Student Solutions Guide for

Elementary Linear Algebra

Third Edition

Larson/Edwards

Bruce H. Edwards

The University of Florida, Gainesville, Florida

D. C. Heath and Company

Lexington, Massachusetts   Toronto

Address editorial correspondence to:
D. C. Heath and Company
125 Spring Street
Lexington, MA 02173

Published simultaneously in Canada.

Printed in the United States of America.

International Standard Book Number: 0-669-39643-5

10 9 8 7 6 5 4 3 2

Preface

This guide is a supplement to *Elementary Linear Algebra,* Third Edition, by Roland E. Larson and Bruce H. Edwards. All references to chapters, sections, exercise numbers, theorems, and definitions apply to the text. The purpose of this supplement is to guide you through linear algebra by providing the basic solution steps for all exercises in the text. This solution guide is not intended to be used as a substitute for working the homework problems yourself. It is one thing to be able to read and understand a solution, but quite another thing to be able to derive the solution on your own.

I have made every effort to see that the solutions given in this guide are correct. However, I would appreciate very much hearing about any errors or other suggestions for improvement.

We would like to thank Meridian Creative Group for typesetting and creating the art for this guide. Finally, I would like to thank my wife, Consuelo, for her support during the many months I worked on this project.

Bruce H. Edwards
The University of Florida
Gainesville, Florida 32611

CONTENTS

CHAPTER 1
Systems of Linear Equations

Section 1.1   Introduction to Systems of Linear Equations

1. Since the equation is in the form $a_1x + a_2y = b$, it *is* linear in the variables x and y.

3. Since the equation cannot be written in the form $a_1x + a_2y = b$, it is *not* linear in the variables x and y.

5. Since the equation cannot be written in the form $a_1x + a_2y = b$, it is *not* linear in the variables x and y.

7. Choosing y as the free variable, we let $y = t$ and obtain
$$2x - 4t = 0$$
$$2x = 4t$$
$$x = 2t$$

   Thus, we can describe the solution set as $x = 2t$ and $y = t$, where t is any real number.

9. Choosing y and z as the free variables, we let $y = s$ and $z = t$, and obtain $x + s + t = 1$ or $x = 1 - s - t$. Thus, we can describe the solution set as $x = 1 - s - t$, $y = s$ and $z = t$, where s and t are any real numbers.

11. Choosing x_2 and x_3 as the free variables, we let $x_2 = s$ and $x_3 = t$ and obtain
$$13x_1 - 26s + 39t = 13$$
$$13x_1 = 13 + 26s - 39t$$
$$x_1 = 1 + 2s - 3t.$$

   Thus, we can describe the solution set as $x_1 = 1 + 2s - 3t$, $x_2 = s$, and $x_3 = t$, where s and t are any real numbers.

13. From Equation 2 we have $x_2 = 3$. Substituting this value into Equation 1 produces $x_1 - 3 = 2$ or $x_1 = 5$. Thus, the system has exactly one solution: $x_1 = 5$ and $x_2 = 3$.

15. From Equation 3 we conclude that $z = 0$. Substituting this value into Equation 2 produces
$$2y + 0 = 3$$
$$y = \tfrac{3}{2}.$$

   Finally, by substituting $y = \tfrac{3}{2}$ and $z = 0$ into Equation 1, we obtain
$$-x + \tfrac{3}{2} - 0 = 0$$
$$x = \tfrac{3}{2}.$$

   Thus, the system has exactly one solution: $x = \tfrac{3}{2}$, $y = \tfrac{3}{2}$, and $z = 0$.

17. From Equation 2 we conclude that $y = 0$. Substituting this value into Equation 1 produces
$$5x + 2(0) = 0$$
$$x = 0.$$

   Thus, the system has exactly one solution: $x = 0$ and $y = 0$.

19.

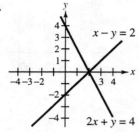

$$2x + y = 4$$
$$x - y = 2$$

Adding the first equation to the second equation produces a new second equation, $3x = 6$, or $x = 2$. Hence, $y = 0$, and the solution is $x = 2$, $y = 0$. This is the point where the two lines intersect.

21.

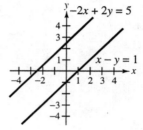

Adding 2 times the first equation to the second equation produces a new second equation.

$$x - y = 1$$
$$0 = 7$$

Since the second equation is an absurdity, we conclude that the original system of equations has no solution. Geometrically, the two lines are parallel.

23. Adding -3 times the first equation to the second equation produces a new second equation.

$$x_1 - x_2 = 0$$
$$x_2 = -1$$

Now, using back-substitution we conclude that the system has exactly one solution: $x_1 = -1$ and $x_2 = -1$.

25. Interchanging the two equations produces the system

$$u + 2v = 120$$
$$2u + v = 120.$$

Adding -2 times the first equation to the second equation produces a new second equation.

$$u + 2v = 120$$
$$-3v = -120$$

Using back-substitution, we have $v = 40$ from the second equation. Substituting this value into the first equation gives $u + 80 = 120$ or $u = 40$. Thus, the system has exactly one solution: $u = 40$ and $v = 40$.

27. Dividing the first equation by 2.5 yields a new first equation.

$$x_1 - 1.2x_2 = 0.6$$
$$10x_1 - 12x_2 = 6$$

Adding -10 times the first equation to the second equation yields a new second equation.

$$x_1 - 1.2x_2 = 0.6$$
$$0 = 0$$

Choosing $x_2 = t$ as the free variable, we obtain $x_1 = 0.6 + 1.2t$. Thus, we can describe the solution set as $x_1 = 0.6 + 1.2t$ and $x_2 = t$, where t is any real number.

29. Dividing the first equation by 9 produces a new first equation.

$$x - \tfrac{1}{3}y = -\tfrac{1}{9}$$
$$\tfrac{1}{5}x + \tfrac{2}{5}y = -\tfrac{1}{3}$$

Adding $-\tfrac{1}{5}$ times the first equation to the second equation produces a new second equation.

$$x - \tfrac{1}{3}y = -\tfrac{1}{9}$$
$$\tfrac{7}{15}y = -\tfrac{14}{45}$$

Multiplying the second equation by $\tfrac{15}{7}$ produces a new second equation.

$$x - \tfrac{1}{3}y = -\tfrac{1}{9}$$
$$y = -\tfrac{2}{3}$$

Now, using back-substitution, we can substitute $y = -\tfrac{2}{3}$ into the first equation to obtain $x + \tfrac{2}{9} = -\tfrac{1}{9}$ or $x = -\tfrac{1}{3}$. Thus we conclude that the system has exactly one solution: $x = -\tfrac{1}{3}$ and $y = -\tfrac{2}{3}$.

31. To begin, we change the form of the first equation.

$$\tfrac{1}{2}x + \tfrac{1}{3}y = \tfrac{23}{6}$$
$$x - 2y = 5$$

Multiplying the first equation by 2 yields a new first equation.

$$x + \tfrac{2}{3}y = \tfrac{23}{3}$$
$$x - 2y = 5$$

Subtracting the first equation from the second equation yields a new second equation.

$$x + \tfrac{2}{3}y = \tfrac{23}{3}$$
$$-\tfrac{8}{3}y = -\tfrac{8}{3}$$

Dividing the second equation by $-8/3$ yields a new second equation.

$$x + \tfrac{2}{3}y = \tfrac{23}{3}$$
$$y = 1$$

Now, using back-substitution we conclude that the system has exactly one solution: $x = 7$ and $y = 1$.

33. Multiplying the first equation by 50 and the second equation by 100 produces a new system.

$$x_1 - 2.5x_2 = -9.5$$
$$3x_1 + 4x_2 = 52$$

Adding -3 times the first equation to the second equation produces a new second equation.

$$x_1 - 2.5x_2 = -9.5$$
$$11.5x_2 = 80.5$$

Now, using back-substitution, we conclude that the system has exactly one solution:
$x_1 = 8$ and $x_2 = 7$.

35. Adding -2 times the first equation to the second equation yields a new second equation.

$$x + y + z = 6$$
$$-3y - z = -9$$
$$3x \quad\quad - z = 0$$

Adding -3 times the first equation to the third equation yields a new third equation.

$$x + y + z = 6$$
$$-3y - z = -9$$
$$-3y - 4z = -18$$

Dividing the second equation by -3 yields a new second equation.

$$x + y + z = 6$$
$$y + \tfrac{1}{3}z = 3$$
$$-3y - 4z = -18$$

Adding 3 times the second equation to the third equation yields a new third equation.

$$x + y + z = 6$$
$$y + \tfrac{1}{3}z = 3$$
$$-3z = -9$$

Dividing the third equation by -3 yields a new third equation.

$$x + y + z = 6$$
$$y + \tfrac{1}{3}z = 3$$
$$z = 3$$

Now, using back-substitution we conclude that the system has exactly one solution:
$x = 1, y = 2$, and $z = 3$.

37. Dividing the first equation by 3 yields a new first equation.

$$x_1 - \tfrac{2}{3}x_2 + \tfrac{4}{3}x_3 = \tfrac{1}{3}$$
$$x_1 + x_2 - 2x_3 = 3$$
$$2x_1 - 3x_2 + 6x_3 = 8$$

Subtracting the first equation from the second equation yields a new second equation.

$$x_1 - \tfrac{2}{3}x_2 + \tfrac{4}{3}x_3 = \tfrac{1}{3}$$
$$\tfrac{5}{3}x_2 + \tfrac{10}{3}x_3 = \tfrac{8}{3}$$
$$2x_1 - 3x_2 + 6x_3 = 8$$

Adding -2 times the first equation to the third equation yields a new third equation.

$$x_1 - \tfrac{2}{3}x_2 + \tfrac{4}{3}x_3 = \tfrac{1}{3}$$
$$\tfrac{5}{3}x_2 + \tfrac{10}{3}x_3 = \tfrac{8}{3}$$
$$\tfrac{5}{3}x_2 + \tfrac{10}{3}x_3 = \tfrac{22}{3}$$

At this point we recognize that Equations 2 and 3 cannot both be satisfied. Thus, the original system of equations has no solution.

39. Adding -2 times the first equation to the second equation yields a new second equation.

$$x_1 + 2x_2 - 7x_3 = -4$$
$$-3x_2 + 15x_3 = 21$$
$$3x_1 + 9x_2 - 36x_3 = -33$$

Adding -3 times the first equation to the third equation yields a new third equation.

$$x_1 + 2x_2 - 7x_3 = -4$$
$$-3x_2 + 15x_3 = 21$$
$$3x_2 - 15x_3 = -21$$

Dividing the second equation by -3 yields a new second equation.

$$x_1 + 2x_2 - 7x_3 = -4$$
$$x_2 - 5x_3 = -7$$
$$3x_2 - 15x_3 = -21$$

Adding -3 times the second equation to the third equation yields a new third equation.

$$x_1 + 2x_2 - 7x_3 = -4$$
$$x_2 - 5x_3 = -7$$
$$0 = 0$$

Adding -2 times the second equation to the first equation yields a new first equation.

$$x_1 + 3x_3 = 10$$
$$x_2 - 5x_3 = -7.$$

Choosing $x_3 = t$ as the free variable we find that the solution is $x_1 = 10 - 3t$, $x_2 = -7 + 5t$, and $x_3 = t$, where t is any real number.

41. Adding -4 times the first equation to the second equation produces a new second equation.

$$\begin{aligned}
x_1 \qquad\;\; + 4x_3 &= \;\;\;13 \\
-2x_2 - 15x_3 &= -45 \\
2x_1 - \;\; 2x_2 - \;\; 7x_3 &= -19
\end{aligned}$$

Adding -2 times the first equation to the third equation produces a new third equation.

$$\begin{aligned}
x_1 \qquad\; + \;\;4x_3 &= \;\;\;13 \\
- \;2x_2 - 15x_3 &= -45 \\
- \;2x_2 - 15x_3 &= -45
\end{aligned}$$

Dividing the second equation by -2, and deleting the redundant third equation, produces

$$\begin{aligned}
x_1 \;\; + \;\;4x_3 &= 13 \\
x_2 + \tfrac{15}{2}x_3 &= \tfrac{45}{2}.
\end{aligned}$$

Choosing $x_3 = t$ as the free variable, we find that the solution is

$x_1 = 13 - 4t$, $x_2 = -\tfrac{15}{2}t + \tfrac{45}{2}$ and $x_3 = t$, where t is any real number.

43. Adding -5 times the first equation to the second equation yields a new second equation.

$$\begin{aligned}
x - 3y + 2z &= \;\;\;18 \\
0 &= -72
\end{aligned}$$

Since the second equation is an absurdity, we conclude that the original system of equations has no solution.

45. Adding -2 times the first equation to the second, 3 times the first equation to the third, and -1 times the first equation to the fourth, produces

$$\begin{aligned}
x + \;\;y + \;\;z + \;\;w &= \;\;\;6 \\
y - 2z - 3w &= -12 \\
7y + 4z + 5w &= \;\;22 \\
y - 2z \qquad\; &= -6.
\end{aligned}$$

Adding -7 times the second equation to the third, and -1 times the second equation to the fourth, produces

$$\begin{aligned}
x + y + \;\;\;z + \;\;\;w &= \;\;\;6 \\
y - \;\;2z - \;\;3w &= -12 \\
18z + 26w &= 106 \\
3w &= \;\;\;6.
\end{aligned}$$

Using back-substitution, we find that the original system has exactly one solution:
$x = 1$, $y = 0$, $z = 3$, and $w = 2$.

47. Using a computer or graphing calculator, you obtain
$x_1 = 11.2415$, $x_2 = -60.9029$, $x_3 = 40.7674$, $x_4 = 27.4267$ (answers might vary slightly).

49. Using a computer or graphing calculator you obtain $x_1 = 8.1124$, $x_2 = -4.5588$, $x_3 = -9.0448$ (answers might vary slightly).

51. $x = y = z = 0$ is clearly a solution.

Dividing the first equation by 4 yields a new first equation.

$$x + \tfrac{3}{4}y + \tfrac{17}{4}z = 0$$
$$5x + 4y + 22z = 0$$
$$4x + 2y + 19z = 0$$

Adding -5 times the first equation to the second equation yields a new second equation.

$$x + \tfrac{3}{4}y + \tfrac{17}{4}z = 0$$
$$\tfrac{1}{4}y + \tfrac{3}{4}z = 0$$
$$4x + 2y + 19z = 0$$

Adding -4 times the first equation to the third equation yields a new third equation.

$$x + \tfrac{3}{4}y + \tfrac{17}{4}z = 0$$
$$\tfrac{1}{4}y + \tfrac{3}{4}z = 0$$
$$-y + 2z = 0$$

Multiplying the second equation by 4 yields a new second equation.

$$x + \tfrac{3}{4}y + \tfrac{17}{4}z = 0$$
$$y + 3z = 0$$
$$-y + 2z = 0$$

Adding the second equation to the third equation yields a new third equation.

$$x + \tfrac{3}{4}y + \tfrac{17}{4}z = 0$$
$$y + 3z = 0$$
$$5z = 0$$

Dividing the third equation by 5 yields a new third equation.

$$x + \tfrac{3}{4}y + \tfrac{17}{4}z = 0$$
$$y + 3z = 0$$
$$z = 0$$

Now, using back-substitution, we conclude that the system has exactly one solution: $x = 0$, $y = 0$, and $z = 0$.

53. $x = y = z = 0$ is clearly a solution.

Dividing the first equation by 5 yields a new first equation.

$$
\begin{aligned}
x + \quad y - \tfrac{1}{5}z &= 0 \\
10x + \quad 5y + 2z &= 0 \\
5x + 15y - 9z &= 0
\end{aligned}
$$

Adding -10 times the first equation to the second equation yields a new second equation.

$$
\begin{aligned}
x + \quad y - \tfrac{1}{5}z &= 0 \\
-5y + 4z &= 0 \\
5x + \quad 15y - 9z &= 0
\end{aligned}
$$

Adding -5 times the first equation to the third equation yields a new third equation.

$$
\begin{aligned}
x + \quad y - \tfrac{1}{5}z &= 0 \\
-5y + 4z &= 0 \\
10y - 8z &= 0
\end{aligned}
$$

Dividing the second equation by -5 yields a new second equation.

$$
\begin{aligned}
x + \quad y - \tfrac{1}{5}z &= 0 \\
y - \tfrac{4}{5}z &= 0 \\
10y - 8z &= 0
\end{aligned}
$$

Adding -10 times the second equation to the third equation yields a new third equation.

$$
\begin{aligned}
x + y - \tfrac{1}{5}z &= 0 \\
y - \tfrac{4}{5}z &= 0 \\
0 &= 0
\end{aligned}
$$

Adding -1 times the second equation to the first equation yields a new first equation.

$$
\begin{aligned}
x + \quad \tfrac{3}{5}z &= 0 \\
y - \tfrac{4}{5}z &= 0
\end{aligned}
$$

Choosing $z = t$ as the free variable we find the solution to be $x = -\tfrac{3}{5}t$, $y = \tfrac{4}{5}t$, and $z = t$, where t is any real number.

55. Since $x_1 = t$ and $x_2 = 3t - 4 = 3x_1 - 4$, one answer is the system

$$
\begin{aligned}
3x_1 - x_2 &= \quad 4 \\
-3x_1 + x_2 &= -4
\end{aligned}
$$

Letting $x_2 = t$, you get $x_1 = \frac{4 + t}{3} = \frac{4}{3} + \frac{t}{3}$.

57. Substituting $X = 1/x$ and $Y = 1/y$ into original system yields

$$12X - 12Y = 7$$
$$3X + 4Y = 0.$$

We reduce this system to row-echelon form.

$$X - Y = \frac{7}{12}$$
$$3X + 4Y = 0$$

$$X - Y = \frac{7}{12}$$
$$7Y = -\frac{7}{4}$$

$$X - Y = \frac{7}{12}$$
$$Y = -\frac{1}{4}$$

Thus, $Y = -1/4$ and $X = 1/3$. Since $X = 1/x$ and $Y = 1/y$, the solution of the original system of equations is $x = 3$ and $y = -4$.

59. We reduce the system to row-echelon form.

$$x + \left(\frac{\sin\theta}{\cos\theta}\right)y = \frac{1}{\cos\theta}$$

$$(-\sin\theta)x + (\cos\theta)y = 0$$

$$x + \left(\frac{\sin\theta}{\cos\theta}\right)y = \frac{1}{\cos\theta}$$

$$\left(\frac{1}{\cos\theta}\right)y = \frac{\sin\theta}{\cos\theta} \quad \left(\text{Since } \frac{\sin^2\theta}{\cos\theta} + \cos\theta = \frac{\sin^2\theta + \cos^2\theta}{\cos\theta} = \frac{1}{\cos\theta}\right)$$

$$x + \left(\frac{\sin\theta}{\cos\theta}\right)y = \frac{1}{\cos\theta}$$

$$y = \sin\theta$$

Substituting $y = \sin\theta$ into the first equation yields

$$x + \left(\frac{\sin\theta}{\cos\theta}\right)\sin\theta = \frac{1}{\cos\theta}$$

$$x = \frac{1 - \sin^2\theta}{\cos\theta} = \frac{\cos^2\theta}{\cos\theta} = \cos\theta.$$

Thus, the solution of the original system of equations is $x = \cos\theta$ and $y = \sin\theta$.

61. Reducing the system to row-echelon form, we have

$$x + \frac{k}{4}y = \frac{7}{4}$$

$$\left(-\frac{k^2}{4} + 1\right)y = -\frac{7}{4}k.$$

Now, if $k = \pm 2$, there is no solution. Otherwise, we see by back-substitution that there would be exactly one solution. Hence, the answer is all k except ± 2.

63. To begin, we reduce the system to row-echelon form.

$$x + \quad ky = 0$$
$$(1 - k^2)y = 0$$

$$x + \quad ky = 0$$
$$y = 0, \quad 1 - k^2 \neq 0$$

$$x \qquad = 0$$
$$y = 0, \quad 1 - k^2 \neq 0$$

Thus, if $1 - k^2 \neq 0$, that is if $k \neq \pm 1$, the system will have exactly one solution.

65. To begin, we reduce the system to row-echelon form.

$$x + 2y + kz = 6$$
$$(8 - 3k)z = -14$$

This system will have a solution unless $8 - 3k = 0$, that is, $k = \frac{8}{3}$.

67. Reducing the system to row-echelon form, we have

$$x + \quad y + \qquad\qquad kz = \qquad 3$$
$$(k - 1)y + \quad (1 - k)z = \qquad -1$$
$$(1 - k)y + \quad (1 - k^2)z = 1 - 3k$$

$$x + \quad y + \qquad kz = \qquad 3$$
$$(k - 1)y + \quad (1 - k)z = \qquad -1$$
$$(-k^2 - k + 2)z = \quad -3k.$$

If $-k^2 - k + 2 = 0$, then there is no solution. Hence, if $k = 1$ or $k = -2$, there is not a unique solution.

69. (a) All three of the lines will intersect in exactly one point (corresponding to the solution point).

(b) All three of the lines will coincide (every point on these lines is a solution point).

(c) The three lines have no common point.

71. Letting $x = -1, 0$ and 1, we obtain the system

$$a - b + c = 0$$
$$c = 0$$
$$a + b + c = 0.$$

Since $c = 0$, we have the new system

$$a - b = 0$$
$$a + b = 0.$$

Adding these equations, we see that $a = 0$. Hence, $a = b = c = 0$ is the only solution.

73. $x - 4y = -3$
        $5x - 6y = 13$

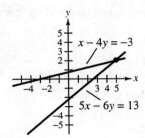

$x - 4y = -3$
    $14y = 28$

$x - 4y = -3$
      $y = 2$

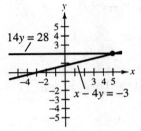

$x = 5$
$y = 2$

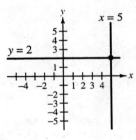

Section 1.2   Gaussian Elimination and Gauss-Jordan Elimination

1. Since the matrix has 3 rows and 2 columns, it has size 3×2.

3. Since the matrix has 1 row and 5 columns, it has size 1×5.

5. Since the matrix has 4 rows and 1 column, it has size 4×1.

7. The matrix satisfies all three conditions in the definition of row-echelon form. Moreover, since each column that has a leading 1 (columns one and two) has zeros elsewhere. The matrix is in reduced row-echelon form.

9. Since the matrix has two non-zero rows without leading 1's, it is not in row-echelon form.

11. The matrix satisfies all three conditions in the definition of row-echelon form. Moreover, since each column that has a leading 1 (columns one and four) has zeros elsewhere, the matrix is in reduced row-echelon form.

13. The matrix satisfies all three conditions in the definition of row-echelon form. Moreover, since there are no leading 1's, the matrix is in reduced row-echelon form.

15. Since the matrix is in reduced row-echelon form, we can simply convert back to a system of linear equations

$$x_1 = 0$$
$$x_2 = 2$$

Thus, the solution set is $x_1 = 0$ and $x_2 = 2$.

17. Since the matrix is in row-echelon form, we convert back to a system of linear equations.

$$x_1 - x_2 \qquad\quad = \quad 3$$
$$x_2 - 2x_3 = \quad 1$$
$$x_3 = -1$$

We can solve this system by back-substitution.

$$x_2 - 2(-1) = \quad 1$$
$$x_2 = -1$$

Substituting $x_2 = -1$ and $x_3 = -1$ into equation 1, we have

$$x_1 - (-1) = 3$$
$$x_1 = 2.$$

Thus, the solution set is $x_1 = 2$, $x_2 = -1$, and $x_3 = -1$.

19. Since the matrix is in row-echelon form, we convert back to a system of linear equations.

$$
\begin{aligned}
x_1 + 2x_2 \quad\;\; + \;\; x_4 &= 4 \\
x_2 + 2x_3 + \;\; x_4 &= 3 \\
x_3 + 2x_4 &= 1 \\
x_4 &= 4
\end{aligned}
$$

We can solve this system by back-substitution.

$$
\begin{aligned}
x_3 &= 1 - & 2x_4 &= 1 - & 2(4) & & = -7 \\
x_2 &= 3 - & 2x_3 - \;\; x_4 &= 3 - 2(-7) -4 &&= \;\; 13 \\
x_1 &= 4 - 2x_2 & - \;\; x_4 &= 4 - 2(13) -4 &&= -26
\end{aligned}
$$

Thus, the solution is: $x_1 = -26, x_2 = 13, x_3 = -7,$ and $x_4 = 4$.

21. The augmented matrix for this system is

$$
\begin{bmatrix} 1 & 2 & 7 \\ 2 & 1 & 8 \end{bmatrix}.
$$

Adding -2 times the first row to the second row yields a new second row.

$$
\begin{bmatrix} 1 & 2 & 7 \\ 0 & -3 & -6 \end{bmatrix}
$$

Dividing the second row by -3 yields a new second row.

$$
\begin{bmatrix} 1 & 2 & 7 \\ 0 & 1 & 2 \end{bmatrix}
$$

Converting back to a system of linear equations produces

$$
\begin{aligned}
x + 2y &= 7 \\
y &= 2.
\end{aligned}
$$

Finally, using back-substitution we find that $x = 3$ and $y = z$.

23. The augmented matrix for this system is

$$
\begin{bmatrix} 1 & -3 & 5 \\ -2 & 6 & -10 \end{bmatrix}.
$$

Adding 2 times the first row to the second row yields a new second row.

$$
\begin{bmatrix} 1 & -3 & 5 \\ 0 & 0 & 0 \end{bmatrix}
$$

Converting back to a system of linear equations produces

$$
x - 3y = 5.
$$

Choosing $y = t$ as the free variable we find that the solution set can be represented by $x = 5 + 3t$ and $y = t$, where t is any real number.

25. The augmented matrix for this system is

$$\begin{bmatrix} -1 & 2 & 1.5 \\ 2 & -4 & 3 \end{bmatrix}.$$

Gaussian elimination produces the following.

$$\begin{bmatrix} -1 & 2 & 1.5 \\ 2 & -4 & 3 \end{bmatrix} \quad \Rightarrow \quad \begin{bmatrix} 1 & -2 & -\frac{3}{2} \\ 2 & -4 & 3 \end{bmatrix} \quad \Rightarrow \quad \begin{bmatrix} 1 & -2 & -\frac{3}{2} \\ 0 & 0 & 6 \end{bmatrix}$$

Since the second row of this matrix corresponds to the equation $0 = 6$, we conclude that the original system has no solution.

27. The augmented matrix for this system is

$$\begin{bmatrix} -3 & 5 & -22 \\ 3 & 4 & 4 \\ 4 & -8 & 32 \end{bmatrix}.$$

Dividing the first row by -3 yields a new first row.

$$\begin{bmatrix} 1 & -\frac{5}{3} & \frac{22}{3} \\ 3 & 4 & 4 \\ 4 & -8 & 32 \end{bmatrix}$$

Adding -3 times the first row to the second row yields a new second row.

$$\begin{bmatrix} 1 & -\frac{5}{3} & \frac{22}{3} \\ 0 & 9 & -18 \\ 4 & -8 & 32 \end{bmatrix}$$

Adding -4 times the first row to the third row yields a new third row.

$$\begin{bmatrix} 1 & -\frac{5}{3} & \frac{22}{3} \\ 0 & 9 & -18 \\ 0 & -\frac{4}{3} & \frac{8}{3} \end{bmatrix}$$

Dividing the second row by 9 yields a new second row.

$$\begin{bmatrix} 1 & -\frac{5}{3} & \frac{22}{3} \\ 0 & 1 & -2 \\ 0 & -\frac{4}{3} & \frac{8}{3} \end{bmatrix}$$

Adding $\frac{4}{3}$ times the second row to the third row yields a new third row.

$$\begin{bmatrix} 1 & -\frac{5}{3} & \frac{22}{3} \\ 0 & 1 & -2 \\ 0 & 0 & 0 \end{bmatrix}$$

Converting back to a system of linear equations produces

$$x - \tfrac{5}{3}y = \tfrac{22}{3}$$
$$y = -2.$$

Finally, using back-substitution we find that the solution set is $x = 4$ and $y = -2$.

29. The augmented matrix for this system is

$$\begin{bmatrix} 1 & 0 & -3 & -2 \\ 3 & 1 & -2 & 5 \\ 2 & 2 & 1 & 4 \end{bmatrix}.$$

Gaussian elimination produces the following.

$$\begin{bmatrix} 1 & 0 & -3 & -2 \\ 3 & 1 & -2 & 5 \\ 2 & 2 & 1 & 4 \end{bmatrix} \Rightarrow \begin{bmatrix} 1 & 0 & -3 & -2 \\ 0 & 1 & 7 & 11 \\ 0 & 2 & 7 & 8 \end{bmatrix} \Rightarrow \begin{bmatrix} 1 & 0 & -3 & -2 \\ 0 & 1 & 7 & 11 \\ 0 & 0 & -7 & -14 \end{bmatrix}$$

Back substitution now yields

$$x_3 = 2$$
$$x_2 = 11 - 7x_3 = 11 - (7)2 = -3$$
$$x_1 = -2 + 3x_3 = -2 + 3(2) = 4.$$

Hence, the solution is: $x_1 = 4$, $x_2 = -3$, and $x_3 = 2$.

31. The augmented matrix for this system is

$$\begin{bmatrix} 1 & 1 & -5 & 3 \\ 1 & 0 & -2 & 1 \\ 2 & -1 & -1 & 0 \end{bmatrix}.$$

Subtracting the first row from the second row yields a new second row.

$$\begin{bmatrix} 1 & 1 & -5 & 3 \\ 0 & -1 & 3 & -2 \\ 2 & -1 & -1 & 0 \end{bmatrix}$$

Adding -2 times the first row to the third row yields a new third row.

$$\begin{bmatrix} 1 & 1 & -5 & 3 \\ 0 & -1 & 3 & -2 \\ 0 & -3 & 9 & -6 \end{bmatrix}$$

Multiplying the second row by -1 yields a new second row.

$$\begin{bmatrix} 1 & 1 & -5 & 3 \\ 0 & 1 & -3 & 2 \\ 0 & -3 & 9 & -6 \end{bmatrix}$$

Adding 3 times the second row to the third row yields a new third row.

$$\begin{bmatrix} 1 & 1 & -5 & 3 \\ 0 & 1 & -3 & 2 \\ 0 & 0 & 0 & 0 \end{bmatrix}$$

Adding -1 times the second row to the first row yields a new first row.

$$\begin{bmatrix} 1 & 0 & -2 & 1 \\ 0 & 1 & -3 & 2 \\ 0 & 0 & 0 & 0 \end{bmatrix}$$

Converting back to a system of linear equations produces

$$x_1 \quad - 2x_3 = 1$$
$$x_2 - 3x_3 = 2.$$

Finally, choosing $x_3 = t$ as the free variable we find the solution set to be $x_1 = 1 + 2t$, $x_2 = 2 + 3t$, and $x_3 = t$, where t is any real number.

33. The augmented matrix for this system is

$$\begin{bmatrix} 1 & 2 & 1 & 8 \\ -3 & -6 & -3 & -21 \end{bmatrix}.$$

Adding 3 times the first row to the second row yields a new second row.

$$\begin{bmatrix} 1 & 2 & 1 & 8 \\ 0 & 0 & 0 & 3 \end{bmatrix}$$

Since the second row corresponds to the equation $0 = 3$, which is an absurdity, we conclude that the system has no solution.

35. The augmented matrix for this system is

$$\begin{bmatrix} 3 & 3 & 12 & 6 \\ 1 & 1 & 4 & 2 \\ 2 & 5 & 20 & 10 \\ -1 & 2 & 8 & 4 \end{bmatrix}.$$

Gaussian elimination produces the following.

$$\begin{bmatrix} 3 & 3 & 12 & 6 \\ 1 & 1 & 4 & 2 \\ 2 & 5 & 20 & 10 \\ -1 & 2 & 8 & 4 \end{bmatrix} \Rightarrow \begin{bmatrix} 1 & 1 & 4 & 2 \\ 1 & 1 & 4 & 2 \\ 2 & 5 & 20 & 10 \\ -1 & 2 & 8 & 4 \end{bmatrix}$$

$$\Rightarrow \begin{bmatrix} 1 & 1 & 4 & 2 \\ 0 & 0 & 0 & 0 \\ 0 & 3 & 12 & 6 \\ 0 & 3 & 12 & 6 \end{bmatrix} \Rightarrow \begin{bmatrix} 1 & 1 & 4 & 2 \\ 0 & 3 & 12 & 6 \\ 0 & 0 & 0 & 0 \\ 0 & 0 & 0 & 0 \end{bmatrix}$$

$$\Rightarrow \begin{bmatrix} 1 & 1 & 4 & 2 \\ 0 & 1 & 4 & 2 \\ 0 & 0 & 0 & 0 \\ 0 & 0 & 0 & 0 \end{bmatrix} \Rightarrow \begin{bmatrix} 1 & 0 & 0 & 0 \\ 0 & 1 & 4 & 2 \\ 0 & 0 & 0 & 0 \\ 0 & 0 & 0 & 0 \end{bmatrix}$$

Letting $z = t$ be the free variable, the solution is: $x = 0$, $y = 2 - 4t$, $z = t$, where t is any real number.

37. Using a computer or graphing calculator, the augmented matrix reduces to

$$\begin{bmatrix} 1 & 0 & 0 & -0.5278 & 23.5361 \\ 0 & 1 & 0 & -4.1111 & 18.5444 \\ 0 & 0 & 1 & -2.1389 & 7.4306 \end{bmatrix}$$

Letting $x_4 = t$ be the free variable, you obtain

$$\begin{aligned} x_1 &= 23.5361 + 0.5278t \\ x_2 &= 18.5444 + 4.1111t \\ x_3 &= 7.4306 + 2.1389t \\ x_4 &= t \end{aligned}$$

39. Using Gaussian elimination on the augmented matrix we have the following.

$$\begin{bmatrix} 1 & -1 & 2 & 2 & 6 & 6 \\ 3 & -2 & 4 & 4 & 12 & 14 \\ 0 & 1 & -1 & -1 & -3 & -3 \\ 2 & -2 & 4 & 5 & 15 & 10 \\ 2 & -2 & 4 & 4 & 13 & 13 \end{bmatrix} \implies \begin{bmatrix} 1 & -1 & 2 & 2 & 6 & 6 \\ 0 & 1 & -2 & -2 & -6 & -4 \\ 0 & 1 & -1 & -1 & -3 & -3 \\ 0 & 0 & 0 & 1 & 3 & -2 \\ 0 & 0 & 0 & 0 & 1 & 1 \end{bmatrix}$$

$$\implies \begin{bmatrix} 1 & -1 & 2 & 2 & 6 & 6 \\ 0 & 1 & -2 & -2 & -6 & -4 \\ 0 & 0 & 1 & 1 & 3 & 1 \\ 0 & 0 & 0 & 1 & 3 & -2 \\ 0 & 0 & 0 & 0 & 1 & 1 \end{bmatrix}$$

Using back-substitution we have

$$\begin{aligned} x_5 &= 1 \\ x_4 &= -2 - 3x_5 = -5 \\ x_3 &= 1 - x_4 - 3x_5 = 3 \\ x_2 &= -4 + 2x_3 + 2x_4 + 6x_5 = -2 \\ x_1 &= 6 + x_2 - 2x_3 - 2x_4 - 6x_5 = 2. \end{aligned}$$

Hence, the solution is: $x_1 = 2$, $x_2 = -2$, $x_3 = 3$, $x_4 = -5$, and $x_5 = 1$.

41. The corresponding system of equations is

$$\begin{aligned} x_1 &= 0 \\ x_2 + x_3 &= 0 \\ 0 &= 0 \end{aligned}$$

Hence, $x_3 = t$ can be any real number, $x_2 = -x_3 = -t$ and $x_1 = 0$.

43. The corresponding system of equations is

$$\begin{aligned} x_1 + x_4 &= 0 \\ x_3 &= 0 \\ 0 &= 0 \end{aligned}$$

Hence, $x_4 = t$ can be any real number, $x_3 = 0$, $x_2 = s$ can be any real number, and $x_1 = -x_4 = -t$.

45. We begin by forming the augmented matrix for the system

$$\begin{bmatrix} 1 & 1 & 0 & 2 \\ 0 & 1 & 1 & 2 \\ 1 & 0 & 1 & 2 \\ a & b & c & 0 \end{bmatrix}.$$

Then we use Gauss-Jordan elimination as follows.

$$\begin{bmatrix} 1 & 1 & 0 & 2 \\ 0 & 1 & 1 & 2 \\ 0 & -1 & 1 & 0 \\ a & b & c & 0 \end{bmatrix} \Rightarrow \begin{bmatrix} 1 & 1 & 0 & 2 \\ 0 & 1 & 1 & 2 \\ 0 & -1 & 1 & 0 \\ 0 & b-a & c & -2a \end{bmatrix}$$

$$\Rightarrow \begin{bmatrix} 1 & 1 & 0 & 2 \\ 0 & 1 & 1 & 2 \\ 0 & 0 & 2 & 2 \\ 0 & b-a & c & -2a \end{bmatrix} \Rightarrow \begin{bmatrix} 1 & 1 & 0 & 2 \\ 0 & 1 & 1 & 2 \\ 0 & 0 & 2 & 2 \\ 0 & 0 & a-b+c & -2b \end{bmatrix}$$

$$\Rightarrow \begin{bmatrix} 1 & 1 & 0 & 2 \\ 0 & 1 & 1 & 2 \\ 0 & 0 & 1 & 1 \\ 0 & 0 & a-b+c & -2b \end{bmatrix} \Rightarrow \begin{bmatrix} 1 & 1 & 0 & 2 \\ 0 & 1 & 1 & 2 \\ 0 & 0 & 1 & 1 \\ 0 & 0 & 0 & a+b+c \end{bmatrix}$$

$$\Rightarrow \begin{bmatrix} 1 & 1 & 0 & 2 \\ 0 & 1 & 0 & 1 \\ 0 & 0 & 1 & 1 \\ 0 & 0 & 0 & a+b+c \end{bmatrix} \Rightarrow \begin{bmatrix} 1 & 0 & 0 & 1 \\ 0 & 1 & 0 & 1 \\ 0 & 0 & 1 & 1 \\ 0 & 0 & 0 & a+b+c \end{bmatrix}$$

Converting back to a system of linear equations

$$x = 1$$
$$y = 1$$
$$z = 1$$
$$0 = a + b + c.$$

We see that the system

(a)   will have a unique solution if $a + b + c = 0$,

(b)   will have no solution if $a + b + c \neq 0$, and

(c)   cannot have an infinite number of solutions.

47. We solve each pair of equations by Gaussian elimination as follows.

(a) Equations 1 and 2:

$$\begin{bmatrix} 4 & -2 & 5 & 16 \\ 1 & 1 & 0 & 0 \end{bmatrix} \implies \begin{bmatrix} 1 & 0 & \frac{5}{6} & \frac{8}{3} \\ 0 & 1 & -\frac{5}{6} & -\frac{8}{3} \end{bmatrix} \implies \begin{array}{l} x = \frac{8}{3} - \frac{5}{6}t, \\ y = -\frac{8}{3} + \frac{5}{6}t, \ z = t \end{array}$$

(b) Equations 1 and 3:

$$\begin{bmatrix} 4 & -2 & 5 & 16 \\ -1 & -3 & 2 & 6 \end{bmatrix} \implies \begin{bmatrix} 1 & 0 & \frac{11}{14} & \frac{36}{14} \\ 0 & 1 & -\frac{13}{14} & -\frac{40}{14} \end{bmatrix} \implies \begin{array}{l} x = \frac{36}{14} - \frac{11}{14}t, \\ y = -\frac{40}{14} + \frac{13}{14}t, \ z = t \end{array}$$

(c) Equations 2 and 3:

$$\begin{bmatrix} 1 & 1 & 0 & 0 \\ -1 & -3 & 2 & 6 \end{bmatrix} \implies \begin{bmatrix} 1 & 0 & 1 & 3 \\ 0 & 1 & -1 & -3 \end{bmatrix} \implies \begin{array}{l} x = 3 - t \\ y = -3 + t, \ z = t \end{array}$$

(d) Each of these systems has an infinite number of solutions.

49. We use Gauss-Jordan elimination as follows.

$$\begin{bmatrix} 1 & 2 \\ -1 & 2 \end{bmatrix} \implies \begin{bmatrix} 1 & 2 \\ 0 & 4 \end{bmatrix} \implies \begin{bmatrix} 1 & 2 \\ 0 & 1 \end{bmatrix} \implies \begin{bmatrix} 1 & 0 \\ 0 & 1 \end{bmatrix}$$

51. We begin by finding all possible first rows.

$$[0 \quad 0], \qquad [0 \quad 1], \qquad [1 \quad 0], \qquad [1 \quad k].$$

For each of these we examine the possible second rows.

$$\begin{bmatrix} 0 & 0 \\ 0 & 0 \end{bmatrix}, \qquad \begin{bmatrix} 0 & 1 \\ 0 & 0 \end{bmatrix}, \qquad \begin{bmatrix} 1 & 0 \\ 0 & 1 \end{bmatrix}, \qquad \begin{bmatrix} 1 & k \\ 0 & 0 \end{bmatrix}$$

These represent all possible 2×2 reduced row-echelon matrices.

53. First off, all a and c cannot both be zero. So, assume $a \neq 0$, and use row reduction as follows.

$$\begin{bmatrix} a & b \\ c & d \end{bmatrix} \implies \begin{bmatrix} a & b \\ 0 & \frac{-cb}{a} + d \end{bmatrix} \implies \begin{bmatrix} a & b \\ 0 & ad - bc \end{bmatrix}$$

Hence, $ab - bc \neq 0$. Similarly, if $c \neq 0$, we can interchange rows and proceed as above. So the original matrix is row equivalent to the identity if and only if $ad - bc \neq 0$.

55. We form the augmented matrix for this system

$$\begin{bmatrix} \lambda - 2 & 1 & 0 \\ 1 & \lambda - 2 & 0 \end{bmatrix}$$

and reduce the system using elementary row operations.

$$\begin{bmatrix} 1 & \lambda - 2 & 0 \\ \lambda - 2 & 1 & 0 \end{bmatrix} \implies \begin{bmatrix} 1 & \lambda - 2 & 0 \\ 0 & \lambda^2 - 4\lambda + 3 & 0 \end{bmatrix}$$

To have a nontrivial solution we must have

$$\lambda^2 - 4\lambda + 3 = 0$$
$$(\lambda - 1)(\lambda - 3) = 0.$$

Thus, if $\lambda = 1$ or $\lambda = 3$, the system will have nontrivial solutions.

57. To show that it is possible we need give only one example, such as

$$x_1 + x_2 + x_3 = 0$$
$$x_1 + x_2 + x_3 = 1$$

which has fewer equations than variables and obviously has no solution.

59. $2 \cos \alpha - \sin\beta = 0$
$4 \cos \alpha + 2 \sin\beta = 4$

(-2) times equation 1 added to equation 2 produces

$$4 \sin\beta = 4 \quad \implies \quad \sin\beta = 1 \quad \implies \quad \beta = \tfrac{\pi}{2}.$$

Then $\cos\alpha = \tfrac{1}{2} \implies \alpha = \tfrac{\pi}{3}, \tfrac{2\pi}{3}.$

61. $\begin{bmatrix} a & b \\ c & d \end{bmatrix} \implies \begin{bmatrix} a - c & b - d \\ c & d \end{bmatrix} \implies \begin{bmatrix} a - c & b - d \\ a & b \end{bmatrix} \implies \begin{bmatrix} -c & -d \\ a & b \end{bmatrix} \implies \begin{bmatrix} c & d \\ a & b \end{bmatrix}$

The rows have been interchanged. In general, the second and third elementary row opeations can be used in this manner to interchange two rows of a matrix. Hence, the first elementary row opertion is, in fact, redundant.

Section 1.3 Applications of Systems of Linear Equations

1. (a) Since there are three points, we choose a second-degree polynomial, $p(x) = a_0 + a_1 x + a_2 x^2$. Then we substitute $x = 2$, 3, and 4 into $p(x)$ and equate the results to $y = 5$, 2, and 5, respectively.

$$a_0 + a_1(2) + a_2(2)^2 = a_0 + 2a_1 + 4a_2 = 5$$
$$a_0 + a_1(3) + a_2(3)^2 = a_0 + 3a_1 + 9a_2 = 2$$
$$a_0 + a_1(4) + a_2(4)^2 = a_0 + 4a_1 + 16a_2 = 5$$

We then form the augmented matrix

$$\begin{bmatrix} 1 & 2 & 4 & 5 \\ 1 & 3 & 9 & 2 \\ 1 & 4 & 16 & 5 \end{bmatrix}$$

and use Gauss-Jordan elimination to obtain the equivalent reduced row-echelon matrix

$$\begin{bmatrix} 1 & 0 & 0 & 29 \\ 0 & 1 & 0 & -18 \\ 0 & 0 & 1 & 3 \end{bmatrix}.$$

Thus, $p(x) = 29 - 18x + 3x^2$.

(b)

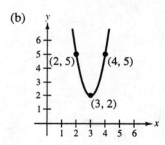

3. (a) Since there are three points, we choose a second-degree polynomial, $p(x) = a_0 + a_1x + a_2x^2$.
Then we substitute $x = 2, 3$, and 5 into $p(x)$ and equate the results to $y = 4, 6$, and 10
respectively.

$$a_0 + a_1(2) + a_2(2)^2 = a_0 + 2a_1 + 4a_2 = 4$$
$$a_0 + a_1(3) + a_2(3)^2 = a_0 + 3a_1 + 9a_2 = 6$$
$$a_0 + a_1(5) + a_2(5)^2 = a_0 + 5a_1 + 25a_2 = 10$$

We use Gauss-Jordan elimination on the augmented matrix for this system.

$$\begin{bmatrix} 1 & 2 & 4 & 4 \\ 1 & 3 & 9 & 6 \\ 1 & 5 & 25 & 10 \end{bmatrix} \implies \begin{bmatrix} 1 & 0 & 0 & 0 \\ 0 & 1 & 0 & 2 \\ 0 & 0 & 1 & 0 \end{bmatrix}$$

Thus, $p(x) = 2x$.

(b)

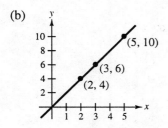

5. (a) Since there are three points, we choose a second-degree polynomial, $p(z) = a_0 + a_1 z + a_2 z^2$. Then we substitute $z = -1, 0, 1$ into $p(z)$ and equate the results to $y = 5, 7$, and 12, respectively.

$$a_0 + a_1(-1) + a_2(-1)^2 = a_0 - a_1 + a_2 = 5$$
$$a_0 + a_1(0) + a_2(0)^2 = a_0 \qquad\quad = 7$$
$$a_0 + a_1(1) + a_2(1)^2 = a_0 + a_1 + a_2 = 12$$

We then form the augmented matrix

$$\begin{bmatrix} 1 & -1 & 1 & 5 \\ 1 & 0 & 0 & 7 \\ 1 & 1 & 1 & 12 \end{bmatrix}$$

and we use Gauss-Jordan elimination to obtain the equivalent reduced row-echelon matrix

$$\begin{bmatrix} 1 & 0 & 0 & 7 \\ 0 & 1 & 0 & \frac{7}{2} \\ 0 & 0 & 1 & \frac{3}{2} \end{bmatrix}$$

Thus, $p(z) = 7 + \frac{7}{2}z + \frac{3}{2}z^2$, $p(x) = 7 + \frac{7}{2}(x - 1987) + \frac{3}{2}(x - 1987)^2$.

(b)

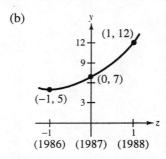

7. We choose a fourth-degree polynomial and substitute $x = 1, 2, 3$, and 4 into $p(x) = a_0 + a_1 x + a_2 x^2 + a_3 x^3 + a_4 x^4$. However, when we substitute $x = 3$ into $p(x)$ and equate it to $y = 2$ and $y = 3$ we get the contradictory equations

$$a_0 + 3a_1 + 9a_2 + 27a_3 + 81a_4 = 2$$
$$a_0 + 3a_1 + 9a_2 + 27a_3 + 81a_4 = 3$$

and must conclude that the system containing these two equations will have no solution. By similar reasoning, we cannot choose $p(y) = b_0 + b_1 y + b_2 y^2 + b_3 y^3 + b_4 y^4$ since $y = 1$ corresponds to both $x = 1$ and $x = 2$.

9. Letting $p(x) = a_0 + a_1 x + a_2 x^2$, we substitute $x = 0, 2,$ and 4 into $p(x)$ and equate the results to $y = 1, 3,$ and 5, respectively.

$$a_0 + a_1(0) + a_2(0)^2 = a_0 \qquad\qquad = 1$$
$$a_0 + a_1(2) + a_2(2)^2 = a_0 + 2a_1 + 4a_2 = 3$$
$$a_0 + a_1(4) + a_2(4)^2 = a_0 + 4a_1 + 16a_2 = 5$$

We use Gauss-Jordan elimination on the augmented matrix for this system.

$$\begin{bmatrix} 1 & 0 & 0 & 1 \\ 1 & 2 & 4 & 3 \\ 1 & 4 & 16 & 5 \end{bmatrix} \implies \begin{bmatrix} 1 & 0 & 0 & 1 \\ 0 & 1 & 0 & 1 \\ 0 & 0 & 1 & 0 \end{bmatrix}$$

Thus, $p(x) = 1 + x$. The graphs of $y = 1/p(x) = 1/(1 + x)$ and that of the function $1 - \frac{7}{15}x + \frac{1}{15}x^2$ are shown below.

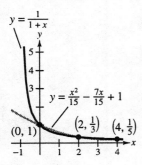

11. To begin, we substitute $x = -1$ and $x = 1$ into $p(x) = a_0 + a_1 x + a_2 x^2 + a_3 x^3$ and equate the results to $y = 2$ and $y = -2$, respectively.

$$a_0 - a_1 + a_2 - a_3 = 2$$
$$a_0 + a_1 + a_2 + a_3 = -2$$

Then, we differentiate p, yielding $p'(x) = a_1 + 2a_2 x + 3a_3 x^2$. We substitute $x = -1$ and $x = 1$ into $p'(x)$ and equate the results to 0.

$$a_1 - 2a_2 + 3a_3 = 0$$
$$a_1 + 2a_2 + 3a_3 = 0$$

Combining these four equations into one system and forming the augmented matrix, we obtain

$$\begin{bmatrix} 1 & -1 & 1 & -1 & 2 \\ 1 & 1 & 1 & 1 & -2 \\ 0 & 1 & -2 & 3 & 0 \\ 0 & 1 & 2 & 3 & 0 \end{bmatrix}.$$

We use Gauss-Jordan elimination to find the equivalent reduced row-echelon matrix

$$\begin{bmatrix} 1 & 0 & 0 & 0 & 0 \\ 0 & 1 & 0 & 0 & -3 \\ 0 & 0 & 1 & 0 & 0 \\ 0 & 0 & 0 & 1 & 1 \end{bmatrix}.$$

Thus, $p(x) = -3x + x^3$. The graph of $y = p(x)$ is shown below.

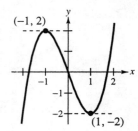

13. To begin, we let $z = x - 1950$ and $p(z) = a_0 + a_1 z + a_2 z^2$. The three data points $(0, 179.3)$, $(10, 203.3)$ and $(30, 226.5)$ yield three linear equations.

$$
\begin{aligned}
a_0 &= 179.3 \\
a_0 + 10a_1 + 100a_2 &= 203.3 \\
a_0 + 30a_1 + 900a_2 &= 226.5
\end{aligned}
$$

The solution to this system is $a_0 = 179.3$, $a_1 = 2.8133$ and $a_2 = -0.0413$. Hence, the second-degree polynomial is $p(x) = 179.3 + 2.8133(x - 1950) - 0.0413(x - 1950)^2$.

To predict the population in 1985 and 1990, we substitute these values into $p(x)$.

$$
\begin{aligned}
p(1985) &= 179.3 + 2.8133(35) - 0.0413(35)^2 \approx 227.17 \\
p(1990) &= 179.3 + 2.8133(40) - 0.0413(40)^2 \approx 225.8
\end{aligned}
$$

15. Choosing a second-degree polynomial approximation, $p(x) = a_0 + a_1 x + a_2 x^2$, we substitute $x = 0, \dfrac{\pi}{2}$, and π into $p(x)$ and equate the results to $y = 0, 1$, and 0, respectively.

$$
\begin{aligned}
a_0 &= 0 \\
a_0 + \frac{\pi}{2}a_1 + \frac{\pi^2}{4}a_2 &= 1 \\
a_0 + \pi a_1 + \pi^2 a_2 &= 0
\end{aligned}
$$

We then form the augmented matrix,

$$
\begin{bmatrix}
1 & 0 & 0 & 0 \\
1 & \frac{\pi}{2} & \frac{\pi^2}{4} & 1 \\
1 & \pi & \pi^2 & 0
\end{bmatrix}
$$

and use Gauss-Jordan elimination to obtain the equivalent reduced row-echelon matrix

$$
\begin{bmatrix}
1 & 0 & 0 & 0 \\
0 & 1 & 0 & \frac{4}{\pi} \\
0 & 0 & 1 & -\frac{4}{\pi^2}
\end{bmatrix}
$$

Thus,

$$
p(x) = \frac{4}{\pi}x - \frac{4}{\pi^2}x^2 = \frac{4}{\pi^2}(\pi x - x^2).
$$

Furthermore,

$$
\begin{aligned}
\sin \frac{\pi}{3} \approx p\left(\frac{\pi}{3}\right) &= \frac{4}{\pi^2}\left[\pi\left(\frac{\pi}{3}\right) - \left(\frac{\pi}{3}\right)^2\right] \\
&= \frac{4}{\pi^2}\left[\frac{2\pi^2}{9}\right] \\
&= \frac{8}{9} \approx 0.889.
\end{aligned}
$$

Note that $\sin \pi/3 = 0.866$ to three significant digits.

17. Substituting $x = -1, 0$ and 1 into $p(x) = a_0 + a_1 x + a_2 x^2$, and equating the result to $y = 0$, we have

$$a_0 - a_1 + a_2 = 0$$
$$a_0 \qquad\quad = 0$$
$$a_0 + a_1 + a_2 = 0.$$

The solution to this system of linear equations is $a_0 = a_1 = a_2 = 0$, which implies that $p(x) = 0$.

19. (a) Each of the network's six junctions gives rise to a linear equation as follows.

$$\text{input} = \text{output}$$
$$600 = x_1 + x_3$$
$$x_1 = x_2 + x_4$$
$$x_2 + x_5 = 500$$
$$x_3 + x_6 = 600$$
$$x_4 + x_7 = x_6$$
$$500 = x_5 + x_7$$

We rearrange these equations, form the augmented matrix, and use Gauss-Jordan elimination.

$$
\begin{bmatrix}
1 & 0 & 1 & 0 & 0 & 0 & 0 & 600 \\
1 & -1 & 0 & -1 & 0 & 0 & 0 & 0 \\
0 & 1 & 0 & 0 & 1 & 0 & 0 & 500 \\
0 & 0 & 1 & 0 & 0 & 1 & 0 & 600 \\
0 & 0 & 0 & 1 & 0 & -1 & 1 & 0 \\
0 & 0 & 0 & 0 & 1 & 0 & 1 & 500
\end{bmatrix}
\Rightarrow
\begin{bmatrix}
1 & 0 & 0 & 0 & 0 & -1 & 0 & 0 \\
0 & 1 & 0 & 0 & 0 & 0 & -1 & 0 \\
0 & 0 & 1 & 0 & 0 & 1 & 0 & 600 \\
0 & 0 & 0 & 1 & 0 & -1 & 1 & 0 \\
0 & 0 & 0 & 0 & 1 & 0 & 1 & 500 \\
0 & 0 & 0 & 0 & 0 & 0 & 0 & 0
\end{bmatrix}
$$

Letting $x_7 = t$ and $x_6 = s$ be the free variables, we can write down the solution as follows.

$$x_1 = s$$
$$x_2 = t$$
$$x_3 = 600 - s$$
$$x_4 = s - t$$
$$x_5 = 500 - t$$
$$x_6 = s$$
$$x_7 = t$$

(b) If $x_6 = x_7 = 0$, then the solution is $x_1 = 0$, $x_2 = 0$, $x_3 = 600$, $x_4 = 0$, $x_5 = 500$, $x_6 = 0$, $x_7 = 0$.

(c) If $x_5 = 1000$ and $x_6 = 0$, then the solution is $x_1 = 0$, $x_2 = -500$, $x_3 = 600$, $x_4 = 500$, $x_5 = 1000$, $x_6 = 0$, and $x_7 = -500$.

21. (a) Each of the network's four junctions gives rise to a linear equation, as follows.

input = output	**junction**
$200 + x_2 = \quad x_1$	1
$x_4 = x_2 + 100$	2
$x_3 = x_4 + 200$	3
$x_1 + 100 = \quad x_3$	4

Rearranging these equations and forming the augmented matrix, we obtain

$$\begin{bmatrix} 1 & -1 & 0 & 0 & 200 \\ 0 & 1 & 0 & -1 & -100 \\ 0 & 0 & 1 & -1 & 200 \\ 1 & 0 & -1 & 0 & -100 \end{bmatrix}.$$

Gauss-Jordan elimination produces the matrix

$$\begin{bmatrix} 1 & 0 & 0 & -1 & 100 \\ 0 & 1 & 0 & -1 & -100 \\ 0 & 0 & 1 & -1 & 200 \\ 0 & 0 & 0 & 0 & 0 \end{bmatrix}.$$

Letting $x_4 = t$, we have $x_1 = 100 + t$, $x_2 = -100 + t$, $x_3 = 200 + t$, and $x_4 = t$, where t is a real number.

(b) When $x_4 = t = 0$, then $x_1 = 100$, $x_2 = -100$, $x_3 = 200$.

(c) When $x_4 = t = 100$, then $x_1 = 200$, $x_2 = 0$, $x_3 = 300$.

23. Applying Kirchoff's first law to either junction produces

$$I_1 + I_3 = I_2$$

and applying the second law to the two paths produces

$$R_1I_1 + R_2I_2 = 4I_1 + 3I_2 = 3$$
$$R_2I_2 + R_3I_3 = 3I_2 + \quad I_3 = 4.$$

Rearranging these equations, forming their augmented matrix, and using Gauss-Jordan elimination yields the following.

$$\begin{bmatrix} 1 & -1 & 1 & 0 \\ 4 & 3 & 0 & 3 \\ 0 & 3 & 1 & 4 \end{bmatrix} \implies \begin{bmatrix} 1 & 0 & 0 & 0 \\ 0 & 1 & 0 & 1 \\ 0 & 0 & 1 & 1 \end{bmatrix}$$

Thus, $I_1 = 0$, $I_2 = 1$, and $I_3 = 1$.

25. (a) To find the general solution, we let A have a volts and B have b volts. Applying Kirchoff's first law to either junction produces

$$I_1 + I_3 = I_2 \qquad \text{(Junction 1 or Junction 2)}$$

and applying the second law to the two paths produces

$$R_1 I_1 + R_2 I_2 = \ \ I_1 + 2I_2 = a \qquad \text{(Path 1)}$$
$$R_2 I_2 + R_3 I_3 = 2I_2 + 4I_3 = b. \qquad \text{(Path 2)}.$$

Rearranging these three equations and forming the augmented matrix yields

$$\begin{bmatrix} 1 & -1 & 1 & 0 \\ 1 & 2 & 0 & a \\ 0 & 2 & 4 & b \end{bmatrix}.$$

Gauss-Jordan elimination produces the matrix

$$\begin{bmatrix} 1 & 0 & 0 & (3a - b)/7 \\ 0 & 1 & 0 & (4a + b)/14 \\ 0 & 0 & 1 & (3b - 2a)/14 \end{bmatrix}.$$

When $a = 5$ and $b = 8$, then $I_1 = 1$, $I_2 = 2$, $I_3 = 1$.

(b) When $a = 2$ and $b = 6$, then $I_1 = 0$, $I_2 = 1$, $I_3 = 1$.

Chapter 1   Review Exercises

1. Choosing y and z as the free variables and letting $y = s$ and $z = t$, we have

$$-4x + 2s - 6t = 1$$
$$-4x = 1 - 2s + 6t$$
$$x = -\tfrac{1}{4} + \tfrac{1}{2}s - \tfrac{3}{2}t.$$

Thus, the solution set may be described as $x = -\tfrac{1}{4} + \tfrac{1}{2}s - \tfrac{3}{2}t,\, y = s,\, z = t$ where s and t are real numbers.

3. This matrix has the characteristic stair-step pattern of leading 1's so that it is in row-echelon form. However, the leading 1 in row three of column four has 1's above it, so the matrix is *not* in reduced row-echelon form.

5. Since the first row begins with -1, this matrix is not in row-echelon form.

7. This matrix corresponds to the system

$$x_1 + 2x_2 = 0$$
$$x_3 = 0.$$

Choosing $x_2 = t$ as the free variable we find that the solution set can be described as $x_1 = -2t,\, x_2 = t$, and $x_3 = 0$, where t is a real number.

9. We row reduce the augmented matrix for this system.

$$\begin{bmatrix} 1 & 1 & 2 \\ 1 & -1 & 0 \end{bmatrix} \Rightarrow \begin{bmatrix} 1 & 1 & 2 \\ 0 & -2 & -2 \end{bmatrix} \Rightarrow \begin{bmatrix} 1 & 1 & 2 \\ 0 & 1 & 1 \end{bmatrix} \Rightarrow \begin{bmatrix} 1 & 0 & 1 \\ 0 & 1 & 1 \end{bmatrix}$$

Converting back to a linear system, the solution is $x = 1$ and $y = 1$.

11. We begin by rearranging the given equations as

$$2x - y = 0$$
$$x - y = -4$$

The augmented matrix for this system is

$$\begin{bmatrix} 2 & -1 & 0 \\ 1 & -1 & -4 \end{bmatrix}$$

which is equivalent to the reduced row-echelon matrix

$$\begin{bmatrix} 1 & 0 & 4 \\ 0 & 1 & 8 \end{bmatrix}.$$

Thus, the solution set is $x = 4$ and $y = 8$.

13. We row reduce the augmented matrix for this system.

$$\begin{bmatrix} 1 & 1 & 0 \\ 2 & 1 & 0 \end{bmatrix} \Rightarrow \begin{bmatrix} 1 & 1 & 0 \\ 0 & -1 & 0 \end{bmatrix} \Rightarrow \begin{bmatrix} 1 & 1 & 0 \\ 0 & 1 & 0 \end{bmatrix} \Rightarrow \begin{bmatrix} 1 & 0 & 0 \\ 0 & 1 & 0 \end{bmatrix}$$

Converting back to a linear system, the solution is $x = 0$ and $y = 0$.

15. The augmented matrix for this system is

$$\begin{bmatrix} 1 & -1 & 9 \\ -1 & 1 & 1 \end{bmatrix}$$

which is equivalent to the reduced row-echelon matrix

$$\begin{bmatrix} 1 & -1 & 0 \\ 0 & 0 & 1 \end{bmatrix}.$$

Since the second row corresponds to $0 = 1$, which is an absurdity, we conclude that the system has no solution.

17. Multiplying both equations by 100 and forming the augmented matrix produces

$$\begin{bmatrix} 20 & 30 & 14 \\ 40 & 50 & 20 \end{bmatrix}.$$

Gauss-Jordan elimination yields the following.

$$\begin{bmatrix} 1 & \frac{3}{2} & \frac{7}{10} \\ 40 & 50 & 20 \end{bmatrix} \Rightarrow \begin{bmatrix} 1 & \frac{3}{2} & \frac{7}{10} \\ 0 & -10 & -8 \end{bmatrix} \Rightarrow \begin{bmatrix} 1 & \frac{3}{2} & \frac{7}{10} \\ 0 & 1 & \frac{4}{5} \end{bmatrix} \Rightarrow \begin{bmatrix} 1 & 0 & -\frac{1}{2} \\ 0 & 1 & \frac{4}{5} \end{bmatrix}$$

Hence, the solution is $x_1 = -\frac{1}{2}$ and $x_2 = \frac{4}{5}$.

19. Expanding the second equation, $3x + 2y = 0$, the augmented matrix for this system is

$$\begin{bmatrix} \frac{1}{2} & -\frac{1}{3} & 0 \\ 3 & 2 & 0 \end{bmatrix}$$

which is equivalent to the reduced row-echelon matrix

$$\begin{bmatrix} 1 & 0 & 0 \\ 0 & 1 & 0 \end{bmatrix}.$$

Thus, the solution set is $x = 0$ and $y = 0$.

21. The augmented matrix for this system is

$$\begin{bmatrix} -1 & 1 & 2 & 1 \\ 2 & 3 & 1 & -2 \\ 5 & 4 & 2 & 4 \end{bmatrix}.$$

which is equivalent to the reduced row-echelon matrix

$$\begin{bmatrix} 1 & 0 & 0 & 2 \\ 0 & 1 & 0 & -3 \\ 0 & 0 & 1 & 3 \end{bmatrix}.$$

Thus, the solution is $x = 2$, $y = -3$, and $z = 3$.

23. We use Gauss-Jordan elimination on the augmented matrix.

$$\begin{bmatrix} 2 & 3 & 3 & 3 \\ 6 & 6 & 12 & 13 \\ 12 & 9 & -1 & 2 \end{bmatrix} \implies \begin{bmatrix} 1 & 0 & 0 & \frac{1}{2} \\ 0 & 1 & 0 & -\frac{1}{3} \\ 0 & 0 & 1 & 1 \end{bmatrix}$$

Thus, $x = \frac{1}{2}$, $y = -\frac{1}{3}$, and $z = 1$.

25. The augmented matrix for this system is

$$\begin{bmatrix} 1 & -2 & 1 & -6 \\ 2 & -3 & 0 & -7 \\ -1 & 3 & -3 & 11 \end{bmatrix}$$

which is equivalent to the reduced row-echelon matrix

$$\begin{bmatrix} 1 & 0 & -3 & 4 \\ 0 & 1 & -2 & 5 \\ 0 & 0 & 0 & 0 \end{bmatrix}.$$

Choosing $z = t$ as the free variable we find that the solution set can be described by $x = 4 + 3t$, $y = 5 + 2t$, and $z = t$, where t is a real number.

27. We use the Gauss-Jordan elimination on the augmented matrix for this system.

$$\begin{bmatrix} 2 & 1 & 2 & 4 \\ 2 & 2 & 0 & 5 \\ 2 & -1 & 6 & 2 \end{bmatrix} \implies \begin{bmatrix} 1 & 0 & 2 & \frac{3}{2} \\ 0 & 1 & -2 & 1 \\ 0 & 0 & 0 & 0 \end{bmatrix}$$

Hence, the solution is $x = \frac{3}{2} - 2t$, $y = 1 + 2t$, $z = t$, where t is any real number.

29. The augmented matrix for this system is

$$\begin{bmatrix} 2 & 1 & 1 & 2 & -1 \\ 5 & -2 & 1 & -3 & 0 \\ -1 & 3 & 2 & 2 & 1 \\ 3 & 2 & 3 & -5 & 12 \end{bmatrix}$$

which is equivalent to the reduced row-echelon matrix

$$\begin{bmatrix} 1 & 0 & 0 & 0 & 1 \\ 0 & 1 & 0 & 0 & 4 \\ 0 & 0 & 1 & 0 & -3 \\ 0 & 0 & 0 & 1 & -2 \end{bmatrix}.$$

Thus, the solution is $x_1 = 1$, $x_2 = 4$, $x_3 = -3$, and $x_4 = -2$.

31. We use Gauss-Jordan elimination on the augmented matrix.

$$\begin{bmatrix} 1 & -2 & -8 & 0 \\ 3 & 2 & 0 & 0 \\ -1 & 1 & 7 & 0 \end{bmatrix} \implies \begin{bmatrix} 1 & 0 & 0 & 0 \\ 0 & 1 & 0 & 0 \\ 0 & 0 & 1 & 0 \end{bmatrix}$$

Hence, the solution is $x_1 = x_2 = x_3 = 0$.

33. The augmented matrix for this system is

$$\begin{bmatrix} 2 & -8 & 4 & 0 \\ 3 & -10 & 7 & 0 \\ 0 & 10 & 5 & 0 \end{bmatrix}$$

which is equivalent to the reduced row-echelon matrix

$$\begin{bmatrix} 1 & 0 & 4 & 0 \\ 0 & 1 & \frac{1}{2} & 0 \\ 0 & 0 & 0 & 0 \end{bmatrix}.$$

Choosing $x_3 = t$ as the free variable, we find that the solution set can be described by $x_1 = -4t$, $x_2 = -\frac{1}{2}t$, and $x_3 = t$, where t is a real number.

35. Forming the augmented matrix

$$\begin{bmatrix} k & 1 & 0 \\ 1 & k & 1 \end{bmatrix}$$

and using Gauss-Jordan elimination, we obtain

$$\begin{bmatrix} 1 & k & 1 \\ k & 1 & 0 \end{bmatrix} \Rightarrow \begin{bmatrix} 1 & k & 1 \\ 0 & 1-k^2 & -k \end{bmatrix} \Rightarrow \begin{bmatrix} 1 & k & 1 \\ 0 & 1 & \frac{k}{k^2-1} \end{bmatrix} \Rightarrow$$

$$\begin{bmatrix} 1 & 0 & \frac{-1}{k^2-1} \\ 0 & 1 & \frac{k}{k^2-1} \end{bmatrix}, \quad k^2 - 1 \neq 0.$$

Thus, the system is inconsistent if $k = \pm 1$.

37. We row reduce the augmented matrix.

$$\begin{bmatrix} 1 & 2 & 3 \\ a & b & -9 \end{bmatrix} \Rightarrow \begin{bmatrix} 1 & 2 & 3 \\ 0 & (b-2a) & (-9-3a) \end{bmatrix}$$

(a) There will be no solution if $b - 2a = 0$ *and* $-9 - 3a \neq 0$.
   That is, if $b = 2a$ and $a \neq -3$.

(b) There will be exactly one solution if $b \neq 2a$.

(c) There will be an infinite number of solutions if $b = 2a$ *and* $a = -3$.
   That is, if $a = -3$ and $b = -6$.

39. You can show that two matrices of the same size are row equivalent if they both row reduce to the same matrix. The two given matrices are row equivalent since each is row equivalent to the identity matrix.

41. Adding a multiple of row one to each row yields the following matrix.

$$
\begin{bmatrix}
1 & 2 & 3 & \cdots & n \\
0 & -n & -2n & \cdots & -(n-1)n \\
0 & -2n & -4n & \cdots & -2(n-1)n \\
\vdots & \vdots & \vdots & & \vdots \\
0 & -(n-1)n & -2(n-1)n & \cdots & -(n-1)(n-1)n
\end{bmatrix}
$$

Every row below row two is a multiple of row two. Therefore, we can reduce these rows to zeros.

$$
\begin{bmatrix}
1 & 2 & 3 & \cdots & n \\
0 & -n & -2n & \cdots & -(n-1)n \\
0 & 0 & 0 & \cdots & 0 \\
\vdots & \vdots & \vdots & & \vdots \\
0 & 0 & 0 & \cdots & 0
\end{bmatrix}
$$

Dividing row two by $-n$ yields a new second row.

$$
\begin{bmatrix}
1 & 2 & 3 & \cdots & n \\
0 & 1 & 2 & \cdots & n-1 \\
0 & 0 & 0 & \cdots & 0 \\
\vdots & \vdots & \vdots & & \vdots \\
0 & 0 & 0 & \cdots & 0
\end{bmatrix}
$$

Adding -2 times row two to row one yields a new first row.

$$
\begin{bmatrix}
1 & 0 & -1 & \cdots & 2-n \\
0 & 1 & 2 & \cdots & n-1 \\
0 & 0 & 0 & \cdots & 0 \\
\vdots & \vdots & \vdots & & \vdots \\
0 & 0 & 0 & \cdots & 0
\end{bmatrix}
$$

This matrix is in reduced row-echelon from.

43. (a) Since there are three points, we choose a second degree polynomial, $p(x) = a_0 + a_1x + a_2x^2$.

By substituting the values at each point into this equation we obtain the system

$$a_0 + 2a_1 + 4a_2 = 5$$
$$a_0 + 3a_1 + 9a_2 = 0$$
$$a_0 + 4a_1 + 16a_2 = 20.$$

Forming the augmented matrix

$$\begin{bmatrix} 1 & 2 & 4 & 5 \\ 1 & 3 & 9 & 0 \\ 1 & 4 & 16 & 20 \end{bmatrix}$$

and using Gauss-Jordan elimination we obtain

$$\begin{bmatrix} 1 & 0 & 0 & 90 \\ 0 & 1 & 0 & -\frac{135}{2} \\ 0 & 0 & 1 & \frac{25}{2} \end{bmatrix}$$

Thus, $p(x) = 90 - \frac{135}{2}x + \frac{25}{2}x^2$.

(b)

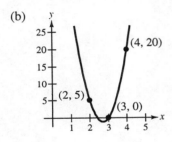

45. We establish the first year as $x = 0$ and substitute the values at each point into $p(x) = a_0 + a_1x + a_2x^2$ to obtain the system

$$a_0 = 50$$
$$a_0 + a_1 + a_2 = 60$$
$$a_0 + 2a_1 + 4a_2 = 75.$$

Forming the augmented matrix

$$\begin{bmatrix} 1 & 0 & 0 & 50 \\ 1 & 1 & 1 & 60 \\ 1 & 2 & 4 & 75 \end{bmatrix}$$

and using Gauss-Jordan elimination, we obtain

$$\begin{bmatrix} 1 & 0 & 0 & 50 \\ 0 & 1 & 0 & \frac{15}{2} \\ 0 & 0 & 1 & \frac{5}{2} \end{bmatrix}.$$

Thus, $p(x) = 50 + \frac{15}{2}x + \frac{5}{2}x^2$. To predict the sales in the fourth year we evaluate $p(x)$ when $x = 3$.

$$p(3) = 50 + \frac{15}{2}(3) + \frac{5}{2}(3)^2 = \$95.$$

47. (a) First we find the equations corresponding to each node in the network.

input	output	node
$x_1 + 200 = x_2 + x_4$		1
$x_6 + 100 = x_1 + x_3$		2
$x_2 + x_3 = x_5 + 300$		3
$x_4 + x_5 = \quad x_6$		4

Rearranging this system and forming the augmented matrix, we have

$$\begin{bmatrix} 1 & -1 & 0 & -1 & 0 & 0 & -200 \\ 1 & 0 & 1 & 0 & 0 & -1 & 100 \\ 0 & 1 & 1 & 0 & -1 & 0 & 300 \\ 0 & 0 & 0 & 1 & 1 & -1 & 0 \end{bmatrix}.$$

The equivalent reduced row-echelon matrix is

$$\begin{bmatrix} 1 & 0 & 1 & 0 & 0 & -1 & 100 \\ 0 & 1 & 1 & 0 & -1 & 0 & 300 \\ 0 & 0 & 0 & 1 & 1 & -1 & 0 \\ 0 & 0 & 0 & 0 & 0 & 0 & 0 \end{bmatrix}.$$

Choosing $x_3 = r, x_5 = s$, and $x_6 = t$ as the free variables, we obtain

$x_1 = 100 - r + t$
$x_2 = 300 - r + s$
$x_4 = -s + t.$

(b) When $x_3 = 100 = r, x_5 = 50 = s$, and $x_6 = 50 = t$, we have

$x_1 = 100 - 100 + 50 = 50$
$x_2 = 300 - 100 + 50 = 250$
$x_4 = -50 + 50 = 0.$

CHAPTER 2
Matrices

Section 2.1   Operations with Matrices

1. (a) $A + B = \begin{bmatrix} 1 & -1 \\ 2 & -1 \end{bmatrix} + \begin{bmatrix} 2 & -1 \\ -1 & 8 \end{bmatrix} = \begin{bmatrix} 1+2 & -1-1 \\ 2-1 & -1+8 \end{bmatrix} = \begin{bmatrix} 3 & -2 \\ 1 & 7 \end{bmatrix}$

(b) $A - B = \begin{bmatrix} 1 & -1 \\ 2 & -1 \end{bmatrix} - \begin{bmatrix} 2 & -1 \\ -1 & 8 \end{bmatrix} = \begin{bmatrix} 1-2 & -1+1 \\ 2+1 & -1-8 \end{bmatrix} = \begin{bmatrix} -1 & 0 \\ 3 & -9 \end{bmatrix}$

(c) $2A = 2\begin{bmatrix} 1 & -1 \\ 2 & -1 \end{bmatrix} = \begin{bmatrix} 2(1) & 2(-1) \\ 2(2) & 2(-1) \end{bmatrix} = \begin{bmatrix} 2 & -2 \\ 4 & -2 \end{bmatrix}$

(d) $2A - B = \begin{bmatrix} 2 & -2 \\ 4 & -2 \end{bmatrix} - \begin{bmatrix} 2 & -1 \\ -1 & 8 \end{bmatrix} = \begin{bmatrix} 0 & -1 \\ 5 & -10 \end{bmatrix}$

3. (a) $A + B = \begin{bmatrix} 6 & -1 \\ 2 & 4 \\ -3 & 5 \end{bmatrix} + \begin{bmatrix} 1 & 4 \\ -1 & 5 \\ 1 & 10 \end{bmatrix} = \begin{bmatrix} 6+1 & -1+4 \\ 2+(-1) & 4+5 \\ -3+1 & 5+10 \end{bmatrix} = \begin{bmatrix} 7 & 3 \\ 1 & 9 \\ -2 & 15 \end{bmatrix}$

(b) $A - B = \begin{bmatrix} 6 & -1 \\ 2 & 4 \\ -3 & 5 \end{bmatrix} - \begin{bmatrix} 1 & 4 \\ -1 & 5 \\ 1 & 10 \end{bmatrix} = \begin{bmatrix} 6-1 & -1-4 \\ 2-(-1) & 4-5 \\ -3-1 & 5-10 \end{bmatrix} = \begin{bmatrix} 5 & -5 \\ 3 & -1 \\ -4 & -5 \end{bmatrix}$

(c) $2A = 2\begin{bmatrix} 6 & -1 \\ 2 & 4 \\ -3 & 5 \end{bmatrix} = \begin{bmatrix} 2(6) & 2(-1) \\ 2(2) & 2(4) \\ 2(-3) & 2(5) \end{bmatrix} = \begin{bmatrix} 12 & -2 \\ 4 & 8 \\ -6 & 10 \end{bmatrix}$

(d) $2A - B = \begin{bmatrix} 12 & -2 \\ 4 & 8 \\ -6 & 10 \end{bmatrix} - \begin{bmatrix} 1 & 4 \\ -1 & 5 \\ 1 & 10 \end{bmatrix} = \begin{bmatrix} 12-1 & -2-4 \\ 4-(-1) & 8-5 \\ -6-1 & 10-10 \end{bmatrix} = \begin{bmatrix} 11 & -6 \\ 5 & 3 \\ -7 & 0 \end{bmatrix}$

5. (a) $A + B = \begin{bmatrix} 2 & 2 & -1 & 0 & 1 \\ 1 & 1 & -2 & 0 & -1 \end{bmatrix} + \begin{bmatrix} 1 & 1 & -1 & 1 & 0 \\ -3 & 4 & 9 & -6 & -7 \end{bmatrix}$

$= \begin{bmatrix} 3 & 3 & -2 & 1 & 1 \\ -2 & 5 & 7 & -6 & -8 \end{bmatrix}$

(b) $A - B = \begin{bmatrix} 2 & 2 & -1 & 0 & 1 \\ 1 & 1 & -2 & 0 & -1 \end{bmatrix} - \begin{bmatrix} 1 & 1 & -1 & 1 & 0 \\ -3 & 4 & 9 & -6 & -7 \end{bmatrix}$

$= \begin{bmatrix} 1 & 1 & 0 & -1 & 1 \\ 4 & -3 & -11 & 6 & 6 \end{bmatrix}$

(c) $2A = 2\begin{bmatrix} 2 & 2 & -1 & 0 & 1 \\ 1 & 1 & -2 & 0 & -1 \end{bmatrix} = \begin{bmatrix} 4 & 4 & -2 & 0 & 2 \\ 2 & 2 & -4 & 0 & -2 \end{bmatrix}$

(d) $2A - B = \begin{bmatrix} 4 & 4 & -2 & 0 & 2 \\ 2 & 2 & -4 & 0 & -2 \end{bmatrix} - \begin{bmatrix} 1 & 1 & -1 & 1 & 0 \\ -3 & 4 & 9 & -6 & -7 \end{bmatrix}$

$= \begin{bmatrix} 3 & 3 & -1 & -1 & 2 \\ 5 & -2 & -13 & 6 & 5 \end{bmatrix}$

7. (a) $c_{21} = 2a_{21} - 3b_{21} = 2(-3) - 3(0) = -6.$

(b) $c_{13} = 2a_{13} - 3b_{13} = 2(4) - 3(-7) = 29.$

9. Expanding both sides of the equation produces

$$\begin{bmatrix} 4x & 4y \\ 4z & -4 \end{bmatrix} = \begin{bmatrix} 2y + 8 & 2z + 2x \\ -2x + 10 & 2 - 2x \end{bmatrix}.$$

By setting corresponding entries equal to each other, we obtain four equations.

$$\begin{array}{rcll} 4x = & 2y + 8 & \Longrightarrow & 4x - 2y = 8 \\ 4y = & 2z + 2x & \Longrightarrow & 2x - 4y + 2z = 0 \\ 4z = & -2x + 10 & \Longrightarrow & 2x + 4z = 10 \\ -4 = & 2 - 2x & \Longrightarrow & 2x = 6 \end{array}$$

Gauss-Jordan elimination produces $x = 3$, $y = 2$, and $z = 1$.

11. (a) $AB = \begin{bmatrix} 1 & 2 \\ 4 & 2 \end{bmatrix}\begin{bmatrix} 2 & -1 \\ -1 & 8 \end{bmatrix} = \begin{bmatrix} 1(2) + 2(-1) & 1(-1) + 2(8) \\ 4(2) + 2(-1) & 4(-1) + 2(8) \end{bmatrix} = \begin{bmatrix} 0 & 15 \\ 6 & 12 \end{bmatrix}$

(b) $BA = \begin{bmatrix} 2 & -1 \\ -1 & 8 \end{bmatrix}\begin{bmatrix} 1 & 2 \\ 4 & 2 \end{bmatrix} = \begin{bmatrix} 2(1) + (-1)(4) & 2(2) + (-1)(2) \\ -1(1) + 8(4) & -1(2) + 8(2) \end{bmatrix} = \begin{bmatrix} -2 & 2 \\ 31 & 14 \end{bmatrix}$

13. (a) $AB = \begin{bmatrix} 3 & -1 \\ 1 & 3 \end{bmatrix}\begin{bmatrix} 1 & -3 \\ 3 & 1 \end{bmatrix} = \begin{bmatrix} 3(1) + (-1)(3) & 3(-3) + (-1)(1) \\ 1(1) + 3(3) & 1(-3) + 3(1) \end{bmatrix} = \begin{bmatrix} 0 & -10 \\ 10 & 0 \end{bmatrix}$

(b) $BA = \begin{bmatrix} 1 & -3 \\ 3 & 1 \end{bmatrix}\begin{bmatrix} 3 & -1 \\ 1 & 3 \end{bmatrix} = \begin{bmatrix} 1(3) + (-3)(1) & 1(-1) + (-3)(3) \\ 3(3) + 1(1) & 3(-1) + 1(3) \end{bmatrix} = \begin{bmatrix} 0 & -10 \\ 10 & 0 \end{bmatrix}$

15. (a) $AB = \begin{bmatrix} 1 & -1 & 7 \\ 2 & -1 & 8 \\ 3 & 1 & -1 \end{bmatrix} \begin{bmatrix} 1 & 1 & 2 \\ 2 & 1 & 1 \\ 1 & -3 & 2 \end{bmatrix}$

$$= \begin{bmatrix} 1(1) + (-1)(2) + 7(1) & 1(1) + (-1)(1) + 7(-3) & 1(2) + (-1)(1) + 7(2) \\ 2(1) + (-1)(2) + 8(1) & 2(1) + (-1)(1) + 8(-3) & 2(2) + (-1)(1) + 8(2) \\ 3(1) + 1(2) + (-1)(1) & 3(1) + 1(1) + (-1)(-3) & 3(2) + 1(1) + (-1)(2) \end{bmatrix}$$

$$= \begin{bmatrix} 6 & -21 & 15 \\ 8 & -23 & 19 \\ 4 & 7 & 5 \end{bmatrix}$$

(b) $BA = \begin{bmatrix} 1 & 1 & 2 \\ 2 & 1 & 1 \\ 1 & -3 & 2 \end{bmatrix} \begin{bmatrix} 1 & -1 & 7 \\ 2 & -1 & 8 \\ 3 & 1 & -1 \end{bmatrix}$

$$= \begin{bmatrix} 1(1) + 1(2) + 2(3) & 1(-1) + 1(-1) + 2(1) & 1(7) + 1(8) + 2(-1) \\ 2(1) + 1(2) + 1(3) & 2(-1) + 1(-1) + 1(1) & 2(7) + 1(8) + 1(-1) \\ 1(1) + (-3)(2) + 2(3) & 1(-1) + (-3)(-1) + 2(1) & 1(7) + (-3)(8) + 2(-1) \end{bmatrix}$$

$$= \begin{bmatrix} 9 & 0 & 13 \\ 7 & -2 & 21 \\ 1 & 4 & -19 \end{bmatrix}$$

17. (a) AB is not defined since A is 3×2 and B is 3×3.

(b) $BA = \begin{bmatrix} 0 & -1 & 0 \\ 4 & 0 & 2 \\ 8 & -1 & 7 \end{bmatrix} \begin{bmatrix} 2 & 1 \\ -3 & 4 \\ 1 & 6 \end{bmatrix}$

$$= \begin{bmatrix} 0(2) + (-1)(-3) + 0(1) & 0(1) + (-1)(4) + 0(6) \\ 4(2) + 0(-3) + 2(1) & 4(1) + 0(4) + 2(6) \\ 8(2) + (-1)(-3) + 7(1) & 8(1) + (-1)(4) + 7(6) \end{bmatrix} = \begin{bmatrix} 3 & -4 \\ 10 & 16 \\ 26 & 46 \end{bmatrix}$$

19. (a) $AB = \begin{bmatrix} -1 & 3 \\ 4 & -5 \\ 0 & 2 \end{bmatrix} \begin{bmatrix} 1 & 2 \\ 0 & 7 \end{bmatrix} = \begin{bmatrix} -1(1) + 3(0) & -1(2) + 3(7) \\ 4(1) + (-5)(0) & 4(2) + (-5)(7) \\ 0(1) + 2(0) & 0(2) + 2(7) \end{bmatrix} = \begin{bmatrix} -1 & 19 \\ 4 & -27 \\ 0 & 14 \end{bmatrix}$

(b) BA is not defined because B is a 2×2 matrix and A is a 3×2 matrix.

21. (a) $AB = \begin{bmatrix} 5 & 0 & 0 \\ 0 & -8 & 0 \\ 0 & 0 & 7 \end{bmatrix} \begin{bmatrix} \frac{1}{5} & 0 & 0 \\ 0 & -\frac{1}{8} & 0 \\ 0 & 0 & \frac{1}{7} \end{bmatrix}$

$= \begin{bmatrix} 5\left(\frac{1}{5}\right) + 0(0) + 0(0) & 5(0) + 0\left(-\frac{1}{8}\right) + 0(0) & 5(0) + 0(0) + 0\left(\frac{1}{7}\right) \\ 0\left(\frac{1}{5}\right) + (-8)(0) + 0(0) & 0(0) + (-8)\left(-\frac{1}{8}\right) + 0(0) & 0(0) + (-8)(0) + 0\left(\frac{1}{7}\right) \\ 0\left(\frac{1}{5}\right) + 0(0) + 7(0) & 0(0) + 0\left(-\frac{1}{8}\right) + 7(0) & 0(0) + 0(0) + 7\left(\frac{1}{7}\right) \end{bmatrix}$

$= \begin{bmatrix} 1 & 0 & 0 \\ 0 & 1 & 0 \\ 0 & 0 & 1 \end{bmatrix}$

(b) $BA = \begin{bmatrix} \frac{1}{5} & 0 & 0 \\ 0 & -\frac{1}{8} & 0 \\ 0 & 0 & \frac{1}{7} \end{bmatrix} \begin{bmatrix} 5 & 0 & 0 \\ 0 & -8 & 0 \\ 0 & 0 & 7 \end{bmatrix}$

$= \begin{bmatrix} \frac{1}{5}(5) + 0(0) + 0(0) & \frac{1}{5}(0) + 0(-8) + 0(0) & \frac{1}{5}(0) + 0(0) + 0(7) \\ 0(5) + \left(-\frac{1}{8}\right)(0) + 0(0) & 0(0) + \left(-\frac{1}{8}\right)(-8) + 0(0) & 0(0) + \left(-\frac{1}{8}\right)(0) + 0(7) \\ 0(5) + 0(0) + \frac{1}{7}(0) & 0(0) + 0(-8) + \frac{1}{7}(0) & 0(0) + 0(0) + \frac{1}{7}(7) \end{bmatrix}$

$= \begin{bmatrix} 1 & 0 & 0 \\ 0 & 1 & 0 \\ 0 & 0 & 1 \end{bmatrix}$

23. (a) $AB = \begin{bmatrix} 6 \\ -2 \\ 1 \\ 6 \end{bmatrix} \begin{bmatrix} 10 & 12 \end{bmatrix} = \begin{bmatrix} 6(10) & 6(12) \\ -2(10) & -2(12) \\ 1(10) & 1(12) \\ 6(10) & 6(12) \end{bmatrix} = \begin{bmatrix} 60 & 72 \\ -20 & -24 \\ 10 & 12 \\ 60 & 72 \end{bmatrix}$

(b) BA is not defined because B is a 1×2 matrix and A is a 4×1 matrix.

25. In matrix form $A\mathbf{x} = \mathbf{b}$, the system is

$\begin{bmatrix} 1 & 3 \\ 2 & -1 \end{bmatrix} \begin{bmatrix} x_1 \\ x_2 \end{bmatrix} = \begin{bmatrix} -1 \\ 3 \end{bmatrix}.$

We use Gauss-Jordan elimination on the augmented matrix.

$\begin{bmatrix} 1 & 3 & -1 \\ 2 & -1 & 3 \end{bmatrix} \implies \begin{bmatrix} 1 & 0 & \frac{8}{7} \\ 0 & 1 & -\frac{5}{7} \end{bmatrix}$

Thus, the solution is $\mathbf{x} = \begin{bmatrix} \frac{8}{7} \\ -\frac{5}{7} \end{bmatrix}.$

27. In the matrix form $A\mathbf{x} = \mathbf{b}$, the system is

$$\begin{bmatrix} 8 & -8 \\ -3 & 2 \end{bmatrix} \begin{bmatrix} x_1 \\ x_2 \end{bmatrix} = \begin{bmatrix} 0 \\ 0 \end{bmatrix}.$$

Using the Gauss-Jordan elimination on the augmented matrix

$$\begin{bmatrix} 8 & -8 & 0 \\ -3 & 2 & 0 \end{bmatrix}$$

we find that

$$\mathbf{x} = \begin{bmatrix} 0 \\ 0 \end{bmatrix}.$$

29. In the matrix form $A\mathbf{x} = \mathbf{b}$, the system is

$$\begin{bmatrix} 1 & 0 & 2 \\ 3 & -2 & 1 \\ -2 & 2 & -1 \end{bmatrix} \begin{bmatrix} x_1 \\ x_2 \\ x_3 \end{bmatrix} = \begin{bmatrix} 5 \\ 8 \\ -3 \end{bmatrix}.$$

Using the Gauss-Jordan elimination on the augmented matrix

$$\begin{bmatrix} 1 & 0 & 2 & 5 \\ 3 & -2 & 1 & 8 \\ -2 & 2 & -1 & -3 \end{bmatrix}$$

we find that

$$\mathbf{x} = \begin{bmatrix} 5 \\ \frac{7}{2} \\ 0 \end{bmatrix}.$$

31. Expanding the left side of the equation produces

$$\begin{bmatrix} 1 & 2 \\ 3 & 5 \end{bmatrix} A = \begin{bmatrix} 1 & 2 \\ 3 & 5 \end{bmatrix} \begin{bmatrix} a_{11} & a_{12} \\ a_{21} & a_{22} \end{bmatrix} = \begin{bmatrix} a_{11} + 2a_{21} & a_{12} + 2a_{22} \\ 3a_{11} + 5a_{21} & 3a_{12} + 5a_{22} \end{bmatrix} = \begin{bmatrix} 1 & 0 \\ 0 & 1 \end{bmatrix}$$

from which we obtain the system

$$\begin{array}{rcl} a_{11} \phantom{+ 2a_{21}} + 2a_{21} \phantom{+ 2a_{22}} &=& 1 \\ a_{12} \phantom{+ 2a_{21}} + 2a_{22} &=& 0 \\ 3a_{11} \phantom{+ 5a_{21}} + 5a_{21} \phantom{+ 5a_{22}} &=& 0 \\ 3a_{12} \phantom{+ 5a_{21}} + 5a_{22} &=& 1. \end{array}$$

Solving by Gauss-Jordan elimination yields $a_{11} = -5$, $a_{12} = 2$, $a_{21} = 3$, and $a_{22} = -1$.

Thus, we have

$$A = \begin{bmatrix} -5 & 2 \\ 3 & -1 \end{bmatrix}.$$

33. Equating the corresponding matrix entries produces the following linear system.

$$
\begin{aligned}
a - b \quad\quad\quad &= -1 \\
2b + c \quad\quad &= 3 \\
c - 2d &= 5 \\
a \quad\quad\quad + d &= -2
\end{aligned}
$$

Using Gaussian elimination, we find that the solution to this system is
$a = -2 - t, b = -t - 1, c = 5 + 2t$, and $d = t$, where t is any real number.

35. We expand $AB = BA$ as follows.

$$
\begin{bmatrix} w & x \\ y & z \end{bmatrix} \begin{bmatrix} 1 & 1 \\ -1 & 1 \end{bmatrix} = \begin{bmatrix} 1 & 1 \\ -1 & 1 \end{bmatrix} \begin{bmatrix} w & x \\ y & z \end{bmatrix}
$$

$$
\begin{bmatrix} w - x & w + x \\ y - z & y + z \end{bmatrix} = \begin{bmatrix} w + y & x + z \\ -w + y & -x + z \end{bmatrix}
$$

This yields the system of equations

$$
\begin{aligned}
-x - y \quad\quad &= 0 \\
w \quad\quad - z &= 0 \\
w \quad\quad - z &= 0 \\
x + y \quad\quad &= 0.
\end{aligned}
$$

Using Gauss-Jordan elimination we solve this system to obtain $w = t, x = -s, y = s$, and $z = t$, where s and t are any real numbers. Thus, $w = z$ and $x = -y$.

37. $AA = \begin{bmatrix} -1 & 0 & 0 \\ 0 & 2 & 0 \\ 0 & 0 & 3 \end{bmatrix} \begin{bmatrix} -1 & 0 & 0 \\ 0 & 2 & 0 \\ 0 & 0 & 3 \end{bmatrix}$

$$
= \begin{bmatrix} -1(-1) + 0(0) + 0(0) & -1(0) + 0(2) + 0(0) & -1(0) + 0(0) + 0(3) \\ 0(-1) + 2(0) + 0(0) & 0(0) + 2(2) + 0(0) & 0(0) + 2(0) + 0(3) \\ 0(-1) + 0(0) + 3(0) & 0(0) + 0(2) + 3(0) & 0(0) + 0(0) + 3(3) \end{bmatrix}
$$

$$
= \begin{bmatrix} 1 & 0 & 0 \\ 0 & 4 & 0 \\ 0 & 0 & 9 \end{bmatrix}
$$

39. Let A and B be diagonal matrices of sizes $n \times n$.

Then,

$$
AB = [c_{ij}] = \left[\sum_{k=1}^{n} a_{ik} b_{kj} \right]
$$

where $c_{ij} = 0$ if $i \neq j$, and $c_{ii} = a_{ii} b_{ii}$ otherwise. The entries of BA are exactly the same.

41. The trace is the sum of the elements on the main diagonal.

$$
1 + (-2) + 3 = 2.
$$

43. (a) $Tr(A + B) = Tr([a_{ij} + b_{ij}]) = \sum_{i=1}^{n}(a_{ii} + b_{ii}) = \sum_{i=1}^{n}a_{ii} + \sum_{i=1}^{n}b_{ii}$

$$= Tr(A) + Tr(B)$$

(b) $Tr(cA) = Tr([ca_{ii}]) = \sum_{i=1}^{n}ca_{ii} = c\sum_{i=1}^{n}a_{ii}$

$$= cTr(A)$$

45. Let $A = \begin{bmatrix} a_{11} & a_{12} \\ a_{21} & a_{22} \end{bmatrix}$.

Then the given matrix equation expands to

$$\begin{bmatrix} a_{11} + a_{21} & a_{12} + a_{22} \\ a_{11} + a_{21} & a_{12} + a_{22} \end{bmatrix} = \begin{bmatrix} 1 & 0 \\ 0 & 1 \end{bmatrix}.$$

Since $a_{11} + a_{21} = 1$ and $a_{11} + a_{21} = 0$ cannot both be true, we conclude that there is no solution.

47. If AB is a square $m \times m$ matrix, then A must be of size $m \times n$ and B of size $n \times m$. Hence, BA is a square matrix (of size $n \times n$).

49. Let rows s and t be identical in the matrix A. $a_{sj} = a_{tj}$, for $j = 1, \ldots, n$. Let

$AB = [c_{ij}]$, where $c_{ij} = \sum_{k=1}^{n}a_{ik}b_{kj}$.

$$c_{sj} = \sum_{k=1}^{n}a_{sk}b_{kj}$$

$$c_{tj} = \sum_{k=1}^{n}a_{tk}b_{kj}$$

Since $a_{sk} = a_{tk}$ for $k = 1, \ldots, n$, rows s and t of AB are the same.

51. If production were increased by 10%, then the new production would be

$$(1.10)\begin{bmatrix} 100 & 90 & 70 & 30 \\ 40 & 20 & 60 & 60 \end{bmatrix} = \begin{bmatrix} 110 & 99 & 77 & 33 \\ 44 & 22 & 66 & 66 \end{bmatrix}.$$

53. $BA = [3.75 \quad 7.00]\begin{bmatrix} 100 & 75 & 75 \\ 125 & 150 & 100 \end{bmatrix}$

$$= [1250 \quad 1131.25 \quad 981.25]$$

This row matrix represents the profit at each of the three outlets.

55. $AB = \left[\begin{array}{cc|cc} 1 & 2 & 0 & 0 \\ 0 & 1 & 0 & 0 \\ \hline 0 & 0 & 2 & 1 \end{array}\right]\left[\begin{array}{cc|c} 1 & 2 & 0 \\ -1 & 1 & 0 \\ \hline 0 & 0 & 1 \\ 0 & 0 & 3 \end{array}\right] = \left[\begin{array}{cc|c} -1 & 4 & 0 \\ -1 & 1 & 0 \\ \hline 0 & 0 & 5 \end{array}\right]$

57. The augmented matrix row reduces as follows.

$$\begin{bmatrix} 1 & -1 & 2 & -1 \\ 3 & -3 & 1 & 7 \end{bmatrix} \Rightarrow \begin{bmatrix} 1 & -1 & 0 & 3 \\ 0 & 0 & 1 & -2 \end{bmatrix}$$

There are an infinite number of solutions. For example, $x_3 = -2, x_2 = 0, x_1 = 3$. Thus,

$$\mathbf{b} = \begin{bmatrix} -1 \\ 7 \end{bmatrix} = 3 \begin{bmatrix} 1 \\ 3 \end{bmatrix} + 0 \begin{bmatrix} -1 \\ -3 \end{bmatrix} - 2 \begin{bmatrix} 2 \\ 1 \end{bmatrix}.$$

59. If $B = [\mathbf{b}_1 \quad \mathbf{b}_2 \quad \cdots \quad \mathbf{b}_p]$ has columns $\mathbf{b}_i$, then AB is formed by multiplying A times each column $\mathbf{b}_i$.

Similarly, if A has rows $\mathbf{a}_1, \ldots, \mathbf{a}_m$, then AB is formed by multiplying each row $\mathbf{a}_i$ by B.

Section 2.2   Properties of Matrix Operations

1. $3\begin{bmatrix} 1 & 2 \\ 3 & 4 \end{bmatrix} + (-4)\begin{bmatrix} 0 & 1 \\ -1 & 2 \end{bmatrix} = \begin{bmatrix} 3 & 6 \\ 9 & 12 \end{bmatrix} + \begin{bmatrix} 0 & -4 \\ 4 & -8 \end{bmatrix} = \begin{bmatrix} 3 & 2 \\ 13 & 4 \end{bmatrix}$

3. $ab(B) = (3)(-4)\begin{bmatrix} 0 & 1 \\ -1 & 2 \end{bmatrix} = (-12)\begin{bmatrix} 0 & 1 \\ -1 & 2 \end{bmatrix} = \begin{bmatrix} 0 & -12 \\ 12 & -24 \end{bmatrix}$

5. $[3 - (-4)]\left(\begin{bmatrix} 1 & 2 \\ 3 & 4 \end{bmatrix} - \begin{bmatrix} 0 & 1 \\ -1 & 2 \end{bmatrix}\right) = 7\begin{bmatrix} 1 & 1 \\ 4 & 2 \end{bmatrix} = \begin{bmatrix} 7 & 7 \\ 28 & 14 \end{bmatrix}$

7. $3X + \begin{bmatrix} -8 & 0 \\ 2 & -10 \\ -6 & 4 \end{bmatrix} = \begin{bmatrix} 1 & 2 \\ -2 & 1 \\ 4 & 4 \end{bmatrix}$

$$3X = \begin{bmatrix} 1 & 2 \\ -2 & 1 \\ 4 & 4 \end{bmatrix} - \begin{bmatrix} -8 & 0 \\ 2 & -10 \\ -6 & 4 \end{bmatrix} = \begin{bmatrix} 9 & 2 \\ -4 & 11 \\ 10 & 0 \end{bmatrix}$$

$$X = \tfrac{1}{3}\begin{bmatrix} 9 & 2 \\ -4 & 11 \\ 10 & 0 \end{bmatrix} = \begin{bmatrix} 3 & \frac{2}{3} \\ -\frac{4}{3} & \frac{11}{3} \\ \frac{10}{3} & 0 \end{bmatrix}$$

9. $X = 3A - 2B = 3\begin{bmatrix} -4 & 0 \\ 1 & -5 \\ -3 & 2 \end{bmatrix} - 2\begin{bmatrix} 1 & 2 \\ -2 & 1 \\ 4 & 4 \end{bmatrix} = \begin{bmatrix} -14 & -4 \\ 7 & -17 \\ -17 & -2 \end{bmatrix}$

11. $B(CA) = \begin{bmatrix} 1 & 3 \\ -1 & 2 \end{bmatrix}\left(\begin{bmatrix} 0 & 1 \\ -1 & 0 \end{bmatrix}\begin{bmatrix} 1 & 2 & 3 \\ 0 & 1 & -1 \end{bmatrix}\right)$

$\quad = \begin{bmatrix} 1 & 3 \\ -1 & 2 \end{bmatrix}\begin{bmatrix} 0 & 1 & -1 \\ -1 & -2 & -3 \end{bmatrix} = \begin{bmatrix} -3 & -5 & -10 \\ -2 & -5 & -5 \end{bmatrix}$

13. $\left(\begin{bmatrix} 1 & 3 \\ -1 & 2 \end{bmatrix} + \begin{bmatrix} 0 & 1 \\ -1 & 0 \end{bmatrix}\right)\begin{bmatrix} 1 & 2 & 3 \\ 0 & 1 & -1 \end{bmatrix} = \begin{bmatrix} 1 & 4 \\ -2 & 2 \end{bmatrix}\begin{bmatrix} 1 & 2 & 3 \\ 0 & 1 & -1 \end{bmatrix}$

$$= \begin{bmatrix} 1 & 6 & -1 \\ -2 & -2 & -8 \end{bmatrix}$$

15. $\left(-2\begin{bmatrix} 1 & 3 \\ -1 & 2 \end{bmatrix}\right)\left(\begin{bmatrix} 0 & 1 \\ -1 & 0 \end{bmatrix} + \begin{bmatrix} 0 & 1 \\ -1 & 0 \end{bmatrix}\right) = \begin{bmatrix} -2 & -6 \\ 2 & -4 \end{bmatrix}\begin{bmatrix} 0 & 2 \\ -2 & 0 \end{bmatrix} = \begin{bmatrix} 12 & -4 \\ 8 & 4 \end{bmatrix}$

17. $AC = \begin{bmatrix} 1 & 2 & 3 \\ 0 & 5 & 4 \\ 3 & -2 & 1 \end{bmatrix}\begin{bmatrix} 0 & 0 & 0 \\ 0 & 0 & 0 \\ 4 & -2 & 3 \end{bmatrix} = \begin{bmatrix} 12 & -6 & 9 \\ 16 & -8 & 12 \\ 4 & -2 & 3 \end{bmatrix}$

$\quad = \begin{bmatrix} 4 & -6 & 3 \\ 5 & 4 & 4 \\ -1 & 0 & 1 \end{bmatrix}\begin{bmatrix} 0 & 0 & 0 \\ 0 & 0 & 0 \\ 4 & -2 & 3 \end{bmatrix} = BC$

But $A \neq B$.

19. $A^2 = \begin{bmatrix} 1 & 2 \\ 0 & -1 \end{bmatrix} \begin{bmatrix} 1 & 2 \\ 0 & -1 \end{bmatrix} = \begin{bmatrix} 1 & 0 \\ 0 & 1 \end{bmatrix} = I$

21. $\begin{bmatrix} 1 & 2 \\ 0 & -1 \end{bmatrix} \left(\begin{bmatrix} 1 & 0 \\ 0 & 1 \end{bmatrix} + \begin{bmatrix} 1 & 2 \\ 0 & -1 \end{bmatrix} \right) = \begin{bmatrix} 1 & 2 \\ 0 & -1 \end{bmatrix} \begin{bmatrix} 2 & 2 \\ 0 & 0 \end{bmatrix} = \begin{bmatrix} 2 & 2 \\ 0 & 0 \end{bmatrix}$

23. (a) $A^T = \begin{bmatrix} 2 & -1 & 3 \\ 4 & 3 & -5 \end{bmatrix}^T = \begin{bmatrix} 2 & 4 \\ -1 & 3 \\ 3 & -5 \end{bmatrix}$

(b) $A^T A = \begin{bmatrix} 2 & 4 \\ -1 & 3 \\ 3 & -5 \end{bmatrix} \begin{bmatrix} 2 & -1 & 3 \\ 4 & 3 & -5 \end{bmatrix} = \begin{bmatrix} 20 & 10 & -14 \\ 10 & 10 & -18 \\ -14 & -18 & 34 \end{bmatrix}$

(c) $AA^T = \begin{bmatrix} 2 & -1 & 3 \\ 4 & 3 & -5 \end{bmatrix} \begin{bmatrix} 2 & 4 \\ -1 & 3 \\ 3 & -5 \end{bmatrix} = \begin{bmatrix} 14 & -10 \\ -10 & 50 \end{bmatrix}$

25. (a) $A^T = \begin{bmatrix} 6 & 0 \\ 0 & -4 \\ 7 & 5 \end{bmatrix}^T = \begin{bmatrix} 6 & 0 & 7 \\ 0 & -4 & 5 \end{bmatrix}$

(b) $A^T A = \begin{bmatrix} 6 & 0 & 7 \\ 0 & -4 & 5 \end{bmatrix} \begin{bmatrix} 6 & 0 \\ 0 & -4 \\ 7 & 5 \end{bmatrix} = \begin{bmatrix} 85 & 35 \\ 35 & 41 \end{bmatrix}$

(c) $AA^T = \begin{bmatrix} 6 & 0 \\ 0 & -4 \\ 7 & 5 \end{bmatrix} \begin{bmatrix} 6 & 0 & 7 \\ 0 & -4 & 5 \end{bmatrix} = \begin{bmatrix} 36 & 0 & 42 \\ 0 & 16 & -20 \\ 42 & -20 & 74 \end{bmatrix}$

27. In general, $AB \neq BA$ for matrices. Hence, $(A + B)(A - B) = A^2 \div BA - AB - B^2 \neq A^2 - B^2$.

29. $(AB)^T = \left(\begin{bmatrix} -1 & 1 & -2 \\ 2 & 0 & 1 \end{bmatrix} \begin{bmatrix} -3 & 0 \\ 1 & 2 \\ 1 & -1 \end{bmatrix} \right)^T = \begin{bmatrix} 2 & 4 \\ -5 & -1 \end{bmatrix}^T = \begin{bmatrix} 2 & -5 \\ 4 & -1 \end{bmatrix}$

$B^T A^T = \begin{bmatrix} -3 & 0 \\ 1 & 2 \\ 1 & -1 \end{bmatrix}^T \begin{bmatrix} -1 & 1 & -2 \\ 2 & 0 & 1 \end{bmatrix}^T = \begin{bmatrix} -3 & 1 & 1 \\ 0 & 2 & -1 \end{bmatrix} \begin{bmatrix} -1 & 2 \\ 1 & 0 \\ -2 & 1 \end{bmatrix}$

$= \begin{bmatrix} 2 & -5 \\ 4 & -1 \end{bmatrix}$

31. $Z = aX + bY$

$\begin{bmatrix} 1 \\ 4 \\ 4 \end{bmatrix} = a \begin{bmatrix} 1 \\ 2 \\ 3 \end{bmatrix} + b \begin{bmatrix} 1 \\ 0 \\ 2 \end{bmatrix}$

$\begin{bmatrix} 1 \\ 4 \\ 4 \end{bmatrix} = \begin{bmatrix} a + b \\ 2a \\ 3a + 2b \end{bmatrix}$

By setting corresponding entries equal and solving the resulting system for a and b, we obtain $a = 2$ and $b = -1$.

33. $aX + bY + cW = a\begin{bmatrix} 1 \\ 2 \\ 3 \end{bmatrix} + b\begin{bmatrix} 1 \\ 0 \\ 2 \end{bmatrix} + c\begin{bmatrix} 0 \\ 0 \\ 1 \end{bmatrix} = \begin{bmatrix} 0 \\ 0 \\ 0 \end{bmatrix}.$

This matrix equation yields the linear system

$$\begin{array}{rl} a + b & = 0 \\ 2a & = 0 \\ 3a + 2b + c & = 0. \end{array}$$

The only solution to this system is $a = b = c = 0$.

35. $A^{19} = \begin{bmatrix} 1^{19} & 0 & 0 \\ 0 & (-1)^{19} & 0 \\ 0 & 0 & 1^{19} \end{bmatrix} = \begin{bmatrix} 1 & 0 & 0 \\ 0 & -1 & 0 \\ 0 & 0 & 1 \end{bmatrix}$

37. There are four possibilities.

$$A = \begin{bmatrix} 3 & 0 \\ 0 & 2 \end{bmatrix}, \quad A = \begin{bmatrix} -3 & 0 \\ 0 & 2 \end{bmatrix}, \quad A = \begin{bmatrix} 3 & 0 \\ 0 & -2 \end{bmatrix}, \quad A = \begin{bmatrix} -3 & 0 \\ 0 & -2 \end{bmatrix}.$$

39. $f(A) = \begin{bmatrix} 2 & 0 \\ 4 & 5 \end{bmatrix}^2 - 5\begin{bmatrix} 2 & 0 \\ 4 & 5 \end{bmatrix} + 2\begin{bmatrix} 1 & 0 \\ 0 & 1 \end{bmatrix}$

$\qquad = \begin{bmatrix} 2 & 0 \\ 4 & 5 \end{bmatrix}\begin{bmatrix} 2 & 0 \\ 4 & 5 \end{bmatrix} - \begin{bmatrix} 10 & 0 \\ 20 & 25 \end{bmatrix} + \begin{bmatrix} 2 & 0 \\ 0 & 2 \end{bmatrix}$

$\qquad = \begin{bmatrix} 4 & 0 \\ 28 & 25 \end{bmatrix} + \begin{bmatrix} -8 & 0 \\ -20 & -23 \end{bmatrix}$

$\qquad = \begin{bmatrix} -4 & 0 \\ 8 & 2 \end{bmatrix}$

41. $f(A) = \begin{bmatrix} 3 & 1 & 4 \\ 0 & 2 & 6 \\ 0 & 0 & 5 \end{bmatrix}^3 - 10\begin{bmatrix} 3 & 1 & 4 \\ 0 & 2 & 6 \\ 0 & 0 & 5 \end{bmatrix}^2 + 31\begin{bmatrix} 3 & 1 & 4 \\ 0 & 2 & 6 \\ 0 & 0 & 5 \end{bmatrix} - 30\begin{bmatrix} 1 & 0 & 0 \\ 0 & 1 & 0 \\ 0 & 0 & 1 \end{bmatrix}$

$\qquad = \begin{bmatrix} 27 & 19 & 256 \\ 0 & 8 & 234 \\ 0 & 0 & 125 \end{bmatrix} - 10\begin{bmatrix} 9 & 5 & 38 \\ 0 & 4 & 42 \\ 0 & 0 & 25 \end{bmatrix} + 31\begin{bmatrix} 3 & 1 & 4 \\ 0 & 2 & 6 \\ 0 & 0 & 5 \end{bmatrix} - 30\begin{bmatrix} 1 & 0 & 0 \\ 0 & 1 & 0 \\ 0 & 0 & 1 \end{bmatrix}$

$\qquad = \begin{bmatrix} 0 & 0 & 0 \\ 0 & 0 & 0 \\ 0 & 0 & 0 \end{bmatrix}$

43. $A + (B + C) = [a_{ij}] + ([b_{ij}] + [c_{ij}]) = ([a_{ij}] + [b_{ij}]) + [c_{ij}] = (A + B) + C$

45. $1A = 1[a_{ij}] = [1a_{ij}] = [a_{ij}] = A$

47. (1) $A + 0_{mn} = [a_{ij}] + [0] = [a_{ij} + 0] = [a_{ij}] = A$

$\quad$ (2) $A + (-A) = [a_{ij}] + [-a_{ij}] = [a_{ij} + (-a_{ij})] = [0] = 0_{mn}$

$\quad$ (3) Let $cA = 0_{mn}$ and suppose $c \neq 0$. Then, $0_{mn} = cA \Rightarrow c^{-1}0_{mn} = c^{-1}(cA) = (c^{-1}c)A = A$
$\quad$ and hence, $A = 0_{mn}$.

49. (1) The entry in the ith row and jth column of AI_n is

$$a_{i1}0 + \cdots + a_{ij}1 + \cdots + a_{in}0 = a_{ij}.$$

(2) The entry in the ith row and jth column of $I_m A$ is

$$0a_{1j} + \cdots + 1a_{ij} + \cdots + 0a_{nj} = a_{ij}.$$

51. $(AA^T)^T = (A^T)^T A^T = AA^T$ which implies that AA^T is symmetric.
Similarly, $(A^T A)^T = A^T (A^T)^T = A^T A$, which implies that $A^T A$ is symmetric.

53. Since

$$A^T = \begin{bmatrix} 0 & -2 \\ 2 & 0 \end{bmatrix} = -\begin{bmatrix} 0 & 2 \\ -2 & 0 \end{bmatrix} = -A$$

the matrix is skew-symmetric.

55. Since

$$A^T = \begin{bmatrix} 0 & 2 & 1 \\ 2 & 0 & 3 \\ 1 & 3 & 0 \end{bmatrix} = A$$

the matrix is symmetric.

57. Since $A^T = -A$, the diagonal element a_{ii} satisfies $a_{ii} = -a_{ii}$, or $a_{ii} = 0$.

59. For any $n \times n$ Matrix A, $\dfrac{A + A^T}{2}$ is symmetric and $\dfrac{A - A^T}{2}$ is skew-symmetric.

Hence, $A = \dfrac{A + A^T}{2} + \dfrac{A - A^T}{2} = B + C$ is the required decomposition.

If $A = \begin{bmatrix} 2 & 5 & 3 \\ -3 & 6 & 0 \\ 4 & 1 & 1 \end{bmatrix}$, then we have

$$\frac{A + A^T}{2} = \begin{bmatrix} 2 & 1 & \frac{7}{2} \\ 1 & 6 & \frac{1}{2} \\ \frac{7}{2} & \frac{1}{2} & 1 \end{bmatrix} = B, \text{ symmetric, and}$$

$$\frac{A - A^T}{2} = \begin{bmatrix} 0 & 4 & -\frac{1}{2} \\ -4 & 0 & -\frac{1}{2} \\ \frac{1}{2} & \frac{1}{2} & 0 \end{bmatrix} = C, \text{ skew-symmetric.}$$

Thus, $A = B + C$.

61. (a) $\begin{bmatrix} 0 & 1 \\ 1 & 0 \end{bmatrix}\begin{bmatrix} -1 & 1 \\ 1 & 0 \end{bmatrix} = \begin{bmatrix} 1 & 0 \\ -1 & 1 \end{bmatrix}$ (many answers possible)

(b) Let A and B be symmetric.
If $AB = BA$, then $(AB)^T = B^T A^T = BA = AB$ and AB is symmetric.
If $(AB)^T = AB$, then $AB = (AB)^T = B^T A^T = BA$ and $AB = BA$.

Section 2.3   The Inverse of a Matrix

1. $AB = \begin{bmatrix} 1 & 2 \\ 3 & 4 \end{bmatrix} \begin{bmatrix} -2 & 1 \\ \frac{3}{2} & -\frac{1}{2} \end{bmatrix} = \begin{bmatrix} 1 & 0 \\ 0 & 1 \end{bmatrix}$

$BA = \begin{bmatrix} -2 & 1 \\ \frac{3}{2} & -\frac{1}{2} \end{bmatrix} \begin{bmatrix} 1 & 2 \\ 3 & 4 \end{bmatrix} = \begin{bmatrix} 1 & 0 \\ 0 & 1 \end{bmatrix}$

3. $AB = \begin{bmatrix} -2 & 2 & 3 \\ 1 & -1 & 0 \\ 0 & 1 & 4 \end{bmatrix} \left(\frac{1}{3}\right) \begin{bmatrix} -4 & -5 & 3 \\ -4 & -8 & 3 \\ 1 & 2 & 0 \end{bmatrix} = \left(\frac{1}{3}\right) \begin{bmatrix} 3 & 0 & 0 \\ 0 & 3 & 0 \\ 0 & 0 & 3 \end{bmatrix}$

$= \begin{bmatrix} 1 & 0 & 0 \\ 0 & 1 & 0 \\ 0 & 0 & 1 \end{bmatrix}$

$BA = \left(\frac{1}{3}\right) \begin{bmatrix} -4 & -5 & 3 \\ -4 & -8 & 3 \\ 1 & 2 & 0 \end{bmatrix} \begin{bmatrix} -2 & 2 & 3 \\ 1 & -1 & 0 \\ 0 & 1 & 4 \end{bmatrix} = \left(\frac{1}{3}\right) \begin{bmatrix} 3 & 0 & 0 \\ 0 & 3 & 0 \\ 0 & 0 & 3 \end{bmatrix}$

$= \begin{bmatrix} 1 & 0 & 0 \\ 0 & 1 & 0 \\ 0 & 0 & 1 \end{bmatrix}$

5. $AB = \begin{bmatrix} 2 & 0 & 0 \\ 0 & -3 & 0 \\ 0 & 0 & 4 \end{bmatrix} \begin{bmatrix} \frac{1}{2} & 0 & 0 \\ 0 & -\frac{1}{3} & 0 \\ 0 & 0 & \frac{1}{4} \end{bmatrix} = \begin{bmatrix} 1 & 0 & 0 \\ 0 & 1 & 0 \\ 0 & 0 & 1 \end{bmatrix}$

$BA = \begin{bmatrix} \frac{1}{2} & 0 & 0 \\ 0 & -\frac{1}{3} & 0 \\ 0 & 0 & \frac{1}{4} \end{bmatrix} \begin{bmatrix} 2 & 0 & 0 \\ 0 & -3 & 0 \\ 0 & 0 & 4 \end{bmatrix} = \begin{bmatrix} 1 & 0 & 0 \\ 0 & 1 & 0 \\ 0 & 0 & 1 \end{bmatrix}$

7. We use the formula

$$A^{-1} = \frac{1}{ad - bc} \begin{bmatrix} d & -b \\ -c & a \end{bmatrix}, \quad \text{where} \quad A = \begin{bmatrix} a & b \\ c & d \end{bmatrix} = \begin{bmatrix} 1 & 2 \\ 3 & 7 \end{bmatrix}.$$

Thus, the inverse is

$$A^{-1} = \frac{1}{(1)(7) - (2)(3)} \begin{bmatrix} 7 & -2 \\ -3 & 1 \end{bmatrix} = \begin{bmatrix} 7 & -2 \\ -3 & 1 \end{bmatrix}.$$

9. We use the formula

$$A^{-1} = \frac{1}{ad - bc} \begin{bmatrix} d & -b \\ -c & a \end{bmatrix}, \quad \text{where} \quad A = \begin{bmatrix} a & b \\ c & d \end{bmatrix} = \begin{bmatrix} -7 & 33 \\ 4 & -19 \end{bmatrix}.$$

Thus, the inverse is

$$A^{-1} = \frac{1}{(-7)(-19) - 33(4)} \begin{bmatrix} -19 & -33 \\ -4 & -7 \end{bmatrix} = \begin{bmatrix} -19 & -33 \\ -4 & -7 \end{bmatrix}.$$

11. From the formula

$$A^{-1} = \frac{1}{ad - bc} \begin{bmatrix} d & -b \\ -c & a \end{bmatrix}, \quad \text{where} \quad A = \begin{bmatrix} a & b \\ c & d \end{bmatrix} = \begin{bmatrix} 2 & 4 \\ 4 & 8 \end{bmatrix},$$

we see that $ad - bc = 2(8) - 4(4) = 0$. Thus, the matrix has no inverse.

13. We use the formula

$$A^{-1} = \frac{1}{ad - bc} \begin{bmatrix} d & -b \\ -c & a \end{bmatrix}, \quad \text{where} \quad A = \begin{bmatrix} a & b \\ c & d \end{bmatrix} = \begin{bmatrix} 2 & 3 \\ 1 & 4 \end{bmatrix}.$$

Thus, the inverse is

$$A^{-1} = \frac{1}{(2)(4) - (3)(1)} \begin{bmatrix} 4 & -3 \\ -1 & 2 \end{bmatrix} = \begin{bmatrix} \frac{4}{5} & -\frac{3}{5} \\ -\frac{1}{5} & \frac{2}{5} \end{bmatrix}.$$

15. We adjoin the identity matrix to form

$$[A : I] = \begin{bmatrix} 1 & 1 & 1 & \vdots & 1 & 0 & 0 \\ 3 & 5 & 4 & \vdots & 0 & 1 & 0 \\ 3 & 6 & 5 & \vdots & 0 & 0 & 1 \end{bmatrix}.$$

Using elementary row operations, we rewrite this matrix in reduced row-echelon form.

$$[I : A^{-1}] = \begin{bmatrix} 1 & 0 & 0 & \vdots & 1 & 1 & -1 \\ 0 & 1 & 0 & \vdots & -3 & 2 & -1 \\ 0 & 0 & 1 & \vdots & 3 & -3 & 2 \end{bmatrix}.$$

Therefore, the inverse is

$$A^{-1} = \begin{bmatrix} 1 & 1 & -1 \\ -3 & 2 & -1 \\ 3 & -3 & 2 \end{bmatrix}.$$

17. We adjoin the identity matrix to form

$$[A : I] = \begin{bmatrix} 1 & 2 & -1 & \vdots & 1 & 0 & 0 \\ 3 & 7 & -10 & \vdots & 0 & 1 & 0 \\ 7 & 16 & -21 & \vdots & 0 & 0 & 1 \end{bmatrix}.$$

Using elementary row operation, we find that we cannot form the identity matrix on the left side.

$$\begin{bmatrix} 1 & 0 & 13 & \vdots & 0 & -16 & 7 \\ 0 & 1 & -7 & \vdots & 0 & 7 & -3 \\ 0 & 0 & 0 & \vdots & 1 & 2 & -1 \end{bmatrix}$$

Therefore, the matrix has no inverse.

19. We adjoin the identity matrix to form

$$[A \vdots I] = \begin{bmatrix} 1 & -2 & -1 & -2 & \vdots & 1 & 0 & 0 & 0 \\ 3 & -5 & -2 & -3 & \vdots & 0 & 1 & 0 & 0 \\ 2 & -5 & -2 & -5 & \vdots & 0 & 0 & 1 & 0 \\ -1 & 4 & 4 & 11 & \vdots & 0 & 0 & 0 & 1 \end{bmatrix}.$$

Using elementary row operations, we reduce the matrix as follows.

$$[I \vdots A^{-1}] = \begin{bmatrix} 1 & 0 & 0 & 0 & \vdots & -24 & 7 & 1 & -2 \\ 0 & 1 & 0 & 0 & \vdots & -10 & 3 & 0 & -1 \\ 0 & 0 & 1 & 0 & \vdots & -29 & 7 & 3 & -2 \\ 0 & 0 & 0 & 1 & \vdots & 12 & -3 & -1 & 1 \end{bmatrix}$$

Therefore, the inverse is

$$A^{-1} = \begin{bmatrix} -24 & 7 & 1 & -2 \\ -10 & 3 & 0 & -1 \\ -29 & 7 & 3 & -2 \\ 12 & -3 & -1 & 1 \end{bmatrix}.$$

21. We adjoin the identity matrix to form

$$[A \vdots I] = \begin{bmatrix} 1 & 1 & 2 & \vdots & 1 & 0 & 0 \\ 3 & 1 & 0 & \vdots & 0 & 1 & 0 \\ -2 & 0 & 3 & \vdots & 0 & 0 & 1 \end{bmatrix}.$$

Using elementary row operations, we rewrite this matrix in reduced row-echelon form.

$$[I \vdots A^{-1}] = \begin{bmatrix} 1 & 0 & 0 & \vdots & -\frac{3}{2} & \frac{3}{2} & 1 \\ 0 & 1 & 0 & \vdots & \frac{9}{2} & -\frac{7}{2} & -3 \\ 0 & 0 & 1 & \vdots & -1 & 1 & 1 \end{bmatrix}$$

Therefore, the inverse is

$$A^{-1} = \begin{bmatrix} -\frac{3}{2} & \frac{3}{2} & 1 \\ \frac{9}{2} & -\frac{7}{2} & -3 \\ -1 & 1 & 1 \end{bmatrix}.$$

23. We adjoin the identity matrix to form

$$[A : I] = \begin{bmatrix} 0.1 & 0.2 & 0.3 & : & 1 & 0 & 0 \\ -0.3 & 0.2 & 0.2 & : & 0 & 1 & 0 \\ 0.5 & 0.5 & 0.5 & : & 0 & 0 & 1 \end{bmatrix}.$$

Using elementary row operations, we reduce the matrix as follows.

$$[I : A^{-1}] = \begin{bmatrix} 1 & 0 & 0 & : & 0 & -2 & 0.8 \\ 0 & 1 & 0 & : & -10 & 4 & 4.4 \\ 0 & 0 & 1 & : & 10 & -2 & -3.2 \end{bmatrix}$$

Therefore, the inverse is

$$A^{-1} = \begin{bmatrix} 0 & -2 & 0.8 \\ -10 & 4 & 4.4 \\ 10 & -2 & -3.2 \end{bmatrix}.$$

25. We adjoin the identity matrix to form

$$[A : I] = \begin{bmatrix} 1 & 0 & 3 & 0 & : & 1 & 0 & 0 & 0 \\ 0 & 2 & 0 & 4 & : & 0 & 1 & 0 & 0 \\ 1 & 0 & 3 & 0 & : & 0 & 0 & 1 & 0 \\ 0 & 2 & 0 & 4 & : & 0 & 0 & 0 & 1 \end{bmatrix}.$$

Using elementary row operations, we find that we cannot form the identity matrix on the left side.

$$[A : I] = \begin{bmatrix} 1 & 0 & 3 & 0 & : & 0 & 0 & 1 & 0 \\ 0 & 1 & 0 & 2 & : & 0 & 0 & 0 & \frac{1}{2} \\ 0 & 0 & 0 & 0 & : & 1 & 0 & -1 & 0 \\ 0 & 0 & 0 & 0 & : & 0 & 1 & 0 & -1 \end{bmatrix} \neq [I : A^{-1}]$$

Therefore, the matrix has no inverse.

27. We adjoin the identity matrix to form

$$[A : I] = \begin{bmatrix} 1 & 0 & 0 & : & 1 & 0 & 0 \\ 3 & 4 & 0 & : & 0 & 1 & 0 \\ 2 & 5 & 5 & : & 0 & 0 & 1 \end{bmatrix}.$$

Using elementary row operations, we rewrite this matrix in reduced row-echelon form.

$$[I : A^{-1}] = \begin{bmatrix} 1 & 0 & 0 & : & 1 & 0 & 0 \\ 0 & 1 & 0 & : & -\frac{3}{4} & \frac{1}{4} & 0 \\ 0 & 0 & 1 & : & \frac{7}{20} & -\frac{1}{4} & \frac{1}{5} \end{bmatrix}$$

Therefore, the inverse is

$$A^{-1} = \begin{bmatrix} 1 & 0 & 0 \\ -\frac{3}{4} & \frac{1}{4} & 0 \\ \frac{7}{20} & -\frac{1}{4} & \frac{1}{5} \end{bmatrix}.$$

29. We adjoin the identity matrix to form

$$[A : I] = \begin{bmatrix} -8 & 0 & 0 & 0 & \vdots & 1 & 0 & 0 & 0 \\ 0 & 1 & 0 & 0 & \vdots & 0 & 1 & 0 & 0 \\ 0 & 0 & 0 & 0 & \vdots & 0 & 0 & 1 & 0 \\ 0 & 0 & 0 & -5 & \vdots & 0 & 0 & 0 & 1 \end{bmatrix}.$$

Using elementary row operations, we find that we cannot form the identity matrix on the left side. Therefore, the matrix A has no inverse.

31. The coefficient matrix for each system is

$$A = \begin{bmatrix} -1 & 1 \\ -2 & 1 \end{bmatrix}$$

and the formula for the inverse of a 2×2 matrix produces

$$A^{-1} = \frac{1}{-1 - (-2)} \begin{bmatrix} 1 & -1 \\ 2 & -1 \end{bmatrix} = \begin{bmatrix} 1 & -1 \\ 2 & -1 \end{bmatrix}.$$

(a) $X = A^{-1}B = \begin{bmatrix} 1 & -1 \\ 2 & -1 \end{bmatrix} \begin{bmatrix} 4 \\ 0 \end{bmatrix} = \begin{bmatrix} 4 \\ 8 \end{bmatrix}$

The solution is $x = 4$ and $y = 8$.

(b) $X = A^{-1}B = \begin{bmatrix} 1 & -1 \\ 2 & -1 \end{bmatrix} \begin{bmatrix} -3 \\ 5 \end{bmatrix} = \begin{bmatrix} -8 \\ -11 \end{bmatrix}$

The solution is $x = -8$ and $y = -11$.

(c) $X = A^{-1}B = \begin{bmatrix} 1 & -1 \\ 2 & -1 \end{bmatrix} \begin{bmatrix} 0 \\ 0 \end{bmatrix} = \begin{bmatrix} 0 \\ 0 \end{bmatrix}$

The solution is $x = 0$ and $y = 0$.

33. The coefficient matrix for each system is

$$A = \begin{bmatrix} 3 & 2 & 2 \\ 2 & 2 & 2 \\ -4 & 4 & 3 \end{bmatrix}.$$

Using the algorithm to invert a matrix, we find that the inverse is

$$A^{-1} = \begin{bmatrix} 1 & -1 & 0 \\ 7 & -8.5 & 1 \\ -8 & 10 & -1 \end{bmatrix}$$

(a) $X = A^{-1}B = \begin{bmatrix} 1 & -1 & 0 \\ 7 & -8.5 & 1 \\ -8 & 10 & -1 \end{bmatrix} \begin{bmatrix} 0 \\ 5 \\ 2 \end{bmatrix} = \begin{bmatrix} -5 \\ -40.5 \\ 48 \end{bmatrix}$

The solution is $x = -5$, $y = -40.5$ and $z = 48$.

(b) $X = A^{-1}B = \begin{bmatrix} 1 & -1 & 0 \\ 7 & -8.5 & 1 \\ -8 & 10 & -1 \end{bmatrix} \begin{bmatrix} -1 \\ 2 \\ 0 \end{bmatrix} = \begin{bmatrix} -3 \\ -24 \\ 28 \end{bmatrix}$

The solution is $x = -3$, $y = -24$ and $z = 28$.

(c) $X = A^{-1}B = \begin{bmatrix} 1 & -1 & 0 \\ 7 & -8.5 & 1 \\ -8 & 10 & -1 \end{bmatrix} \begin{bmatrix} 0 \\ 0 \\ 0 \end{bmatrix} = \begin{bmatrix} 0 \\ 0 \\ 0 \end{bmatrix}.$

The solution is $x = y = z = 0$.

35. (a) $(AB)^{-1} = B^{-1}A^{-1} = \begin{bmatrix} 7 & -3 \\ 2 & 0 \end{bmatrix} \begin{bmatrix} 2 & 5 \\ -7 & 6 \end{bmatrix} = \begin{bmatrix} 35 & 17 \\ 4 & 10 \end{bmatrix}$

(b) $(A^T)^{-1} = (A^{-1})^T = \begin{bmatrix} 2 & 5 \\ -7 & 6 \end{bmatrix}^T = \begin{bmatrix} 2 & -7 \\ 5 & 6 \end{bmatrix}$

(c) $A^2 = (A^{-1})^2 = \begin{bmatrix} 2 & 5 \\ -7 & 6 \end{bmatrix} \begin{bmatrix} 2 & 5 \\ -7 & 6 \end{bmatrix} = \begin{bmatrix} -31 & 40 \\ -56 & 1 \end{bmatrix}$

(d) $(2A)^{-1} = \frac{1}{2}A^{-1} = \frac{1}{2} \begin{bmatrix} 2 & 5 \\ -7 & 6 \end{bmatrix} = \begin{bmatrix} 1 & \frac{5}{2} \\ -\frac{7}{2} & 3 \end{bmatrix}$

37. (a) $(AB)^{-1} = B^{-1}A^{-1} = \begin{bmatrix} 2 & 4 & \frac{5}{2} \\ -\frac{3}{4} & 2 & \frac{1}{4} \\ \frac{1}{4} & \frac{1}{2} & 2 \end{bmatrix} \begin{bmatrix} 1 & -\frac{1}{2} & \frac{3}{4} \\ \frac{3}{2} & \frac{1}{2} & -2 \\ \frac{1}{4} & 1 & \frac{1}{2} \end{bmatrix} = \begin{bmatrix} \frac{69}{8} & \frac{7}{2} & -\frac{21}{4} \\ \frac{37}{16} & \frac{13}{8} & -\frac{71}{16} \\ \frac{3}{2} & \frac{17}{8} & \frac{3}{16} \end{bmatrix}$

(b) $(A^T)^{-1} = (A^{-1})^T = \begin{bmatrix} 1 & \frac{3}{2} & \frac{1}{4} \\ -\frac{1}{2} & \frac{1}{2} & 1 \\ \frac{3}{4} & -2 & \frac{1}{2} \end{bmatrix}$

(c) $A^{-2} = (A^{-1})^2 = \begin{bmatrix} 1 & -\frac{1}{2} & \frac{3}{4} \\ \frac{3}{2} & \frac{1}{2} & -2 \\ \frac{1}{4} & 1 & \frac{1}{2} \end{bmatrix}^2 = \begin{bmatrix} \frac{7}{16} & 0 & \frac{17}{8} \\ \frac{7}{4} & -\frac{5}{2} & -\frac{7}{8} \\ \frac{15}{8} & \frac{7}{8} & -\frac{25}{16} \end{bmatrix}$

(d) $(2A)^{-1} = \frac{1}{2}A^{-1} = \begin{bmatrix} \frac{1}{2} & -\frac{1}{4} & \frac{3}{8} \\ \frac{3}{4} & \frac{1}{4} & -1 \\ \frac{1}{8} & \frac{1}{2} & \frac{1}{4} \end{bmatrix}$

39. The inverse of A is given by

$$A^{-1} = \frac{1}{2x - 9} \begin{bmatrix} -3 & -x \\ 2 & 3 \end{bmatrix}.$$

Letting $A^{-1} = A$, we find that $1/(2x - 9) = -1$. Thus, $x = 4$.

41. First we find $2A$.

$$2A = [(2A)^{-1}]^{-1} = \frac{1}{4 - 6} \begin{bmatrix} 4 & -2 \\ -3 & 1 \end{bmatrix} = \begin{bmatrix} -2 & 1 \\ \frac{3}{2} & -\frac{1}{2} \end{bmatrix}$$

Then, we divide by 2 to obtain

$$A = \tfrac{1}{2}(2A) = \tfrac{1}{2} \begin{bmatrix} -2 & 1 \\ \frac{3}{2} & -\frac{1}{2} \end{bmatrix} = \begin{bmatrix} -1 & \frac{1}{2} \\ \frac{3}{4} & -\frac{1}{4} \end{bmatrix}.$$

43. We use mathematical induction. The property is clearly true if $k = 1$. Suppose the property is true for $k = n$, and consider the case for $k = n + 1$.

$$(A^{n+1})^{-1} = (AA^n)^{-1} = (A^n)^{-1}A^{-1} = \underbrace{(A^{-1}\cdots A^{-1})}_{n \text{ times}} A^{-1} = \underbrace{A^{-1}\cdots A^{-1}}_{n + 1 \text{ times}}$$

45. Let A be symmetric and nonsingular. Then $A^T = A$ and $(A^{-1})^T = (A^T)^{-1} = A^{-1}$.

47. $(I - 2A)(I - 2A) = I^2 - 2IA - 2AI + 4A^2$

$\qquad\qquad\qquad = I - 4A + 4A^2$

$\qquad\qquad\qquad = I - 4A + 4A \qquad$ (since $A = A^2$)

$\qquad\qquad\qquad = I$

Thus, $(I - 2A)^{-1} = I - 2A$.

49. Since A is invertible, we can multiply both sides of the equation $AB = 0$ by A^{-1} to obtain the following.

$$A^{-1}(AB) = A^{-1}O$$
$$(A^{-1}A)B = O$$
$$B = O$$

51. No. For instance,

$$\begin{bmatrix} 1 & 0 \\ 0 & 1 \end{bmatrix} + \begin{bmatrix} -1 & 0 \\ 0 & -1 \end{bmatrix} = \begin{bmatrix} 0 & 0 \\ 0 & 0 \end{bmatrix}.$$

53. To find the inverses, we take the reciprocals of the diagonal entries.

(a) $A^{-1} = \begin{bmatrix} -1 & 0 & 0 \\ 0 & \frac{1}{3} & 0 \\ 0 & 0 & \frac{1}{2} \end{bmatrix}$ (b) $A^{-1} = \begin{bmatrix} 2 & 0 & 0 \\ 0 & 3 & 0 \\ 0 & 0 & 4 \end{bmatrix}$

55. $H = I - 2\mathbf{uu}^T$.

$$H^T = (I - 2\mathbf{uu}^T)^T = I - 2(\mathbf{uu}^T)^T = I - 2\mathbf{uu}^T = H$$

Thus, H is symmetric.

$$\begin{aligned} HH &= (I - 2\mathbf{uu}^T)(I - 2\mathbf{uu}^T) \\ &= I - 4\mathbf{uu}^T + 4\mathbf{uu}^T\mathbf{uu}^T \\ &= I - 4\mathbf{uu}^T + 4\mathbf{uu}^T, \qquad \text{since } u^T u = 1 \\ &= I \end{aligned}$$

Thus, $H^{-1} = H$ and H is nonsingular.

Section 2.4   Elementary Matrices

1. The matrix *is* elementary. It can be obtained by multiplying the second row of I_2 by 2.

3. The matrix *is* elementary. Two times the first row was added to the second row.

5. The matrix is *not* elementary. The first row was multiplied by 2 and the second and third rows were interchanged.

7. The matrix is *not* elementary. The third row was multiplied by 0.

9. This matrix *is* elementary. It can be obtained by multiplying the second row of I_4 by -5, and adding the result to the third row.

11. *B* is obtained by interchanging the first and third rows of *A*. Thus,

$$E = \begin{bmatrix} 0 & 0 & 1 \\ 0 & 1 & 0 \\ 1 & 0 & 0 \end{bmatrix}.$$

13. *A* is obtained by interchanging the first and third rows of *B*. Thus,

$$E = \begin{bmatrix} 0 & 0 & 1 \\ 0 & 1 & 0 \\ 1 & 0 & 0 \end{bmatrix}.$$

15. To obtain the inverse matrix, we reverse the elementary row operation that produced it. Thus, we interchange the first and second rows of I_2 to obtain

$$E^{-1} = \begin{bmatrix} 0 & 1 \\ 1 & 0 \end{bmatrix}.$$

17. To obtain the inverse matrix, we reverse the elementary row operation that produced it. Thus, we add -4 times the first row of I_2 to the second row to obtain

$$E^{-1} = \begin{bmatrix} 1 & 0 \\ -4 & 1 \end{bmatrix}.$$

19. To obtain the inverse matrix, we reverse the elementary row operation that produced it. Thus, we interchange the first and third rows to obtain

$$E^{-1} = \begin{bmatrix} 0 & 0 & 1 \\ 0 & 1 & 0 \\ 1 & 0 & 0 \end{bmatrix}.$$

21. To obtain the inverse matrix, we reverse the elementary row operation that produced it. Thus, we divide the first row of I_3 by *k* to obtain

$$E^{-1} = \begin{bmatrix} \dfrac{1}{k} & 0 & 0 \\ 0 & 1 & 0 \\ 0 & 0 & 1 \end{bmatrix}, \quad k \neq 0.$$

23. To obtain the inverse matrix, we reverse the elementary row operation that produced it. Thus, we add $-k$ times the third row to the second row to obtain

$$E^{-1} = \begin{bmatrix} 1 & 0 & 0 & 0 \\ 0 & 1 & -k & 0 \\ 0 & 0 & 1 & 0 \\ 0 & 0 & 0 & 1 \end{bmatrix}.$$

25.

Matrix	Elementary Row Operation	Elementary Matrix
$\begin{bmatrix} 1 & 2 \\ 0 & -2 \end{bmatrix}$	Add -1 times row one to row two.	$E_1 = \begin{bmatrix} 1 & 0 \\ -1 & 1 \end{bmatrix}$
$\begin{bmatrix} 1 & 0 \\ 0 & -2 \end{bmatrix}$	Add row two to row one.	$E_2 = \begin{bmatrix} 1 & 1 \\ 0 & 1 \end{bmatrix}$
$\begin{bmatrix} 1 & 0 \\ 0 & 1 \end{bmatrix}$	Divide row two by -2.	$E_3 = \begin{bmatrix} 1 & 0 \\ 0 & -\frac{1}{2} \end{bmatrix}$

Since $E_3 E_2 E_1 A = I_2$, we can factor A as follows.

$$A = E_1^{-1} E_2^{-1} E_3^{-1} = \begin{bmatrix} 1 & 0 \\ 1 & 1 \end{bmatrix} \begin{bmatrix} 1 & -1 \\ 0 & 1 \end{bmatrix} \begin{bmatrix} 1 & 0 \\ 0 & -2 \end{bmatrix}$$

Note that this factorization is not unique. For example, another factorization is

$$A = \begin{bmatrix} 0 & 1 \\ 1 & 0 \end{bmatrix} \begin{bmatrix} 1 & 0 \\ 1 & 1 \end{bmatrix} \begin{bmatrix} 1 & 0 \\ 0 & 2 \end{bmatrix}.$$

27. We reduce the matrix $A = \begin{bmatrix} 4 & -1 \\ 3 & -1 \end{bmatrix}$ as follows.

Matrix	Elementary Row Operation	Elementary Matrix
$\begin{bmatrix} 1 & 0 \\ 3 & -1 \end{bmatrix}$	(-1) times row two to row one	$E_1 = \begin{bmatrix} 1 & -1 \\ 0 & 1 \end{bmatrix}$
$\begin{bmatrix} 1 & 0 \\ 0 & -1 \end{bmatrix}$	-3 times row one to row two	$E_2 = \begin{bmatrix} 1 & 0 \\ -3 & 1 \end{bmatrix}$
$\begin{bmatrix} 1 & 0 \\ 0 & 1 \end{bmatrix}$	-1 times row two	$E_3 = \begin{bmatrix} 1 & 0 \\ 0 & -1 \end{bmatrix}$

Since $E_3 E_2 E_1 A = I_2$, one way to factor A is as follows.

$$A = E_1^{-1} E_2^{-1} E_3^{-1} = \begin{bmatrix} 1 & 1 \\ 0 & 1 \end{bmatrix} \begin{bmatrix} 1 & 0 \\ 3 & 1 \end{bmatrix} \begin{bmatrix} 1 & 0 \\ 0 & -1 \end{bmatrix}$$

29.

Matrix	Elementary Row Operation	Elementary Matrix

$$\begin{bmatrix} 1 & -2 & 0 \\ 0 & 1 & 0 \\ 0 & 0 & 1 \end{bmatrix} \qquad \text{Add row one to row two.} \qquad E_1 = \begin{bmatrix} 1 & 0 & 0 \\ 1 & 1 & 0 \\ 0 & 0 & 1 \end{bmatrix}$$

$$\begin{bmatrix} 1 & 0 & 0 \\ 0 & 1 & 0 \\ 0 & 0 & 1 \end{bmatrix} \qquad \text{Add 2 times row two to row one.} \qquad E_2 = \begin{bmatrix} 1 & 2 & 0 \\ 0 & 1 & 0 \\ 0 & 0 & 1 \end{bmatrix}$$

Since $E_2 E_1 A = I_3$, one way to factor A is

$$A = E_1^{-1} E_2^{-1} = \begin{bmatrix} 1 & 0 & 0 \\ -1 & 1 & 0 \\ 0 & 0 & 1 \end{bmatrix} \begin{bmatrix} 1 & -2 & 0 \\ 0 & 1 & 0 \\ 0 & 0 & 1 \end{bmatrix}.$$

31. We reduce the matrix $A = \begin{bmatrix} 2 & 0 & -8 \\ 2 & 2 & 2 \\ 0 & 2 & 7 \end{bmatrix}$ as follows.

Matrix	Elementary Row Operation	Elementary Matrix
$\begin{bmatrix} 1 & 0 & -4 \\ 2 & 2 & 2 \\ 0 & 2 & 7 \end{bmatrix}$	$\frac{1}{2}$ times row one	$E_1 = \begin{bmatrix} \frac{1}{2} & 0 & 0 \\ 0 & 1 & 0 \\ 0 & 0 & 1 \end{bmatrix}$
$\begin{bmatrix} 1 & 0 & -4 \\ 0 & 2 & 10 \\ 0 & 2 & 7 \end{bmatrix}$	-2 times row one to row two	$E_2 = \begin{bmatrix} 1 & 0 & 0 \\ -2 & 1 & 0 \\ 0 & 0 & 1 \end{bmatrix}$
$\begin{bmatrix} 1 & 0 & -4 \\ 0 & 1 & 5 \\ 0 & 2 & 7 \end{bmatrix}$	$\frac{1}{2}$ times row two	$E_3 = \begin{bmatrix} 1 & 0 & 0 \\ 0 & \frac{1}{2} & 0 \\ 0 & 0 & 1 \end{bmatrix}$
$\begin{bmatrix} 1 & 0 & -4 \\ 0 & 1 & 5 \\ 0 & 0 & -3 \end{bmatrix}$	-2 times row two to row three	$E_4 = \begin{bmatrix} 1 & 0 & 0 \\ 0 & 1 & 0 \\ 0 & -2 & 1 \end{bmatrix}$
$\begin{bmatrix} 1 & 0 & -4 \\ 0 & 1 & 5 \\ 0 & 0 & 1 \end{bmatrix}$	$-\frac{1}{3}$ times row three	$E_5 = \begin{bmatrix} 1 & 0 & 0 \\ 0 & 1 & 0 \\ 0 & 0 & -\frac{1}{3} \end{bmatrix}$
$\begin{bmatrix} 1 & 0 & -4 \\ 0 & 1 & 0 \\ 0 & 0 & 1 \end{bmatrix}$	-5 times row three to row two	$E_6 = \begin{bmatrix} 1 & 0 & 0 \\ 0 & 1 & -5 \\ 0 & 0 & 1 \end{bmatrix}$
$\begin{bmatrix} 1 & 0 & 0 \\ 0 & 1 & 0 \\ 0 & 0 & 1 \end{bmatrix}$	4 times row three to row one	$E_7 = \begin{bmatrix} 1 & 0 & 4 \\ 0 & 1 & 0 \\ 0 & 0 & 1 \end{bmatrix}$

Thus, one way to factor A is

$$A = E_1^{-1} E_2^{-1} \ldots E_7^{-1} =$$

$$\begin{bmatrix} 2 & 0 & 0 \\ 0 & 1 & 0 \\ 0 & 0 & 1 \end{bmatrix} \begin{bmatrix} 1 & 0 & 0 \\ 2 & 1 & 0 \\ 0 & 0 & 1 \end{bmatrix} \begin{bmatrix} 1 & 0 & 0 \\ 0 & 2 & 0 \\ 0 & 0 & 1 \end{bmatrix} \begin{bmatrix} 1 & 0 & 0 \\ 0 & 1 & 0 \\ 0 & 2 & 1 \end{bmatrix}$$

$$\begin{bmatrix} 1 & 0 & 0 \\ 0 & 1 & 0 \\ 0 & 0 & -3 \end{bmatrix} \begin{bmatrix} 1 & 0 & 0 \\ 0 & 1 & 5 \\ 0 & 0 & 1 \end{bmatrix} \begin{bmatrix} 1 & 0 & -4 \\ 0 & 1 & 0 \\ 0 & 0 & 1 \end{bmatrix}.$$

33. (a) EA has the same rows as A except the two rows that are interchanged in E will be interchanged in EA.

(b) Multiplying a matrix on the left by E interchanges the same two rows that are interchanged from I_n in E. Thus, multiplying E by itself interchanges the rows twice and we have $E^2 = I_n$.

35. $A^{-1} = \begin{bmatrix} 1 & 0 & 0 \\ 0 & 1 & 0 \\ 0 & 0 & c \end{bmatrix}^{-1} \begin{bmatrix} 1 & 0 & 0 \\ b & 1 & 0 \\ 0 & 0 & 1 \end{bmatrix}^{-1} \begin{bmatrix} 1 & a & 0 \\ 0 & 1 & 0 \\ 0 & 0 & 1 \end{bmatrix}^{-1}$

$= \begin{bmatrix} 1 & 0 & 0 \\ 0 & 1 & 0 \\ 0 & 0 & 1/c \end{bmatrix} \begin{bmatrix} 1 & 0 & 0 \\ -b & 1 & 0 \\ 0 & 0 & 1 \end{bmatrix} \begin{bmatrix} 1 & -a & 0 \\ 0 & 1 & 0 \\ 0 & 0 & 1 \end{bmatrix} = \begin{bmatrix} 1 & -a & 0 \\ -b & 1 + ab & 0 \\ 0 & 0 & 1/c \end{bmatrix}.$

37. No. For example,

$\begin{bmatrix} 1 & 0 \\ 2 & 1 \end{bmatrix} \begin{bmatrix} 1 & 1 \\ 0 & 1 \end{bmatrix} = \begin{bmatrix} 1 & 1 \\ 2 & 3 \end{bmatrix}$, which is not elementary.

39. Since the matrix is lower triangular, an LU-factorization is

$\begin{bmatrix} 1 & 0 \\ -2 & 1 \end{bmatrix} \begin{bmatrix} 1 & 0 \\ 0 & 1 \end{bmatrix}$

41.   <u>Matrix</u>   <u>Elementary Matrix</u>

$\begin{bmatrix} 3 & 0 & 1 \\ 6 & 1 & 1 \\ -3 & 1 & 0 \end{bmatrix} = A$

$\begin{bmatrix} 3 & 0 & 1 \\ 0 & 1 & -1 \\ -3 & 1 & 0 \end{bmatrix}$ $\begin{bmatrix} 1 & 0 & 0 \\ -2 & 1 & 0 \\ 0 & 0 & 1 \end{bmatrix} = E_1$

$\begin{bmatrix} 3 & 0 & 1 \\ 0 & 1 & -1 \\ 0 & 1 & 1 \end{bmatrix}$ $\begin{bmatrix} 1 & 0 & 0 \\ 0 & 1 & 0 \\ 1 & 0 & 1 \end{bmatrix} = E_2$

$\begin{bmatrix} 3 & 0 & 1 \\ 0 & 1 & -1 \\ 0 & 0 & 2 \end{bmatrix} = U$ $\begin{bmatrix} 1 & 0 & 0 \\ 0 & 1 & 0 \\ 0 & -1 & 1 \end{bmatrix} = E_3$

$E_3 E_2 E_1 A = U \implies A = E_1^{-1} E_2^{-1} E_3^{-1} U = \begin{bmatrix} 1 & 0 & 0 \\ 2 & 1 & 0 \\ -1 & 1 & 1 \end{bmatrix} \begin{bmatrix} 3 & 0 & 1 \\ 0 & 1 & -1 \\ 0 & 0 & 2 \end{bmatrix} = LU$

43. (a)   <u>Matrix</u>   <u>Elementary Matrix</u>

$$\begin{bmatrix} 2 & 1 & 0 \\ 0 & 1 & -1 \\ -2 & 1 & 1 \end{bmatrix} = A$$

$$\begin{bmatrix} 2 & 1 & 0 \\ 0 & 1 & -1 \\ 0 & 2 & 1 \end{bmatrix} \qquad \begin{bmatrix} 1 & 0 & 0 \\ 0 & 1 & 0 \\ 1 & 0 & 1 \end{bmatrix} = E_1$$

$$\begin{bmatrix} 2 & 1 & 0 \\ 0 & 1 & -1 \\ 0 & 0 & 3 \end{bmatrix} = U \qquad \begin{bmatrix} 1 & 0 & 0 \\ 0 & 1 & 0 \\ 0 & -2 & 1 \end{bmatrix} = E_2$$

$$E_2 E_1 A = U \implies A = E_1^{-1} E_2^{-1} U = \begin{bmatrix} 1 & 0 & 0 \\ 0 & 1 & 0 \\ -1 & 2 & 1 \end{bmatrix} \begin{bmatrix} 2 & 1 & 0 \\ 0 & 1 & -1 \\ 0 & 0 & 3 \end{bmatrix} = LU$$

(b) $Ly = b:$ $\begin{bmatrix} 1 & 0 & 0 \\ 0 & 1 & 0 \\ -1 & 2 & 1 \end{bmatrix} \begin{bmatrix} y_1 \\ y_2 \\ y_3 \end{bmatrix} = \begin{bmatrix} 1 \\ 2 \\ -2 \end{bmatrix}$

$y_1 = 1,\ y_2 = 2,$ and $-y_1 + 2y_2 + y_3 = -2 \implies y_3 = -5$

(c) $Ux = y:$ $\begin{bmatrix} 2 & 1 & 0 \\ 0 & 1 & -1 \\ 0 & 0 & 3 \end{bmatrix} \begin{bmatrix} x_1 \\ x_2 \\ x_3 \end{bmatrix} = \begin{bmatrix} 1 \\ 2 \\ -5 \end{bmatrix}$

$x_3 = -\frac{5}{3},\ x_2 - x_3 = 2 \implies x_2 = \frac{1}{3}$ and $2x_1 + x_2 = 1 \implies x_1 = \frac{1}{3}.$

Thus, the solution to the system $Ax = b$ is $x_1 = \frac{1}{3},\ x_2 = \frac{1}{3},\ x_3 = -\frac{5}{3}.$

45. You could first factor the matrix $A = LU$. Then for each right hand side b_i, solve $Ly = b_i$ and $Ux = y$.

47. $A^2 = \begin{bmatrix} 1 & 0 \\ 0 & 0 \end{bmatrix}^2 = \begin{bmatrix} 1 & 0 \\ 0 & 0 \end{bmatrix} = A.$

Because $A^2 = A$, A is idempotent.

49. $A^2 = \begin{bmatrix} 2 & 3 \\ -1 & -2 \end{bmatrix} \begin{bmatrix} 2 & 3 \\ -1 & -2 \end{bmatrix} = \begin{bmatrix} 1 & 0 \\ 0 & 1 \end{bmatrix} \neq A.$

Because $A^2 \neq A$, A is *not* idempotent.

51. $A^2 = \begin{bmatrix} 0 & 0 & 1 \\ 0 & 1 & 0 \\ 1 & 0 & 0 \end{bmatrix} \begin{bmatrix} 0 & 0 & 1 \\ 0 & 1 & 0 \\ 1 & 0 & 0 \end{bmatrix} = \begin{bmatrix} 1 & 0 & 0 \\ 0 & 1 & 0 \\ 0 & 0 & 1 \end{bmatrix}.$

Because $A^2 \neq A$, A is *not* idempotent.

53. We begin by finding A^2.

$$A^2 = \begin{bmatrix} 1 & 0 \\ a & b \end{bmatrix} \begin{bmatrix} 1 & 0 \\ a & b \end{bmatrix} = \begin{bmatrix} 1 & 0 \\ a(1+b) & b^2 \end{bmatrix}$$

Setting $A^2 = A$ yields the equations $a = a(1+b)$ and $b = b^2$. The second equation is satisfied when $b = 1$ or $b = 0$. If $b = 1$, then $a = 0$, and if $b = 0$, then a can be any real number.

55. Since A is idempotent and invertible, we have

$$
\begin{aligned}
A^2 &= A \\
A^{-1}A^2 &= A^{-1}A \\
(A^{-1}A)A &= I \\
A &= I.
\end{aligned}
$$

57. We have $(AB)^2 = (AB)(AB) = A(BA)B = A(AB)B$
$$= (AA)(BB) = AB.$$

Hence, $(AB)^2 = AB$, and AB is idempotent.

59. $A = E_k \cdots E_2 E_1 B$, for $E_1, \ldots, E_k$ elementary.
$B = F_t \cdots F_2 F_1 C$, for $F_1, \ldots, F_t$ elementary.

Then

$$A = E_k \cdots E_2 E_1 B = (E_k \cdots E_2 E_1)(F_t \cdots F_2 F_1 C)$$

which shows that A is row equivalent to C.

Section 2.5 Applications of Matrix Operations

1. The matrix is *not* stochastic because every entry of a stochastic matrix must satisfy the inequality $0 \le a_{ij} \le 1$.

3. This matrix *is* stochastic since each entry is between 0 and 1, and each column adds up to 1.

5. The matrix *is* stochastic because $0 \le a_{ij} \le 1$ and each column adds up to 1.

7. We form the matrix representing the given transition probabilities. [A represents people who purchased the product and B represents people who did not.]

$$P = \begin{bmatrix} 0.80 & 0.30 \\ 0.20 & 0.70 \end{bmatrix} \begin{matrix} A \\ B \end{matrix} \Big\} \text{ To}$$

with columns labeled From A B

The state matrix representing the current population is

$$X = \begin{bmatrix} 100 \\ 900 \end{bmatrix} \begin{matrix} A \\ B \end{matrix}$$

The state matrix for next month is

$$PX = \begin{bmatrix} 0.80 & 0.30 \\ 0.20 & 0.70 \end{bmatrix} \begin{bmatrix} 100 \\ 900 \end{bmatrix} = \begin{bmatrix} 350 \\ 650 \end{bmatrix}.$$

The state matrix for the month after next is

$$P(PX) = \begin{bmatrix} 0.80 & 0.30 \\ 0.20 & 0.70 \end{bmatrix} \begin{bmatrix} 350 \\ 650 \end{bmatrix} = \begin{bmatrix} 475 \\ 525 \end{bmatrix}.$$

Thus, next month 350 people will purchase the product. In two months 475 people will purchase the product.

9. We form the matrix representing the given transition probabilities. [N represents nonsmokers, S_0 represents those who smoke one pack or less, and S_1 represents those who smoke more than one pack.]

$$
\begin{array}{c}
\overbrace{\hspace{3.5cm}}^{\text{From}} \\
\begin{array}{ccc}
N & S_0 & S_1
\end{array}
\end{array}
$$

$$
P = \begin{bmatrix} 0.93 & 0.10 & 0.05 \\ 0.05 & 0.80 & 0.10 \\ 0.02 & 0.10 & 0.85 \end{bmatrix} \begin{array}{l} N \\ S_0 \\ S_1 \end{array} \Bigg\} \text{ To}
$$

The state matrix representing the current population is

$$
X = \begin{bmatrix} 5000 \\ 2500 \\ 2500 \end{bmatrix} \begin{array}{l} N \\ S_0 \\ S_1 \end{array}
$$

The state matrix for the next month is

$$
PX = \begin{bmatrix} 0.93 & 0.10 & 0.05 \\ 0.05 & 0.80 & 0.10 \\ 0.02 & 0.10 & 0.85 \end{bmatrix} \begin{bmatrix} 5000 \\ 2500 \\ 2500 \end{bmatrix} = \begin{bmatrix} 5025 \\ 2500 \\ 2475 \end{bmatrix}.
$$

The state matrix for the month after next is

$$
P(PX) = \begin{bmatrix} 0.93 & 0.10 & 0.05 \\ 0.05 & 0.80 & 0.10 \\ 0.02 & 0.10 & 0.85 \end{bmatrix} \begin{bmatrix} 5025 \\ 2500 \\ 2475 \end{bmatrix} = \begin{bmatrix} 5047 \\ 2498.75 \\ 2454.25 \end{bmatrix}.
$$

Thus, next month the population will be grouped as follows: 5025 nonsmokers, 2500 smokers of one pack or less per day, and 2475 smokers of more than one pack per day. In two months the population will be grouped as follows: 5047 nonsmokers, 2499 smokers of one pack or less per day, and 2454 smokers of more than one pack per day.

11. We form the matrix representing the given transition probabilities.

[*A* represents more than one hour of TV, *B* less than one hour].

$$P = \begin{matrix} & \overbrace{\begin{matrix} A & B \end{matrix}}^{\text{From}} \\ \begin{bmatrix} 0 & 0.25 \\ 1 & 0.75 \end{bmatrix} & \left.\begin{matrix} A \\ B \end{matrix}\right\} \text{To} \end{matrix}$$

The state matrix representing the current distribution is

$$X = \begin{bmatrix} 100 \\ 100 \end{bmatrix}.$$

The state matrix for one day later is

$$PX = \begin{bmatrix} 0 & 0.25 \\ 1 & 0.75 \end{bmatrix} \begin{bmatrix} 100 \\ 100 \end{bmatrix} = \begin{bmatrix} 25 \\ 175 \end{bmatrix}.$$

In two days the state matrix is

$$P(PX) = \begin{bmatrix} 0 & 0.25 \\ 1 & 0.75 \end{bmatrix} \begin{bmatrix} 25 \\ 175 \end{bmatrix} \approx \begin{bmatrix} 44 \\ 156 \end{bmatrix}.$$

In thirty days, the state matrix will be

$$P^{30}X = \begin{bmatrix} 40 \\ 160 \end{bmatrix}.$$

Thus, 25 will watch TV for more than an hour tomorrow, 44 the day after tomorrow, and 40 in thirty days.

13. Since the columns in a stochastic matrix add up to 1, we can represent two stochastic matrices as

$$P = \begin{bmatrix} a & b \\ 1-a & 1-b \end{bmatrix} \quad \text{and} \quad Q = \begin{bmatrix} c & d \\ 1-c & 1-d \end{bmatrix}.$$

Then,

$$PQ = \begin{bmatrix} a & b \\ 1-a & 1-b \end{bmatrix} \begin{bmatrix} c & d \\ 1-c & 1-d \end{bmatrix}$$

$$= \begin{bmatrix} ac+b-bc & ad+b-bd \\ c-ac+1-b-c+bc & d-ad+1-b-d+bd \end{bmatrix}.$$

The columns of *PQ* add up to 1, and the entries are non-negative, since those of *P* and *Q* are non-negative.

15. Divide the message into groups of three and form the uncoded matrices.

S	E	L		L	—	C		O	N	S		O	L	I		D	A	T		E	D	—
[19	5	12]		[12	0	3]		[15	14	19]		[15	12	9]		[4	1	20]		[5	4	0]

Multiplying each uncoded row matrix on the right by A yields the coded row matrices

$$[\,19\quad 5\quad 12\,]\,A = [\,19\quad 5\quad 12\,] \begin{bmatrix} 1 & -1 & 0 \\ 1 & 0 & -1 \\ -6 & 2 & 3 \end{bmatrix} = [\,-48\quad 5\quad 31\,]$$

$$[\,12\quad 0\quad 3\,]\,A = [\,-6\quad -6\quad 9\,]$$

$$[\,15\quad 14\quad 19\,]\,A = [\,-85\quad 23\quad 43\,]$$

$$[\,15\quad 12\quad 9\,]\,A = [\,-27\quad 3\quad 15\,]$$

$$[\,4\quad 1\quad 20\,]\,A = [\,-115\quad 36\quad 59\,]$$

$$[\,5\quad 4\quad 0\,]\,A = [\,9\quad -5\quad -4\,]$$

Thus, the coded message is

$$-48, 5, 31, -6, -6, 9, -85, 23, 43, -27, 3, 15, -115, 36, 59, 9, -5, -4.$$

17. Divide the message into pairs of letters and form the coded matrices.

C	O		M	E		—	H		O	M		E	—		S	O		O	N
[3	15]		[13	5]		[0	8]		[15	13]		[5	0]		[19	15]		[15	14]

Multiplying each uncoded row matrix on the right by A yields the coded row matrices.

$$[\,3\quad 15\,] \begin{bmatrix} 1 & 2 \\ 3 & 5 \end{bmatrix} = [\,48\quad 81\,]$$

$$[\,13\quad 5\,] \begin{bmatrix} 1 & 2 \\ 3 & 5 \end{bmatrix} = [\,28\quad 51\,]$$

$$[\,0\quad 8\,] \begin{bmatrix} 1 & 2 \\ 3 & 5 \end{bmatrix} = [\,24\quad 40\,]$$

$$[\,15\quad 13\,] \begin{bmatrix} 1 & 2 \\ 3 & 5 \end{bmatrix} = [\,54\quad 95\,]$$

$$[\,5\quad 0\,] \begin{bmatrix} 1 & 2 \\ 3 & 5 \end{bmatrix} = [\,5\quad 10\,]$$

$$[\,19\quad 15\,] \begin{bmatrix} 1 & 2 \\ 3 & 5 \end{bmatrix} = [\,64\quad 113\,]$$

$$[\,15\quad 14\,] \begin{bmatrix} 1 & 2 \\ 3 & 5 \end{bmatrix} = [\,57\quad 100\,]$$

Thus, the coded message is

$$48, 81, 28, 51, 24, 40, 54, 95, 5, 10, 64, 113, 57, 100.$$

19. We find $A^{-1} = \begin{bmatrix} -5 & 2 \\ 3 & -1 \end{bmatrix}$

and multiply each coded row matrix on the right by A^{-1} to find the associated uncoded row matrix.

$$[\,11 \quad 21\,]\begin{bmatrix} -5 & 2 \\ 3 & -1 \end{bmatrix} = [\,8 \quad 1\,] \qquad \Rightarrow \qquad \text{H, A}$$

$$[\,64 \quad 112\,]\begin{bmatrix} -5 & 2 \\ 3 & -1 \end{bmatrix} = [\,16 \quad 16\,] \qquad \Rightarrow \qquad \text{P, P}$$

$$[\,25 \quad 50\,]\begin{bmatrix} -5 & 2 \\ 3 & -1 \end{bmatrix} = [\,25 \quad 0\,] \qquad \Rightarrow \qquad \text{Y, \_\_}$$

$$[\,29 \quad 53\,]\begin{bmatrix} -5 & 2 \\ 3 & -1 \end{bmatrix} = [\,14 \quad 5\,] \qquad \Rightarrow \qquad \text{N, E}$$

$$[\,23 \quad 46\,]\begin{bmatrix} -5 & 2 \\ 3 & -1 \end{bmatrix} = [\,23 \quad 0\,] \qquad \Rightarrow \qquad \text{W, \_\_}$$

$$[\,40 \quad 75\,]\begin{bmatrix} -5 & 2 \\ 3 & -1 \end{bmatrix} = [\,25 \quad 5\,] \qquad \Rightarrow \qquad \text{Y, E}$$

$$[\,55 \quad 92\,]\begin{bmatrix} -5 & 2 \\ 3 & -1 \end{bmatrix} = [\,1 \quad 18\,] \qquad \Rightarrow \qquad \text{A, R}$$

Thus, the message is HAPPY__ NEW__YEAR.

21. We find $A^{-1} = \begin{bmatrix} 1 & 0 & -1 \\ 0 & -1 & -1 \\ -3 & 2 & 6 \end{bmatrix}$,

and multiply each coded row matrix on the right by A^{-1} to find the associated uncoded row matrix.

$$[\,33 \quad 9 \quad 9\,]A^{-1} = [\,33 \quad 9 \quad 9\,]\begin{bmatrix} 1 & 0 & -1 \\ 0 & -1 & -1 \\ -3 & 2 & 6 \end{bmatrix} = [\,6 \quad 9 \quad 12\,] \Rightarrow \textit{F, I, L}$$

$$[\,55 \quad 28 \quad 14\,]A^{-1} = [\,13 \quad 0 \quad 1\,] \quad \Rightarrow \quad \textit{M, \_\_, A}$$

$$[\,95 \quad 50 \quad 25\,]A^{-1} = [\,20 \quad 0 \quad 5\,] \quad \Rightarrow \quad \textit{T, \_\_, E}$$

$$[\,99 \quad 53 \quad 29\,]A^{-1} = [\,12 \quad 5 \quad 22\,] \quad \Rightarrow \quad \textit{L, E, V}$$

$$[\,-22 \quad -32 \quad -9\,]A^{-1} = [\,5 \quad 14 \quad 0\,] \quad \Rightarrow \quad \textit{E, N, \_\_}$$

Thus, the message is FILM __ AT__ ELEVEN.

23. We let $A^{-1} = \begin{bmatrix} a & b \\ c & d \end{bmatrix}$

and find that

$$— \quad R.$$

$$[-18 \quad -18] \begin{bmatrix} a & b \\ c & d \end{bmatrix} = [0 \quad 18]$$

$$[-18(a+c) \quad -18(b+d)] = [0 \quad 18].$$

Thus, $c = -a$ and $d = -1 - b$. Using these values we find that

$$O \quad N$$

$$[1 \quad 16] \begin{bmatrix} a & b \\ -a & -(1+b) \end{bmatrix} = [15 \quad 14]$$

$$[-15a \quad -15b - 16] = [15 \quad 14].$$

Thus, $a = -1$, $b = -2$, $c = 1$, and $d = 1$. Using the matrix

$$A^{-1} = \begin{bmatrix} -1 & -2 \\ 1 & 1 \end{bmatrix}$$

we multiply each coded row matrix to yield the uncoded row matrices

[13 5], [5 20], [0 13], [5 0], [20 15], [14 9], [7 8], [20 0], [0 18], [15 14].

This corresponds to the message

MEET __ ME __ TONIGHT __ RON.

25. We use the given information to find D.

$$\overbrace{\text{User}}$$

$$D = \begin{bmatrix} 0.10 & 0.20 \\ 0.80 & 0.10 \end{bmatrix} \begin{matrix} \text{Coal} \\ \text{Steel} \end{matrix} \Big\} \text{Supplier}$$

The equation $X = DX + E$ may be rewritten in the form $(I - D)X = E$; that is,

$$\begin{bmatrix} 0.90 & -0.20 \\ -0.80 & 0.90 \end{bmatrix} X = \begin{bmatrix} 10,000 \\ 20,000 \end{bmatrix}.$$

We can solve this system by using Gauss-Jordan elimination to obtain

$$X = \begin{bmatrix} 20,000 \\ 40,000 \end{bmatrix}.$$

27. From the given matrix D, we form the linear system $X = DX + E$, which can be written as

$(I - D)X = E$

$$\begin{bmatrix} 0.6 & -0.5 & -0.5 \\ -0.3 & 1 & -0.3 \\ -0.2 & -0.2 & 1.0 \end{bmatrix} X = \begin{bmatrix} 1000 \\ 1000 \\ 1000 \end{bmatrix}.$$

Solving this system, we find $X = \begin{bmatrix} 8622 \\ 4685 \\ 3661.4 \end{bmatrix}.$

29. (a) The line that best fits the given points is shown on the graph.

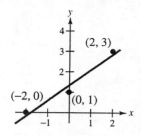

(b) Using the matrices

$$X = \begin{bmatrix} 1 & -2 \\ 1 & 0 \\ 1 & 2 \end{bmatrix} \quad \text{and} \quad Y = \begin{bmatrix} 0 \\ 1 \\ 3 \end{bmatrix}$$

we have $X^T X = \begin{bmatrix} 1 & 1 & 1 \\ -2 & 0 & 2 \end{bmatrix} \begin{bmatrix} 1 & -2 \\ 1 & 0 \\ 1 & 2 \end{bmatrix} = \begin{bmatrix} 3 & 0 \\ 0 & 8 \end{bmatrix}$

$$X^T Y = \begin{bmatrix} 1 & 1 & 1 \\ -2 & 0 & 2 \end{bmatrix} \begin{bmatrix} 0 \\ 1 \\ 3 \end{bmatrix} = \begin{bmatrix} 4 \\ 6 \end{bmatrix}$$

$$A = (X^T X)^{-1} X^T Y = \begin{bmatrix} \frac{1}{3} & 0 \\ 0 & \frac{1}{8} \end{bmatrix} \begin{bmatrix} 4 \\ 6 \end{bmatrix} = \begin{bmatrix} \frac{4}{3} \\ \frac{3}{4} \end{bmatrix}.$$

Thus, the least squares regression line is $y = \frac{3}{4}x + \frac{4}{3}$.

(c) Solving $Y = XA + E$ for E, we have

$$E = Y - XA = \begin{bmatrix} 0 \\ 1 \\ 3 \end{bmatrix} - \begin{bmatrix} 1 & -2 \\ 1 & 0 \\ 1 & 2 \end{bmatrix} \begin{bmatrix} \frac{4}{3} \\ \frac{3}{4} \end{bmatrix} = \begin{bmatrix} \frac{1}{6} \\ -\frac{1}{3} \\ \frac{1}{6} \end{bmatrix}.$$

Thus, the sum of the squares error is

$$E^T E = \begin{bmatrix} \frac{1}{6} & -\frac{1}{3} & \frac{1}{6} \end{bmatrix} \begin{bmatrix} \frac{1}{6} \\ -\frac{1}{3} \\ \frac{1}{6} \end{bmatrix} = \frac{1}{6}.$$

31. (a) The line that best fits the given points is shown on the graph.

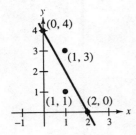

(b) Using the matrices

$$X = \begin{bmatrix} 1 & 0 \\ 1 & 1 \\ 1 & 1 \\ 1 & 2 \end{bmatrix} \quad \text{and} \quad Y = \begin{bmatrix} 4 \\ 3 \\ 1 \\ 0 \end{bmatrix}$$

we have $X^T X = \begin{bmatrix} 1 & 1 & 1 & 1 \\ 0 & 1 & 1 & 2 \end{bmatrix} \begin{bmatrix} 1 & 0 \\ 1 & 1 \\ 1 & 1 \\ 1 & 2 \end{bmatrix} = \begin{bmatrix} 4 & 4 \\ 4 & 6 \end{bmatrix}$

$$X^T Y = \begin{bmatrix} 1 & 1 & 1 & 1 \\ 0 & 1 & 1 & 2 \end{bmatrix} \begin{bmatrix} 4 \\ 3 \\ 1 \\ 0 \end{bmatrix} = \begin{bmatrix} 8 \\ 4 \end{bmatrix}$$

$$A = (X^T X)^{-1} X^T Y = \frac{1}{8} \begin{bmatrix} 6 & -4 \\ -4 & 4 \end{bmatrix} \begin{bmatrix} 8 \\ 4 \end{bmatrix} = \begin{bmatrix} 4 \\ -2 \end{bmatrix}.$$

Thus, the least squares regression line is $y = 4 - 2x$.

(c) Solving $Y = XA + E$ for E, we have

$$E = Y - XA = \begin{bmatrix} 4 \\ 3 \\ 1 \\ 0 \end{bmatrix} - \begin{bmatrix} 1 & 0 \\ 1 & 1 \\ 1 & 1 \\ 1 & 2 \end{bmatrix} \begin{bmatrix} 4 \\ -2 \end{bmatrix} = \begin{bmatrix} 4 \\ 3 \\ 1 \\ 0 \end{bmatrix} - \begin{bmatrix} 4 \\ 2 \\ 2 \\ 0 \end{bmatrix} = \begin{bmatrix} 0 \\ 1 \\ -1 \\ 0 \end{bmatrix}.$$

Thus, the sum of the squares error is

$$E^T E = \begin{bmatrix} 0 & 1 & -1 & 0 \end{bmatrix} \begin{bmatrix} 0 \\ 1 \\ -1 \\ 0 \end{bmatrix} = 2.$$

33. Using the matrices

$$X = \begin{bmatrix} 1 & -2 \\ 1 & -1 \\ 1 & 0 \\ 1 & 1 \end{bmatrix} \quad \text{and} \quad Y = \begin{bmatrix} 0 \\ 1 \\ 1 \\ 2 \end{bmatrix}$$

we have

$$X^T X = \begin{bmatrix} 4 & -2 \\ -2 & 6 \end{bmatrix} \quad X^T Y = \begin{bmatrix} 4 \\ 1 \end{bmatrix}$$

$$A = (X^T X)^{-1} X^T Y = \begin{bmatrix} 0.3 & 0.1 \\ 0.1 & 0.2 \end{bmatrix} \begin{bmatrix} 4 \\ 1 \end{bmatrix} = \begin{bmatrix} 1.3 \\ 0.6 \end{bmatrix}.$$

Thus, the least squares regression line is $y = 0.6x + 1.3$.

35. Using the matrices

$$X = \begin{bmatrix} 1 & -3 \\ 1 & 1 \\ 1 & 2 \end{bmatrix} \quad \text{and} \quad Y = \begin{bmatrix} 0 \\ 4 \\ 6 \end{bmatrix}$$

we have

$$X^T X = \begin{bmatrix} 3 & 0 \\ 0 & 14 \end{bmatrix} \quad \text{and} \quad X^T Y = \begin{bmatrix} 10 \\ 16 \end{bmatrix}$$

$$A = (X^T X)^{-1} X^T Y = \begin{bmatrix} \frac{1}{3} & 0 \\ 0 & \frac{1}{14} \end{bmatrix} \begin{bmatrix} 10 \\ 16 \end{bmatrix} = \begin{bmatrix} \frac{10}{3} \\ \frac{8}{7} \end{bmatrix}.$$

Thus, the least squares regression line is $y = \frac{8}{7}x + \frac{10}{3}$.

37. Using the matrices

$$X = \begin{bmatrix} 1 & -3 \\ 1 & -1 \\ 1 & 1 \\ 1 & 3 \end{bmatrix} \quad \text{and} \quad Y = \begin{bmatrix} 4 \\ 2 \\ 1 \\ 0 \end{bmatrix}$$

we have

$$X^T X = \begin{bmatrix} 1 & 1 & 1 & 1 \\ -3 & -1 & 1 & 3 \end{bmatrix} \begin{bmatrix} 1 & -3 \\ 1 & -1 \\ 1 & 1 \\ 1 & 3 \end{bmatrix} = \begin{bmatrix} 4 & 0 \\ 0 & 20 \end{bmatrix}$$

$$X^T Y = \begin{bmatrix} 1 & 1 & 1 & 1 \\ -3 & -1 & 1 & 3 \end{bmatrix} \begin{bmatrix} 4 \\ 2 \\ 1 \\ 0 \end{bmatrix} = \begin{bmatrix} 7 \\ -13 \end{bmatrix}$$

$$A = (X^T X)^{-1} X^T Y = \begin{bmatrix} \frac{1}{4} & 0 \\ 0 & \frac{1}{20} \end{bmatrix} \begin{bmatrix} 7 \\ -13 \end{bmatrix} = \begin{bmatrix} \frac{7}{4} \\ -\frac{13}{20} \end{bmatrix}.$$

Thus, the least squares regression line is $y = \frac{7}{4} - \frac{13}{20}x$.

39. Using the matrices

$$X = \begin{bmatrix} 1 & 0 \\ 1 & 1 \\ 1 & 2 \end{bmatrix} \quad \text{and} \quad Y = \begin{bmatrix} 0 \\ 1 \\ 4 \end{bmatrix}$$

we have

$$X^T X = \begin{bmatrix} 3 & 3 \\ 3 & 5 \end{bmatrix} \quad \text{and} \quad X^T Y = \begin{bmatrix} 5 \\ 9 \end{bmatrix}$$

$$A = (X^T X)^{-1}(X^T Y) = \begin{bmatrix} -\frac{1}{3} \\ 2 \end{bmatrix}.$$

Thus, the least squares regression line is $y = 2x - \frac{1}{3}$.

41. Using the matrices

$$X = \begin{bmatrix} 1 & 0 \\ 1 & 4 \\ 1 & 5 \\ 1 & 8 \\ 1 & 10 \end{bmatrix} \quad \text{and} \quad Y = \begin{bmatrix} 6 \\ 3 \\ 0 \\ -4 \\ -5 \end{bmatrix}$$

we have

$$X^T X = \begin{bmatrix} 5 & 27 \\ 27 & 205 \end{bmatrix} \quad X^T Y = \begin{bmatrix} 0 \\ -70 \end{bmatrix}$$

$$A = (X^T X)^{-1}(X^T Y) \approx \begin{bmatrix} 6.385 \\ -1.182 \end{bmatrix}.$$

Thus, the least squares regression line is $y \approx -1.182x + 6.385$.

43. (a) Using the matrices

$$X = \begin{bmatrix} 1 & 1.00 \\ 1 & 1.25 \\ 1 & 1.50 \end{bmatrix} \quad \text{and} \quad Y = \begin{bmatrix} 450 \\ 375 \\ 330 \end{bmatrix}.$$

we find that the coefficient matrix is

$$A = (X^T X)^{-1} X^T Y = \begin{bmatrix} 3.00 & 3.75 \\ 3.75 & 4.8125 \end{bmatrix}^{-1} \begin{bmatrix} 1155 \\ 1413.75 \end{bmatrix}$$

$$= \frac{8}{3} \begin{bmatrix} 4.8125 & -3.75 \\ -3.75 & 3.00 \end{bmatrix} \begin{bmatrix} 1155 \\ 1413.75 \end{bmatrix}$$

$$= \begin{bmatrix} 685 \\ -240 \end{bmatrix}.$$

Thus, the least squares regression line is $y = 685 - 240x$.

(b) When $x = 1.40$, $y = 685 - 240(1.40) = 349$.

Chapter 2   Review Exercises

1. $\begin{bmatrix} 2 & 1 & 0 \\ 0 & 5 & -4 \end{bmatrix} - 3 \begin{bmatrix} 5 & 3 & -6 \\ 0 & -2 & 5 \end{bmatrix} = \begin{bmatrix} 2 & 1 & 0 \\ 0 & 5 & -4 \end{bmatrix} - \begin{bmatrix} 15 & 9 & -18 \\ 0 & -6 & 15 \end{bmatrix}$

$$= \begin{bmatrix} -13 & -8 & 18 \\ 0 & 11 & -19 \end{bmatrix}$$

3. $\begin{bmatrix} 1 & 2 \\ 5 & -4 \\ 6 & 0 \end{bmatrix} \begin{bmatrix} 6 & -2 & 8 \\ 4 & 0 & 0 \end{bmatrix} = \begin{bmatrix} 1(6) + 2(4) & 1(-2) + 2(0) & 1(8) + 2(0) \\ 5(6) - 4(4) & 5(-2) - 4(0) & 5(8) - 4(0) \\ 6(6) + 0(4) & 6(-2) + 0(0) & 6(8) + 0(0) \end{bmatrix}$

$$= \begin{bmatrix} 14 & -2 & 8 \\ 14 & -10 & 40 \\ 36 & -12 & 48 \end{bmatrix}$$

5. $\begin{bmatrix} 1 & 3 & 2 \\ 0 & 2 & -4 \\ 0 & 0 & 3 \end{bmatrix} \begin{bmatrix} 4 & -3 & 2 \\ 0 & 3 & -1 \\ 0 & 0 & 2 \end{bmatrix} = \begin{bmatrix} 1(4) & 1(-3) + 3(3) & 1(2) + 3(-1) + 2(2) \\ 0 & 2(3) & 2(-1) + (-4)(2) \\ 0 & 0 & 3(2) \end{bmatrix}$

$$= \begin{bmatrix} 4 & 6 & 3 \\ 0 & 6 & -10 \\ 0 & 0 & 6 \end{bmatrix}$$

7. Multiplying the left side of the equation yields $\begin{bmatrix} 5x + 4y \\ -x + y \end{bmatrix} = \begin{bmatrix} 2 \\ -22 \end{bmatrix}$.

Thus, the corresponding system of linear equations is

$$5x + 4y = \quad 2$$
$$-x + \ y = -22.$$

9. Letting

$$A = \begin{bmatrix} 2 & 3 & 1 \\ 2 & -3 & -3 \\ 4 & -2 & 3 \end{bmatrix}, \quad \mathbf{x} = \begin{bmatrix} x_1 \\ x_2 \\ x_3 \end{bmatrix} \text{ and } \mathbf{b} = \begin{bmatrix} 10 \\ 22 \\ -2 \end{bmatrix}$$

the given system can be written in matrix form

$$A\mathbf{x} = \mathbf{b}.$$

11. $A^T A = \begin{bmatrix} 1 & 0 \\ 2 & 1 \\ -3 & 2 \end{bmatrix} \begin{bmatrix} 1 & 2 & -3 \\ 0 & 1 & 2 \end{bmatrix} = \begin{bmatrix} 1 & 2 & -3 \\ 2 & 5 & -4 \\ -3 & -4 & 13 \end{bmatrix}$

$AA^T = \begin{bmatrix} 1 & 2 & -3 \\ 0 & 1 & 2 \end{bmatrix} \begin{bmatrix} 1 & 0 \\ 2 & 1 \\ -3 & 2 \end{bmatrix} = \begin{bmatrix} 14 & -4 \\ -4 & 5 \end{bmatrix}$

13. We use the formula for the inverse of a 2×2 matrix.

$$A^{-1} = \frac{1}{ad - bc} \begin{bmatrix} d & -b \\ -c & a \end{bmatrix} = \frac{1}{3(-1) - (-1)(2)} \begin{bmatrix} -1 & 1 \\ -2 & 3 \end{bmatrix} = \begin{bmatrix} 1 & -1 \\ 2 & -3 \end{bmatrix}$$

15. We begin by adjoining the identity matrix to the given matrix.

$$[A : I] = \begin{bmatrix} 2 & 3 & 1 & \vdots & 1 & 0 & 0 \\ 2 & -3 & -3 & \vdots & 0 & 1 & 0 \\ 4 & 0 & 3 & \vdots & 0 & 0 & 1 \end{bmatrix}$$

This matrix reduces to $[I : A^{-1}] = \begin{bmatrix} 1 & 0 & 0 & \vdots & \frac{3}{20} & \frac{3}{20} & \frac{1}{10} \\ 0 & 1 & 0 & \vdots & \frac{3}{10} & -\frac{1}{30} & -\frac{2}{15} \\ 0 & 0 & 1 & \vdots & -\frac{1}{5} & -\frac{1}{5} & \frac{1}{5} \end{bmatrix}$.

Thus, the inverse matrix is

$$A^{-1} = \begin{bmatrix} \frac{3}{20} & \frac{3}{20} & \frac{1}{10} \\ \frac{3}{10} & -\frac{1}{30} & -\frac{2}{15} \\ -\frac{1}{5} & -\frac{1}{5} & \frac{1}{5} \end{bmatrix}.$$

17.

$$\overset{A}{\begin{bmatrix} 5 & 4 \\ -1 & 1 \end{bmatrix}} \overset{\mathbf{x}}{\begin{bmatrix} x_1 \\ x_2 \end{bmatrix}} = \overset{\mathbf{b}}{\begin{bmatrix} 2 \\ -22 \end{bmatrix}}$$

Since

$$A^{-1} = \frac{1}{5(1) - 4(-1)} \begin{bmatrix} 1 & -4 \\ 1 & 5 \end{bmatrix} = \begin{bmatrix} \frac{1}{9} & -\frac{4}{9} \\ \frac{1}{9} & \frac{5}{9} \end{bmatrix}$$

we solve the equation $A\mathbf{x} = \mathbf{b}$ as follows.

$$\mathbf{x} = A^{-1}\mathbf{b} = \begin{bmatrix} \frac{1}{9} & -\frac{4}{9} \\ \frac{1}{9} & \frac{5}{9} \end{bmatrix} \begin{bmatrix} 2 \\ -22 \end{bmatrix} = \begin{bmatrix} 10 \\ -12 \end{bmatrix}$$

19. Since

$$(3A)^{-1} = \begin{bmatrix} 4 & -1 \\ 2 & 3 \end{bmatrix},$$

we can use the formula for the inverse of a 2×2 matrix to obtain

$$3A = \begin{bmatrix} 4 & -1 \\ 2 & 3 \end{bmatrix}^{-1} = \frac{1}{4(3) - (-1)(2)} \begin{bmatrix} 3 & 1 \\ -2 & 4 \end{bmatrix} = \frac{1}{14} \begin{bmatrix} 3 & 1 \\ -2 & 4 \end{bmatrix}.$$

Hence, $A = \dfrac{1}{42} \begin{bmatrix} 3 & 1 \\ -2 & 4 \end{bmatrix}.$

21. Because the given matrix represents the addition of 4 times the third row to the first row of I_3, we reverse the operation and subtract 4 times the third row from the first row.

$$E^{-1} = \begin{bmatrix} 1 & 0 & -4 \\ 0 & 1 & 0 \\ 0 & 0 & 1 \end{bmatrix}$$

23. We begin by finding a sequence of elementary row operations that can be used to write A in reduced row-echelon form.

Matrix	Elementary Row Operation	Elementary Matrix
$\begin{bmatrix} 1 & \frac{3}{2} \\ 0 & 1 \end{bmatrix}$	Divide row one by 2.	$E_1 = \begin{bmatrix} \frac{1}{2} & 0 \\ 0 & 1 \end{bmatrix}$
$\begin{bmatrix} 1 & 0 \\ 0 & 1 \end{bmatrix}$	Subtract $\frac{3}{2}$ times row two from row one.	$E_2 = \begin{bmatrix} 1 & -\frac{3}{2} \\ 0 & 1 \end{bmatrix}$

Thus, we can factor A as follows.

$$A = E_1^{-1} E_2^{-1} = \begin{bmatrix} 2 & 0 \\ 0 & 1 \end{bmatrix} \begin{bmatrix} 1 & \frac{3}{2} \\ 0 & 1 \end{bmatrix}$$

25. We begin by finding a sequence of elementary row operations to write A in reduced row-echelon form.

Matrix	Elementary Row Operation	Elementary Matrix
$\begin{bmatrix} 1 & 0 & 1 \\ 0 & 1 & -2 \\ 0 & 0 & 1 \end{bmatrix}$	$\frac{1}{4}$ times row 3.	$E_1 = \begin{bmatrix} 1 & 0 & 0 \\ 0 & 1 & 0 \\ 0 & 0 & \frac{1}{4} \end{bmatrix}$
$\begin{bmatrix} 1 & 0 & 1 \\ 0 & 1 & 0 \\ 0 & 0 & 1 \end{bmatrix}$	Add two times row three to row two.	$E_2 = \begin{bmatrix} 1 & 0 & 0 \\ 0 & 1 & 2 \\ 0 & 0 & 1 \end{bmatrix}$
$\begin{bmatrix} 1 & 0 & 0 \\ 0 & 1 & 0 \\ 0 & 0 & 1 \end{bmatrix}$	Add -1 times row three to row one.	$E_3 = \begin{bmatrix} 1 & 0 & -1 \\ 0 & 1 & 0 \\ 0 & 0 & 1 \end{bmatrix}$

Thus, we can factor A as follows.

$$A = E_1^{-1} E_2^{-1} E_3^{-1} =$$

$$\begin{bmatrix} 1 & 0 & 0 \\ 0 & 1 & 0 \\ 0 & 0 & 4 \end{bmatrix} \begin{bmatrix} 1 & 0 & 0 \\ 0 & 1 & -2 \\ 0 & 0 & 1 \end{bmatrix} \begin{bmatrix} 1 & 0 & 1 \\ 0 & 1 & 0 \\ 0 & 0 & 1 \end{bmatrix}.$$

27. Letting $A = \begin{bmatrix} a & b \\ c & d \end{bmatrix}$, we have

$$A^2 = \begin{bmatrix} a & b \\ c & d \end{bmatrix} \begin{bmatrix} a & b \\ c & d \end{bmatrix} = \begin{bmatrix} a^2 + bc & ab + bd \\ ca + dc & cb + d^2 \end{bmatrix} = \begin{bmatrix} 1 & 0 \\ 0 & 1 \end{bmatrix}.$$

Hence, many answers are possible.

$$\begin{bmatrix} 1 & 0 \\ 0 & 1 \end{bmatrix}, \begin{bmatrix} -1 & 0 \\ 0 & -1 \end{bmatrix}, \begin{bmatrix} -1 & 0 \\ 0 & 1 \end{bmatrix}, \text{ etc.}$$

29. Let $A = \begin{bmatrix} a & b \\ c & d \end{bmatrix}$

then $A^2 = \begin{bmatrix} a & b \\ c & d \end{bmatrix} \begin{bmatrix} a & b \\ c & d \end{bmatrix} = \begin{bmatrix} a^2 + bc & b(a + d) \\ c(a + d) & bc + d^2 \end{bmatrix}.$

Solving $A^2 = A$ gives the system of nonlinear equations

$$a^2 + bc = a$$
$$d^2 + bc = d$$
$$b(a + d) = b$$
$$c(a + d) = c.$$

From this system, we conclude that any of the following matrices are solutions to the equation $A^2 = A$.

$$\begin{bmatrix} 0 & 0 \\ 0 & 0 \end{bmatrix}, \begin{bmatrix} 0 & 0 \\ t & 1 \end{bmatrix}, \begin{bmatrix} 0 & t \\ 0 & 1 \end{bmatrix}, \begin{bmatrix} 1 & 0 \\ t & 0 \end{bmatrix}, \begin{bmatrix} 1 & t \\ 0 & 0 \end{bmatrix}, \begin{bmatrix} 1 & 0 \\ 0 & 1 \end{bmatrix}$$

31. (a) Letting $W = aX + bY + cZ$ yields the system of linear equations

$$\begin{aligned} a - b + 3c &= 3 \\ 2a \quad\quad + 4c &= 2 \\ 3b - c &= -4 \\ a + 2b + 2c &= -1 \end{aligned}$$

which has the solution $a = -1, b = -1, c = 1$.

(b) Letting $Z = aX + bY$ yields the system of linear equations

$$\begin{aligned} a - b &= 3 \\ 2a \quad\quad &= 4 \\ 3b &= -1 \\ a + 2b &= 2 \end{aligned}$$

which has no solution.

33. We have

$$\begin{aligned} (A^{-1} + B^{-1})(A(A + B)^{-1}B) &= A^{-1}A(A + B)^{-1}B + B^{-1}A(A + B)^{-1}B \\ &= (I + B^{-1}A)(A + B)^{-1}B) \\ &= (B^{-1}B + B^{-1}A)(A + B)^{-1}B \\ &= B^{-1}(B + A)(A + B)^{-1}B \\ &= B^{-1}B \\ &= I. \end{aligned}$$

35.

Matrix	Elementary Matrix

$$\begin{bmatrix} 2 & 5 \\ 6 & 14 \end{bmatrix} = A$$

$$\begin{bmatrix} 2 & 5 \\ 0 & -1 \end{bmatrix} = U \qquad\qquad \begin{bmatrix} 1 & 0 \\ -3 & 1 \end{bmatrix} = E$$

$$EA = U \qquad \Rightarrow \qquad A = E^{-1}U = \begin{bmatrix} 1 & 0 \\ 3 & 1 \end{bmatrix}\begin{bmatrix} 2 & 5 \\ 0 & -1 \end{bmatrix} = LU$$

37.   <u>Matrix</u>   <u>Elementary Matrix</u>

$$\begin{bmatrix} 1 & 0 & 1 \\ 2 & 1 & 2 \\ 3 & 2 & 6 \end{bmatrix} = A$$

$$\begin{bmatrix} 1 & 0 & 1 \\ 0 & 1 & 0 \\ 3 & 2 & 6 \end{bmatrix} \qquad \begin{bmatrix} 1 & 0 & 0 \\ -2 & 1 & 0 \\ 0 & 0 & 1 \end{bmatrix} = E_1$$

$$\begin{bmatrix} 1 & 0 & 1 \\ 0 & 1 & 0 \\ 0 & 2 & 3 \end{bmatrix} \cdot \qquad \begin{bmatrix} 1 & 0 & 0 \\ 0 & 1 & 0 \\ -3 & 0 & 1 \end{bmatrix} = E_2$$

$$\begin{bmatrix} 1 & 0 & 1 \\ 0 & 1 & 0 \\ 0 & 0 & 3 \end{bmatrix} = U \qquad \begin{bmatrix} 1 & 0 & 0 \\ 0 & 1 & 0 \\ 0 & -2 & 1 \end{bmatrix} = E_3$$

$$E_3 E_2 E_1 A = U \quad \Rightarrow \quad A = E_1^{-1} E_2^{-1} E_3^{-1} U = LU = \begin{bmatrix} 1 & 0 & 0 \\ 2 & 1 & 0 \\ 3 & 2 & 1 \end{bmatrix} \begin{bmatrix} 1 & 0 & 1 \\ 0 & 1 & 0 \\ 0 & 0 & 3 \end{bmatrix}.$$

$$L\mathbf{y} = \mathbf{b}: \begin{bmatrix} 1 & 0 & 0 \\ 2 & 1 & 0 \\ 3 & 2 & 1 \end{bmatrix} \begin{bmatrix} y_1 \\ y_2 \\ y_3 \end{bmatrix} = \begin{bmatrix} 3 \\ 7 \\ 8 \end{bmatrix} \quad \Rightarrow \quad \mathbf{y} = \begin{bmatrix} 3 \\ 1 \\ -3 \end{bmatrix}$$

$$U\mathbf{x} = \mathbf{y}: \begin{bmatrix} 1 & 0 & 1 \\ 0 & 1 & 0 \\ 0 & 0 & 3 \end{bmatrix} \begin{bmatrix} x_1 \\ x_2 \\ x_3 \end{bmatrix} = \begin{bmatrix} 3 \\ 1 \\ -3 \end{bmatrix} \Rightarrow \mathbf{x} = \begin{bmatrix} 4 \\ 1 \\ -1 \end{bmatrix}$$

39. This matrix is *not* stochastic. The second and third columns do not add up to 1.

41. $PX = \begin{bmatrix} \frac{1}{2} & \frac{1}{4} \\ \frac{1}{2} & \frac{3}{4} \end{bmatrix} \begin{bmatrix} 128 \\ 64 \end{bmatrix} = \begin{bmatrix} 80 \\ 112 \end{bmatrix}$

$P^2 X = P \begin{bmatrix} 80 \\ 112 \end{bmatrix} = \begin{bmatrix} 68 \\ 124 \end{bmatrix};$

$P^3 X = P \begin{bmatrix} 64 \\ 124 \end{bmatrix} = \begin{bmatrix} 65 \\ 127 \end{bmatrix}.$

43. We begin by forming the matrix of transition probabilities.

From Region

$$P = \begin{bmatrix} 0.85 & 0.15 & 0.10 \\ 0.10 & 0.80 & 0.10 \\ 0.05 & 0.05 & 0.80 \end{bmatrix} \begin{matrix} 1 \\ 2 \\ 3 \end{matrix} \Bigg\} \text{To Region}$$

(a) The population in each region after one year is given by

$$PX = \begin{bmatrix} 0.85 & 0.15 & 0.10 \\ 0.10 & 0.80 & 0.10 \\ 0.05 & 0.05 & 0.80 \end{bmatrix} \begin{bmatrix} 100,000 \\ 100,000 \\ 100,000 \end{bmatrix}$$

$$= \begin{bmatrix} 110,000 \\ 100,000 \\ 90,000 \end{bmatrix} \begin{matrix} \text{Region 1} \\ \text{Region 2} \\ \text{Region 3} \end{matrix}$$

(b) The population in each region after three years is given by

$$P^3X = \begin{bmatrix} 0.665375 & 0.322375 & 0.2435 \\ 0.219 & 0.562 & 0.219 \\ 0.115625 & 0.115625 & 0.5375 \end{bmatrix} \begin{bmatrix} 100,000 \\ 100,000 \\ 100,000 \end{bmatrix}$$

$$= \begin{bmatrix} 123,125 \\ 100,000 \\ 76,875 \end{bmatrix} \begin{matrix} \text{Region 1} \\ \text{Region 2} \\ \text{Region 3} \end{matrix}$$

45. The uncoded row matrices are

O	N	E	—	I	F	—	B	Y	—	L	A	N	D
[15	14]	[5	0]	[9	6]	[0	2]	[25	0]	[12	1]	[14	4] .

Multiplying each 1×2 matrix on the right by A yields the coded row matrices

[103 44], [25 10], [57 24], [4 2], [125 50], [62 25], [78 32].

Thus, the coded message is

103, 44, 25, 10, 57, 24, 4, 2, 125, 50, 62, 25, 78, 32.

47. We find A^{-1} to be

$$A^{-1} = \begin{bmatrix} 3 & 2 \\ 4 & 3 \end{bmatrix}$$

and the coded row matrices are

$[-45 \ 34]$, $[36 \ -24]$, $[-43 \ 37]$, $[-23 \ 22]$, $[-37 \ 29]$, $[57 \ -38]$, $[-39 \ 31]$.

Multiplying each coded row matrix on the right by A^{-1} yields the uncoded row matrices

A	L	L	—	S	Y	S	T	E	M	S	—	G	O
[1	12]	[12	0]	[19	25]	[19	20]	[5	13]	[19	0]	[7	15] .

The decoded message is ALL__SYSTEMS__GO.

49. First we find the input-output matrix D.

$$\overset{\text{User Industry}}{\overbrace{}}$$

$$\begin{matrix} & A & B \end{matrix}$$

$$D = \begin{bmatrix} 0.20 & 0.50 \\ 0.30 & 0.10 \end{bmatrix} \begin{matrix} A \\ B \end{matrix} \Bigg\} \text{Supplier Industry}$$

Then we solve the equation $X = DX + E$ for X to obtain $(I - D)X = E$, which corresponds to solving the augmented matrix

$$\begin{bmatrix} 0.80 & -0.50 & \vdots & 40{,}000 \\ -0.30 & 0.90 & \vdots & 80{,}000 \end{bmatrix}.$$

The solution to this system gives us

$$X \approx \begin{bmatrix} 133{,}333 \\ 133{,}333 \end{bmatrix}.$$

51. Using the matrices

$$X = \begin{bmatrix} 1 & 1 \\ 1 & 2 \\ 1 & 3 \end{bmatrix} \quad \text{and} \quad Y = \begin{bmatrix} 5 \\ 4 \\ 2 \end{bmatrix}$$

we have

$$X^T X = \begin{bmatrix} 3 & 6 \\ 6 & 14 \end{bmatrix} \quad \text{and} \quad X^T Y = \begin{bmatrix} 11 \\ 19 \end{bmatrix}$$

$$A = (X^T Y)^{-1} X^T Y = \begin{bmatrix} \frac{7}{3} & -1 \\ -1 & \frac{1}{2} \end{bmatrix} \begin{bmatrix} 11 \\ 19 \end{bmatrix} = \begin{bmatrix} \frac{20}{3} \\ -\frac{3}{2} \end{bmatrix}.$$

Thus, the least squares regression line is $y = -\frac{3}{2}x + \frac{20}{3}$.

53. Using the matrices

$$X = \begin{bmatrix} 1 & -2 \\ 1 & -1 \\ 1 & 0 \\ 1 & 1 \\ 1 & 2 \end{bmatrix} \quad \text{and} \quad Y = \begin{bmatrix} 4 \\ 2 \\ 1 \\ -2 \\ -3 \end{bmatrix}$$

we have

$$X^T X = \begin{bmatrix} 5 & 0 \\ 0 & 10 \end{bmatrix} \quad X^T Y = \begin{bmatrix} 2 \\ -18 \end{bmatrix}$$

$$A = (X^T X)^{-1} X^T Y = \begin{bmatrix} \frac{1}{5} & 0 \\ 0 & \frac{1}{10} \end{bmatrix} \begin{bmatrix} 2 \\ -18 \end{bmatrix} \begin{bmatrix} 0.4 \\ -1.8 \end{bmatrix}.$$

Thus, the least squares regression line is $y = -1.8x + 0.4$.

55. (a) We begin by finding the matrices X and Y.

$$X = \begin{bmatrix} 1 & 1.0 \\ 1 & 1.5 \\ 1 & 2.0 \\ 1 & 2.5 \end{bmatrix} \quad \text{and} \quad Y = \begin{bmatrix} 32 \\ 41 \\ 48 \\ 53 \end{bmatrix}$$

Then

$$X^T X = \begin{bmatrix} 1 & 1 & 1 & 1 \\ 1.0 & 1.5 & 2.0 & 2.5 \end{bmatrix} \begin{bmatrix} 1 & 1.0 \\ 1 & 1.5 \\ 1 & 2.0 \\ 1 & 2.5 \end{bmatrix} = \begin{bmatrix} 4 & 7 \\ 7 & 13.5 \end{bmatrix}$$

and

$$X^T Y = \begin{bmatrix} 1 & 1 & 1 & 1 \\ 1.0 & 1.5 & 2.0 & 2.5 \end{bmatrix} \begin{bmatrix} 32 \\ 41 \\ 48 \\ 53 \end{bmatrix} = \begin{bmatrix} 174 \\ 322 \end{bmatrix}.$$

The matrix of coefficients is

$$A = (X^T X)^{-1} X^T Y = \frac{1}{5} \begin{bmatrix} 13.5 & -7 \\ -7 & 4 \end{bmatrix} \begin{bmatrix} 174 \\ 322 \end{bmatrix} = \begin{bmatrix} 19 \\ 14 \end{bmatrix}.$$

Thus, the least squares regression line is $y = 19 + 14x$.

(b) When $x = 1.6$ (160 pounds per acre), $y = 41.4$ (bushels per acre).

CHAPTER 3
Determinants

Section 3.1   The Determinant of a Matrix

1. The determinant of a matrix of order 1 is the entry in the matrix. Thus, $\det[1] = 1$.

3. $\begin{vmatrix} 2 & 1 \\ 3 & 4 \end{vmatrix} = 2(4) - 3(1) = 5$

5. $\begin{vmatrix} 5 & 2 \\ -6 & 3 \end{vmatrix} = 5(3) - (-6)(2) = 27$

7. $\begin{vmatrix} -7 & 6 \\ \frac{1}{2} & 3 \end{vmatrix} = -7(3) - (\frac{1}{2})(6) = -24$

9. $\begin{vmatrix} 2 & 6 \\ 0 & 3 \end{vmatrix} = 2(3) - 0(6) = 6$

11. $\begin{vmatrix} \lambda - 3 & 2 \\ 4 & \lambda - 1 \end{vmatrix} = (\lambda - 3)(\lambda - 1) - 4(2) = \lambda^2 - 4\lambda - 5$

13. (a) The minors of the matrix are as follows.

$M_{11} = |4| = 4$

$M_{12} = |3| = 3$

$M_{21} = |2| = 2$

$M_{22} = |1| = 1$

(b) The cofactors of the matrix are as follows.

$C_{11} = (-1)^2 M_{11} = 4 \quad C_{12} = (-1)^3 M_{12} = -3$
$C_{21} = (-1)^3 M_{21} = -2 \quad C_{22} = (-1)^4 M_{22} = 1$

15. (a) The minors of the matrix are as follows.

$$M_{11} = \begin{vmatrix} 5 & 6 \\ -3 & 1 \end{vmatrix} = 23$$

$$M_{12} = \begin{vmatrix} 4 & 6 \\ 2 & 1 \end{vmatrix} = -8$$

$$M_{13} = \begin{vmatrix} 4 & 5 \\ 2 & -3 \end{vmatrix} = -22$$

$$M_{21} = \begin{vmatrix} 2 & 1 \\ -3 & 1 \end{vmatrix} = 5$$

$$M_{22} = \begin{vmatrix} -3 & 1 \\ 2 & 1 \end{vmatrix} = -5$$

$$M_{23} = \begin{vmatrix} -3 & 2 \\ 2 & -3 \end{vmatrix} = 5$$

$$M_{31} = \begin{vmatrix} 2 & 1 \\ 5 & 6 \end{vmatrix} = 7$$

$$M_{32} = \begin{vmatrix} -3 & 1 \\ 4 & 6 \end{vmatrix} = -22$$

$$M_{33} = \begin{vmatrix} -3 & 2 \\ 4 & 5 \end{vmatrix} = -23$$

(b) The cofactors of the matrix are as follows.

$$C_{11} = (-1)^2 M_{11} = 23 \qquad C_{12} = (-1)^3 M_{12} = 8 \qquad C_{13} = (-1)^4 M_{13} = -22$$

$$C_{21} = (-1)^3 M_{21} = -5 \qquad C_{22} = (-1)^4 M_{22} = -5 \qquad C_{23} = (-1)^5 M_{23} = -5$$

$$C_{31} = (-1)^4 M_{31} = 7 \qquad C_{32} = (-1)^5 M_{32} = 22 \qquad C_{33} = (-1)^6 M_{33} = -23$$

17. (a) We found the cofactors of the matrix in Exercise 15. Now we find the determinant by expanding along the second row.

$$\begin{vmatrix} -3 & 2 & 1 \\ 4 & 5 & 6 \\ 2 & -3 & 1 \end{vmatrix} = 4C_{21} + 5C_{22} + 6C_{23}$$

$$= 4(-5) + 5(-5) + 6(-5) = -75$$

(b) Expanding along the second column, we have

$$\begin{vmatrix} -3 & 2 & 1 \\ 4 & 5 & 6 \\ 2 & -3 & 1 \end{vmatrix} = 2C_{12} + 5C_{22} - 3C_{32}$$

$$= 2(8) + 5(-5) - 3(22) = -75.$$

19. We choose to expand along the second row because it has a zero.

$$\begin{vmatrix} 1 & 4 & -2 \\ 3 & 2 & 0 \\ -1 & 4 & 3 \end{vmatrix} = -3\begin{vmatrix} 4 & -2 \\ 4 & 3 \end{vmatrix} + 2\begin{vmatrix} 1 & -2 \\ -1 & 3 \end{vmatrix} - 0\begin{vmatrix} 1 & 4 \\ -1 & 4 \end{vmatrix}$$

$$= -3(20) + 2(1) = -58$$

21. We choose to expand along the first column because it has two zeros.

$$\begin{vmatrix} 2 & 4 & 6 \\ 0 & 3 & 1 \\ 0 & 0 & -5 \end{vmatrix} = 2\begin{vmatrix} 3 & 1 \\ 0 & -5 \end{vmatrix} - 0\begin{vmatrix} 4 & 6 \\ 0 & -5 \end{vmatrix} + 0\begin{vmatrix} 4 & 6 \\ 3 & 1 \end{vmatrix}$$

$$= 2(-15) = -30$$

23. We choose to expand along the second row because it has all zeros.

$$\begin{vmatrix} 6 & 3 & -7 \\ 0 & 0 & 0 \\ 4 & -6 & 3 \end{vmatrix} = -0\begin{vmatrix} 3 & -7 \\ -6 & 3 \end{vmatrix} + 0\begin{vmatrix} 6 & -7 \\ 4 & 3 \end{vmatrix} - 0\begin{vmatrix} 6 & 3 \\ 4 & -6 \end{vmatrix} = 0$$

Note that when a matrix has a row (or column) that is all zeros, its determinant is zero.

25. We expand along the first row.

$$\begin{vmatrix} 0.1 & 0.2 & 0.3 \\ -0.3 & 0.2 & 0.2 \\ 0.5 & 0.4 & 0.4 \end{vmatrix} = 0.1\begin{vmatrix} 0.2 & 0.2 \\ 0.4 & 0.4 \end{vmatrix} - 0.2\begin{vmatrix} -0.3 & 0.2 \\ 0.5 & 0.4 \end{vmatrix} + 0.3\begin{vmatrix} -0.3 & 0.2 \\ 0.5 & 0.4 \end{vmatrix}$$

$$= 0.1(0) - 0.2(-.22) + 0.3(-.22)$$

$$= -0.022$$

27. We use the third row since it has a zero.

$$\begin{vmatrix} x & y & 1 \\ 2 & 3 & 1 \\ 0 & -1 & 1 \end{vmatrix} = -(-1)\begin{vmatrix} x & 1 \\ 2 & 1 \end{vmatrix} + 1\begin{vmatrix} x & y \\ 2 & 3 \end{vmatrix}$$

$$= x - 2 + 3x - 2y$$

$$= 4x - 2y - 2$$

29. We expand along the second row since it has two zeros.

$$\begin{vmatrix} 3 & 6 & -5 & 4 \\ -2 & 0 & 6 & 0 \\ 1 & 1 & 2 & 2 \\ 0 & 3 & -1 & -1 \end{vmatrix} = 2 \begin{vmatrix} 6 & -5 & 4 \\ 1 & 2 & 2 \\ 3 & -1 & -1 \end{vmatrix} - 6 \begin{vmatrix} 3 & 6 & 4 \\ 1 & 1 & 2 \\ 0 & 3 & -1 \end{vmatrix}$$

The determinants of the two 3×3 matrices are

$$\begin{vmatrix} 6 & -5 & 4 \\ 1 & 2 & 2 \\ 3 & -1 & -1 \end{vmatrix} = 6 \begin{vmatrix} 2 & 2 \\ -1 & -1 \end{vmatrix} + 5 \begin{vmatrix} 1 & 2 \\ 3 & -1 \end{vmatrix} + 4 \begin{vmatrix} 1 & 2 \\ 3 & -1 \end{vmatrix}$$

$$= 6(0) + 5(-7) + 4(-7)$$

$$= -63$$

$$\begin{vmatrix} 3 & 6 & 4 \\ 1 & 1 & 2 \\ 0 & 3 & -1 \end{vmatrix} = 3 \begin{vmatrix} 1 & 2 \\ 3 & -1 \end{vmatrix} - 6 \begin{vmatrix} 1 & 2 \\ 0 & -1 \end{vmatrix} + 4 \begin{vmatrix} 1 & 1 \\ 0 & 3 \end{vmatrix}$$

$$= 3(-7) - 6(-1) + 4(3)$$

$$= -3.$$

Thus, the determinant of the original matrix is

$$2(-63) - 6(-3) = -108.$$

31. We use the first column since it has two zeros.

$$\begin{vmatrix} 5 & 3 & 0 & 6 \\ 4 & 6 & 4 & 12 \\ 0 & 2 & -3 & 4 \\ 0 & 1 & -2 & 2 \end{vmatrix} = 5 \begin{vmatrix} 6 & 4 & 12 \\ 2 & -3 & 4 \\ 1 & -2 & 2 \end{vmatrix} - 4 \begin{vmatrix} 3 & 0 & 6 \\ 2 & -3 & 4 \\ 1 & -2 & 2 \end{vmatrix}$$

The determinants of the two 3×3 matrices are

$$\begin{vmatrix} 6 & 4 & 12 \\ 2 & -3 & 4 \\ 1 & -2 & 2 \end{vmatrix} = 6 \begin{vmatrix} -3 & 4 \\ -2 & 2 \end{vmatrix} - 2 \begin{vmatrix} 4 & 12 \\ -2 & 2 \end{vmatrix} + 1 \begin{vmatrix} 4 & 12 \\ -3 & 4 \end{vmatrix}$$

$$= 6(2) - 2(32) + 52$$

$$= 0$$

and

$$\begin{vmatrix} 3 & 0 & 6 \\ 2 & -3 & 4 \\ 1 & -2 & 2 \end{vmatrix} = 3 \begin{vmatrix} -3 & 4 \\ -2 & 2 \end{vmatrix} - 0 \begin{vmatrix} 2 & 4 \\ 1 & 2 \end{vmatrix} + 6 \begin{vmatrix} 2 & -3 \\ 1 & -2 \end{vmatrix}$$

$$= 3(2) + 6(-1)$$

$$= 0.$$

Thus, we have

$$\begin{vmatrix} 5 & 3 & 0 & 6 \\ 4 & 6 & 4 & 12 \\ 0 & 2 & -3 & 4 \\ 0 & 1 & -2 & 2 \end{vmatrix} = 5(0) - 4(0) = 0.$$

33. We expand along the first row since it has two zeros.

$$
\begin{vmatrix} 3 & 0 & 7 & 0 \\ 2 & 6 & 11 & 12 \\ 4 & 1 & -1 & 2 \\ 1 & 5 & 2 & 10 \end{vmatrix} = 3 \begin{vmatrix} 6 & 11 & 12 \\ 1 & -1 & 2 \\ 5 & 2 & 10 \end{vmatrix} + 7 \begin{vmatrix} 2 & 6 & 12 \\ 4 & 1 & 2 \\ 1 & 5 & 10 \end{vmatrix}
$$

The determinants of the two 3×3 matrices are

$$
\begin{vmatrix} 6 & 11 & 12 \\ 1 & -1 & 2 \\ 5 & 2 & 10 \end{vmatrix} = 6 \begin{vmatrix} -1 & 2 \\ 2 & 10 \end{vmatrix} - 11 \begin{vmatrix} 1 & 2 \\ 5 & 10 \end{vmatrix} + 12 \begin{vmatrix} 1 & -1 \\ 5 & 2 \end{vmatrix}
$$

$$
= 6(-14) - 11(0) + 12(7)
$$

$$
= 0
$$

$$
\begin{vmatrix} 2 & 6 & 12 \\ 4 & 1 & 2 \\ 1 & 5 & 10 \end{vmatrix} = 2 \begin{vmatrix} 1 & 2 \\ 5 & 10 \end{vmatrix} - 6 \begin{vmatrix} 4 & 2 \\ 1 & 10 \end{vmatrix} + 12 \begin{vmatrix} 4 & 1 \\ 1 & 5 \end{vmatrix}
$$

$$
= 2(0) = -6(38) + 12(19)
$$

$$
= 0.
$$

Thus, the determinant of the original matrix is

$$
3(0) + 7(0) = 0.
$$

35. We expand along the first column, and then along the first column of the 4×4 matrix.

$$
\begin{vmatrix} 5 & 2 & 0 & 0 & -2 \\ 0 & 1 & 4 & 3 & 2 \\ 0 & 0 & 2 & 6 & 3 \\ 0 & 0 & 3 & 4 & 1 \\ 0 & 0 & 0 & 0 & 2 \end{vmatrix} = 5 \begin{vmatrix} 1 & 4 & 3 & 2 \\ 0 & 2 & 6 & 3 \\ 0 & 3 & 4 & 1 \\ 0 & 0 & 0 & 2 \end{vmatrix} = 5(1) \begin{vmatrix} 2 & 6 & 3 \\ 3 & 4 & 1 \\ 0 & 0 & 2 \end{vmatrix}
$$

We now expand along the third row, and obtain

$$
5(1) \begin{vmatrix} 2 & 6 & 3 \\ 3 & 4 & 1 \\ 0 & 0 & 2 \end{vmatrix} = 5(2) \begin{vmatrix} 2 & 6 \\ 3 & 4 \end{vmatrix} = 10(-10) = -100.
$$

37. The determinant of a triangular matrix is the product of the elements on its main diagonal.

$$
\begin{vmatrix} -2 & 0 & 0 \\ 4 & 6 & 0 \\ -3 & 7 & 2 \end{vmatrix} = -2(6)(2) = -24
$$

39. The determinant of a triangular matrix is the product of the elements on its main diagonal.

$$\begin{vmatrix} 5 & 8 & -4 & 2 \\ 0 & 0 & 6 & 0 \\ 0 & 0 & 2 & 2 \\ 0 & 0 & 0 & -1 \end{vmatrix} = 5(0)(2)(-1) = 0$$

41. The determinant of a triangular matrix is the product of the elements on the main diagonal.

$$\begin{vmatrix} -1 & 4 & 2 & 1 & -3 \\ 0 & 3 & -4 & 5 & 2 \\ 0 & 0 & 2 & 7 & 0 \\ 0 & 0 & 0 & 5 & -1 \\ 0 & 0 & 0 & 0 & 1 \end{vmatrix} = (-1)(3)(2)(5)(1) = -30$$

43. The determinant is

$$\begin{vmatrix} \lambda - 1 & -4 \\ -2 & \lambda + 1 \end{vmatrix} = (\lambda - 1)(\lambda + 1) - (-4)(-2) = \lambda^2 - 9.$$

Setting $\lambda^2 - 9 = 0$ yields $\lambda = \pm 3$.

45. Expanding along the first row, we see that the determinant of a 4×4 matrix involves four 3×3 determinants. Each of these 3×3 determinants requires 6 triple products. Hence, there are $4(6) = 24$ quadruple products.

47. Expanding the determinant along the first row yields

$$\begin{vmatrix} 1 & 1 & 1 \\ a & b & c \\ a^2 & b^2 & c^2 \end{vmatrix} = (bc^2 - cb^2) - (ac^2 - ca^2) + (ab^2 - a^2b) = bc^2 + ca^2 + ab^2 - ba^2 - ac^2 - cb^2.$$

Expanding the right side yields

$$(a - b)(b - c)(c - a) = (ab - b^2 - ac + bc)(c - a)$$
$$= abc - cb^2 - ac^2 + bc^2 - ba^2 + ab^2 + ca^2 - abc$$
$$= bc^2 + ca^2 + ab^2 - ba^2 - ac^2 - cb^2.$$

49. Expanding along the first row, we have

$$\begin{vmatrix} x & 0 & c \\ -1 & x & b \\ 0 & -1 & a \end{vmatrix} = x \begin{vmatrix} x & b \\ -1 & a \end{vmatrix} + c \begin{vmatrix} -1 & x \\ 0 & -1 \end{vmatrix} = x(ax + b) + c(1)$$
$$= ax^2 + bx + c.$$

51. If you expand along the row of zeros, you see that the determinant is zero.

Section 3.2   Evaluation of a Determinant Using Elementary Operations

1. Because the first row is a multiple of the second row, the determinant is zero.

3. Because the second row is composed all of zeros, the determinant is zero.

5. Because the second and third columns are interchanged, the sign of the determinant is changed.

7. Because 5 has been factored out of the first row, the first determinant is 5 times the second one.

9. Because each row in the matrix on the left is divided by 5 to yield the matrix on the right, the determinant of the matrix on the left is 5^3 times the determinant of the matrix on the right.

11. Because a multiple to the first row of the matrix on the left was added to the second row to produce the matrix on the right, the determinants are equal.

13. Because a multiple of the second column of the matrix on the left was added to the third column to produce the matrix on the right, the determinants are equal.

15. $\begin{vmatrix} 1 & 7 & -3 \\ 1 & 3 & 1 \\ 4 & 8 & 1 \end{vmatrix} = \begin{vmatrix} 1 & 7 & -3 \\ 0 & -4 & 4 \\ 4 & 8 & 1 \end{vmatrix}$

$$= \begin{vmatrix} 1 & 7 & -3 \\ 0 & -4 & 4 \\ 0 & -20 & 13 \end{vmatrix}$$

$$= \begin{vmatrix} 1 & 7 & -3 \\ 0 & -4 & 4 \\ 0 & 0 & -7 \end{vmatrix} = 1(-4)(-7) = 28$$

17. $\begin{vmatrix} 2 & -1 & -1 \\ 1 & 3 & 2 \\ 1 & 1 & 3 \end{vmatrix} = - \begin{vmatrix} 1 & 3 & 2 \\ 2 & -1 & -1 \\ 1 & 1 & 3 \end{vmatrix}$

$$= - \begin{vmatrix} 1 & 3 & 2 \\ 0 & -7 & -5 \\ 0 & -2 & 1 \end{vmatrix} = (-1)(-7 - 10) = 17$$

19.
$$\begin{vmatrix} 4 & 3 & -2 \\ 5 & 4 & 1 \\ -2 & 3 & 4 \end{vmatrix} = 4 \begin{vmatrix} 14 & 11 & 0 \\ 5 & 4 & 1 \\ -22 & -13 & 0 \end{vmatrix}$$

$$= (-1) \begin{vmatrix} 14 & 11 \\ -22 & -13 \end{vmatrix}$$

$$= (-1) \big(14(-13) - (-22)(11)\big)$$

$$= (-1)(60) = -60$$

21.
$$\begin{vmatrix} 5 & -8 & 0 \\ 9 & 7 & 4 \\ -8 & 7 & 1 \end{vmatrix} = \begin{vmatrix} 5 & -8 & 0 \\ 41 & -21 & 0 \\ -8 & 7 & 1 \end{vmatrix} = 1(-105 + 328) = 223$$

23.
$$\begin{vmatrix} 4 & -7 & 9 & 1 \\ 6 & 2 & 7 & 0 \\ 3 & 6 & -3 & 3 \\ 0 & 7 & 4 & -1 \end{vmatrix} = \begin{vmatrix} 4 & -7 & 9 & 1 \\ 6 & 2 & 7 & 0 \\ -9 & 27 & -30 & 0 \\ 4 & 0 & 13 & 0 \end{vmatrix}$$

$$= - \begin{vmatrix} 6 & 2 & 7 \\ -9 & 27 & -30 \\ 4 & 0 & 13 \end{vmatrix}$$

$$= 3 \begin{vmatrix} 6 & 2 & 7 \\ 3 & -9 & 10 \\ 4 & 0 & 13 \end{vmatrix}$$

$$= 3 \begin{vmatrix} 0 & 20 & -13 \\ 3 & -9 & 10 \\ 4 & 0 & 13 \end{vmatrix}$$

$$= 3[(-3)260 + 4(200 - 117)] = -1344$$

25. $\begin{vmatrix} 1 & -2 & 7 & 9 \\ 3 & -4 & 5 & 5 \\ 3 & 6 & 1 & -1 \\ 4 & 5 & 3 & 2 \end{vmatrix} = 2 \begin{vmatrix} 1 & -2 & 7 & 9 \\ 0 & 2 & -16 & -22 \\ 0 & 12 & -20 & -28 \\ 0 & 13 & -25 & -34 \end{vmatrix}$

$\qquad\qquad = 2 \begin{vmatrix} 1 & -2 & 7 & 9 \\ 0 & 1 & -8 & -11 \\ 0 & 12 & -20 & -28 \\ 0 & 13 & -25 & -34 \end{vmatrix}$

$\qquad\qquad = 2 \begin{vmatrix} 1 & -2 & 7 & 9 \\ 0 & 1 & -8 & -11 \\ 0 & 0 & 76 & 104 \\ 0 & 0 & 79 & 109 \end{vmatrix}$

$\qquad\quad = 2(1)(1) \begin{vmatrix} 76 & 104 \\ 79 & 109 \end{vmatrix}$

$\qquad\quad = 2\big(76(109) - 79(104)\big) = 136$

27.
$$
\begin{vmatrix} 1 & -1 & 8 & 4 & 2 \\ 2 & 6 & 0 & -4 & 3 \\ 2 & 0 & 2 & 6 & 2 \\ 0 & 2 & 8 & 0 & 0 \\ 0 & 1 & 1 & 2 & 2 \end{vmatrix} =
\begin{vmatrix} 1 & -1 & 8 & 4 & 2 \\ 0 & 8 & -16 & -12 & -1 \\ 0 & 2 & -14 & -2 & -2 \\ 0 & 2 & 8 & 0 & 0 \\ 0 & 1 & 1 & 2 & 2 \end{vmatrix}
$$

$$
= \begin{vmatrix} 1 & -1 & 8 & 4 & 2 \\ 0 & 0 & -24 & -28 & -17 \\ 0 & 0 & -16 & -6 & -6 \\ 0 & 0 & 6 & -4 & -4 \\ 0 & 1 & 1 & 2 & 2 \end{vmatrix}
$$

$$
= (-1) \begin{vmatrix} -24 & -28 & -17 \\ -16 & -6 & -6 \\ 6 & -4 & -4 \end{vmatrix}
$$

$$
= 2 \begin{vmatrix} -24 & -28 & -17 \\ -16 & -6 & -6 \\ -3 & 2 & 2 \end{vmatrix}
$$

$$
= 2 \begin{vmatrix} -24 & -28 & -17 \\ -25 & 0 & 0 \\ -3 & 2 & 2 \end{vmatrix} = 50(-56 + 34) = -1100
$$

29.
$$
\begin{vmatrix} 1 & 0 & 0 \\ 0 & k & 0 \\ 0 & 0 & 1 \end{vmatrix} = k \begin{vmatrix} 1 & 0 & 0 \\ 0 & 1 & 0 \\ 0 & 0 & 1 \end{vmatrix} = k
$$

31.
$$
\begin{vmatrix} 0 & 1 & 0 \\ 1 & 0 & 0 \\ 0 & 0 & 1 \end{vmatrix} = - \begin{vmatrix} 1 & 0 & 0 \\ 0 & 1 & 0 \\ 0 & 0 & 1 \end{vmatrix} = -1
$$

33.
$$
\begin{vmatrix} 1 & 0 & 0 \\ k & 1 & 0 \\ 0 & 0 & 1 \end{vmatrix} = \begin{vmatrix} 1 & 0 & 0 \\ 0 & 1 & 0 \\ 0 & 0 & 1 \end{vmatrix} = 1
$$

35. We expand the two determinants on the left.

$$\begin{vmatrix} a_{11} & a_{12} & a_{13} \\ a_{21} & a_{22} & a_{23} \\ a_{31} & a_{32} & a_{33} \end{vmatrix} + \begin{vmatrix} b_{11} & a_{12} & a_{13} \\ b_{21} & a_{22} & a_{23} \\ b_{31} & a_{32} & a_{33} \end{vmatrix}$$

$$= a_{11} \begin{vmatrix} a_{22} & a_{23} \\ a_{32} & a_{33} \end{vmatrix} - a_{21} \begin{vmatrix} a_{12} & a_{13} \\ a_{32} & a_{33} \end{vmatrix} + a_{31} \begin{vmatrix} a_{12} & a_{13} \\ a_{22} & a_{23} \end{vmatrix}$$

$$+ b_{11} \begin{vmatrix} a_{22} & a_{23} \\ a_{32} & a_{33} \end{vmatrix} - b_{21} \begin{vmatrix} a_{12} & a_{13} \\ a_{32} & a_{33} \end{vmatrix} + b_{31} \begin{vmatrix} a_{12} & a_{13} \\ a_{22} & a_{23} \end{vmatrix}$$

$$= (a_{11} + b_{11}) \begin{vmatrix} a_{22} & a_{23} \\ a_{32} & a_{33} \end{vmatrix} - (a_{21} + b_{21}) \begin{vmatrix} a_{12} & a_{13} \\ a_{32} & a_{33} \end{vmatrix} + (a_{31} + b_{31}) \begin{vmatrix} a_{12} & a_{13} \\ a_{22} & a_{23} \end{vmatrix}$$

$$= \begin{vmatrix} (a_{11} + b_{11}) & a_{12} & a_{13} \\ (a_{21} + b_{21}) & a_{22} & a_{23} \\ (a_{31} + b_{31}) & a_{32} & a_{33} \end{vmatrix}$$

37. $\begin{vmatrix} \cos \theta & \sin \theta \\ -\sin \theta & \cos \theta \end{vmatrix} = \cos \theta \, (\cos \theta) - (-\sin \theta)(\sin \theta) = \cos^2 \theta + \sin^2 \theta = 1$

39. Suppose B is obtained from A by adding a multiple of a row of A to another row of A. More specifically, suppose c times the jth row of A is added to the ith row of A.

$$B = \begin{bmatrix} a_{11} & \cdots & a_{1n} \\ \vdots & & \\ (a_{i1} + ca_{j1}) & \cdots & (a_{in} + ca_{jn}) \\ \vdots & & \\ a_{n1} & \cdots & a_{nn} \end{bmatrix}$$

Expanding along this row, we have

$$\det B = (a_{i1} + ca_{j1})\, C_{i1} + \cdots + (a_{in} + ca_{jn})C_{in}$$

$$= [a_{i1}C_{i1} + \cdots + a_{in}\, C_{in}] + [ca_{j1}C_{i1} + \cdots + ca_{jn}C_{in}]$$

The first bracketed expression is det A, so we only need to prove that the second bracketed expression is zero.

We use math induction. For $n = 2$, we have (assuming $i = 2$ and $j = 1$)

$$ca_{11}C_{21} + ca_{12}C_{22} = \det \begin{bmatrix} a_{11} & a_{12} \\ ca_{11} & ca_{12} \end{bmatrix} = 0 \text{ (because row 2 is a multiple of row 1)}$$

Assuming the expression is true for $n - 1$, we have

$$ca_{ji}C_{i1} + \cdots + ca_{jn}C_{in} = 0$$

by expanding along any row different from i and j, and applying the induction hypothesis.

41. Cofactor expansion would cost:

$(3{,}628{,}799)\,(0.001) + (6{,}235{,}300)\,(0.003) = \$22{,}334.70.$

Row reduction would cost much less:

$(285)\,(0.001) + (339)\,(0.003) = \$1.30$

Section 3.3   Properties of Determinants

1. (a) $|A| = \begin{vmatrix} -1 & 0 \\ 0 & 3 \end{vmatrix} = -3$

    (b) $|B| = \begin{vmatrix} 2 & 0 \\ 0 & -1 \end{vmatrix} = -2$

    (c) $AB = \begin{bmatrix} -1 & 0 \\ 0 & 3 \end{bmatrix} \begin{bmatrix} 2 & 0 \\ 0 & -1 \end{bmatrix} = \begin{bmatrix} -2 & 0 \\ 0 & -3 \end{bmatrix}$

    (d) $|AB| = \begin{vmatrix} -2 & 0 \\ 0 & -3 \end{vmatrix} = 6$

    Note that $|A||B| = -3(-2) = 6 = |AB|$.

3. (a) $|A| = \begin{vmatrix} -2 & 1 \\ 4 & -2 \end{vmatrix} = 0$

    (b) $|B| = \begin{vmatrix} 1 & 1 \\ 0 & -1 \end{vmatrix} = -1$

    (c) $AB = \begin{bmatrix} -2 & 1 \\ 4 & -2 \end{bmatrix} \begin{bmatrix} 1 & 1 \\ 0 & -1 \end{bmatrix} = \begin{bmatrix} -2 & -3 \\ 4 & 6 \end{bmatrix}$

    (d) $|AB| = \begin{vmatrix} -2 & -3 \\ 4 & 6 \end{vmatrix} = 0$

    Note that $|A||B| = 0(-1) = 0 = |AB|$.

5. (a) $|A| = \begin{vmatrix} -1 & 2 & 1 \\ 1 & 0 & 1 \\ 0 & 1 & 0 \end{vmatrix} = 2$

    (b) $|B| = \begin{vmatrix} -1 & 0 & 0 \\ 0 & 2 & 0 \\ 0 & 0 & 3 \end{vmatrix} = -6$

    (c) $AB = \begin{bmatrix} -1 & 2 & 1 \\ 1 & 0 & 1 \\ 0 & 1 & 0 \end{bmatrix} \begin{bmatrix} -1 & 0 & 0 \\ 0 & 2 & 0 \\ 0 & 0 & 3 \end{bmatrix} = \begin{bmatrix} 1 & 4 & 3 \\ -1 & 0 & 3 \\ 0 & 2 & 0 \end{bmatrix}$

    (d) $|AB| = \begin{vmatrix} 1 & 4 & 3 \\ -1 & 0 & 3 \\ 0 & 2 & 0 \end{vmatrix} = -12$

    Note that $|A||B| = 2(-6) = -12 = |AB|$.

7. $|A| = \begin{vmatrix} 4 & 2 \\ 6 & -8 \end{vmatrix} = 2^2 \begin{vmatrix} 2 & 1 \\ 3 & -4 \end{vmatrix} = 4(-11) = -44$

9. $|A| = \begin{vmatrix} -3 & 6 & 9 \\ 6 & 9 & 12 \\ 9 & 12 & 15 \end{vmatrix} = 3^3 \begin{vmatrix} -1 & 2 & 3 \\ 2 & 3 & 4 \\ 3 & 4 & 5 \end{vmatrix}$

$= 3^3 \begin{vmatrix} -1 & 2 & 3 \\ 0 & 7 & 10 \\ 0 & 10 & 14 \end{vmatrix} = (-27)(-2) = 54$

11. (a) $|A| = \begin{vmatrix} -1 & 1 \\ 2 & 0 \end{vmatrix} = -2$

   (b) $|B| = \begin{vmatrix} 1 & -1 \\ -2 & 0 \end{vmatrix} = -2$

   (c) $|A + B| = \left| \begin{bmatrix} -1 & 1 \\ 2 & 0 \end{bmatrix} + \begin{bmatrix} 1 & -1 \\ -2 & 0 \end{bmatrix} \right| = \begin{vmatrix} 0 & 0 \\ 0 & 0 \end{vmatrix} = 0$

   Note that $|A| + |B| = -2 + (-2) = -4 \neq |A + B|$.

13. First we observe that $|A| = \begin{vmatrix} 6 & -11 \\ 4 & -5 \end{vmatrix} = 14$.

   (a) $|A^T| = |A| = 14$

   (b) $|A^2| = |A||A| = |A|^2 = 196$

   (c) $|AA^T| = |A||A^T| = 14(14) = 196$

   (d) $|2A| = 4|A| = 56$

   (e) $A^{-1} = \dfrac{1}{|A|} = \dfrac{1}{14}$.

15. First we observe that $|A| = \begin{vmatrix} 2 & 0 & 5 \\ 4 & -1 & 6 \\ 3 & 2 & 1 \end{vmatrix} = 29$

   (a) $|A^T| = |A| = 29$

   (b) $|A^2| = |A||A| = 29^2 = 841$

   (c) $|AA^T| = |A||A^T| = 29(29) = 841$

   (d) $|2A| = 2^3|A| = 8(29) = 232$

   (e) $A^{-1} = \dfrac{1}{|A|} = \dfrac{1}{29}$.

17. (a) $|AB| = |A||B| = -5(3) = -15$

(b) $|A^3| = |A|^3 = (-5)^3 = -125$

(c) $|3B| = 3^4|B| = 81(3) = 243$

(d) $|(AB)^T| = |AB| = -15$

(e) $|A^{-1}| = \dfrac{1}{|A|} = -\dfrac{1}{5}$

19. Because

$$\begin{vmatrix} 5 & 4 \\ 10 & 8 \end{vmatrix} = 0$$

the matrix is singular.

21. Because

$$\begin{vmatrix} 14 & 7 \\ 2 & 3 \end{vmatrix} = 28 \neq 0,$$

the matrix is nonsingular.

23. Because

$$\begin{vmatrix} \frac{1}{2} & \frac{3}{2} & 2 \\ \frac{2}{3} & -\frac{1}{3} & 0 \\ 1 & 1 & 1 \end{vmatrix} = \frac{5}{6} \neq 0$$

the matrix is nonsingular.

25. Because

$$\begin{vmatrix} 1 & 0 & -8 & 2 \\ 0 & 8 & -1 & 10 \\ 0 & 0 & 0 & 1 \\ 0 & 0 & 0 & 2 \end{vmatrix} = 0,$$

the matrix is singular.

27. The coefficient matrix of the system is

$$\begin{bmatrix} 1 & -1 & 1 \\ 2 & -1 & 1 \\ 3 & -2 & 2 \end{bmatrix}$$

which has a determinant of

$$\begin{vmatrix} 1 & -1 & 1 \\ 2 & -1 & 1 \\ 3 & -2 & 2 \end{vmatrix} = 0.$$

Because the determinant is zero, the system does not have a unique solution.

29. The coefficient matrix of the system is

$$\begin{vmatrix} 2 & 1 & 5 & 1 \\ 1 & 1 & -3 & -4 \\ 2 & 2 & 2 & -3 \\ 1 & 5 & -6 & 0 \end{vmatrix}.$$

Because the determinant of this matrix is 115, and hence nonzero, the system has a unique solution.

31. We find the values of k necessary to make A singular by setting $|A| = 0$.

$$\begin{aligned} |A| &= \begin{vmatrix} k-1 & 3 \\ 2 & k-2 \end{vmatrix} \\ &= (k-1)(k-2) - 6 \\ &= k^2 - 3k - 4 \\ &= (k-4)(k+1) = 0 \end{aligned}$$

Thus, $|A| = 0$ when $k = -1, 4$.

33. We are given $AB = I$, which implies that $|AB| = |A||B| = |I| = 1$. Hence, both $|A|$ and $|B|$ must be nonzero, since their product is 1.

35. Let

$$A = \begin{bmatrix} 1 & 0 \\ 0 & 0 \end{bmatrix} \text{ and } B = \begin{bmatrix} 0 & 1 \\ 0 & 0 \end{bmatrix}.$$

Then

$$|A| + |B| = 0 + 0 = 0, \text{ and } |A + B| = \begin{vmatrix} 1 & 1 \\ 0 & 0 \end{vmatrix} = 0.$$

(The answer is not unique.)

37. For each i, $i = 1, 2, \ldots, n$, the ith row of A can be written as

$$a_{i1}, \quad a_{i2}, \quad \ldots, \quad a_{in-1}, \quad -\sum_{j=1}^{n-1} a_{ij}$$

Therefore, the last column can be reduced to all zeros by adding the other columns of A to it. Since A can be reduced to a matrix with a column of zeros, $|A| = 0$.

39. Since A is invertible, we have $|I| = |AA^{-1}| = |A||A^{-1}| = 1$. Since all the entires of A and A^{-1} are integers, we must have both $|A|$ and $|A^{-1}|$ integers. Hence, if the product of two integers is 1, the integers must be 1 or -1. Thus, $|A| = \pm 1$.

41. $P^{-1}AP \neq A$ in general. For example,

$$P = \begin{bmatrix} 1 & 2 \\ 3 & 5 \end{bmatrix}, \ P^{-1} = \begin{bmatrix} -5 & 2 \\ 3 & -1 \end{bmatrix}, \ A = \begin{bmatrix} 2 & 1 \\ -1 & 0 \end{bmatrix},$$

$$P^{-1}AP = \begin{bmatrix} -27 & -49 \\ 16 & 29 \end{bmatrix} \neq A.$$

However, the determinant $|A|$ and $|P^{-1}AP|$ are equal.

$$|P^{-1}AP| = |P^{-1}||A||P| = |P^{-1}||P||A| = \frac{1}{|P|}|P||A| = |A|.$$

43. Let A be an $n \times n$ matrix satisfying $A^T = -A$.

Then,

$$|A| = |A^T| = |-A| = (-1)^n |A|.$$

45. The inverse of this matrix is

$$\begin{bmatrix} 0 & 1 \\ 1 & 0 \end{bmatrix}^{-1} = \begin{bmatrix} 0 & 1 \\ 1 & 0 \end{bmatrix}.$$

Hence $A^T = A^{-1}$.

Thus, $\begin{bmatrix} 0 & 1 \\ 1 & 0 \end{bmatrix}$ *is* orthogonal.

47. Since the matrix has no inverse (its determinant is 0), it is not orthogonal.

49. The inverse of this elementary matrix is

$$A^{-1} = \begin{bmatrix} 1 & 0 & 0 \\ 0 & 0 & 1 \\ 0 & 1 & 0 \end{bmatrix}.$$

Because $A^{-1} = A^T$, the matrix *is* orthogonal.

51. If $A^T = A^{-1}$, then $|A^T| = |A^{-1}|$ and we have

$$|AA^{-1}| = |A||A^{-1}| = |A||A^T| = |A|^2 = 1 \Rightarrow |A| = \pm 1.$$

53. $|SB| = |S||B| = 0 \ |B| = 0 \Rightarrow SB$ is singular.

55. $A\mathbf{x}_1 = \begin{bmatrix} 1 & 2 \\ 0 & -3 \end{bmatrix} \begin{bmatrix} 1 \\ 0 \end{bmatrix} = \begin{bmatrix} 1 \\ 0 \end{bmatrix}$

$A\mathbf{x}_2 = \begin{bmatrix} 1 & 2 \\ 0 & -3 \end{bmatrix} \begin{bmatrix} -1 \\ 2 \end{bmatrix} = \begin{bmatrix} 3 \\ -6 \end{bmatrix} = -3 \begin{bmatrix} -1 \\ 2 \end{bmatrix}$

57. $A\mathbf{x}_1 = \begin{bmatrix} 1 & 1 & 1 \\ 0 & 1 & 0 \\ 1 & 1 & 1 \end{bmatrix} \begin{bmatrix} 1 \\ 0 \\ 1 \end{bmatrix} = \begin{bmatrix} 2 \\ 0 \\ 2 \end{bmatrix} = 2 \begin{bmatrix} 1 \\ 0 \\ 1 \end{bmatrix}$

$A\mathbf{x}_2 = \begin{bmatrix} 1 & 1 & 1 \\ 0 & 1 & 0 \\ 1 & 1 & 1 \end{bmatrix} \begin{bmatrix} -1 \\ 0 \\ 1 \end{bmatrix} = \begin{bmatrix} 0 \\ 0 \\ 0 \end{bmatrix} = 0 \begin{bmatrix} -1 \\ 0 \\ 1 \end{bmatrix}$

$A\mathbf{x}_3 = \begin{bmatrix} 1 & 1 & 1 \\ 0 & 1 & 0 \\ 1 & 1 & 1 \end{bmatrix} \begin{bmatrix} -1 \\ 1 \\ -1 \end{bmatrix} = \begin{bmatrix} -1 \\ 1 \\ -1 \end{bmatrix} = 1 \begin{bmatrix} -1 \\ 1 \\ -1 \end{bmatrix}$

59. $|\lambda I - A| = \begin{vmatrix} \lambda - 4 & 5 \\ -2 & \lambda + 3 \end{vmatrix} = \lambda^2 - \lambda - 2 = (\lambda - 2)(\lambda + 1)$

For $\lambda = 2$: $\begin{bmatrix} -2 & 5 \\ -2 & 5 \end{bmatrix} \Rightarrow \begin{bmatrix} -2 & 5 \\ 0 & 0 \end{bmatrix} \Rightarrow \vec{\mathbf{x}} = \begin{bmatrix} 5 \\ 2 \end{bmatrix}$

For $\lambda = -1$: $\begin{bmatrix} -5 & 5 \\ -2 & 2 \end{bmatrix} \Rightarrow \begin{bmatrix} 1 & -1 \\ 0 & 0 \end{bmatrix} \Rightarrow \vec{\mathbf{x}} = \begin{bmatrix} 1 \\ 1 \end{bmatrix}.$

61. $|\lambda I - A| = \begin{vmatrix} \lambda - 1 & 1 & 1 \\ -1 & \lambda - 3 & -1 \\ 3 & -1 & \lambda + 1 \end{vmatrix}$

$= (\lambda - 1)(\lambda^2 - 2\lambda - 4) + 1(\lambda + 2) + 3(2 - \lambda)$

$= \lambda^3 - 3\lambda^2 - 4\lambda + 12$

$= (\lambda - 2)(\lambda + 2)(\lambda - 3)$

$\lambda = 2$: $\begin{bmatrix} 1 & 1 & 1 \\ -1 & -1 & -1 \\ 3 & -1 & 3 \end{bmatrix} \Rightarrow \begin{bmatrix} 1 & 1 & 1 \\ 0 & -4 & 0 \\ 0 & 0 & 0 \end{bmatrix} \Rightarrow \begin{bmatrix} 1 & 0 & 1 \\ 0 & 1 & 0 \\ 0 & 0 & 0 \end{bmatrix} \Rightarrow \mathbf{x} = \begin{bmatrix} 1 \\ 0 \\ -1 \end{bmatrix}$

$\lambda = -2$: $\begin{bmatrix} -3 & 1 & 1 \\ -1 & -5 & -1 \\ 3 & -1 & -1 \end{bmatrix} \Rightarrow \begin{bmatrix} 1 & 5 & 1 \\ 0 & 16 & 4 \\ 0 & 0 & 0 \end{bmatrix} \Rightarrow \begin{bmatrix} 1 & 5 & 1 \\ 0 & 4 & 1 \\ 0 & 0 & 0 \end{bmatrix} \Rightarrow \mathbf{x} = \begin{bmatrix} -1 \\ 1 \\ -4 \end{bmatrix}$

$\lambda = 3$: $\begin{bmatrix} 2 & 1 & 1 \\ -1 & 0 & -1 \\ 3 & -1 & 4 \end{bmatrix} \Rightarrow \begin{bmatrix} 1 & 0 & 1 \\ 0 & 1 & -1 \\ 0 & -1 & 1 \end{bmatrix} \Rightarrow \begin{bmatrix} 1 & 0 & 1 \\ 0 & 1 & -1 \\ 0 & 0 & 0 \end{bmatrix} \Rightarrow \mathbf{x} = \begin{bmatrix} -1 \\ 1 \\ 1 \end{bmatrix}$

Section 3.4   Applications of Determinants

1. The matrix of cofactors is

$$\begin{bmatrix} |4| & -|3| \\ -|2| & |1| \end{bmatrix} = \begin{bmatrix} 4 & -3 \\ -2 & 1 \end{bmatrix}.$$

Thus, the adjoint of A is

$$\text{adj}(A) = \begin{bmatrix} 4 & -3 \\ -2 & 1 \end{bmatrix}^T = \begin{bmatrix} 4 & -2 \\ -3 & 1 \end{bmatrix}.$$

Since $|A| = -2$, the inverse of A is

$$A^{-1} = \frac{1}{|A|}\,\text{adj}(A) = -\frac{1}{2}\begin{bmatrix} 4 & -2 \\ -3 & 1 \end{bmatrix} = \begin{bmatrix} -2 & 1 \\ \frac{3}{2} & -\frac{1}{2} \end{bmatrix}$$

3. The matrix of cofactors is

$$\begin{bmatrix} \begin{vmatrix} 2 & 6 \\ -4 & -12 \end{vmatrix} & -\begin{vmatrix} 0 & 6 \\ 0 & -12 \end{vmatrix} & \begin{vmatrix} 0 & 2 \\ 0 & -4 \end{vmatrix} \\ -\begin{vmatrix} 0 & 0 \\ -4 & -12 \end{vmatrix} & \begin{vmatrix} 1 & 0 \\ 0 & -12 \end{vmatrix} & -\begin{vmatrix} 1 & 0 \\ 0 & -4 \end{vmatrix} \\ \begin{vmatrix} 0 & 0 \\ 2 & 6 \end{vmatrix} & -\begin{vmatrix} 1 & 0 \\ 0 & 6 \end{vmatrix} & \begin{vmatrix} 1 & 0 \\ 0 & 2 \end{vmatrix} \end{bmatrix} = \begin{bmatrix} 0 & 0 & 0 \\ 0 & -12 & 4 \\ 0 & -6 & 2 \end{bmatrix}.$$

Thus, the adjoint of A is

$$\text{adj}(A) = \begin{bmatrix} 0 & 0 & 0 \\ 0 & -12 & -6 \\ 0 & 4 & 2 \end{bmatrix}.$$

Since row 3 of A is a multiple of row 2, the determinant is zero, and thus A has no inverse.

5. The matrix of cofactors is

$$
\begin{bmatrix}
\begin{vmatrix} 4 & 3 \\ 1 & -1 \end{vmatrix} & -\begin{vmatrix} 2 & 3 \\ 0 & -1 \end{vmatrix} & \begin{vmatrix} 2 & 4 \\ 0 & 1 \end{vmatrix} \\[12pt]
-\begin{vmatrix} -5 & -7 \\ 1 & -1 \end{vmatrix} & \begin{vmatrix} -3 & -7 \\ 0 & -1 \end{vmatrix} & -\begin{vmatrix} -3 & -5 \\ 0 & 1 \end{vmatrix} \\[12pt]
\begin{vmatrix} -5 & -7 \\ 4 & 3 \end{vmatrix} & -\begin{vmatrix} -3 & -7 \\ 2 & 3 \end{vmatrix} & \begin{vmatrix} -3 & -5 \\ 2 & 4 \end{vmatrix}
\end{bmatrix}
=
\begin{bmatrix}
-7 & 2 & 2 \\
-12 & 3 & 3 \\
13 & -5 & -2
\end{bmatrix}.
$$

Thus, the adjoint is $\mathrm{adj}(A) = \begin{bmatrix} -7 & -12 & 13 \\ 2 & 3 & -5 \\ 2 & 3 & -2 \end{bmatrix}$.

Since $|A| = -3$, the inverse of A is

$$
A^{-1} = \frac{1}{|A|}\,\mathrm{adj}(A) = -\frac{1}{3}\begin{bmatrix} -7 & -12 & 13 \\ 2 & 3 & -5 \\ 2 & 3 & -2 \end{bmatrix} = \begin{bmatrix} \frac{7}{3} & 4 & -\frac{13}{3} \\ -\frac{2}{3} & -1 & \frac{5}{3} \\ -\frac{2}{3} & -1 & \frac{2}{3} \end{bmatrix}.
$$

7. The matrix of cofactors is

$$
\begin{bmatrix}
\begin{vmatrix} -1 & 4 & 1 \\ 0 & 1 & 2 \\ 1 & 1 & 2 \end{vmatrix} & -\begin{vmatrix} 3 & 4 & 1 \\ 0 & 1 & 2 \\ -1 & 1 & 2 \end{vmatrix} & \begin{vmatrix} 3 & -1 & 1 \\ 0 & 0 & 2 \\ -1 & 1 & 2 \end{vmatrix} & -\begin{vmatrix} 3 & -1 & 4 \\ 0 & 0 & 1 \\ -1 & 1 & 1 \end{vmatrix} \\
-\begin{vmatrix} 2 & 0 & 1 \\ 0 & 1 & 2 \\ 1 & 1 & 2 \end{vmatrix} & \begin{vmatrix} -1 & 0 & 1 \\ 0 & 1 & 2 \\ -1 & 1 & 2 \end{vmatrix} & -\begin{vmatrix} -1 & 2 & 1 \\ 0 & 0 & 2 \\ -1 & 1 & 2 \end{vmatrix} & \begin{vmatrix} -1 & 2 & 0 \\ 0 & 0 & 1 \\ -1 & 1 & 1 \end{vmatrix} \\
\begin{vmatrix} 2 & 0 & 1 \\ -1 & 4 & 1 \\ 1 & 1 & 2 \end{vmatrix} & -\begin{vmatrix} -1 & 0 & 1 \\ 3 & 4 & 1 \\ -1 & 1 & 2 \end{vmatrix} & \begin{vmatrix} -1 & 2 & 1 \\ 3 & -1 & 1 \\ -1 & 1 & 2 \end{vmatrix} & -\begin{vmatrix} -1 & 2 & 0 \\ 3 & -1 & 4 \\ -1 & 1 & 1 \end{vmatrix} \\
-\begin{vmatrix} 2 & 0 & 1 \\ -1 & 4 & 1 \\ 0 & 1 & 2 \end{vmatrix} & \begin{vmatrix} -1 & 0 & 1 \\ 3 & 4 & 1 \\ 0 & 1 & 2 \end{vmatrix} & -\begin{vmatrix} -1 & 2 & 1 \\ 3 & -1 & 1 \\ 0 & 0 & 2 \end{vmatrix} & \begin{vmatrix} -1 & 2 & 0 \\ 3 & -1 & 4 \\ 0 & 0 & 1 \end{vmatrix}
\end{bmatrix}
$$

$$
= \begin{bmatrix}
7 & 7 & -4 & 2 \\
1 & 1 & 2 & -1 \\
9 & 0 & -9 & 9 \\
-13 & -4 & 10 & -5
\end{bmatrix}.
$$

Thus, the adjoint of A is

$$
\text{adj}(A) = \begin{bmatrix}
7 & 1 & 9 & -13 \\
7 & 1 & 0 & -4 \\
-4 & 2 & -9 & 10 \\
2 & -1 & 9 & -5
\end{bmatrix}.
$$

Since $\det(A) = 9$, the inverse of A is

$$
A^{-1} = \frac{1}{|A|}\text{adj}(A) = \begin{bmatrix}
\frac{7}{9} & \frac{1}{9} & 1 & -\frac{13}{9} \\
\frac{7}{9} & \frac{1}{9} & 0 & -\frac{4}{9} \\
-\frac{4}{9} & \frac{2}{9} & -1 & \frac{10}{9} \\
\frac{2}{9} & -\frac{1}{9} & 1 & -\frac{5}{9}
\end{bmatrix}.
$$

9. If all the entries of A are integers, then so are those of the adjoint of A. Since $A^{-1} = \dfrac{1}{|A|}\text{adj}(A)$, and $|A| = 1$, the entries of A^{-1} must be integers.

11. Since adj $(A) = |A|A^{-1}$, we have

$$
|\text{adj}(A)| = ||A|A^{-1}| = |A|^n |A^{-1}| = |A|^n \frac{1}{|A|} = |A|^{n-1}.
$$

13. $|\text{adj}(A)| = \begin{vmatrix} -2 & 1 \\ 0 & 1 \end{vmatrix} = -2$

$\quad\;\; |A| = \begin{vmatrix} 1 & 0 \\ 1 & -2 \end{vmatrix} = -2$

Thus, $|\text{adj}(A)| = |A|$.

15. Since $\text{adj}(A^{-1}) = |A^{-1}|A$ and $(\text{adj}(A))^{-1} = (|A|A^{-1})^{-1} = \dfrac{1}{|A|}A,$

we have $\text{adj}(A^{-1}) = (\text{adj}(A))^{-1}.$

17. The coefficient matrix is

$$A = \begin{bmatrix} 1 & 2 \\ -1 & 1 \end{bmatrix}, \qquad \text{where } |A| = 3.$$

Because $|A| \neq 0$, we can use Cramer's Rule. We replace column one with the column of constants to obtain

$$A_1 = \begin{bmatrix} 5 & 2 \\ 1 & 1 \end{bmatrix}, \qquad |A_1| = 3.$$

Similarly, we replace column two with the column of constants to obtain

$$A_2 = \begin{bmatrix} 1 & 5 \\ -1 & 1 \end{bmatrix}, \qquad |A_2| = 6.$$

Then we solve for x_1 and x_2.

$$x_1 = \frac{|A_1|}{|A|} = \frac{3}{3} = 1$$

$$x_2 = \frac{|A_2|}{|A|} = \frac{6}{3} = 2$$

19. The coefficient matrix is

$$A = \begin{bmatrix} 3 & 4 \\ 5 & 3 \end{bmatrix}, \qquad \text{where } |A| = -11.$$

Because $|A| \neq 0$, we can use Cramer's Rule.

$$A_1 = \begin{bmatrix} -2 & 4 \\ 4 & 3 \end{bmatrix}, \qquad |A_1| = -22$$

$$A_2 = \begin{bmatrix} 3 & -2 \\ 5 & 4 \end{bmatrix}, \qquad |A_2| = 22$$

The solution is as follows.

$$x_1 = \frac{|A_1|}{|A|} = \frac{-22}{-11} = 2$$

$$x_2 = \frac{|A_2|}{|A|} = \frac{22}{-11} = -2$$

21. The coefficient matrix is

$$A = \begin{bmatrix} 20 & 8 \\ 12 & -24 \end{bmatrix}, \qquad \text{where } |A| = -576.$$

Because $|A| \neq 0$, we can use Cramer's Rule.

$$A_1 = \begin{bmatrix} 11 & 8 \\ 21 & -24 \end{bmatrix}, \qquad |A_1| = -432$$

$$A_2 = \begin{bmatrix} 20 & 11 \\ 12 & 21 \end{bmatrix}, \qquad |A_2| = 288$$

The solution is

$$x_1 = \frac{|A_1|}{|A|} = \frac{-432}{-576} = \frac{3}{4}$$

$$x_2 = \frac{|A_2|}{|A|} = \frac{288}{-576} = -\frac{1}{2}.$$

23. The coefficient matrix is

$$A = \begin{bmatrix} -0.4 & 0.8 \\ 2 & -4 \end{bmatrix}, \qquad \text{where } |A| = 0.$$

Because $|A| = 0$, Cramer's Rule cannot be applied. (The system does not have a solution.)

25. The coefficient matrix is

$$A = \begin{bmatrix} 3 & 6 \\ 6 & 12 \end{bmatrix}, \qquad \text{where } |A| = 0.$$

Because $|A| = 0$, Cramer's Rule cannot be applied. (The system has an infinite number of solutions.)

27. The coefficient matrix is

$$A = \begin{bmatrix} 4 & -1 & -1 \\ 2 & 2 & 3 \\ 5 & -2 & -2 \end{bmatrix}, \quad \text{where } |A| = 3.$$

Because $|A| \neq 0$, we can use Cramer's Rule.

$$A_1 = \begin{bmatrix} 1 & -1 & -1 \\ 10 & 2 & 3 \\ -1 & -2 & -2 \end{bmatrix}, \ |A_1| = 3$$

$$A_2 = \begin{bmatrix} 4 & 1 & -1 \\ 2 & 10 & 3 \\ 5 & -1 & -2 \end{bmatrix}, \quad |A_2| = 3$$

$$A_3 = \begin{bmatrix} 4 & -1 & 1 \\ 2 & 2 & 10 \\ 5 & -2 & -1 \end{bmatrix}, \quad |A_3| = 6$$

The solution is

$$x_1 = \frac{|A_1|}{|A|} = \frac{3}{3} = 1$$

$$x_2 = \frac{|A_2|}{|A|} = \frac{3}{3} = 1$$

$$x_3 = \frac{|A_3|}{|A|} = \frac{6}{3} = 2.$$

29. The coefficient matrix is

$$A = \begin{bmatrix} 3 & 4 & 4 \\ 4 & -4 & 6 \\ 6 & -6 & 0 \end{bmatrix}, \quad \text{where } |A| = 252.$$

Because $|A| \neq 0$, we can use Cramer's Rule.

$$A_1 = \begin{bmatrix} 11 & 4 & 4 \\ 11 & -4 & 6 \\ 3 & -6 & 0 \end{bmatrix}, \quad |A_1| = 252$$

$$A_2 = \begin{bmatrix} 3 & 11 & 4 \\ 4 & 11 & 6 \\ 6 & 3 & 0 \end{bmatrix}, \quad |A_2| = 126$$

$$A_3 = \begin{bmatrix} 3 & 4 & 11 \\ 4 & -4 & 11 \\ 6 & -6 & 3 \end{bmatrix}, \quad |A_3| = 378$$

The solution is

$$x_1 = \frac{|A_1|}{|A|} = \frac{252}{252} = 1$$

$$x_2 = \frac{|A_2|}{|A|} = \frac{126}{252} = \frac{1}{2}$$

$$x_3 = \frac{|A_3|}{|A|} = \frac{378}{252} = \frac{3}{2}.$$

31. The coefficient matrix is

$$A = \begin{bmatrix} 3 & 3 & 5 \\ 3 & 5 & 9 \\ 5 & 9 & 17 \end{bmatrix}, \quad \text{where } |A| = 4.$$

Because $|A| \neq 0$, we can use Cramer's Rule.

$$A_1 = \begin{bmatrix} 1 & 3 & 5 \\ 2 & 5 & 9 \\ 4 & 9 & 17 \end{bmatrix}, \quad |A_1| = 0$$

$$A_2 = \begin{bmatrix} 3 & 1 & 5 \\ 3 & 2 & 9 \\ 5 & 4 & 17 \end{bmatrix}, \quad |A_2| = -2$$

$$A_3 = \begin{bmatrix} 3 & 3 & 1 \\ 3 & 5 & 2 \\ 5 & 9 & 4 \end{bmatrix}, \quad |A_3| = 2$$

The solution is

$$x_1 = \frac{|A_1|}{|A|} = \frac{0}{4} = 0$$

$$x_2 = \frac{|A_2|}{|A|} = -\frac{2}{4} = -\frac{1}{2}$$

$$x_3 = \frac{|A_3|}{|A|} = \frac{2}{4} = \frac{1}{2}.$$

33. The coefficient matrix is

$$A = \begin{bmatrix} 7 & -3 & 0 & 2 \\ -2 & 1 & 0 & -1 \\ 4 & 0 & 1 & -2 \\ -1 & 1 & 0 & -1 \end{bmatrix}, \quad \text{where } |A| = 1.$$

To solve for x_1, we compute the determinant of A_1.

$$A_1 = \begin{bmatrix} 41 & -3 & 0 & 2 \\ -13 & 1 & 0 & -1 \\ 12 & 0 & 1 & -2 \\ -8 & 1 & 0 & -1 \end{bmatrix}. \quad |A_1| = 5$$

Then, $x_1 = |A_1|/|A| = 5/1 = 5.$

35. The coefficient matrix is

$$A = \begin{bmatrix} 5 & -3 & 1 \\ 2 & 2 & -3 \\ 1 & -7 & 8 \end{bmatrix}, \quad \text{where } |A| = 16.$$

To solve for x_1, we compute the determinant of A_1.

$$A_1 = \begin{bmatrix} 2 & -3 & 1 \\ 4 & 2 & -3 \\ -6 & -7 & 8 \end{bmatrix}, \quad |A_1| = 16.$$

Then, $x_1 = |A_1|/|A| = 16/16 = 1$.

37. The coefficient matrix is

$$A = \begin{bmatrix} k & 1-k \\ 1-k & k \end{bmatrix}, \quad \text{where } |A| = k^2 - (1-k)^2 = 2k - 1.$$

Replacing the ith column of A with the column of constants yields A_i.

$$A_1 = \begin{bmatrix} 1 & 1-k \\ 3 & k \end{bmatrix}, \quad |A_1| = 4k - 3$$

$$A_2 = \begin{bmatrix} k & 1 \\ 1-k & 3 \end{bmatrix}, \quad |A_2| = 4k - 1$$

The solution is

$$x = \frac{|A_1|}{|A|} = \frac{4k-3}{2k-1}$$

$$y = \frac{|A_2|}{|A|} = \frac{4k-1}{2k-1}.$$

Note that when $k = \frac{1}{2}$, $|A| = 2k - 1 = 0$ and the system will be inconsistent.

39. We use the formula for area as follows.

$$\text{Area} = \pm \frac{1}{2} \begin{vmatrix} x_1 & y_1 & 1 \\ x_2 & y_2 & 1 \\ x_3 & y_3 & 1 \end{vmatrix}$$

Since

$$\begin{vmatrix} x_1 & y_1 & 1 \\ x_2 & y_2 & 1 \\ x_3 & y_3 & 1 \end{vmatrix} = \begin{vmatrix} 0 & 0 & 1 \\ 2 & 0 & 1 \\ 0 & 3 & 1 \end{vmatrix} = 6,$$

the area is $\frac{1}{2}(6) = 3$.

41. We use the formula for area as follows.

$$\text{Area} = \pm \frac{1}{2} \begin{vmatrix} x_1 & y_1 & 1 \\ x_2 & y_2 & 1 \\ x_3 & y_3 & 1 \end{vmatrix} = \pm \frac{1}{2} \begin{vmatrix} -1 & 2 & 1 \\ 2 & 2 & 1 \\ -2 & 4 & 1 \end{vmatrix} = \pm \frac{1}{2}(6) = 3$$

43. We use the fact that

$$\begin{vmatrix} x_1 & y_1 & 1 \\ x_2 & y_2 & 1 \\ x_3 & y_3 & 1 \end{vmatrix} = \begin{vmatrix} 1 & 2 & 1 \\ 3 & 4 & 1 \\ 5 & 6 & 1 \end{vmatrix} = 0$$

to determine that the three points are collinear.

45. We use the fact that

$$\begin{vmatrix} x_1 & y_1 & 1 \\ x_2 & y_2 & 1 \\ x_3 & y_3 & 1 \end{vmatrix} = \begin{vmatrix} -2 & 5 & 1 \\ 0 & -1 & 1 \\ 3 & -9 & 1 \end{vmatrix} = 2$$

to determine that the three points are not collinear.

47. We use the equation

$$\begin{vmatrix} x & y & 1 \\ x_1 & y_1 & 1 \\ x_2 & y_2 & 1 \end{vmatrix} = 0$$

to find the equation of the line. Thus,

$$\begin{vmatrix} x & y & 1 \\ 0 & 0 & 1 \\ 3 & 4 & 1 \end{vmatrix} = 3y - 4x = 0$$

or $y = \frac{4}{3}x$.

49. We find the equation as follows.

$$0 = \begin{vmatrix} x & y & 1 \\ x_1 & y_1 & 1 \\ x_2 & y_2 & 1 \end{vmatrix} = \begin{vmatrix} x & y & 1 \\ -2 & 3 & 1 \\ -2 & -4 & 1 \end{vmatrix} = 7x + 14$$

Thus, an equation for the line is $x = -2$.

51. We use the formula for volume as follows.

$$\text{Volume} = \pm\frac{1}{6}\begin{vmatrix} x_1 & y_1 & z_1 & 1 \\ x_2 & y_2 & z_2 & 1 \\ x_3 & y_3 & z_3 & 1 \\ x_4 & y_4 & z_4 & 1 \end{vmatrix}$$

Since

$$\begin{vmatrix} x_1 & y_1 & z_1 & 1 \\ x_2 & y_2 & z_2 & 1 \\ x_3 & y_3 & z_3 & 1 \\ x_4 & y_4 & z_4 & 1 \end{vmatrix} = \begin{vmatrix} 1 & 0 & 0 & 1 \\ 0 & 1 & 0 & 1 \\ 0 & 0 & 1 & 1 \\ 1 & 1 & 1 & 1 \end{vmatrix} = -2,$$

the volume of the tetrahedron is $-\frac{1}{6}(-2) = \frac{1}{3}$.

53. We use the formula for volume as follows.

$$\text{Volume} = \pm\frac{1}{6}\begin{vmatrix} x_1 & y_1 & z_1 & 1 \\ x_2 & y_2 & z_2 & 1 \\ x_3 & y_3 & z_3 & 1 \\ x_4 & y_4 & z_4 & 1 \end{vmatrix} = \frac{1}{6}\begin{vmatrix} 3 & -1 & 1 & 1 \\ 4 & -4 & 4 & 1 \\ 1 & 1 & 1 & 1 \\ 0 & 0 & 1 & 1 \end{vmatrix} = \pm\frac{1}{6}(-12) = 2$$

55. We use the fact that

$$\begin{vmatrix} x_1 & y_1 & z_1 & 1 \\ x_2 & y_2 & z_2 & 1 \\ x_3 & y_3 & z_3 & 1 \\ x_4 & y_4 & z_4 & 1 \end{vmatrix} = \begin{vmatrix} -4 & 1 & 0 & 1 \\ 0 & 1 & 2 & 1 \\ 4 & 3 & -1 & 1 \\ 0 & 0 & 1 & 1 \end{vmatrix} = 28$$

to determine that the four points are not coplanar.

57. We use the fact that

$$\begin{vmatrix} x_1 & y_1 & z_1 & 1 \\ x_2 & y_2 & z_2 & 1 \\ x_3 & y_3 & z_3 & 1 \\ x_4 & y_4 & z_4 & 1 \end{vmatrix} = \begin{vmatrix} 0 & 0 & -1 & 1 \\ 0 & -1 & 0 & 1 \\ 1 & 1 & 0 & 1 \\ 2 & 1 & 2 & 1 \end{vmatrix} = 0$$

to determine that the four points are coplanar.

59. We use the equation

$$\begin{vmatrix} x & y & z & 1 \\ x_1 & y_1 & z_1 & 1 \\ x_2 & y_2 & z_2 & 1 \\ x_3 & y_3 & z_3 & 1 \end{vmatrix} = 0$$

to find the equation of the plane. Thus,

$$\begin{vmatrix} x & y & z & 1 \\ 1 & -2 & 1 & 1 \\ -1 & -1 & 7 & 1 \\ 2 & -1 & 3 & 1 \end{vmatrix} = x \begin{vmatrix} -2 & 1 & 1 \\ -1 & 7 & 1 \\ -1 & 3 & 1 \end{vmatrix} - y \begin{vmatrix} 1 & 1 & 1 \\ -1 & 7 & 1 \\ 2 & 3 & 1 \end{vmatrix}$$

$$+ z \begin{vmatrix} 1 & -2 & 1 \\ -1 & -1 & 1 \\ 2 & -1 & 1 \end{vmatrix} - \begin{vmatrix} 1 & -2 & 1 \\ -1 & -1 & 7 \\ 2 & -1 & 3 \end{vmatrix} = 0$$

or $4x - 10y + 3z = 27$.

61. We find the equation as follows.

$$0 = \begin{vmatrix} x & y & z & 1 \\ x_1 & y_1 & z_1 & 1 \\ x_2 & y_2 & z_2 & 1 \\ x_3 & y_3 & z_3 & 1 \end{vmatrix} = \begin{vmatrix} x & y & z & 1 \\ 0 & 0 & 0 & 1 \\ 1 & -1 & 0 & 1 \\ 0 & 1 & -1 & 1 \end{vmatrix}$$

$$= x \begin{vmatrix} 0 & 0 & 1 \\ -1 & 0 & 1 \\ 1 & -1 & 1 \end{vmatrix} - y \begin{vmatrix} 0 & 0 & 1 \\ 1 & 0 & 1 \\ 0 & -1 & 1 \end{vmatrix} + z \begin{vmatrix} 0 & 0 & 1 \\ 1 & -1 & 1 \\ 0 & 1 & 1 \end{vmatrix} - \begin{vmatrix} 0 & 0 & 0 \\ 1 & -1 & 0 \\ 0 & 1 & -1 \end{vmatrix}$$

$$= x + y + z = 0$$

Chapter 3   Review Exercises

1. Using the formula for the determinant of a 2 × 2 matrix, we have

$$\begin{vmatrix} 4 & -1 \\ 2 & 2 \end{vmatrix} = 4(2) - 2(-1)$$

$$= 10.$$

3. Using the formula for the determinant of a 2 × 2 matrix, we have

$$\begin{vmatrix} -3 & 1 \\ 6 & -2 \end{vmatrix} = (-3)(-2) - 6(1)$$

$$= 0.$$

5. Expansion by cofactors along the first column produces

$$\begin{vmatrix} 1 & 4 & -2 \\ 0 & -3 & 1 \\ 1 & 1 & -1 \end{vmatrix} = 1\begin{vmatrix} -3 & 1 \\ 1 & -1 \end{vmatrix} - 0\begin{vmatrix} 4 & -2 \\ 1 & -1 \end{vmatrix} + 1\begin{vmatrix} 4 & -2 \\ -3 & 1 \end{vmatrix}$$

$$= 1(2) + (-2)$$

$$= 0.$$

7. The determinant of a diagonal matrix is the product of the entires along the main diagonal.

$$\begin{vmatrix} -2 & 0 & 0 \\ 0 & -3 & 0 \\ 0 & 0 & -1 \end{vmatrix} = (-2)(-3)(-1)$$

$$= -6$$

9. Expansion by cofactors along the first column produces

$$\begin{vmatrix} -3 & 6 & 9 \\ 9 & 12 & -3 \\ 0 & 15 & -6 \end{vmatrix} = -3\begin{vmatrix} 12 & -3 \\ 15 & -6 \end{vmatrix} - 9\begin{vmatrix} 6 & 9 \\ 15 & -6 \end{vmatrix} + 0\begin{vmatrix} 6 & 9 \\ 12 & -3 \end{vmatrix}$$

$$= 81 + 1539 + 0$$

$$= 1620.$$

11. Expansion by cofactors along the second column produces

$$
\begin{vmatrix} 2 & 0 & -1 & 4 \\ -1 & 2 & 0 & 3 \\ 3 & 0 & 1 & 2 \\ -2 & 0 & 3 & 1 \end{vmatrix} = 2 \begin{vmatrix} 2 & -1 & 4 \\ 3 & 1 & 2 \\ -2 & 3 & 1 \end{vmatrix} = 2 \begin{vmatrix} 5 & 0 & 6 \\ 3 & 1 & 2 \\ -11 & 0 & -5 \end{vmatrix} = 2 \begin{vmatrix} 5 & 6 \\ -11 & -5 \end{vmatrix}
$$

$$
= 2(-25 + 66)
$$

$$
= 82.
$$

13.

$$
\begin{vmatrix} -4 & 1 & 2 & 3 \\ 1 & -2 & 1 & 2 \\ 2 & -1 & 3 & 4 \\ 1 & 2 & 2 & -1 \end{vmatrix} = - \begin{vmatrix} 1 & 2 & 2 & -1 \\ 1 & -2 & 1 & 2 \\ 2 & -1 & 3 & 4 \\ -4 & 1 & 2 & 3 \end{vmatrix}
$$

$$
= - \begin{vmatrix} 1 & 2 & 2 & -1 \\ 0 & -4 & -1 & 3 \\ 0 & -5 & -1 & 6 \\ 0 & 9 & 10 & -1 \end{vmatrix}
$$

$$
= - \begin{vmatrix} 1 & 2 & 2 & -1 \\ 0 & 1 & 0 & -3 \\ 0 & -5 & -1 & 6 \\ 0 & 9 & 10 & -1 \end{vmatrix}
$$

$$
= - \begin{vmatrix} 1 & 2 & 2 & -1 \\ 0 & 1 & 0 & -3 \\ 0 & 0 & -1 & -9 \\ 0 & 0 & 10 & 26 \end{vmatrix}
$$

$$
= - \begin{vmatrix} 1 & 2 & 2 & -1 \\ 0 & 1 & 0 & -3 \\ 0 & 0 & -1 & -9 \\ 0 & 0 & 0 & -64 \end{vmatrix}
$$

$$
= -64
$$

15.
$$\begin{vmatrix} -1 & 1 & -1 & 0 & 0 \\ 0 & 1 & -1 & 0 & 1 \\ 1 & 0 & 1 & -1 & 0 \\ 0 & -1 & 0 & 1 & -1 \\ 0 & 1 & 1 & -1 & 1 \end{vmatrix} = \begin{vmatrix} -1 & 1 & -1 & 0 & 0 \\ 0 & 1 & -1 & 0 & 1 \\ 0 & 1 & 0 & -1 & 0 \\ 0 & -1 & 0 & 1 & -1 \\ 0 & 1 & 1 & -1 & 1 \end{vmatrix}$$

$$= (-1) \begin{vmatrix} 1 & -1 & 0 & 1 \\ 1 & 0 & -1 & 0 \\ -1 & 0 & 1 & -1 \\ 1 & 1 & -1 & 1 \end{vmatrix}$$

$$= (-1) \begin{vmatrix} 1 & -1 & 0 & 1 \\ 1 & 0 & -1 & 0 \\ -1 & 0 & 1 & -1 \\ 2 & 0 & -1 & 2 \end{vmatrix}$$

$$= (-1) \begin{vmatrix} 1 & -1 & 0 \\ -1 & 1 & -1 \\ 2 & -1 & 2 \end{vmatrix} = (-1)(1 + 0) = -1$$

17. The determinant of a diagonal matrix is the product of its main diagonal entries. Thus,

$$\begin{vmatrix} -1 & 0 & 0 & 0 & 0 \\ 0 & -1 & 0 & 0 & 0 \\ 0 & 0 & -1 & 0 & 0 \\ 0 & 0 & 0 & -1 & 0 \\ 0 & 0 & 0 & 0 & -1 \end{vmatrix} = (-1)^5 = -1.$$

19. (a) $|A| = \begin{vmatrix} -1 & 2 \\ 0 & 1 \end{vmatrix} = -1$

(b) $|B| = \begin{vmatrix} 3 & 4 \\ 2 & 1 \end{vmatrix} = -5$

(c) $AB = \begin{bmatrix} -1 & 2 \\ 0 & 1 \end{bmatrix} \begin{bmatrix} 3 & 4 \\ 2 & 1 \end{bmatrix} = \begin{bmatrix} 1 & -2 \\ 2 & 1 \end{bmatrix}$

(d) $|AB| = \begin{vmatrix} 1 & -2 \\ 2 & 1 \end{vmatrix} = 5$

Note that $|A||B| = |AB| = 5$.

21. First we find

$$|A| = \begin{vmatrix} -2 & 6 \\ 1 & 3 \end{vmatrix} = -12.$$

(a) $|A^T| = |A| = -12$

(b) $|A^3| = |A|^3 = (-12)^3 = -1728$

(c) $|A^TA| = |A^T||A| = -12(-12) = 144$

(d) $|5A| = 5^2|A| = 25(-12) = -300$

23. (a) $|A| = \begin{vmatrix} 1 & 0 & -4 \\ 0 & 3 & 2 \\ -2 & 7 & 6 \end{vmatrix} = \begin{vmatrix} 1 & 0 & -4 \\ 0 & 3 & 2 \\ 0 & 7 & -2 \end{vmatrix} = \begin{vmatrix} 3 & 2 \\ 7 & -2 \end{vmatrix} = -20$

(b) $|A^{-1}| = \dfrac{1}{A} = -\dfrac{1}{20}$

25. Because the determinant of the coefficient matrix is

$$\begin{vmatrix} 5 & 4 \\ -1 & 1 \end{vmatrix} = 9 \neq 0,$$

the system has a unique solution.

27. Because the determinant of the coefficient matrix is

$$\begin{vmatrix} -1 & 1 & 2 \\ 2 & 3 & 1 \\ 5 & 4 & 2 \end{vmatrix} = -15 \neq 0,$$

the system has a unique solution.

29. Because the determinant of the coefficient matrix is

$$\begin{vmatrix} 1 & 2 & 6 \\ 2 & 5 & 15 \\ 3 & 1 & 3 \end{vmatrix} = 0,$$

the system does not have a unique solution.

31. Using the fact that $|cA| = c^n|A|$, where A is an $n \times n$ matrix, we obtain

$$|4A| = 4^3|A| = 64(2) = 128.$$

33. We expand the left-hand determinant along the third row

$$\begin{vmatrix} a_{11} & a_{12} & a_{13} \\ a_{21} & a_{22} & a_{23} \\ (a_{31} + c_{31}) & (a_{32} + c_{32}) & (a_{33} + c_{33}) \end{vmatrix}$$

$$= (a_{31} + c_{31}) \begin{vmatrix} a_{12} & a_{13} \\ a_{22} & a_{23} \end{vmatrix} - (a_{32} + c_{32}) \begin{vmatrix} a_{11} & a_{13} \\ a_{21} & a_{23} \end{vmatrix}$$

$$+ (a_{33} + c_{33}) \begin{vmatrix} a_{11} & a_{12} \\ a_{21} & a_{22} \end{vmatrix}$$

$$= a_{31} \begin{vmatrix} a_{12} & a_{13} \\ a_{22} & a_{23} \end{vmatrix} + c_{31} \begin{vmatrix} a_{12} & a_{13} \\ a_{22} & a_{23} \end{vmatrix} - a_{32} \begin{vmatrix} a_{11} & a_{13} \\ a_{21} & a_{23} \end{vmatrix} - c_{32} \begin{vmatrix} a_{11} & a_{13} \\ a_{21} & a_{23} \end{vmatrix}$$

$$+ a_{33} \begin{vmatrix} a_{11} & a_{12} \\ a_{21} & a_{22} \end{vmatrix} + c_{33} \begin{vmatrix} a_{11} & a_{12} \\ a_{21} & a_{22} \end{vmatrix}.$$

The first, third and fifth terms in this sum correspond to the determinant

$$\begin{vmatrix} a_{11} & a_{12} & a_{13} \\ a_{21} & a_{22} & a_{23} \\ a_{31} & a_{32} & a_{33} \end{vmatrix}$$

expanded along the third row. Similarly, the second, fourth and sixth terms of the sum correspond to the determinant

$$\begin{vmatrix} a_{11} & a_{12} & a_{13} \\ a_{21} & a_{22} & a_{23} \\ c_{31} & c_{32} & c_{33} \end{vmatrix}$$

expanded along the third row.

35. We can see that each row consists of $n - 1$ ones and one element equal to $1 - n$.
The sum of these elements is then

$$(n - 1)1 + (1 - n) = 0.$$

In Section 3.3, Exercise 37, we showed that a matrix whose rows each add up to zero has a determinant of zero. Thus, the determinant of this matrix is zero.

37. $|\lambda I - A| = \begin{vmatrix} \lambda + 3 & -10 \\ -5 & \lambda - 2 \end{vmatrix} = \lambda^2 + \lambda - 56 = (\lambda + 8)(\lambda - 7)$

$$\lambda = -8: \begin{bmatrix} -5 & -10 \\ -5 & -10 \end{bmatrix} \Rightarrow \begin{bmatrix} 1 & 2 \\ 0 & 0 \end{bmatrix} \Rightarrow \mathbf{x} = \begin{bmatrix} 2 \\ -1 \end{bmatrix}$$

$$\lambda = 7: \begin{bmatrix} 10 & -10 \\ -5 & 5 \end{bmatrix} \Rightarrow \begin{bmatrix} 1 & -1 \\ 0 & 0 \end{bmatrix} \Rightarrow \mathbf{x} = \begin{bmatrix} 1 \\ 1 \end{bmatrix}.$$

39. By definition of the Jacobian, we have

$$J(u, v) = \begin{vmatrix} \dfrac{\partial x}{\partial u} & \dfrac{\partial x}{\partial v} \\[2mm] \dfrac{\partial y}{\partial u} & \dfrac{\partial y}{\partial v} \end{vmatrix} = \begin{vmatrix} -\dfrac{1}{2} & \dfrac{1}{2} \\[2mm] \dfrac{1}{2} & \dfrac{1}{2} \end{vmatrix} = -\dfrac{1}{4} - \dfrac{1}{4} = -\dfrac{1}{2}.$$

41. $J(u, v, w) = \begin{vmatrix} \dfrac{1}{2} & \dfrac{1}{2} & 0 \\[2mm] \dfrac{1}{2} & -\dfrac{1}{2} & 0 \\[2mm] 2vw & 2uw & 2uv \end{vmatrix}$

$$= 2uv\left(-\dfrac{1}{4} - \dfrac{1}{4}\right)$$

$$= -uv$$

43. Row reduction is generally preferred for matrices with few zeros. For a matrix with many zeros, it is often easier to expand along a row or column having many zeros.

45. The matrix of cofactors is given by

$$\begin{bmatrix} \begin{vmatrix} 1 & 0 \\ -1 & 1 \end{vmatrix} & -\begin{vmatrix} 2 & 0 \\ 2 & 1 \end{vmatrix} & \begin{vmatrix} 2 & 1 \\ 2 & -1 \end{vmatrix} \\[4mm] -\begin{vmatrix} 0 & 0 \\ -1 & 1 \end{vmatrix} & \begin{vmatrix} 1 & 0 \\ 2 & 1 \end{vmatrix} & -\begin{vmatrix} 1 & 0 \\ 2 & -1 \end{vmatrix} \\[4mm] \begin{vmatrix} 0 & 0 \\ 1 & 0 \end{vmatrix} & -\begin{vmatrix} 1 & 0 \\ 2 & 0 \end{vmatrix} & \begin{vmatrix} 1 & 0 \\ 2 & 1 \end{vmatrix} \end{bmatrix} = \begin{bmatrix} 1 & -2 & -4 \\ 0 & 1 & 1 \\ 0 & 0 & 1 \end{bmatrix}.$$

Thus, the adjoint is

$$\text{adj} \begin{bmatrix} 1 & 0 & 0 \\ 2 & 1 & 0 \\ 2 & -1 & 1 \end{bmatrix} = \begin{bmatrix} 1 & 0 & 0 \\ -2 & 1 & 0 \\ -4 & 1 & 1 \end{bmatrix}.$$

47. The determinant of the coefficient matrix is

$$\begin{vmatrix} 0.2 & -0.1 \\ 0.4 & -0.5 \end{vmatrix} = -0.06 \neq 0.$$

Thus, the system has a unique solution. We form the matrices A_1 and A_2 and find their determinant as follows.

$$A_1 = \begin{bmatrix} 0.07 & -0.1 \\ -0.01 & -0.5 \end{bmatrix}, \quad |A_1| = -0.036$$

$$A_2 = \begin{bmatrix} 0.2 & 0.07 \\ 0.4 & -0.01 \end{bmatrix}, \quad |A_2| = -0.03$$

Thus,

$$x = \frac{|A_1|}{|A|} = \frac{-0.036}{-0.06} = 0.6$$

$$y = \frac{|A_2|}{|A|} = \frac{-0.03}{-0.06} = 0.5.$$

49. The determinant of the coefficient matrix is

$$\begin{vmatrix} 2 & 3 & 3 \\ 6 & 6 & 12 \\ 12 & 9 & -1 \end{vmatrix} = 168 \neq 0$$

Thus, the system has a unique solution. Using Cramer's Rule

$$A_1 = \begin{bmatrix} 3 & 3 & 3 \\ 13 & 6 & 12 \\ 2 & 9 & -1 \end{bmatrix} \quad |A_1| = \quad 84$$

$$A_2 = \begin{bmatrix} 2 & 3 & 3 \\ 6 & 13 & 12 \\ 12 & 2 & -1 \end{bmatrix} \quad |A_2| = \quad -56$$

$$A_3 = \begin{bmatrix} 2 & 3 & 3 \\ 6 & 6 & 13 \\ 12 & 9 & 2 \end{bmatrix} \quad |A_3| = \quad 168.$$

Thus,

$$x_1 = \frac{|A_1|}{|A|} = \frac{84}{168} = \frac{1}{2}$$

$$x_2 = \frac{|A_2|}{|A|} = \frac{-56}{168} = -\frac{1}{3}$$

$$x_3 = \frac{|A_3|}{|A|} = \frac{168}{168} = \quad 1.$$

51. The formula for area yields

$$\text{Area} = \pm\frac{1}{2}\begin{vmatrix} x_1 & y_1 & 1 \\ x_2 & y_2 & 1 \\ x_3 & y_3 & 1 \end{vmatrix} = \pm\frac{1}{2}\begin{vmatrix} 1 & 0 & 1 \\ 5 & 0 & 1 \\ 5 & 8 & 1 \end{vmatrix}$$

$$= \pm\frac{1}{2}(-8)(1 - 5) = 16.$$

53. We use the equation

$$\begin{vmatrix} x & y & 1 \\ x_1 & y_1 & 1 \\ x_2 & y_2 & 1 \end{vmatrix} = 0$$

to find the equation of the line

$$\begin{vmatrix} x & y & 1 \\ -4 & 0 & 1 \\ 4 & 4 & 1 \end{vmatrix} = -4x + 8y - 16 = 0, \text{ or } 2y - x = 4$$

55. The equation of the plane is given by the equation

$$\begin{vmatrix} x & y & z & 1 \\ 0 & 0 & 0 & 1 \\ 1 & 0 & 3 & 1 \\ 0 & 3 & 4 & 1 \end{vmatrix} = 0.$$

Expanding by cofactors along the second row yields

$$\begin{vmatrix} x & y & z \\ 1 & 0 & 3 \\ 0 & 3 & 4 \end{vmatrix} = 0$$

or $9x + 4y - 3z = 0$.

Chapters 1-3 Solutions — Cumulative Test

1. $\begin{bmatrix} 1 & -2 & 3 \\ -1 & 6 & -1 \end{bmatrix} \Rightarrow \begin{bmatrix} 1 & -2 & 3 \\ 0 & 4 & 2 \end{bmatrix} \Rightarrow \begin{bmatrix} 1 & 0 & 4 \\ 0 & 2 & 1 \end{bmatrix}$ $\quad \begin{aligned} x_1 &= 4 \\ x_2 &= \tfrac{1}{2} \end{aligned}$

2. $\begin{bmatrix} 4 & 1 & -3 & 11 \\ 2 & -3 & 2 & 9 \\ 1 & 1 & 1 & -3 \end{bmatrix} \Rightarrow \begin{bmatrix} 1 & 0 & 0 & 2 \\ 0 & 1 & 0 & -3 \\ 0 & 0 & 1 & -2 \end{bmatrix}$ $\quad \begin{aligned} x_1 &= 2 \\ x_2 &= -3 \\ x_3 &= -2 \end{aligned}$

3. $\begin{bmatrix} 0 & 1 & -1 & 0 & | & 2 \\ 1 & 0 & 2 & -1 & | & 0 \\ 1 & 2 & 0 & -1 & | & 4 \end{bmatrix} \Rightarrow \begin{bmatrix} 1 & 0 & 2 & -1 & | & 0 \\ 0 & 1 & -1 & 0 & | & 2 \\ 0 & 0 & 0 & 0 & | & 0 \end{bmatrix}$ $\quad \begin{aligned} x_1 &= s - 2t \\ x_2 &= 2 + t \\ x_3 &= t \\ x_4 &= s \end{aligned}$

4. $\begin{bmatrix} 1 & 2 & 1 & -2 \\ 0 & 0 & 2 & -4 \\ -2 & -4 & 1 & -2 \end{bmatrix} \Rightarrow \begin{bmatrix} 1 & 2 & 0 & 0 \\ 0 & 0 & 1 & -2 \\ 0 & 0 & 0 & 0 \end{bmatrix}$ $\quad \begin{aligned} x_1 &= -2s \\ x_2 &= s \\ x_3 &= 2t \\ x_4 &= t \end{aligned}$

5. $\begin{bmatrix} 1 & 2 & -1 & | & 3 \\ -1 & -1 & 1 & | & 2 \\ -1 & 1 & 1 & | & k \end{bmatrix} \Rightarrow \begin{bmatrix} 1 & 2 & -1 & | & 3 \\ 0 & 1 & 0 & | & 5 \\ 0 & 3 & 0 & | & 3+k \end{bmatrix} \Rightarrow \begin{bmatrix} 1 & 2 & -1 & | & 3 \\ 0 & 1 & 0 & | & 5 \\ 0 & 0 & 0 & | & -12+k \end{bmatrix}$

$k = 12$ (for consistent system)

6. $A + B = \begin{bmatrix} 1 & 1 & 1 \\ 7 & 3 & -3 \end{bmatrix} \quad 2A - 3B = \begin{bmatrix} 2 & 7 & -8 \\ -6 & -9 & 19 \end{bmatrix}$

7. $AB = \begin{bmatrix} 1 & 2 \\ 1 & 1 \\ 1 & 0 \end{bmatrix};$ $\quad BA$ not defined

8. $BA = \begin{bmatrix} 12.50 & 9.00 & 21.50 \end{bmatrix} \begin{bmatrix} 200 & 300 \\ 600 & 350 \\ 250 & 400 \end{bmatrix}$

$= \begin{bmatrix} 13,275.00 & 15,500.00 \end{bmatrix}$

This product represents the total value of the three models at each of the two warehouses.

9. $2A - B = \begin{bmatrix} -2 & 2 \\ 4 & 6 \end{bmatrix} - \begin{bmatrix} x & 2 \\ y & 5 \end{bmatrix} = \begin{bmatrix} 1 & 0 \\ 0 & 1 \end{bmatrix} \Rightarrow \begin{aligned} -2 - x &= 1 \\ 4 - y &= 0 \\ x &= -3 \\ y &= 4 \end{aligned}$

10. $A^T A = \begin{bmatrix} 17 & 22 & 27 \\ 22 & 29 & 36 \\ 27 & 36 & 45 \end{bmatrix}$

11. $\begin{bmatrix} -2 & 3 \\ 4 & 6 \end{bmatrix}^{-1}$ does not exist; $\begin{bmatrix} -2 & 3 \\ 3 & 6 \end{bmatrix}^{-1} = \dfrac{-1}{21}\begin{bmatrix} 6 & -3 \\ -3 & -2 \end{bmatrix}$

12. $\begin{bmatrix} 1 & 1 & 0 \\ -3 & 6 & 5 \\ 0 & 1 & 0 \end{bmatrix}^{-1} = \begin{bmatrix} 1 & 0 & -1 \\ 0 & 0 & 1 \\ \frac{6}{10} & \frac{2}{10} & -\frac{18}{10} \end{bmatrix}$

13. $\begin{bmatrix} 2 & -4 \\ 1 & 0 \end{bmatrix} \Rightarrow \begin{bmatrix} 1 & 0 \\ 2 & -4 \end{bmatrix} \Rightarrow \begin{bmatrix} 1 & 0 \\ 0 & -4 \end{bmatrix} \Rightarrow \begin{bmatrix} 1 & 0 \\ 0 & 1 \end{bmatrix}$

$\begin{bmatrix} 1 & 0 \\ 0 & -\frac{1}{4} \end{bmatrix}\begin{bmatrix} 1 & 0 \\ -2 & 1 \end{bmatrix}\begin{bmatrix} 0 & 1 \\ 1 & 0 \end{bmatrix}\begin{bmatrix} 2 & -4 \\ 1 & 0 \end{bmatrix} = \begin{bmatrix} 1 & 0 \\ 0 & 1 \end{bmatrix}$

$A = \begin{bmatrix} 0 & 1 \\ 1 & 0 \end{bmatrix}\begin{bmatrix} 1 & 0 \\ 2 & 1 \end{bmatrix}\begin{bmatrix} 1 & 0 \\ 0 & -4 \end{bmatrix}.$

14. $= -\det\begin{bmatrix} 1 & -1 & 2 \\ 0 & 1 & 3 \\ 5 & 8 & -4 \end{bmatrix} = -\det\begin{bmatrix} 1 & -1 & 2 \\ 0 & 1 & 3 \\ 0 & 13 & -14 \end{bmatrix} = 14 + 39 = +53$

15. (a) $\det A = 14$

    (b) $\det B = -10$

    (c) $\det AB = -140$

    (d) $\det\left(A^{-1}\right) = \dfrac{1}{|A|} = \dfrac{1}{14}$

16. (a) $|3A| = 3^4 \cdot 7 = 567$

    (b) $|A^T| = |A| = 7$

    (c) $|A^{-1}| = \dfrac{1}{7}$

    (d) $|A^3| = 7^3 = 343$

17. $\left.\begin{array}{r} a - b + c = 2 \\ c = 1 \\ 4a + 2b + c = 6 \end{array}\right\}$ $\begin{array}{l} a = \frac{7}{6} \\ b = \frac{1}{6} \\ c = 1 \end{array}$

$y = \frac{7}{6}x^2 + \frac{1}{6}x + 1$

18. $a\begin{bmatrix} 1 \\ 0 \\ 1 \end{bmatrix} + b\begin{bmatrix} 1 \\ 1 \\ 0 \end{bmatrix} + c\begin{bmatrix} 0 \\ 1 \\ 1 \end{bmatrix} = \begin{bmatrix} 1 \\ 2 \\ 3 \end{bmatrix}$ $\begin{array}{l} a = 1 \\ b = 0 \\ c = 2 \end{array}$

19. No. C could be singular. $\begin{bmatrix} 0 & 0 \\ 0 & 1 \end{bmatrix} \begin{bmatrix} 0 & 1 \\ 0 & 0 \end{bmatrix} = \begin{bmatrix} 0 & 1 \\ 0 & 0 \end{bmatrix} \begin{bmatrix} 0 & 1 \\ 0 & 0 \end{bmatrix}$

$\qquad\qquad\qquad\qquad\quad\ A \qquad\quad C \qquad\quad\ B \qquad\quad C$

20. $(B^T B)^T = B^T (B^T)^T = B^T B$

21. Let B, C be inverses of A. Then
$B = (CA)B = C(AB) = C$

22. (a) A row equivalent to B if there exist elementary matrices $E_1, \cdots, E_k$ such that $A = E_k \cdots E_1 B$

   (b) A row equivalent to $B \implies A = E_k \cdots E_1 B$ $(E_1, \cdots, E_k$ elementary)

   B row equivalent to $C \implies B = F_l \cdots F_1 C$ $(F_1, \cdots, F_e$ elementary)

   Then $A = E_k \cdots E_1 (F_l \cdots F_1) C \implies A$ row equivalent to C

23. $\left. \begin{array}{l} \det (AA^T) = \det A^2 \\ \det (A(-A)) = (-1)^n \det A^2 \end{array} \right\}$ $\det A^2 = 0 \implies \det A = 0$

24. (a) $\begin{bmatrix} 0 & 0 \\ 0 & 0 \end{bmatrix}, \begin{bmatrix} 1 & 0 \\ 0 & 1 \end{bmatrix}, \begin{bmatrix} 1 & 0 \\ 0 & 0 \end{bmatrix}$

   (b) $\det A = \det A^2 = (\det A)^2 \implies \det A = 0, 1$

25. (a)   not necessarily: $\begin{bmatrix} 1 & 0 \\ 0 & 1 \end{bmatrix} + \begin{bmatrix} -1 & 0 \\ 0 & -1 \end{bmatrix} = \begin{bmatrix} 0 & 0 \\ 0 & 0 \end{bmatrix}$

   (b)   Yes. $\det (AB) = \det A \cdot \det B \neq 0$

26. $\begin{bmatrix} 0 & 0 \\ 0 & 0 \end{bmatrix}, \begin{bmatrix} 0 & 1 \\ 0 & 0 \end{bmatrix}, \begin{bmatrix} 1 & a \\ 0 & 0 \end{bmatrix}, \begin{bmatrix} 1 & 0 \\ 0 & 1 \end{bmatrix}$

CHAPTER 4
Vector Spaces

Section 4.1   Vectors In R^n

1. $\mathbf{v} = \frac{3}{2}\mathbf{u} = \frac{3}{2}(2, -1) = (3, -\frac{3}{2})$

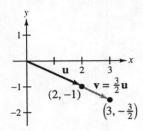

3. $\mathbf{v} = \mathbf{u} + 2\mathbf{w}$

$= (2, -1) + 2(1, 2)$

$= (2, -1) + (2, 4)$

$= (2 + 2, -1 + 4) = (4, 3)$

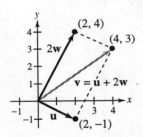

5. $\mathbf{v} = \frac{1}{2}(3\mathbf{u} + \mathbf{w}) = \frac{1}{2}(3(2, -1) + (1, 2)) = \frac{1}{2}((6, -3) + (1, 2))$

$= \frac{1}{2}(7, -1) = (\frac{7}{2}, -\frac{1}{2})$

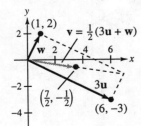

7. (a) $2\mathbf{v} = 2(2, 3) = (2(2), 2(3)) = (4, 6)$

(b) $-3\mathbf{v} = -3(2, 3) = (-3(2), -3(3)) = (-6, -9)$

(c) $\frac{1}{2}\mathbf{v} = \frac{1}{2}(2, 3) = (\frac{1}{2}(2), \frac{1}{2}(3)) = (1, \frac{3}{2})$

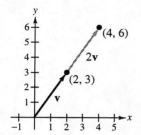   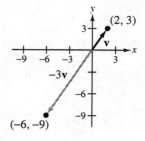   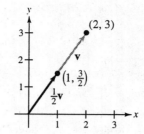

9. $\mathbf{u} - \mathbf{v} = (1, 2, 3) - (2, 2, -1) = (-1, 0, 4)$

$\mathbf{v} - \mathbf{u} = (2, 2, -1) - (1, 2, 3) = (1, 0, -4)$

11. $2\mathbf{u} + 4\mathbf{v} - \mathbf{w} = 2(1, 2, 3) + 4(2, 2, -1) - (4, 0, -4)$

$$= (2, 4, 6) + (8, 8, -4) - (4, 0, -4)$$

$$= (2 + 8 - 4, 4 + 8 - 0, 6 + (-4) - (-4))$$

$$= (6, 12, 6)$$

13. $2\mathbf{z} - 3\mathbf{u} = \mathbf{w}$ implies that $2\mathbf{z} = 3\mathbf{u} + \mathbf{w}$, or $\mathbf{z} = \frac{3}{2}\mathbf{u} + \frac{1}{2}\mathbf{w}$.

Hence, $\mathbf{z} = \frac{3}{2}(1, 2, 3) + \frac{1}{2}(4, 0, -4) = (\frac{3}{2}, 3, \frac{9}{2}) + (2, 0, -2) = (\frac{7}{2}, 3, \frac{5}{2})$.

15. (a) $2\mathbf{v} = 2(1, 2, 2) = (2, 4, 4)$

(b) $-\mathbf{v} = -(1, 2, 2) = (-1, -2, -2)$

(c) $\frac{1}{2}\mathbf{v} = \frac{1}{2}(1, 2, 2) = (\frac{1}{2}, 1, 1)$

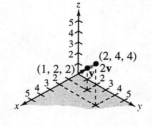   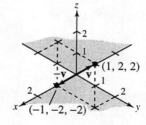   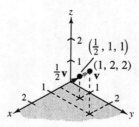

17. (a) Since $(-6, -4, 10) = -2(3, 2, -5)$, $\mathbf{u}$ is a scalar multiple of $\mathbf{z}$.

(b) Since $(2, \frac{4}{3}, -\frac{10}{3}) = \frac{2}{3}(3, 2, -5)$, $\mathbf{v}$ is a scalar multiple of $\mathbf{z}$.

(c) Since $(6, 4, 10) \neq c(3, 2, -5)$ for any c, $\mathbf{w}$ is *not* a scalar multiple of $\mathbf{z}$.

19. (a) $\mathbf{u} - \mathbf{v} = (4, 0, -3, 5) - (0, 2, 5, 4)$

$= (4 - 0, 0 - 2, -3 - 5, 5 - 4)$

$= (4, -2, -8, 1)$

(b) $2(\mathbf{u} + 3\mathbf{v}) = 2[(4, 0, -3, 5) + 3(0, 2, 5, 4)]$

$= 2[(4, 0, -3, 5) + (0, 6, 15, 12)]$

$= 2(4 + 0, 0 + 6, -3 + 15, 5 + 12)$

$= 2(4, 6, 12, 17) = (8, 12, 24, 34)$

21. (a) $\mathbf{u} - \mathbf{v} = (-7, 0, 0, 0, 9) - (2, -3, -2, 3, 3) = (-9, 3, 2, -3, 6)$

(b) $2(\mathbf{u} + 3\mathbf{v}) = 2[(-7, 0, 0, 0, 9) + 3(2, -3, -2, 3, 3)]$

$= 2[(-7, 0, 0, 0, 9) + (6, -9, -6, 9, 9)]$

$= 2(-1, -9, -6, 9, 18)$

$= (-2, -18, -12, 18, 36)$

23. $2\mathbf{w} = \mathbf{u} - 3\mathbf{v}$

$\mathbf{w} = \frac{1}{2}\mathbf{u} - \frac{3}{2}\mathbf{v}$

$= \frac{1}{2}(1, -1, 0, 1) - \frac{3}{2}(0, 2, 3, -1)$

$= (\frac{1}{2}, -\frac{1}{2}, 0, \frac{1}{2}) - (0, 3, \frac{9}{2}, -\frac{3}{2})$

$= (\frac{1}{2} - 0, -\frac{1}{2} - 3, 0 - \frac{9}{2}, \frac{1}{2} - (-\frac{3}{2}))$

$= (\frac{1}{2}, -\frac{7}{2}, -\frac{9}{2}, 2)$

25. The equation

$$a\mathbf{u} + b\mathbf{w} = \mathbf{v}$$

$$a(1, 2) + b(1, -1) = (2, 1)$$

yields the system

$$a + b = 2$$

$$2a - b = 1.$$

Solving this system produces $a = 1$ and $b = 1$. Thus, $\mathbf{v} = \mathbf{u} + \mathbf{w}$.

27. The equation

$$a\mathbf{u} + b\mathbf{w} = \mathbf{v}$$

$$a(1, 2) + b(1, -1) = (3, 0)$$

yields the system

$$a + b = 3$$

$$2a - b = 0.$$

Solving this system produces $a = 1$ and $b = 2$. Thus, $\mathbf{v} = \mathbf{u} + 2\mathbf{w}$.

29. $2\mathbf{u} + \mathbf{v} - 3\mathbf{w} = \mathbf{0}$

$$\begin{aligned}
\mathbf{w} &= \tfrac{2}{3}\mathbf{u} + \tfrac{1}{3}\mathbf{v} \\
&= \tfrac{2}{3}(0, 2, 7, 5) + \tfrac{1}{3}(-3, 1, 4, -8) \\
&= (0, \tfrac{4}{3}, \tfrac{14}{3}, \tfrac{10}{3}) + (-1, \tfrac{1}{3}, \tfrac{4}{3}, -\tfrac{8}{3}) \\
&= (0 + (-1), \tfrac{4}{3} + \tfrac{1}{3}, \tfrac{14}{3} + \tfrac{4}{3}, \tfrac{10}{3} - \tfrac{8}{3}) \\
&= (-1, \tfrac{5}{3}, 6, \tfrac{2}{3})
\end{aligned}$$

31. The equation

$$a\mathbf{u}_1 + b\mathbf{u}_2 + c\mathbf{u}_3 = \mathbf{v}$$

$$a(2, 3, 5) + b(1, 2, 4) + c(-2, 2, 3) = (10, 1, 4)$$

yields the system

$$2a + b - 2c = 10$$
$$3a + 2b + 2c = 1$$
$$5a + 4b + 3c = 4$$

Solving this system produces $a = 1$, $b = 2$, and $c = -3$. Thus, $\mathbf{v} = \mathbf{u}_1 + 2\mathbf{u}_2 - 3\mathbf{u}_3$.

33. The equation

$$a\mathbf{u}_1 + b\mathbf{u}_2 + c\mathbf{u}_3 = \mathbf{v}$$

$$a(1, 1, 2, 2) + b(2, 3, 5, 6) + c(-3, 1, -4, 2) = (0, 5, 3, 0)$$

yields the system

$$a + 2b - 3c = 0$$
$$a + 3b + c = 5$$
$$2a + 5b - 4c = 3$$
$$2a + 6b + 2c = 0.$$

The second and fourth equations cannot both be true. Thus, the system has no solution. It is not possible to write $\mathbf{v}$ as a linear combination of $\mathbf{u}_1,$ $\mathbf{u}_2,$ and $\mathbf{u}_3$.

35. The equation

$$a\mathbf{v}_1 + b\mathbf{v}_2 + c\mathbf{v}_3 = \mathbf{0}$$

$$a(1, 0, 1) + b(-1, 1, 2) + c(0, 1, 4) = (0, 0, 0)$$

yields the homogenous system

$$a - b = 0$$
$$b + c = 0$$
$$a + 2b + 4c = 0.$$

This system has only the trivial solution $a = b = c = 0$. Thus, we cannot find a nontrivial way of writing $\mathbf{0}$ as a combination of $\mathbf{v}_1,$ $\mathbf{v}_2,$ and $\mathbf{v}_3$.

37. (1) $\mathbf{u} + \mathbf{v} = (2, -1, 3, 6) + (1, 4, 0, 1) = (3, 3, 3, 7)$ is a vector in R^4.

    (2) $\mathbf{u} + \mathbf{v} = (2, -1, 3, 6) + (1, 4, 0, 1) = (3, 3, 3, 7)$ and

        $\mathbf{v} + \mathbf{u} = (1, 4, 0, 1) + (2, -1, 3, 6) = (3, 3, 3, 7)$

        Hence, $\mathbf{u} + \mathbf{v} = \mathbf{v} + \mathbf{u}.$

    (3) $(\mathbf{u} + \mathbf{v}) + \mathbf{w} = [(2, -1, 3, 6) + 1, 4, 0, 1)] + (3, 0, 2, 0) = (3, 3, 3, 7) + (3, 0, 2, 0)$

              $= (6, 3, 5, 7)$

      $\mathbf{u} + (\mathbf{v} + \mathbf{w}) = (2, -1, 3, 6) + [(1, 4, 0, 1) + (3, 0, 2, 0)] = (2, -1, 3, 6) + (4, 4, 2, 1)$

              $= (6, 3, 5, 7)$

        Hence, $(\mathbf{u} + \mathbf{v}) + \mathbf{w} = \mathbf{u} + (\mathbf{v} + \mathbf{w}).$

    (4) $\mathbf{u} + \mathbf{0} = (2, -1, 3, 6) + (0, 0, 0, 0) = (2, -1, 3, 6) = \mathbf{u}$

    (5) $\mathbf{u} + (-\mathbf{u}) = (2, -1, 3, 6) + (-2, 1, -3, -6) = (0, 0, 0, 0) = \mathbf{0}$

    (6) $c\mathbf{u} = 5(2, -1, 3, 6) = (10, -5, 15, 30)$ is a vector in R^4.

    (7) $c(\mathbf{u} + \mathbf{v}) = 5[(2, -1, 3, 6) + (1, 4, 0, 1)] = 5(3, 3, 3, 7) = (15, 15, 15, 35)$

      $c\mathbf{u} + c\mathbf{v} = 5(2, -1, 3, 6) + 5(1, 4, 0, 1) = (10, -5, 15, 30) + (5, 20, 0, 5)$

           $= (15, 15, 15, 35)$

        Hence, $c(\mathbf{u} + \mathbf{v}) = c\mathbf{u} + c\mathbf{v}.$

    (8) $(c + d)\mathbf{u} = (5 + (-2)) (2, -1, 3, 6) = 3(2, -1, 3, 6) = (6, -3, 9, 18)$

      $c\mathbf{u} + d\mathbf{u} = 5(2, -1, 3, 6) + (-2) (2, -1, 3, 6) = (10, -5, 15, 30) + (-4, 2, -6, -12)$

          $= (6, -3, 9, 18)$

        Hence, $(c + d)\mathbf{u} = c\mathbf{u} + d\mathbf{u}.$

    (9) $c(d\mathbf{u}) = 5((-2) (2, -1, 3, 6)) = 5(-4, 2, -6, -12) = (-20, 10, -30, -60)$

      $(cd)\mathbf{u} = (5(-2)) (2, -1, 3, 6) = -10(2, -1, 3, 6) = (-20, 10, -30, -60)$

        Hence, $c (d\mathbf{u}) = (cd)\mathbf{u}.$

    (10) $1(\mathbf{u}) = 1(2, -1, 3, 6) = (2, -1, 3, 6) = \mathbf{u}$

39. We prove the remaining eight properties.

    (1) $\mathbf{u} + \mathbf{v} = (u_1, u_2) + (v_1, v_2) = (u_1 + v_1, u_2 + v_2)$ is a vector in the plane.

    (2) $\mathbf{u} + \mathbf{v} = (u_1, u_2) + (v_1, v_2) = (u_1 + v_1, u_2 + v_2) = (v_1 + u_1, v_2 + u_2)$

        $= (v_1, v_2) + (u_1, u_2) = \mathbf{v} + \mathbf{u}$

    (4) $\mathbf{u} + \mathbf{0} = (u_1, u_2) + (0, 0) = (u_1 + 0, u_2 + 0) = (u_1, u_2) = \mathbf{u}$

    (5) $\mathbf{u} + (-\mathbf{u}) = (u_1, u_2) + (-u_1, -u_2) = (u_1 - u_1, u_2 - u_2) = (0, 0) = \mathbf{0}$

    (6) $c\mathbf{u} = c(u_1, u_2) = (cu_1, cu_2)$ is a vector in the plane.

    (7) $c(\mathbf{u} + \mathbf{v}) = c [(u_1, u_2) + (v_1, v_2)] = c(u_1 + v_1, u_2 + v_2)$

        $= (c(u_1 + v_1), c(u_2 + v_2)) = (cu_1 + cv_1, cu_2 + cu_2)$

        $= (cu_1, cu_2) + (cv_1 + cv_2)$

        $= c(u_1, u_2) + c(v_1 + v_2) = c\mathbf{u} + c\mathbf{v}$

    (9) $(c + d)\mathbf{u} = (c + d) (u_1, u_2) = ((c + d)u_1, (c + d)u_2)$

        $= (cu_1 + du_1, cu_2 + du_2)$

        $= (cu_1, cu_2) + (du_1 + du_2)$

        $= c(u_1, u_2) + d(u_1 + u_2) = c\mathbf{u} + d\mathbf{u}$

    (10) $1(\mathbf{u}) = 1(u_1, u_2) = (u_1, u_2) = \mathbf{u}$

41. We prove the remaining five parts of the Theorem.

(2) Suppose that $\mathbf{v} + \mathbf{u} = 0$.

Then,

$(-\mathbf{v}) + (\mathbf{v} + \mathbf{u}) = (-\mathbf{v}) + 0$

$((-\mathbf{v}) + \mathbf{v}) + \mathbf{u} = -\mathbf{v}$

$\qquad\qquad \mathbf{0} + \mathbf{u} = -\mathbf{v}$

$\qquad\qquad\qquad \mathbf{u} = -\mathbf{v}.$

(3) $0\mathbf{v} = (0 + 0)\mathbf{v} = 0\mathbf{v} + 0\mathbf{v}$, which implies that

$\qquad 0\mathbf{v} + (-0\mathbf{v}) = (0\mathbf{v} + 0\mathbf{v}) + (-0\mathbf{v})$

$\qquad\qquad\qquad \mathbf{0} = 0\mathbf{v} + (0\mathbf{v} + (-0\mathbf{v}))$

$\qquad\qquad\qquad \mathbf{0} = 0\mathbf{v} + \mathbf{0}$

$\qquad\qquad\qquad \mathbf{0} = 0\mathbf{v}.$

(4) $c\mathbf{0} = c(\mathbf{0} + \mathbf{0}) = c\mathbf{0} + c\mathbf{0}$, which implies that

$\qquad c\mathbf{0} + (-c\mathbf{0}) = (c\mathbf{0} + c\mathbf{0}) + (-c\mathbf{0})$

$\qquad\qquad\qquad \mathbf{0} = c\mathbf{0} + (c\mathbf{0} + (-c\mathbf{0}))$

$\qquad\qquad\qquad \mathbf{0} = c\mathbf{0} + \mathbf{0}$

$\qquad\qquad\qquad \mathbf{0} = c\mathbf{0}.$

(5) We are given that $c\mathbf{v} = \mathbf{0}$. If $c = 0$, we are done. If not, then c^{-1} exists, and we have

$c^{-1}(c\mathbf{v}) = c^{-1}\mathbf{0}$

$(c^{-1}c)\mathbf{v} = \mathbf{0}$

$\qquad 1\mathbf{v} = \mathbf{0}$

$\qquad \mathbf{v} = \mathbf{0}.$

(6) $-(-\mathbf{v}) + (-\mathbf{v}) = \mathbf{0}$ and $\mathbf{v} + (-\mathbf{v}) = \mathbf{0}$, and so by property 2, $-(-\mathbf{v}) = \mathbf{v}$.

43. If $\mathbf{b} = x_1\mathbf{a}_1 + \cdots + X_n\mathbf{a}_n$ is a linear combination of the columns of A, then a solution to $A\mathbf{x} = \mathbf{b}$ is

$$\mathbf{x} = \begin{bmatrix} x_1 \\ \vdots \\ x_n \end{bmatrix}$$

The system $A\mathbf{x} = \mathbf{b}$ is inconsistent if $\mathbf{b}$ is not a linear combination of the columns of A.

Section 4.2   Vector Spaces

1. The additive identity of R^4 is the vector $(0, 0, 0, 0)$.

3. The additive identity of $M_{2,3}$ is the 2×3 zero matrix

$$\begin{bmatrix} 0 & 0 & 0 \\ 0 & 0 & 0 \end{bmatrix}.$$

5. P_3 is the set of all polynominals of degree less than or equal to 3. Its additive identity is

$$0(x) = 0x^3 + 0x^2 + 0x + 0 = 0.$$

7. In R^4, the additive inverse of (v_1, v_2, v_3, v_4) is $(-v_1, -v_2, -v_3, -v_4)$.

9. $M_{2,3}$ is the set of all 2×3 matrices. The additive inverse of

$$\begin{bmatrix} a_{11} & a_{12} & a_{13} \\ a_{21} & a_{22} & a_{23} \end{bmatrix}$$

is $-\begin{bmatrix} a_{11} & a_{12} & a_{13} \\ a_{21} & a_{22} & a_{23} \end{bmatrix} = \begin{bmatrix} -a_{11} & -a_{12} & -a_{13} \\ -a_{21} & -a_{22} & -a_{23} \end{bmatrix}.$

11. P_3 is the set of all polynominals of degree less than or equal to 3. The additive inverse of $a_3x^3 + a_2x^2 + a_1x + a_0$ is

$$-(a_3x^3 + a_2x^2 + a_1x + a_0) = -a_3x^3 - a_2x^2 - a_1x - a_0.$$

13. $M_{4,6}$ with the standard operations is a vector space. All ten vector space axioms hold.

15. This set is *not* a vector space. The set is not closed under addition or scalar multiplication. For example, $(-x^5 + x^4) + (x^5 - x^3) = x^4 - x^3$ is not a fifth-degree polynomial.

17. This set is a vector space. All ten vector space axioms hold.

19. This set is a vector space. All ten vector space axioms hold.

21. This set is *not* a vector space because it is not closed under addition. A counterexample is

$$\begin{bmatrix} 1 & 0 \\ 0 & 0 \end{bmatrix} + \begin{bmatrix} 0 & 0 \\ 0 & 1 \end{bmatrix} = \begin{bmatrix} 1 & 0 \\ 0 & 1 \end{bmatrix}.$$

Each matrix on the left is singular, while their sum is nonsingular.

23. This set is a vector space. All ten vector space axioms hold.

25. (a) Axiom 8 fails. For example,

$$(1 + 2)(1, 1) = 3(1, 1) = (3, 1) \quad \left(\text{Since } c(x, y) = (cx, y)\right)$$

$$1(1, 1) + 2(1, 1) = (1, 1) + (2, 1) = (3, 2).$$

Thus, R^2 is not a vector space with these operations.

(b) Axiom 2 fails. For example,

$$(1, 2) + (2, 1) = (1, 0)$$

$$(2, 1) + (1, 2) = (2, 0).$$

Thus, R^2 is not a vector space with these operations.

(c) Axiom 6 fails. For example, $(-1)(1, 1) = (\sqrt{-1}, \sqrt{-1})$, which is not in R^2.

Thus, R^2 is not a vector space with these operations.

27. We verify the ten axioms in the definition of vector space.

(1) $\mathbf{u} + \mathbf{v} = \begin{bmatrix} u_1 & u_2 \\ u_3 & u_4 \end{bmatrix} + \begin{bmatrix} v_1 & v_2 \\ v_3 & v_4 \end{bmatrix} = \begin{bmatrix} u_1 + v_1 & u_2 + v_2 \\ u_3 + v_3 & u_4 + v_4 \end{bmatrix}$ is in $M_{2,2}$

(2) $\mathbf{u} + \mathbf{v} = \begin{bmatrix} u_1 & u_2 \\ u_3 & u_4 \end{bmatrix} + \begin{bmatrix} v_1 & v_2 \\ v_3 & v_4 \end{bmatrix} = \begin{bmatrix} u_1 + v_1 & u_2 + v_2 \\ u_3 + v_3 & u_4 + v_4 \end{bmatrix}$

$$= \begin{bmatrix} v_1 + u_2 & v_2 + u_2 \\ v_3 + u_4 & v_4 + u_4 \end{bmatrix} = \begin{bmatrix} v_1 & v_2 \\ v_3 & v_4 \end{bmatrix} + \begin{bmatrix} u_1 & u_2 \\ u_3 & u_4 \end{bmatrix} = \mathbf{v} + \mathbf{u}$$

(3) $\mathbf{u} + (\mathbf{v} + \mathbf{w}) = \begin{bmatrix} u_1 & u_2 \\ u_3 & u_4 \end{bmatrix} + \left(\begin{bmatrix} u_1 & u_2 \\ u_3 & u_4 \end{bmatrix} + \begin{bmatrix} w_1 & w_2 \\ w_3 & w_4 \end{bmatrix} \right)$

$$= \begin{bmatrix} u_1 & u_2 \\ u_3 & u_4 \end{bmatrix} + \begin{bmatrix} v_1 + w_1 & v_2 + w_2 \\ v_3 + w_3 & v_4 + w_4 \end{bmatrix}$$

$$= \begin{bmatrix} u_1 + (v_1 + w_1) & u_2 + (v_2 + w_2) \\ u_3 + (v_3 + w_3) & u_4 + (v_4 + w_4) \end{bmatrix}$$

$$= \begin{bmatrix} (u_1 + v_1) + w_1 & (u_2 + v_2) + w_2 \\ (u_3 + v_3) + w_3 & (u_4 + v_4) + w_4 \end{bmatrix}$$

$$= \begin{bmatrix} u_1 + v_1 & u_2 + v_2 \\ u_3 + v_3 & u_4 + v_4 \end{bmatrix} + \begin{bmatrix} w_1 & w_2 \\ w_3 & w_4 \end{bmatrix}$$

$$= \left(\begin{bmatrix} u_1 & u_2 \\ u_3 & u_4 \end{bmatrix} + \begin{bmatrix} v_1 & v_2 \\ v_3 & v_4 \end{bmatrix} \right) = \begin{bmatrix} w_1 & w_2 \\ w_3 & w_4 \end{bmatrix} = (\mathbf{u} + \mathbf{v}) + \mathbf{w}$$

(4) The zero vector is

$$\mathbf{0} = \begin{bmatrix} 0 & 0 \\ 0 & 0 \end{bmatrix} \cdot \text{ Hence,}$$

$$\mathbf{u} + \mathbf{0} = \begin{bmatrix} u_1 & u_2 \\ u_3 & u_4 \end{bmatrix} + \begin{bmatrix} 0 & 0 \\ 0 & 0 \end{bmatrix} = \begin{bmatrix} u_1 & u_2 \\ u_3 & u_4 \end{bmatrix} = \mathbf{u}$$

(5) For every

$$\mathbf{u} = \begin{bmatrix} u_1 & u_2 \\ u_3 & u_4 \end{bmatrix}, \text{ we have } -\mathbf{u} = \begin{bmatrix} -u_1 & -u_2 \\ -u_3 & -u_4 \end{bmatrix}.$$

$$\mathbf{u} + (-\mathbf{u}) = \begin{bmatrix} u_1 & u_2 \\ u_3 & u_4 \end{bmatrix} + \begin{bmatrix} -u_1 & -u_2 \\ -u_3 & -u_4 \end{bmatrix}$$

$$= \begin{bmatrix} 0 & 0 \\ 0 & 0 \end{bmatrix}$$

$$= \mathbf{0}.$$

(6) $c\mathbf{u} = c \begin{bmatrix} u_1 & u_2 \\ u_3 & u_4 \end{bmatrix} = \begin{bmatrix} cu_1 & cu_2 \\ cu_3 & cu_4 \end{bmatrix}$ is in $M_{2,2}$.

$$(7)\ c(\mathbf{u} + \mathbf{v}) = c\left(\begin{bmatrix} u_1 & u_2 \\ u_3 & u_4 \end{bmatrix} + \begin{bmatrix} v_1 & v_2 \\ v_3 & v_4 \end{bmatrix}\right) = c\begin{bmatrix} u_1 + v_1 & u_2 + v_2 \\ u_3 + v_3 & u_4 + v_4 \end{bmatrix}$$

$$= \begin{bmatrix} c(u_1 + v_1) & c(u_2 + v_2) \\ c(u_3 + v_3) & c(u_4 + v_4) \end{bmatrix} = \begin{bmatrix} cu_1 + cv_1 & cu_2 + cv_2 \\ cu_3 + cv_3 & cu_4 + cv_4 \end{bmatrix}$$

$$= \begin{bmatrix} cu_1 & cu_2 \\ cu_3 & cu_4 \end{bmatrix} + \begin{bmatrix} cu_1 & cu_2 \\ cu_3 & cu_4 \end{bmatrix} = c\begin{bmatrix} u_1 & u_2 \\ u_3 & u_4 \end{bmatrix} + c\begin{bmatrix} v_1 & v_2 \\ v_3 & v_4 \end{bmatrix}$$

$$= c\mathbf{u} + c\mathbf{v}$$

$$(8)\ (c + d)\mathbf{u} = (c + d)\begin{bmatrix} u_1 & u_2 \\ u_3 & u_4 \end{bmatrix} = \begin{bmatrix} (c + d)u_1 & (c + d)u_2 \\ (c + d)u_3 & (c + d)u_4 \end{bmatrix}$$

$$= \begin{bmatrix} cu_1 + du_1 & cu_2 + du_2 \\ cu_3 + du_3 & cu_4 + du_4 \end{bmatrix} = \begin{bmatrix} cu_1 & cu_2 \\ cu_3 & cu_4 \end{bmatrix} + \begin{bmatrix} du_1 & du_2 \\ du_3 & du_4 \end{bmatrix}$$

$$= c\begin{bmatrix} u_1 & u_2 \\ u_3 & u_4 \end{bmatrix} + d\begin{bmatrix} u_1 & u_2 \\ u_3 & u_4 \end{bmatrix} = c\mathbf{u} + d\mathbf{u}$$

$$(9)\ c(d\mathbf{u}) = c\left(d\begin{bmatrix} u_1 & u_2 \\ u_3 & u_4 \end{bmatrix}\right) = c\begin{bmatrix} du_1 & du_2 \\ du_3 & du_4 \end{bmatrix} = \begin{bmatrix} c(du_1) & c(du_2) \\ c(du_3) & c(du_4) \end{bmatrix}$$

$$= \begin{bmatrix} (cd)u_1 & (cd)u_2 \\ (cd)u_3 & (cd)u_4 \end{bmatrix} = (cd)\begin{bmatrix} u_1 & u_2 \\ u_3 & u_4 \end{bmatrix} = (cd)\mathbf{u}$$

$$(10)\ 1(\mathbf{u}) = 1\begin{bmatrix} u_1 & u_2 \\ u_3 & u_4 \end{bmatrix} = \begin{bmatrix} 1u_1 & 1u_2 \\ 1u_3 & 1u_4 \end{bmatrix} = \mathbf{u}$$

29. This set is not a vector space because Axiom 5 fails. The additive identity is $(1, 1)$ and hence $(0, 0)$ has no additive inverse. Axioms 7 and 8 also fail.

31. Suppose there were two zero vectors, $\mathbf{0}$ and $\mathbf{Q}$. Then since $\mathbf{v} + \mathbf{0} = \mathbf{v} + \mathbf{Q}$ for all $\mathbf{v}$, we have

$$\mathbf{0} = \mathbf{0} + \mathbf{Q} = \mathbf{Q}.$$

33.
$$\mathbf{u} + \mathbf{w} = \mathbf{v} + \mathbf{w}$$
$$(\mathbf{u} + \mathbf{w}) + (-\mathbf{w}) = (\mathbf{v} + \mathbf{w}) + (-\mathbf{w})$$
$$\mathbf{u} + (\mathbf{w} + (-\mathbf{w})) = \mathbf{v} + (\mathbf{w} + (-\mathbf{w}))$$
$$\mathbf{u} + \mathbf{0} = \mathbf{v} + \mathbf{0}$$
$$\mathbf{u} = \mathbf{v}$$

35. $(-1)\mathbf{v} + 1(\mathbf{v}) = (-1 + 1)\mathbf{v} = 0\mathbf{v} = \mathbf{0}$. Also, $-\mathbf{v} + \mathbf{v} = \mathbf{0}$. Hence, $(-1)\mathbf{v}$ and $-\mathbf{v}$ are both additive inverses of $\mathbf{v}$. Since the additive inverse of a vector is unique (Problem 32),
$$(-1)\mathbf{v} = -\mathbf{v}.$$

Section 4.3   Subspaces of Vector Spaces

1. Because W is nonempty and $W \subset R^4$, we need only check that W is closed under addition and scalar multiplication. Given

$$(x_1, x_2, x_3, 0) \in W \quad \text{and} \quad (y_1, y_2, y_3, 0) \in W,$$

it follows that

$$(x_1, x_2, x_3, 0) + (y_1, y_2, y_3, 0) = (x_1 + y_1, x_2 + y_2, x_3 + y_3, 0) \in W.$$

Furthermore, for any real number c and $(x_1, x_2, x_3, 0) \in W$, it follows that

$$c(x_1, x_2, x_3, 0) = (cx_1, cx_2, cx_3, 0) \in W.$$

3. Because W is nonempty and $W \subset M_{2,2}$, we need only check that W is closed under addition and scalar multiplication. Given

$$\begin{bmatrix} 0 & a_1 \\ b_1 & 0 \end{bmatrix} \in W \quad \text{and} \quad \begin{bmatrix} 0 & a_2 \\ b_2 & 0 \end{bmatrix} \in W$$

it follows that

$$\begin{bmatrix} 0 & a_1 \\ b_1 & 0 \end{bmatrix} + \begin{bmatrix} 0 & a_2 \\ b_2 & 0 \end{bmatrix} = \begin{bmatrix} 0 & a_1 + a_2 \\ b_1 + b_2 & 0 \end{bmatrix} \in W.$$

Furthermore, for any real number c and

$$\begin{bmatrix} 0 & a \\ b & o \end{bmatrix} \in W$$

it follows that

$$c\begin{bmatrix} 0 & a \\ b & 0 \end{bmatrix} = \begin{bmatrix} 0 & ca \\ cb & 0 \end{bmatrix} \in W.$$

5. Recall from calculus that continuity implies integrability, thus $W \subset V$. Furthermore, because W is nonempty, we need only check that W is closed under addition and scalar multiplication. Given continuous functions $\mathbf{f}, \mathbf{g} \in W$, it follows that $\mathbf{f} + \mathbf{g}$ is continuous, thus, $\mathbf{f} + \mathbf{g} \in W$. Also, for any real number c and for a continuous function $\mathbf{f} \in W$, $c\mathbf{f}$ is continuous. Thus, $c\mathbf{f} \in W$.

7. The vectors in W are of the form $(a, b, -1)$. This set is not closed under addition or scalar multiplication. For example,

$$(0, 0, -1) + (0, 0, -1) = (0, 0, -2) \notin W$$

and

$$2(0, 0, -1) = (0, 0, -2) \notin W.$$

9. Consider $f(x) = e^x$, which is continuous and nonnegative. Thus, $\mathbf{f} \in W$. The function $(-1)\mathbf{f} = -\mathbf{f}$ is negative. Thus, $-\mathbf{f} \notin W$, and W is not closed under scalar multiplication.

11. This set is not closed under addition.

For example,

$$\begin{bmatrix} 1 & 0 \\ 0 & 0 \end{bmatrix} + \begin{bmatrix} 0 & 0 \\ 0 & 1 \end{bmatrix} = \begin{bmatrix} 1 & 0 \\ 0 & 1 \end{bmatrix} \notin W.$$

13. (a) This set is *not* a subspace of $C(-\infty, \infty)$ because it is not closed under scalar multiplication.
   (b) This set is a subspace of $C(-\infty, \infty)$ because it is closed under addition and scalar multiplication.
   (c) This set is a subspace of $C(-\infty, \infty)$ because it is closed under addition and scalar multiplication.
   (d) This set is a subspace of $C(-\infty, \infty)$ because it is closed under addition and scalar multiplication.
   (e) This set is a subspace of $C(-\infty, \infty)$ because it is closed under addition and scalar multiplication.
   (f) This set is *not* a subspace of $C(-\infty, \infty)$ because it is not closed under addition or scalar multiplication.

15. W is a subspace of R^3, because it is nonempty and closed under addition and scalar multiplication.

17. Note that $W \subset R^3$ and W is nonempty. If $(a_1, b_1, a_1 + 2b_1)$ and $(a_2, b_2, a_2 + 2b_2)$ are vectors in W, then their sum

$$(a_1, b_1, a_1 + 2b_1) + (a_2, b_2, a_2 + 2b_2) = (a_1 + a_2, b_1 + b_2, (a_1 + a_2) + 2(b_1 + b_2))$$

is also in W. Furthermore, for any real number c and $(a, b, a + 2b)$ in W,

$$c(a, b, a + 2b) = (ca, cb, ca + 2cb)$$

is in W. Because W is closed under addition and scalar multiplication, W is a subspace of R^3.

19. W is not a subspace of R^3 because it is not closed under addition or scalar multiplication.

For example, $(1, 1, 1) \in W$, but

$$(1, 1, 1) + (1, 1, 1) = (2, 2, 2) \notin W.$$

Or,

$$2(1, 1, 1) = (2, 2, 2) \notin W.$$

21. Let W be a nonempty subset of a vector space V. On the one hand, if W is a subspace of V, then for any scalars a, b, and any vectors $\mathbf{x}, \mathbf{y} \in W$, $a\mathbf{x} \in W$ and $b\mathbf{y} \in W$, and hence, $a\mathbf{x} + b\mathbf{y} \in W$.

On the other hand, assume that $a\mathbf{x} + b\mathbf{y}$ is an element of W where a, b are scalars, and $\mathbf{x}, \mathbf{y} \in W$. To show that W is a subspace, we must verify the closure axioms. If $\mathbf{x}, \mathbf{y} \in W$, then $\mathbf{x} + \mathbf{y} \in W$ (by taking $a = b = 1$). Finally, if a is a scalar, $a\mathbf{x} \in W$ (by taking $b = 0$).

23. The set W is a nonempty subset of V. To show closure, let $a_1\mathbf{x} + b_1\mathbf{y} + c_1\mathbf{z} \in W$ and $a_2\mathbf{x} + b_2\mathbf{y} + c_2\mathbf{z} \in W$.

Their sum is in W, since

$$(a_1\mathbf{x} + b_1\mathbf{y} + c_1\mathbf{z}) + (a_2\mathbf{x} + b_2\mathbf{y} + c_2\mathbf{z}) =$$

$$(a_1 + a_2)\mathbf{x} + (b + b_2)\mathbf{y} + (c_1 + c_2)\mathbf{z}.$$

Also, if c is a scalar,

$$c(a_1\mathbf{x} + b_1\mathbf{y} + c_1\mathbf{z}) = (ca_1)\mathbf{x} + (cb_1)\mathbf{y} + (cc_1)\mathbf{z} \in W.$$

25. W is nonempty since $A\mathbf{0} = \mathbf{0} \Rightarrow \mathbf{0} \in W$. If $\mathbf{x}, \mathbf{y} \in W$ then $A\mathbf{x} = A\mathbf{y} = \mathbf{0}$. Thus, $A(\mathbf{x} + \mathbf{y}) = A\mathbf{x} + A\mathbf{y} = \mathbf{0} + \mathbf{0} = \mathbf{0} \Rightarrow \mathbf{x} + \mathbf{y} \in W$.

If $\mathbf{x} \in W$ and $c \in R$, then $A\mathbf{x} = \mathbf{0}$. Thus, $A(c\mathbf{x}) = c(A\mathbf{x}) = C\mathbf{0} = \mathbf{0} \Rightarrow c\mathbf{x} \in W$.

27. The set W is a nonempty subset of $M_{2,2}$. (For instance, $A \in W$). To show closure, let $X, Y \in W \Rightarrow AX = XA$ and $AY = YA$. Then, $(X + Y)A = XA + YA = AX + AY = A(X + Y) \Rightarrow X + Y \in W$. Similarly, if c is a scalar, then $(cX)A = c(XA) = c(AX) = A(cX) \Rightarrow cX \in W$.

29. $V + W$ is nonempty since $\mathbf{0} = \mathbf{0} + \mathbf{0} \in V + W$.

Let $u_1, u_2 \in V + W$. Then $u_1 = v_1 + w_1$, $u_2 = v_2 + w_2$, where $v_i \in V$ and $W_i \in W$. Thus,

$$u_1 + u_2 = (v_1 + w_1) + (v_2 + w_2) = (v_1 + v_2) + (w_1 + w_2) \in V + W.$$

For scalar c,

$$cu_1 = c(v_1 + w_1) = cv_1 + cw_1 \in V + W.$$

If $v = \{1x, 0): x$ is a real number$\}$ and $w = \{(0, y):y$ is a real number$\}$, then $v + w = \mathbf{R}^2$.

Section 4.4   Spanning Sets and Linear Independence

1. (a) Solving the equation

$$c_1(2, -1, 3) + c_2(5, 0, 4) = (0, -5, 7)$$

for c_1 and c_2 yields the system

$$2c_1 + 5c_2 = 0$$
$$-c_1 = -5$$
$$3c_1 + 4c_2 = 7.$$

The solution to this system is $c_1 = 5$ and $c_2 = -2$. Thus, **u** can be written as a linear combination of vectors in S.

(b) We proceed as in (a), substituting $(16, -\frac{1}{2}, \frac{27}{2})$ for $(0, -5, 7)$, which yields the system

$$2c_1 + 5c_2 = 16$$
$$-c_1 = -\tfrac{1}{2}$$
$$3c_1 + 4c_2 = \tfrac{27}{2}.$$

The solution to this system is $c_1 = \frac{1}{2}$ and $c_2 = 3$. Thus, **v** can be written as a linear combination of vectors in S.

(c) We proceed as in (a), substituting $(3, 6, -2)$ for $(0, -5, 7)$, which yields the system

$$2c_1 + 5c_2 = 3$$
$$-c_1 = 6$$
$$3c_1 + 4c_2 = -2.$$

This system has no solution. Thus, **w** cannot be written as a linear combination of the vectors in S.

3. (a) Solving the equation

$$c_1(2, 0, 7) + c_2(2, 4, 5) + c_3(2, -12, 13) = (4, -20, 24)$$

for c_1 c_2, and c_3, yields the system

$$
\begin{aligned}
2c_1 + 2c_2 + 2c_3 &= 4 \\
4c_2 - 12c_3 &= -20 \\
7c_1 + 5c_2 + 13c_3 &= 24.
\end{aligned}
$$

One solution is $c_1 = 7$, $c_2 = -5$, and $c_3 = 0$. Thus, **u** can be written as a linear combination of vectors in S.

(b) We proceed as in (a), substituting $(-1, 0, 0)$ for $(4, -20, 24)$, which yields the system

$$
\begin{aligned}
2c_1 + 2c_2 + 2c_3 &= -1 \\
4c_2 - 12c_3 &= 0 \\
7c_1 + 5c_2 + 13c_3 &= 0.
\end{aligned}
$$

This system has no solution. Thus, **v** cannot be written as a linear combination of vectors in S.

(c) We proceed as in (a), substituting $(6, 24, 9)$ for $(4, -20, 24)$, which yields the system

$$
\begin{aligned}
2c_1 + 2c_2 + 2c_3 &= 6 \\
4c_2 - 12c_3 &= 24 \\
7c_1 + 5c_2 + 13c_3 &= 9.
\end{aligned}
$$

One solution is $c_1 = -3$, $c_2 = 6$, and $c_3 = 0$. Thus, **w** can be written as a linear combination of vectors in S.

5. Let $\mathbf{u} = (u_1, u_2)$ be any vector in R^2. Solving the equation

$$c_1(2, 1) + c_2(-1, 2) = (u_1, u_2)$$

for c_1 and c_2 yields the system

$$
\begin{aligned}
2c_1 - c_2 &= u_1 \\
c_1 + 2c_2 &= u_2.
\end{aligned}
$$

This system has a unique solution because the determinant of the coefficient matrix is nonzero. Thus, S spans R^2.

7. S does not span R^2 since only vectors of the form $t(-3, 5)$, are in span (S). For example, $(0, 1)$ is not in span (S). S spans a line in R^2.

9. S does not span R^2 since only vectors of the form $t(1, -2)$, are in span (S). For example, $(0, 1)$ is not in span (S). S spans a line in R^2.

11. Let $\mathbf{u} = (u_1, u_2, u_3)$ be any vector in R^3. Solving the equation

$$c_1(4, 7, 3) + c_2(-1, 2, 6) + c_3(2, -3, 5) = (u_1, u_2, u_3)$$

for c_1, c_2, and c_3 yields the system

$$\begin{aligned} 4c_1 - c_2 + 2c_3 &= u_1 \\ 7c_1 + 2c_2 - 3c_3 &= u_2 \\ 3c_1 + 6c_2 + 5c_3 &= u_3. \end{aligned}$$

This system has a unique solution since the determinant of the coefficient matrix is nonzero. Thus, S spans R^3.

13. This set does not span R^3. S spans a plane in R^3.

15. Let $\mathbf{u} = (u_1, u_2, u_3)$ be any vector in R^3. Solving the equation

$$c_1(1, -2, 0) + c_2(0, 0, 1) + c_3(-1, 2, 0) = (u_1, u_2, u_3)$$

for c_1 and c_2, and c_3 yields the system

$$\begin{aligned} c_1 \quad - c_3 &= u_1 \\ -2c_1 \quad + 2c_3 &= u_2 \\ c_2 \quad &= u_3. \end{aligned}$$

This system has an infinite number of solutions if $u_2 = -2u_1$, otherwise it has no solution. For instance $(1, 1, 1)$ is not in the span of S. Thus, S does not span R^3. The subspace spanned by S is span $(S) = (a, -2a, b) : a$ and b are any real numbers, which is a plane in R^3.

17. Since $(-2, 2)$ is not a scalar multiple of $(3, 5)$, the set S is linearly independent.

19. This set is linearly dependent since

$$1(0, 0) + 0(1, -1) = (0, 0).$$

21. Since $(1, -4, 1)$ is not a scalar multiple of $(6, 3, 2)$, the set S is linearly independent.

23. Since these vectors are multiples of each other, the set S is linearly dependent.

25. From the vector equation

$$c_1(-4, -3, 4) + c_2(1, -2, 3) + c_3(6, 0, 0) = \mathbf{0}$$

we obtain the homogenous system

$$\begin{aligned} -4c_1 + c_2 + 6c_3 &= 0 \\ -3c_1 - 2c_2 \quad &= 0 \\ 4c_1 + 3c_2 \quad &= 0. \end{aligned}$$

This system has only the trivial solution $c_1 = c_2 = c_3 = 0$. Hence, the set S, is linearly independent.

27. From the vector equation

$$c_1(4, -3, 6, 2) + c_2(1, 8, 3, 1) + c_3(3, -2, -1, 0) = (0, 0, 0, 0)$$

we obtain the homogenous system

$$
\begin{aligned}
4c_1 + c_2 + 3c_3 &= 0 \\
-3c_1 + 8c_2 - 2c_3 &= 0 \\
6c_1 + 3c_2 - c_3 &= 0 \\
2c_1 + c_2 &= 0.
\end{aligned}
$$

This system has only the trivial solution $c_1 = c_2 = c_3 = 0$. Hence, the set S, is linearly independent.

29. One example of a nontrivial linear combination of vectors in S whose sum is the zero vector is

$$2(3, 4) - 8(-1, 1) - 7(2, 0) = (0, 0).$$

Solving this equation for $(2, 0)$ yields

$$(2, 0) = \tfrac{2}{7}(3, 4) - \tfrac{8}{7}(-1, 1).$$

31. One example of a nontrivial linear combination of vectors in S whose sum is the zero vector is

$$(1, 1, 1) - (1, 1, 0) - 0(0, 1, 1) - (0, 0, 1) = (0, 0, 0).$$

Solving this equation for $(1, 1, 1)$ yields

$$(1, 1, 1) = (1, 1, 0) + (0, 0, 1) + 0(0, 1, 1).$$

33. (a) From the vector equation

$$c_1(t, 1, 1) + c_2(1, t, 1) + c_3(1, 1, t) = (0, 0, 0)$$

we obtain the homogenous system

$$
\begin{aligned}
tc_1 + c_2 + c_3 &= 0 \\
c_1 + tc_2 + c_3 &= 0 \\
c_1 + c_2 + tc_3 &= 0.
\end{aligned}
$$

The coefficient matrix of this system will have a nonzero determinant if $t^3 - 3t + 2 \neq 0$. Thus, the vectors will be linearly independent for all values of t other than $t = -2$ or $t = 1$.

(b) Proceeding as in (a), we obtain the homogenous system

$$
\begin{aligned}
tc_1 + c_2 + c_3 &= 0 \\
c_1 + c_3 &= 0 \\
c_1 + c_2 + 3tc_3 &= 0.
\end{aligned}
$$

The coefficient matrix of this system will have a nonzero determinant if $2 - 4t \neq 0$. Thus, the vectors will be linearly independent for all values of t other than $t = \tfrac{1}{2}$.

35. (a) From the vector equation

$$c_1 \begin{bmatrix} 2 & -3 \\ 4 & 1 \end{bmatrix} + c_2 \begin{bmatrix} 0 & 5 \\ 1 & -2 \end{bmatrix} = \begin{bmatrix} 6 & -19 \\ 10 & 7 \end{bmatrix}$$

we obtain the linear system

$$
\begin{array}{rcl}
2c_1 & = & 6 \\
-3c_1 + 5c_2 & = & -19 \\
4c_1 + c_2 & = & 10 \\
c_1 - 2c_2 & = & 7.
\end{array}
$$

The solution to this system is $c_1 = 3$ and $c_2 = -2$.

Hence,

$$\begin{bmatrix} 6 & -19 \\ 10 & 7 \end{bmatrix} = 3 \begin{bmatrix} 2 & -3 \\ 4 & 1 \end{bmatrix} - 2 \begin{bmatrix} 0 & 5 \\ 1 & -2 \end{bmatrix}.$$

(b) Processing as in (a), we obtain the system

$$
\begin{array}{rcl}
2c_1 & = & 6 \\
-3c_1 + 5c_2 & = & 2 \\
4c_1 + c_2 & = & 9 \\
c_1 - 2c_2 & = & 11.
\end{array}
$$

This system is inconsistent, and hence the matrix is not a linear combination of A and B.

(c) Proceeding as in (a), we obtain

$$\begin{bmatrix} -2 & 28 \\ 1 & -11 \end{bmatrix} = - \begin{bmatrix} 2 & -3 \\ 4 & 1 \end{bmatrix} + 5 \begin{bmatrix} 0 & 5 \\ 1 & -2 \end{bmatrix}$$

and hence the matrix is a linear combination of A and B.

(d) Proceeding as in (a), we obtain the trivial combination

$$\begin{bmatrix} 0 & 0 \\ 0 & 0 \end{bmatrix} = 0 \begin{bmatrix} 2 & -3 \\ 4 & 1 \end{bmatrix} + 0 \begin{bmatrix} 0 & 5 \\ 1 & -2 \end{bmatrix}.$$

37. (a) From the vector equation

$$c_1(2 - x) + c_2(2x - x^2) + c_3(6 - 5x + x^2) = 0 + 0x + 0x^2$$

we obtain the homogenous system

$$\begin{aligned} 2c_1 \quad\quad + 6c_3 &= 0 \\ -c_1 + 2c_2 - 5c_3 &= 0 \\ -c_2 + c_3 &= 0. \end{aligned}$$

This system has infinitely many solutions. For instance, $c_1 = -3, c_2 = 1, c_3 = 1$.
Thus, S is linearly dependent.

(b) From the vector equation $c_1(x^2 - 1) + c_2(2x + 5) = 0 + 0x + 0x^2$
we obtain the homogenous system

$$\begin{aligned} -c_1 + 5c_2 &= 0 \\ 2c_2 &= 0 \\ c_1 \quad\quad &= 0. \end{aligned}$$

This system has only the trivial solution. Thus, S is linearly independent.

(c) From the vector equation

$$c_1(x^2 + 3x + 1) + c_2(2x^2 + x - 1) + c_3(4x) = 0 + 0x + 0x^2$$

we obtain the homogenous system

$$\begin{aligned} c_1 - c_2 \quad\quad &= 0 \\ 3c_1 + c_2 + 4c_3 &= 0 \\ c_1 + 2c_2 \quad\quad &= 0. \end{aligned}$$

This system has only the trivial solution. Thus, S is linearly independent.

39. (a) Because $(-2, 4) = -2(1, -2)$, S is linearly dependent.

(b) Because $2(1, -6, 2) = (2, -12, 4)$, S is linearly dependent.

(c) Because $(0, 0) = 0(1, 0)$, S is linearly dependent.

41. Since the matrix $\begin{pmatrix} 1 & 2 & -1 \\ 0 & 1 & 1 \\ 2 & 5 & -1 \end{pmatrix}$ row reduces to $\begin{pmatrix} 1 & 0 & -3 \\ 0 & 1 & 1 \\ 0 & 0 & 0 \end{pmatrix}$

and $\begin{pmatrix} -2 & -6 & 0 \\ 1 & 1 & -2 \end{pmatrix}$ row reduces to $\begin{pmatrix} 1 & 0 & -3 \\ 0 & 1 & 1 \end{pmatrix}$,

you see that S_1 and S_2 span the same subspace.

You could also verify this by showing that each vector in S_1 is in the span of S_2, and conversely, each vector in S_2 is in the span of S_1. For example,

$$(1, 2, -1) = -\tfrac{1}{4}(-2, -6, 0) + \tfrac{1}{2}(1, 1, -2).$$

43. Since $3 = 3\sin^2 x + 3\cos^2 x = 3(\sin^2 x + \cos^2 x)$, the set is linearly dependent.

45. The matrix $\begin{bmatrix} 1 & 1 & 1 \\ 1 & 1 & 0 \\ 1 & 0 & 0 \end{bmatrix}$ row reduces to $\begin{bmatrix} 1 & 0 & 0 \\ 0 & 1 & 0 \\ 0 & 0 & 1 \end{bmatrix}$,

which shows that the equation

$$c_1(1, 1, 1) + c_2(1, 1, 0) + c_3(1, 0, 0) = (0, 0, 0)$$

only has the trivial solution. Thus, the three vectors are linearly independent. Furthermore, the vectors span R^3 because the coefficient matrix of the linear system

$$\begin{bmatrix} 1 & 1 & 1 \\ 1 & 1 & 0 \\ 1 & 0 & 0 \end{bmatrix} \begin{bmatrix} c_1 \\ c_2 \\ c_3 \end{bmatrix} = \begin{bmatrix} u_1 \\ u_2 \\ u_3 \end{bmatrix}$$

is nonsingular.

47. Let S be a set of linearly independent vectors and $T \subset S$. If $T = \{\mathbf{v}_1, \cdots, \mathbf{v}_k\}$ and T were linearly dependent, then there would exist constants $c_1, \cdots, c_k$, not all zero, satisfying $c_1\mathbf{v}_1 + \cdots + c_k\mathbf{v}_k = \mathbf{0}$. But, $\mathbf{v}_i \in S$, and S is linearly independent, which is impossible. Thus, T is linearly independent.

49. If a set of vectors $\{\mathbf{v}_1, \mathbf{v}_2, \cdots\}$ contains the zero vector, then $\mathbf{0} = 0\mathbf{v}_1 + \ldots + 0\mathbf{v}_k + 1 \cdot \mathbf{0}$ which implies that the set is linearly dependent.

51. If the set $\{\mathbf{v}_1, \cdots, \mathbf{v}_{k-1}\}$ spanned $\mathbf{v}$, then

$$\mathbf{v}_k = c_1\mathbf{v}_1 + \cdots + c_{k-1}\mathbf{v}_{k-1}$$

for some scalars $c_1, \cdots, c_{k-1}$. Thus,

$$c\mathbf{v}_1 + \cdots + c_{k-1}\mathbf{v}_{k-1} - \mathbf{v}_k = \mathbf{0}$$

which is impossible since $\{\mathbf{v}_1, \cdots, \mathbf{v}_k\}$ were linearly independent.

53. Theorem 4.8 requires that only one of the vectors be a linear combination of the others. In this case, $(-1, 0, 2) = 0(1, 2, 3) - (1, 0, -2)$, and hence, there is no contradiction.

55. Consider the vector equation

$$c_1(\mathbf{u} + \mathbf{v}) + c_2(\mathbf{u} - \mathbf{v}) = \mathbf{0}.$$

Regrouping, we have

$$(c_1 + c_2)\mathbf{u} + (c_1 - c_2)\mathbf{v} = \mathbf{0}.$$

Since $\mathbf{u}$ and $\mathbf{v}$ are linearly independent, $c_1 + c_2 = c_1 - c_2 = 0$. Hence, $c_1 = c_2 = 0$, and the vectors $\mathbf{u} + \mathbf{v}$ and $\mathbf{u} - \mathbf{v}$ are linearly independent.

57. On $[0, 1]$, $\quad f_2(x) = |x| = x = \frac{1}{3}(3x)$.

$$= \frac{1}{3}f_1(x)$$

$$\Rightarrow \{f_1, f_2\} \text{ dependent}$$

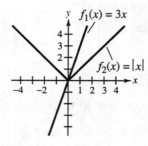

On $[-1, 1]$, f_1 and f_2 are not multiples of each other. For if they were, $cf_1(x) = f_2(x)$, then $c(3x) = |x|$. But if $x = 1$, $c = \frac{1}{3}$, whereas if $x = -1$, $c = -\frac{1}{3}$.

59. On the one hand, if **u** and **v** are linearly dependent, then there exist constants c_1 and c_2, not both zero, such that $c_1\mathbf{u} + c_2\mathbf{v} = \mathbf{0}$. Without loss of generality, we can assume $c_1 \neq 0$, and obtain $\mathbf{u} = -\dfrac{c_2}{c_1}\,\mathbf{v}$.

On the other hand, if one vector is a scalar multiple of another, $\mathbf{u} = c\mathbf{v}$, then $\mathbf{u} - c\mathbf{v} = \mathbf{0}$, which implies that **u** and **v** are linearly dependent.

Section 4.5   Basis and Dimension

1. There are six vectors in the standard basis for R^6.

$$\{(1, 0, 0, 0, 0, 0), (0, 1, 0, 0, 0, 0), (0, 0, 1, 0, 0, 0),$$

$$(0, 0, 0, 1, 0, 0), (0, 0, 0, 0, 1, 0), (0, 0, 0, 0, 0, 1)\}$$

3. There are eight vectors in the standard basis.

$$\left\{ \begin{bmatrix} 1 & 0 & 0 & 0 \\ 0 & 0 & 0 & 0 \end{bmatrix}, \begin{bmatrix} 0 & 1 & 0 & 0 \\ 0 & 0 & 0 & 0 \end{bmatrix}, \begin{bmatrix} 0 & 0 & 1 & 0 \\ 0 & 0 & 0 & 0 \end{bmatrix}, \begin{bmatrix} 0 & 0 & 0 & 1 \\ 0 & 0 & 0 & 0 \end{bmatrix}, \right.$$

$$\left. \begin{bmatrix} 0 & 0 & 0 & 0 \\ 1 & 0 & 0 & 0 \end{bmatrix}, \begin{bmatrix} 0 & 0 & 0 & 0 \\ 0 & 1 & 0 & 0 \end{bmatrix}, \begin{bmatrix} 0 & 0 & 0 & 0 \\ 0 & 0 & 1 & 0 \end{bmatrix}, \begin{bmatrix} 0 & 0 & 0 & 0 \\ 0 & 0 & 0 & 1 \end{bmatrix} \right\}$$

5. A basis for R^2 can only have two vectors. Because S has three vectors, it is not a basis for R^2.

7. S is linearly dependent and does not span R^2 (For instance, $(1, 1) \notin$ span (S)).

9. A basis for R^3 contains three linearly independent vectors. Because

$$-2(1, 3, 0) + (4, 1, 2) + (-2, 5, -2) = (0, 0, 0)$$

S is linearly dependent and is, therefore, not a basis for R^3.

11. S is linearly dependent and does not span R^3. For instance, $(0, 0, 1) \notin$ span (S).

13. A basis for P_2 can have only three vectors. Because S has four vectors, it is not a basis for P_2.

15. A basis for $M_{2,2}$ must have four vectors. Because S has only two vectors, it is not a basis for $M_{2,2}$.

17. Because $\{v_1, v_2\}$ consists of exactly two linearly independent vectors, it is a basis for R^2.

19. Because v_1 and v_2 are multiples of each other. They do not form a basis for R^2.

21. Since the vectors in S are not scalar multiples of one another, they are linearly independent. Because S consists of exactly two linearly independent vectors, it is a basis for R^2.

23. To determine if the vectors of S are linearly independent, we find the solution to

$$c_1(0, 3, -2) + c_2(4, 0, 3) + c_3(-8, 15, -16) = (0, 0, 0)$$

which corresponds to the solution of

$$\begin{aligned} 4c_2 - 8c_3 &= 0 \\ 3c_1 \phantom{{}+{}} + 15c_3 &= 0 \\ -2c_1 + 3c_2 - 16c_3 &= 0. \end{aligned}$$

Since this system has nontrivial solutions (for instance, $c_1 = -5$, $c_2 = 2$ and $c_3 = 1$), the vectors are linearly dependent, and S is not a basis for R^3.

25. To determine if the vectors of S are linearly independent, we find the solution to

$$c_1(-1, 2, 0, 0) + c_2(2, 0, -1, 0) + c_3(3, 0, 0, 4) + c_4(0, 0, 5, 0) = (0, 0, 0, 0)$$

which corresponds to the solution of

$$
\begin{aligned}
-c_1 + 2c_2 + 3c_3 &= 0 \\
2c_1 &= 0 \\
-c_2 + 5c_4 &= 0 \\
4c_3 &= 0.
\end{aligned}
$$

This system has only the trivial solution. Thus, S consists of exactly four linearly independent vectors, and is therefore a basis for R^4.

27. We form the equation

$$c_1 \begin{bmatrix} 2 & 0 \\ 0 & 3 \end{bmatrix} + c_2 \begin{bmatrix} 1 & 4 \\ 0 & 1 \end{bmatrix} + c_3 \begin{bmatrix} 0 & 1 \\ 3 & 2 \end{bmatrix} + c_4 \begin{bmatrix} 0 & 1 \\ 2 & 0 \end{bmatrix} = \begin{bmatrix} 0 & 0 \\ 0 & 0 \end{bmatrix}$$

which yields the homogenous system

$$
\begin{aligned}
2c_1 + c_2 &= 0 \\
4c_2 + c_3 + c_4 &= 0 \\
3c_3 + 2c_4 &= 0 \\
3c_1 + c_2 + 2c_3 &= 0.
\end{aligned}
$$

This system has only the trivial solution. Thus, S consists of exactly four linearly independent vectors, and is therefore a basis for $M_{2,2}$.

29. We form the equation

$$c_1(t^3 - 2t^2 + 1) + c_2(t^2 - 4) + c_3(t^3 + 2t) + c_4(5t) = 0 + 0t + 0t^2 + 0t^3$$

which yields the homogenous system

$$
\begin{aligned}
c_1 + c_3 &= 0 \\
-2c_1 + c_2 &= 0 \\
2c_3 + 5c_4 &= 0 \\
c_1 - 4c_2 &= 0.
\end{aligned}
$$

This system has only the trivial solution. Thus, S consists of exactly four linearly independent vectors, and is, therefore, a basis for P_3.

31. We form the equation

$$c_1(4, 3, 2) + c_2(0, 3, 2) + c_3(0, 0, 2) = (0, 0, 0)$$

which yields the homogenous system

$$
\begin{aligned}
4c_1 &= 0 \\
3c_1 + 3c_2 &= 0 \\
2c_1 + 2c_2 + 2c_3 &= 0.
\end{aligned}
$$

This system has only the trivial solution, so S is a basis for R^3. Solving the system

$$
\begin{aligned}
4c_1 &= 8 \\
3c_1 + 3c_2 &= 3 \\
2c_1 + 2c_2 + 2c_3 &= 8
\end{aligned}
$$

yields $c_1 = 2$, $c_2 = -1$, and $c_3 = 3$. Thus,

$$\mathbf{u} = 2(4, 3, 2) - (0, 3, 2) + 3(0, 0, 2) = (8, 3, 8).$$

33. We form the equation

$$c_1\left(\tfrac{2}{3}, \tfrac{5}{2}, 1\right) + c_2\left(1, \tfrac{3}{2}, 0\right) + c_3(2, 12, 6) = (0, 0, 0)$$

which yields the homogenous system

$$
\begin{aligned}
\tfrac{2}{3}c_1 + c_2 + 2c_3 &= 0 \\
\tfrac{5}{2}c_1 + \tfrac{3}{2}c_2 + 12c_3 &= 0 \\
c_1 \qquad\quad + 6c_3 &= 0.
\end{aligned}
$$

Since this system has nontrivial solutions (for instance, $c_1 = 6$, $c_2 = -2$ and $c_3 = -1$), the vectors are linearly dependent. Hence, S is not a basis for R^3.

35. Because a basis for R^6 has six linearly independent vectors, the dimension of R^6 is 6.

37. Because a basis for P_7 has eight linearly independent vectors, the dimension of P_7 is 8.

39. One basis for $D_{3,3}$ is

$$
\left\{
\begin{bmatrix} 1 & 0 & 0 \\ 0 & 0 & 0 \\ 0 & 0 & 0 \end{bmatrix},
\begin{bmatrix} 0 & 0 & 0 \\ 0 & 1 & 0 \\ 0 & 0 & 0 \end{bmatrix},
\begin{bmatrix} 0 & 0 & 0 \\ 0 & 0 & 0 \\ 0 & 0 & 1 \end{bmatrix}
\right\}.
$$

Since a basis for $D_{3,3}$ has 3 vectors,

$$\dim(D_{3,3}) = 3.$$

41. The following subsets of two vectors form a basis for R^2.

$$\{(1, 0), (0, 1)\}, \{(1, 0), (1, 1)\}, \{(0, 1), (1, 1)\}.$$

43. We can add any vector that is not a multiple of $(1, 1)$. For instance, the set $\{(1, 1), (1, 0)\}$ is a basis for R^2.

45. (a) W is a line through the origin.

(b) A basis for W is $\{(2, 1)\}$.

(c) The dimension of W is 1.

47. (a) W is a line through the origin.

(b) A basis for W is $\{(2, 1, -1)\}$.

(c) The dimension of W is 1.

49. (a) A basis for W is $\{(2, 1, 0, 1), (-1, 0, 1, 0)\}$.

(c) The dimension of W is 2.

51. (a) A basis for W is $\{(0, 6, 1, -1)\}$.

(c) The dimension of W is 1.

53. The statement is false. Any set of $n - 1$ vectors will not span a vector space of dimension n.

55. The statement is true. Theorem 4.10 states that if V has a basis consisting of n vectors, then every set containing more than n vectors is linearly dependent.

57. Since the set $S_1 = \{c\mathbf{v}_1, \cdots, c\mathbf{v}_n\}$ has n vectors, we only need to show that they are linearly independent. Consider the equation

$$a_1(c\mathbf{v}_1) + a_2(c\mathbf{v}_2) + \cdots + a_n(c\mathbf{v}_n) = \mathbf{0}$$

$$c(a_1\mathbf{v}_1 + a_2\mathbf{v}_2 + \cdots + a_n\mathbf{v}_n) = \mathbf{0}$$

$$a_1\mathbf{v}_1 + a_2\mathbf{v}_2 + \cdots + a_n\mathbf{v}_n = \mathbf{0}$$

Since $\{\mathbf{v}_1, \cdots, \mathbf{v}_n\}$ are linearly independent, the coefficients $a_1, \cdots, a_n$ must all be zero. Hence, S_1 is linearly independent.

59. Let $W \subset V$ and $\dim V = n$. Let $\mathbf{w}_1, \cdots, \mathbf{w}_k$ be a basis for W. Since $W \subset V$, the vectors $\mathbf{w}_1, \cdots, \mathbf{w}_k$ are linearly independent in V. If span $(\mathbf{w}_1, \cdots, \mathbf{w}_k) = V$, then $\dim W = \dim V$. If not, let $\mathbf{v} \in V$, $\mathbf{v} \notin W$. Then $\dim W < \dim V$.

61. (a)

S_1–basis:	$\{(1, 0, 0), (1, 1, 0)\}$	$\dim S_1 = 2$
S_2–basis:	$\{(0, 0, 1), (0, 1, 0)\}$	$\dim S_2 = 2$
$S_1 \cap S_2$–basis:	$\{(0, 1, 0)\}$	$\dim(S_1 \cap S_2) = 1$
$S_1 + S_2$–basis:	$\{(1, 0, 0), (0, 1, 0), (0, 0, 1)\}$	$\dim(S_1 + S_2) = 3$

(Answers are not unique.)

(b) No, it is not possible.

63. If S spans V, we are done. If not, let $\mathbf{v}_1 \notin \text{Span}\,(S)$, and consider the linearly independent set

$S_1 = S \cup \{\mathbf{v}_1\}$. If S_1 spans V we are done. If not, let $\mathbf{v}_2 \notin \text{Span}\,(S_1)$ and continue as before. Since the vector space is finite-dimensional, this process will ultimately produce a basis of V containing S.

Section 4.6   Rank of a Matrix and Systems of Linear Equations

1. (a) Because this matrix row reduces to

$$\begin{bmatrix} 1 & 0 \\ 0 & 1 \end{bmatrix}$$

the rank of the matrix is 2.

(b) A basis for the row space is $\{(1, 0), (0, 1)\}$.

(c) Row-reducing the transpose of the original matrix produces the identity matrix again, and hence, a basis for the column space is $\{(1, 0), (0, 1)\}$.

3. (a) Because this matrix row reduces to

$$\begin{bmatrix} 1 & 2 \\ 0 & 1 \end{bmatrix} \text{ or } \begin{bmatrix} 1 & 0 \\ 0 & 1 \end{bmatrix}$$

the rank of the matrix is 2.

(b) A basis for the row space of the matrix is $\{(1, 2), (0, 1)\}$ (or $\{(1, 0), (0, 1)\}$).

(c) Row-reducing the transpose of the original matrix produces

$$\begin{bmatrix} 1 & \frac{1}{2} \\ 0 & 1 \end{bmatrix} \text{ or } \begin{bmatrix} 1 & 0 \\ 0 & 1 \end{bmatrix}.$$

Thus, a basis for the column space of the matrix is $\{(1, \frac{1}{2}), (0, 1)\}$ (or $\{(1, 0), (0, 1)\}$).

5. (a) Because this matrix row reduces to

$$\begin{bmatrix} 1 & 0 & \frac{1}{4} \\ 0 & 1 & \frac{3}{2} \\ 0 & 0 & 0 \end{bmatrix}$$

the rank of the matrix is 2.

(b) A basis for the row space is $\{(1, 0, \frac{1}{4}), (0, 1, \frac{3}{2})\}$.

(c) Row-reducing the transpose of the original matrix produces

$$\begin{bmatrix} 1 & 0 & -\frac{2}{5} \\ 0 & 1 & \frac{3}{5} \\ 0 & 0 & 0 \end{bmatrix}.$$

Hence, a basis for the column space is $\{(1, 0, -\frac{2}{5}), (0, 1, \frac{3}{5})\}$.

Equivalently, a basis for the column space consists of columns 1 and 2 of the original matrix: $\{(4, 6, 2), (20, -5, -11)\}$.

7. (a) Because this matrix row reduces to

$$\begin{bmatrix} 1 & 2 & -2 & 0 \\ 0 & 0 & 0 & 1 \\ 0 & 0 & 0 & 0 \end{bmatrix}$$

the rank of the matrix is 2.

(b) A basis for the row space of the matrix is $\{(1, 2, -2, 0), (0, 0, 0, 1)\}$.

(c) Row-reducing the transpose of the original matrix produces

$$\begin{bmatrix} 1 & 0 & \frac{19}{7} \\ 0 & 1 & \frac{8}{7} \\ 0 & 0 & 0 \\ 0 & 0 & 0 \end{bmatrix}.$$

Thus, a basis for the column space of the matrix is $\{(1, 0, \frac{19}{7}), (0, 1, \frac{8}{7})\}$.
Equivalently, a basis for the column space consists of columns 1 and 2
of the original matrix: $\{(-2, 3, -2), (5, -4, 9)\}$.

9. We begin by forming the matrix whose rows are vectors in S.

$$\begin{bmatrix} 2 & 9 & -2 & 53 \\ -3 & 2 & 3 & -2 \\ 8 & -3 & -8 & 17 \\ 0 & -3 & 0 & 15 \end{bmatrix}$$

This matrix reduces to

$$\begin{bmatrix} 1 & 0 & -1 & 0 \\ 0 & 1 & 0 & 0 \\ 0 & 0 & 0 & 1 \\ 0 & 0 & 0 & 0 \end{bmatrix}.$$

Thus, a basis for span (S) is $\{(1, 0, -1, 0), (0, 1, 0, 0), (0, 0, 0, 1)\}$.

11. We form the matrix whose rows are the vectors in S, and then row-reduce.

$$\begin{bmatrix} -3 & 2 & 5 & 28 \\ -6 & 1 & -8 & -1 \\ 14 & -10 & 12 & -10 \\ 0 & 5 & 12 & 50 \end{bmatrix} \Rightarrow \begin{bmatrix} 1 & 0 & 0 & 0 \\ 0 & 1 & 0 & 0 \\ 0 & 0 & 1 & 0 \\ 0 & 0 & 0 & 1 \end{bmatrix}$$

Thus, a basis for span (S) is

$$\{(1, 0, 0, 0), (0, 1, 0, 0), (0, 0, 1, 0), (0, 0, 0, 1)\}.$$

13. Solving the system $A\mathbf{x} = 0$ yields only the trivial solution $\mathbf{x} = (0, 0)$. Thus, the dimension of the
solution space is 0. The solution space consists of the zero vector itself.

15. Solving the system $A\mathbf{x} = 0$ yields solutions of the form $(-2s - 3t, s, t)$, where s and t are any
real numbers. The dimension of the solution space is 2, and a basis is $\{(-2, 1, 0), (-3, 0, 1)\}$.

17. Solving the system $A\mathbf{x} = 0$ yields solutions of the form $(-t, 2t, t)$, where t is any real number.
The dimension of the solution space is 1, and a basis for the solution space is $\{(-1, 2, 1)\}$.

19. This system yields solutions of the form $(-t, -3t, 2t)$, where t is any real number. The dimension of the solution space is 1, and a basis is $\{(-1, -3, 2)\}$.

21. This system yields solutions of the form $(2s - 3t, s, t)$, where s and t are any real numbers. The dimension of the solution space is 2, and a basis for the solution space is $\{(2, 1, 0), (-3, 0, 1)\}$.

23. This system yields solutions of the form $\left(\frac{4}{3}t, -\frac{3}{2}t, -t, t\right)$, where t is any real number. The dimension of the solution space is 1, and a basis is $\{(\frac{4}{3}, -\frac{3}{2}, -1, 1)\}$.

25. (a) The system $A\mathbf{x} = \mathbf{b}$ is consistent since its augmented matrix reduces to

$$\begin{bmatrix} 1 & 0 & -2 & 3 \\ 0 & 1 & 4 & 5 \\ 0 & 0 & 0 & 0 \\ 0 & 0 & 0 & 0 \end{bmatrix}.$$

(b) The solutions of $A\mathbf{x} = \mathbf{b}$ are of the form $(3 + 2t, 5 - 4t, t)$ where t is any real number. That is,

$$\mathbf{x} = t \begin{bmatrix} 2 \\ -4 \\ 1 \end{bmatrix} + \begin{bmatrix} 3 \\ 5 \\ 0 \end{bmatrix},$$

where

$$\mathbf{x}_h = t \begin{bmatrix} 2 \\ -4 \\ 1 \end{bmatrix} \quad \text{and} \quad \mathbf{x}_p = \begin{bmatrix} 3 \\ 5 \\ 0 \end{bmatrix}.$$

27. (a) The system $A\mathbf{x} = \mathbf{b}$ is inconsistent since its augmented matrix reduces to

$$\begin{bmatrix} 1 & 0 & 4 & 2 & 0 \\ 0 & 1 & -2 & 4 & 0 \\ 0 & 0 & 0 & 0 & 1 \end{bmatrix}.$$

29. (a) The system $A\mathbf{x} = \mathbf{b}$ is consistent since its augmented matrix reduces to

$$\begin{bmatrix} 1 & 2 & 0 & 0 & -5 & 1 \\ 0 & 0 & 1 & 0 & 6 & 2 \\ 0 & 0 & 0 & 1 & 4 & -3 \\ 0 & 0 & 0 & 0 & 0 & 0 \end{bmatrix}.$$

(b) The solutions of the system are of the form

$$(1 - 2s + 5t, s, 2 - 6t, -3 - 4t, t),$$

where s and t are any real numbers. That is,

$$\mathbf{x} = s\begin{bmatrix} -2 \\ 1 \\ 0 \\ 0 \\ 0 \end{bmatrix} + t\begin{bmatrix} 5 \\ 0 \\ -6 \\ -4 \\ 1 \end{bmatrix} + \begin{bmatrix} 1 \\ 0 \\ 2 \\ -3 \\ 0 \end{bmatrix},$$

where

$$\mathbf{x}_h = s\begin{bmatrix} -2 \\ 1 \\ 0 \\ 0 \\ 0 \end{bmatrix} + t\begin{bmatrix} 5 \\ 0 \\ -6 \\ -4 \\ 1 \end{bmatrix} \quad \text{and} \quad \mathbf{x}_p = \begin{bmatrix} 1 \\ 0 \\ 2 \\ -3 \\ 0 \end{bmatrix}.$$

31. The vector $\mathbf{b}$ is in the column space of A if the equation $A\mathbf{x} = \mathbf{b}$ is consistent. Since $A\mathbf{x} = \mathbf{b}$ has the solution

$$\mathbf{x} = \begin{bmatrix} 1 \\ 2 \end{bmatrix},$$

$\mathbf{b}$ is in the column space of A. Furthermore,

$$\mathbf{b} = 1\begin{bmatrix} -1 \\ 4 \end{bmatrix} + 2\begin{bmatrix} 2 \\ 0 \end{bmatrix} = \begin{bmatrix} 3 \\ 4 \end{bmatrix}.$$

33. The vector $\mathbf{b}$ is in the column space of A if the equation $A\mathbf{x} = \mathbf{b}$ is consistent. Since $A\mathbf{x} = \mathbf{b}$ has the solution

$$\mathbf{x} = \begin{bmatrix} -\frac{5}{4} \\ \frac{3}{4} \\ -\frac{1}{2} \end{bmatrix},$$

$\mathbf{b}$ is in the column space of A. Furthermore,

$$\mathbf{b} = -\frac{5}{4}\begin{bmatrix} 1 \\ -1 \\ 2 \end{bmatrix} + \frac{3}{4}\begin{bmatrix} 3 \\ 1 \\ 0 \end{bmatrix} - \frac{1}{2}\begin{bmatrix} 0 \\ 0 \\ 1 \end{bmatrix} = \begin{bmatrix} 1 \\ 2 \\ -3 \end{bmatrix}.$$

35. The rank of the matrix is at most 3. Thus, the dimension of the row space is at most 3, and any four vectors in the row space must form a linearly dependent set.

37. Assume that A is an $m \times n$ matrix where $n > m$. Then the set of n column vectors of A are vectors in R^m and must be linearly dependent. Similarly, if $m > n$, then the set of m row vectors of A are vectors in R^n, and must be linearly dependent.

39. (a) Let

$$A = \begin{bmatrix} 1 & 0 \\ 0 & 1 \end{bmatrix} \quad \text{and} \quad B = \begin{bmatrix} 0 & 1 \\ 1 & 0 \end{bmatrix}. \quad \text{Then } A + B = \begin{bmatrix} 1 & 1 \\ 1 & 1 \end{bmatrix}.$$

Note that rank(A) = rank(B) = 2, and rank ($A + B$) = 1.

(b) Let

$$A = \begin{bmatrix} 1 & 0 \\ 0 & 0 \end{bmatrix} \quad \text{and} \quad B = \begin{bmatrix} 0 & 1 \\ 0 & 0 \end{bmatrix}. \quad \text{Then } A + B = \begin{bmatrix} 1 & 1 \\ 0 & 0 \end{bmatrix}.$$

Note that rank(A) = rank(B) = 1, and rank ($A + B$) = 1.

(c) Let

$$A = \begin{bmatrix} 1 & 0 \\ 0 & 0 \end{bmatrix} \quad \text{and} \quad B = \begin{bmatrix} 0 & 0 \\ 0 & 1 \end{bmatrix}. \quad \text{Then } A + B = \begin{bmatrix} 1 & 0 \\ 0 & 1 \end{bmatrix}.$$

Note that rank(A) = rank(B) = 1, and rank ($A + B$) = 2.

41. (a) Since the row (or column) space has dimension no larger than the smallest of m and n, $r \le m$ (since $m < n$).

(b) There are r vectors in a basis for the row space of A.

(c) There are r vectors in a basis for the column space of A.

(d) The row space of A is a subspace of R^n.

(e) The column space of A is a subspace of R^m.

43. Consider the first row of the product AB.

$$\begin{bmatrix} a_{11} & \cdots & a_{1n} \\ \vdots & & \vdots \\ a_{m1} & \cdots & a_{mn} \end{bmatrix} \begin{bmatrix} b_{11} & \cdots & b_{1k} \\ \vdots & & \vdots \\ b_{n1} & \cdots & b_{nk} \end{bmatrix} =$$

$$\begin{matrix} \mathbf{A} & & \mathbf{B} \end{matrix}$$

$$\begin{bmatrix} (a_{11}b_{11} + \cdots + a_{1n}b_{n1}) \cdots (a_{11}b_{1k} + \cdots + a_{1n}b_{nk}) \\ \vdots \\ (a_{m1}b_{11} + \cdots + a_{mn}b_{n1}) \cdots (a_{m1}b_{1k} + \cdots + a_{mn}b_{nk}) \end{bmatrix}.$$

$$\mathbf{AB}$$

First row of $AB = [(a_{11}b_{11} + \cdots + a_{1n}b_{n1}), \cdots, (a_{11}b_{1k} + \cdots + a_{1n}b_{nk})]$.

We can express this first row as

$$a_{11}(b_{11}, b_{12}, \cdots b_{1k}) + a_{12}(b_{21}, \cdots, b_{2k}) + \cdots + a_{1n}(b_{n1}, b_{n2}, \cdots, b_{nk}),$$

which means that the first row of AB is in the row space of B. The same argument applies to the other rows of A. A similar argument can be used to show that the column vectors of AB are in the column space of A. The first column of AB is

$$\begin{bmatrix} a_{11}b_{11} + \cdots + a_{1n}b_{n1} \\ \vdots \\ a_{m1}b_{11} + \cdots + a_{mn}b_{n1} \end{bmatrix} = b_{11} \begin{bmatrix} a_{11} \\ \vdots \\ a_{m1} \end{bmatrix} + \cdots + b_{n1} \begin{bmatrix} a_{1n} \\ \vdots \\ a_{mn} \end{bmatrix}.$$

45. Let $A\mathbf{x} = \mathbf{b}$ be a system of linear equations in n variables.

(1) If rank (A) = rank $([A \vdots \mathbf{b}]) = n$, then $\mathbf{b}$ is in the column space of A, and hence $A\mathbf{x} = \mathbf{b}$ has a unique solution.

(2) If rank (A) = rank $([A \vdots \mathbf{b}]) < n$, then $\mathbf{b}$ is in the column space of A and rank $(A) < n$, which implies that $A\mathbf{x} = \mathbf{b}$ has an infinite number of solutions.

(3) If rank (A) = rank $([A \vdots \mathbf{b}])$, then $\mathbf{b}$ is *not* in the column space of A, and the system is inconsistent.

47. Let A be an $m \times n$ matrix.

(a) If $A\mathbf{x} = \mathbf{b}$ is consistent for all vectors $\mathbf{b}$, then the augmented matrix $[A \vdots \mathbf{b}]$ cannot row-reduce to $[U \vdots \mathbf{b}']$ where the last row of U consists of all zeros. Thus, the rank of A is m.

Conversely, if the rank of A is m, then rank (A) = rank $([A \vdots \mathbf{b}])$ for all vectors $\mathbf{b}$, which implies that $A\mathbf{x} = \mathbf{b}$ is consistent.

(b) $A\mathbf{x}$ is a linear combination $x_1\mathbf{a}_1 + \cdots + x_n\mathbf{a}_n$ of the columns of A. Thus,

$$A\mathbf{x} = x_1\mathbf{a}_1 + \cdots + x_n\mathbf{a}_n = \mathbf{0}$$

has only the trivial solution $x_1 = \cdots = x_n$ if and only if $\mathbf{a}_1, \cdots, \mathbf{a}_n$ are linearly independent.

49. Let $\mathbf{x} \in N(A) \implies A\mathbf{x} = \mathbf{0} \implies A^T A\mathbf{x} = \mathbf{0} \implies \mathbf{x} \in N(A^T A)$.

Section 4.7   Coordinates and Change of Basis

1. Since $[\mathbf{x}]_B = \begin{bmatrix} 4 \\ 1 \end{bmatrix}$, we can write

$$\mathbf{x} = 4(2, -1) + 1(0, 1) = (8, -3).$$

Moreover, since $(8, -3) = 8(1, 0) - 3(0, 1)$, it follows that the coordinates of $\mathbf{x}$ relative to S are

$$[\mathbf{x}]_S = \begin{bmatrix} 8 \\ -3 \end{bmatrix}.$$

3. Since $[\mathbf{x}]_B = \begin{bmatrix} 2 \\ 3 \\ 1 \end{bmatrix}$, we can write

$$\mathbf{x} = 2(1, 0, 1) + 3(1, 1, 0) + 1(0, 1, 1) = (5, 4, 3).$$

Moreover, since $(5, 4, 3) = 5(1, 0, 0) + 4(0, 1, 0) + 3(0, 0, 1)$, it follows that the coordinates of $\mathbf{x}$ relative to S are

$$[\mathbf{x}]_S = \begin{bmatrix} 5 \\ 4 \\ 3 \end{bmatrix}.$$

5. Since $[\mathbf{x}]_B = \begin{bmatrix} 1 \\ -2 \\ 3 \\ -1 \end{bmatrix}$, we can write

$$\mathbf{x} = 1(0, 0, 0, 1) - 2(0, 0, 1, 1) + 3(0, 1, 1, 1) - 1(1, 1, 1, 1) = (-1, 2, 0, 1),$$

which implies that the coordinates of $\mathbf{x}$ relative to the standard basis S are

$$[\mathbf{x}]_S = \begin{bmatrix} -1 \\ 2 \\ 0 \\ 1 \end{bmatrix}.$$

7. We begin by writing $\mathbf{x}$ as a linear combination of the vectors in B.

$$\mathbf{x} = (12, 6) = c_1(4, 0) + c_2(0, 3)$$

Equating corresponding components yields the following system of linear equations.

$$\begin{aligned} 4c_1 \qquad &= 12 \\ 3c_2 &= 6 \end{aligned}$$

The solution of this system is $c_1 = 3$ and $c_2 = 2$. Thus, $\mathbf{x} = 3(4, 0) + 2(0, 3)$, and the coordinate vector of $\mathbf{x}$ relative to B is

$$[\mathbf{x}]_B = \begin{bmatrix} 3 \\ 2 \end{bmatrix}.$$

9. We begin by writing $\mathbf{x}$ as a linear combination of the vectors in B.

$$\mathbf{x} = (3, 19, 2) = c_1(8, 11, 0) + c_2(7, 0, 10) + c_3(1, 4, 6)$$

Equating corresponding components yields the following system of linear equations.

$$\begin{aligned} 8c_1 + 7c_2 + c_3 &= 3 \\ 11c_1 \qquad\quad + 4c_3 &= 19 \\ 10c_2 + 6c_3 &= 2 \end{aligned}$$

The solution of this system is $c_1 = 1$, $c_2 = -1$, and $c_3 = 2$. Thus, $\mathbf{x} = 1(8, 11, 0) + (-1)(7, 0, 10) + 2(1, 4, 6)$, and the coordinate vector of $\mathbf{x}$ relative to B is

$$[\mathbf{x}]_B = \begin{bmatrix} 1 \\ -1 \\ 2 \end{bmatrix}.$$

11. We begin by writing $\mathbf{x}$ as a linear combination of the vectors in B.

$$\mathbf{x} = (11, 18, -7) = c_1(4, 3, 3) + c_2(-11, 0, 11) + c_3(0, 9, 2)$$

Equating corresponding components yields the following system of linear equations.

$$\begin{aligned} 4c_1 - 11c_2 \qquad\quad &= 11 \\ 3c_1 \qquad\quad + 9c_3 &= 18 \\ 3c_1 + 11c_2 + 2c_3 &= -7 \end{aligned}$$

The solution to this system is $c_1 = 0$, $c_2 = -1$, and $c_3 = 2$. Thus, $\mathbf{x} = (11, 18, -7) = 0(4, 3, 3) - 1(-11, 0, 11) + 2(0, 9, 2)$ and

$$[\mathbf{x}]_B = \begin{bmatrix} 0 \\ -1 \\ 2 \end{bmatrix}.$$

13. We begin by forming the matrix

$$[B' \;\vdots\; B] = \begin{bmatrix} 2 & 1 & \vdots & 1 & 0 \\ 4 & 3 & \vdots & 0 & 1 \end{bmatrix}$$

and then use Gauss-Jordan elimination to produce

$$[I_2 \;\vdots\; P^{-1}] = \begin{bmatrix} 1 & 0 & \vdots & \frac{3}{2} & -\frac{1}{2} \\ 0 & 1 & \vdots & -2 & 1 \end{bmatrix}.$$

Thus, the transition matrix from B to B' is

$$P^{-1} = \begin{bmatrix} \frac{3}{2} & -\frac{1}{2} \\ -2 & 1 \end{bmatrix}.$$

15. We begin by forming the matrix

$$[B' : B] = \begin{bmatrix} 1 & 0 & : & 2 & -1 \\ 0 & 1 & : & 4 & 3 \end{bmatrix}.$$

Since this matrix is already in the form $[I_2 : P^{-1}]$, we see that the transition matrix from B to B' is

$$P^{-1} = \begin{bmatrix} 2 & -1 \\ 4 & 3 \end{bmatrix}.$$

17. We begin by forming the matrix

$$[B' : B] = \begin{bmatrix} 1 & 0 & 6 & : & 1 & 0 & 0 \\ 0 & 2 & 0 & : & 0 & 1 & 0 \\ 0 & 8 & 12 & : & 0 & 0 & 1 \end{bmatrix}$$

and then use the Gauss-Jordan elimination to produce

$$[I_3 : P^{-1}] = \begin{bmatrix} 1 & 0 & 0 & : & 1 & 2 & -\frac{1}{2} \\ 0 & 1 & 0 & : & 0 & \frac{1}{2} & 0 \\ 0 & 0 & 1 & : & 0 & -\frac{1}{3} & \frac{1}{12} \end{bmatrix}.$$

Thus, the transition matrix from B to B' is

$$P^{-1} = \begin{bmatrix} 1 & 2 & -\frac{1}{2} \\ 0 & \frac{1}{2} & 0 \\ 0 & -\frac{1}{3} & \frac{1}{12} \end{bmatrix}.$$

19. We begin by forming the matrix

$$[B' : B] = \begin{bmatrix} 1 & 0 & 0 & : & 1 & 1 & 1 \\ 0 & 1 & 0 & : & 3 & 5 & 4 \\ 0 & 0 & 1 & : & 3 & 6 & 5 \end{bmatrix}$$

Since this matrix is already in the form $[I_3 : P^{-1}]$, we see that the transition matrix from B to B' is

$$P^{-1} = \begin{bmatrix} 1 & 1 & 1 \\ 3 & 5 & 4 \\ 3 & 6 & 5 \end{bmatrix}.$$

21. We begin by forming the matrix

$$[B' \vdots B] = \begin{bmatrix} 1 & -2 & -1 & -2 & \vdots & 1 & 0 & 0 & 0 \\ 3 & -5 & -2 & -3 & \vdots & 0 & 1 & 0 & 0 \\ 2 & -5 & -2 & -5 & \vdots & 0 & 0 & 1 & 0 \\ -1 & 4 & 4 & 11 & \vdots & 0 & 0 & 0 & 1 \end{bmatrix}$$

and then use Gauss-Jordan elimination to produce

$$[I_4 \vdots P^{-1}] = \begin{bmatrix} 1 & 0 & 0 & 0 & \vdots & -24 & 7 & 1 & -2 \\ 0 & 1 & 0 & 0 & \vdots & -10 & 3 & 0 & -1 \\ 0 & 0 & 1 & 0 & \vdots & -29 & 7 & 3 & -2 \\ 0 & 0 & 0 & 1 & \vdots & 12 & -3 & -1 & 1 \end{bmatrix}.$$

Thus, the transition matrix from B to B' is

$$P^{-1} = \begin{bmatrix} -24 & 7 & 1 & -2 \\ -10 & 3 & 0 & -1 \\ -29 & 7 & 3 & -2 \\ 12 & -3 & -1 & 1 \end{bmatrix}.$$

23. (a) $[B' \vdots B] = \begin{bmatrix} -12 & -4 & \vdots & 1 & -2 \\ 0 & 4 & \vdots & 3 & -2 \end{bmatrix} \Rightarrow \begin{bmatrix} 1 & 0 & \vdots & -\frac{1}{3} & \frac{1}{3} \\ 0 & 1 & \vdots & \frac{3}{4} & -\frac{1}{2} \end{bmatrix} = [I \vdots P^{-1}]$

(b) $[B \vdots B'] = \begin{bmatrix} 1 & -2 & \vdots & -12 & -4 \\ 3 & -2 & \vdots & 0 & 4 \end{bmatrix} \Rightarrow \begin{bmatrix} 1 & 0 & \vdots & 6 & 4 \\ 0 & 1 & \vdots & 9 & 4 \end{bmatrix} = [I \vdots P]$

(c) $P^{-1}P = \begin{bmatrix} -\frac{1}{3} & \frac{1}{3} \\ \frac{3}{4} & -\frac{1}{2} \end{bmatrix} \begin{bmatrix} 6 & 4 \\ 9 & 4 \end{bmatrix} = \begin{bmatrix} 1 & 0 \\ 0 & 1 \end{bmatrix}$

(d) $[\mathbf{x}]_B = P[\mathbf{x}]_{B'} = \begin{bmatrix} 6 & 4 \\ 9 & 4 \end{bmatrix} \begin{bmatrix} -1 \\ 3 \end{bmatrix} = \begin{bmatrix} 6 \\ 3 \end{bmatrix}$

25. (a) $[B' \vdots B] = \begin{bmatrix} 2 & 1 & 0 & \vdots & 1 & 0 & 1 \\ 1 & 0 & 2 & \vdots & 0 & 1 & 1 \\ 1 & 0 & 1 & \vdots & 2 & 3 & 1 \end{bmatrix} \Rightarrow \begin{bmatrix} 1 & 0 & 0 & \vdots & 4 & 5 & 1 \\ 0 & 1 & 0 & \vdots & -7 & -10 & -1 \\ 0 & 0 & 1 & \vdots & -2 & -2 & 0 \end{bmatrix} = [I \vdots P^{-1}]$

(b) $[B \vdots B'] = \begin{bmatrix} 1 & 0 & 1 & \vdots & 2 & 1 & 0 \\ 0 & 1 & 1 & \vdots & 1 & 0 & 2 \\ 2 & 3 & 1 & \vdots & 1 & 0 & 1 \end{bmatrix} \Rightarrow \begin{bmatrix} 1 & 0 & 0 & \vdots & \frac{1}{2} & \frac{1}{2} & -\frac{5}{4} \\ 0 & 1 & 0 & \vdots & -\frac{1}{2} & -\frac{1}{2} & \frac{3}{4} \\ 0 & 0 & 1 & \vdots & \frac{3}{2} & \frac{1}{2} & \frac{5}{4} \end{bmatrix} = [I \vdots P]$

(c) $P^{-1}P = \begin{bmatrix} 4 & 5 & 1 \\ -7 & -10 & -1 \\ -2 & -2 & 0 \end{bmatrix} \begin{bmatrix} \frac{1}{2} & \frac{1}{2} & -\frac{5}{4} \\ -\frac{1}{2} & -\frac{1}{2} & \frac{3}{4} \\ \frac{3}{2} & \frac{1}{2} & \frac{5}{4} \end{bmatrix} = \begin{bmatrix} 1 & 0 & 0 \\ 0 & 1 & 0 \\ 0 & 0 & 1 \end{bmatrix}$

(d) $[\mathbf{x}]_B = P[\mathbf{x}]_{B'} = \begin{bmatrix} \frac{1}{2} & \frac{1}{2} & -\frac{5}{4} \\ -\frac{1}{2} & -\frac{1}{2} & \frac{3}{4} \\ \frac{3}{2} & \frac{1}{2} & \frac{5}{4} \end{bmatrix} \begin{bmatrix} 1 \\ 2 \\ -1 \end{bmatrix} = \begin{bmatrix} \frac{11}{4} \\ -\frac{9}{4} \\ \frac{5}{4} \end{bmatrix}$

27. The standard basis in P_2 is $S = \{1, x, x^2\}$ and since

$$\mathbf{p} = 4(1) + 11(x) + 1(x^2),$$

it follows that

$$(\mathbf{p})_s = \begin{bmatrix} 4 \\ 11 \\ 1 \end{bmatrix}.$$

29. The standard basis in $M_{3,1}$ is

$$S = \left\{ \begin{bmatrix} 1 \\ 0 \\ 0 \end{bmatrix}, \begin{bmatrix} 0 \\ 1 \\ 0 \end{bmatrix}, \begin{bmatrix} 0 \\ 0 \\ 1 \end{bmatrix} \right\}$$

and since

$$X = 0 \begin{bmatrix} 1 \\ 0 \\ 0 \end{bmatrix} + 3 \begin{bmatrix} 0 \\ 1 \\ 0 \end{bmatrix} + 2 \begin{bmatrix} 0 \\ 0 \\ 1 \end{bmatrix},$$

it follows that

$$(\mathbf{x})_s = \begin{bmatrix} 0 \\ 3 \\ 2 \end{bmatrix}.$$

31. If P is the transition matrix from B'' to B', then $P[\mathbf{x}]_{B''} = [\mathbf{x}]_{B'}$. If Q is the transition matrix from B' to B, then $Q[\mathbf{x}]_{B'} = [\mathbf{x}]_B$. Hence,

$$[\mathbf{x}]_B = Q[\mathbf{x}]_{B'} = QP[\mathbf{x}]_{B''}.$$

which means that QP is the transition matrix from B'' to B.

33. If B is the standard basis, then

$$[B' \vdots B] = [B' \vdots I] \quad \Rightarrow \quad [I \vdots (B')^{-1}]$$

shows that P^{-1}, the transition matrix from B to B', is $(B')^{-1}$.

If B' is the standard basis, then

$$[B' \vdots B] = [I \vdots B]$$

shows that P^{-1}, the transition matrix from B to B', is B.

Section 4.8   Applications of Vector Spaces

1. (a) If $y = e^x$, then $y'' = e^x$ and $y'' + y = 2e^x \neq 0$. Thus, e^x is not a solution to the equation.

    (b) If $y = \sin x$, then $y'' = -\sin x$ and $y'' + y = 0$. Thus, $\sin x$ is a solution to the equation.

    (c) If $y = \cos x$, then $y'' = -\cos x$ and $y'' + y = 0$. Thus, $\cos x$ is a solution to the equation.

    (d) If $y = \sin x - \cos x$, then $y'' = -\sin x + \cos x$ and $y'' + y = 0$. Thus, $\sin x - \cos x$ is a solution to the equation.

3. (a) If $y = e^{-2x}$, then $y' = -2e^{-2x}$ and $y'' = 4e^{-2x}$. Thus,
    $$y'' + 4y' + 4y = 4e^{-2x} + 4(-2e^{-2x}) + 4(e^{-2x}) = 0,\text{ and } e^{-2x}\text{ is a solution.}$$

    (b) If $y = xe^{-2x}$, then $y' = (1 - 2x)e^{-2x}$ and $y'' = (4x - 4)e^{-2x}$. Thus,
    $$y'' + 4y' + 4y = (4x - 4)e^{-2x} + 4(1 - 2x)e^{-2x} + 4xe^{-2x} = 0,\text{ and } xe^{-2x}\text{ is a solution.}$$

    (c) If $y = x^2 e^{-2x}$, then $y' = (2x - 2x^2)e^{-2x}$ and $y'' = (4x^2 - 8x + 2)e^{-2x}$. Thus,
    $$y'' + 4y' + 4y = (4x^2 - 8x + 2)e^{-2x} + 4(2x - 2x^2)e^{-2x} + 4(x^2 e^{-2x}) \neq 0,\text{ and } x^2 e^{-2x}$$
    is not a solution.

    (d) If $y = (x + 2)e^{-2x}$, then $y' = (-3 - 2x)3^{-2x}$ and $y'' = (4 + 4x)e^{-2x}$. Thus,
    $$y'' = 4y' + 4y = (4 + 4x)e^{-2x} + 4(-3 - 2x)e^{-2x} + 4(x + 2)e^{-2x} = 0,\text{ and } (x + 2)e^{-2x}$$
    is a solution.

5. $W(e^x, e^{-x}) = \begin{vmatrix} e^x & e^{-x} \\ \frac{d}{dx}(e^x) & \frac{d}{dx}(e^{-x}) \end{vmatrix} = \begin{vmatrix} e^x & e^{-x} \\ e^x & -e^{-x} \end{vmatrix} = -2$

7. $W(e^{-x}, xe^{-x}, (x + 3)e^{-x}) = \begin{vmatrix} e^{-x} & xe^{-x} & (x + 3)e^{-x} \\ -e^{-x} & (1 - x)e^{-x} & (-x - 2)e^{-x} \\ e^{-x} & (x - 2)e^{-x} & (x + 1)e^{-x} \end{vmatrix}$

$$= e^{-3x} \begin{vmatrix} 1 & x & x + 3 \\ -1 & 1 - x & -x - 2 \\ 1 & x - 2 & x + 1 \end{vmatrix}$$

$$= e^{-3x} \begin{vmatrix} 1 & x & x + 3 \\ 0 & 1 & 1 \\ 0 & -2 & -2 \end{vmatrix} = 0$$

9. Since

$$W(\sin x, \cos x) = \begin{vmatrix} \sin x & \cos x \\ \cos x & -\sin x \end{vmatrix} = -\sin^2 x - \cos^2 x = -1 \neq 0,$$

the set is linearly independent.

11. $W(e^{-2x}, xe^{-2x}, (2x + 1)e^{-2x}) = \begin{vmatrix} e^{-2x} & xe^{-2x} & (2x + 1)e^{-2x} \\ -2e^{-2x} & (1 - 2x)e^{-2x} & -4xe^{-2x} \\ 4e^{-2x} & (4x - 4)e^{-2x} & (8x - 4)e^{-2x} \end{vmatrix}$

$$= e^{-6x} \begin{vmatrix} 1 & x & 2x + 1 \\ -2 & 1 - 2x & -4x \\ 4 & 4x - 4 & 8x - 4 \end{vmatrix}$$

$$= e^{-6x} \begin{vmatrix} 1 & x & 2x + 1 \\ 0 & 1 & 2 \\ 0 & -4 & -8 \end{vmatrix}$$

$$= 0,$$

the set is linearly dependent.

13. Since

$$W(2, -1 + 2 \sin x, 1 + \sin x) = \begin{vmatrix} 2 & -1 + 2 \sin x & 1 + \sin x \\ 0 & 2 \cos x & \cos x \\ 0 & -2 \sin x & -\sin x \end{vmatrix}$$

$$= -4 \cos x \sin x + 4 \cos x \sin x = 0,$$

the set is linearly dependent.

15. Note that $e^{-x} + xe^{-x}$ is the sum of the first two expressions in the set. Thus, the set is linearly dependent.

17. From Exercise 9 we have a set of two linearly independent solutions. Since $y'' + y = 0$ is second-degree, it has a general solution of the form $C_1 \sin x + C_2 \cos x$.

19. From Exercise 12 we have a set of three linearly independent solutions. Since $y''' + y' = 0$ is third order, it has a general solution of the form $c_1 + c_2 \sin x + c_3 \cos x$.

21. Clearly $\cos ax$ and $\sin ax$ satisfy the differential equation $y'' + a^2y = 0$. Since $W(\cos ax, \sin ax) = a \neq 0$, they are linearly independent. Hence, the general solution is $y = c_1 \cos ax + c_2 \sin ax$.

23. We first calculate the Wronskian of the two functions

$$W(e^{ax}, xe^{ax}) = \begin{vmatrix} e^{ax} & xe^{ax} \\ ae^{ax} & (ax + 1)e^{ax} \end{vmatrix} = (ax + 1)e^{2ax} - axe^{2ax} = e^{2ax}.$$

Since $W(e^{ax}, xe^{ax}) \neq 0$ and the functions are solutions to $y'' - 2ay' + a^2y = 0$, they are linearly independent.

25. No, this is not true. For instance, consider the nonhomogenous differential equation $y'' = 1$. Two solutions are $y_1 = x^2 / 2$ and $y_2 = x^2 / 2 + 1$, but $y_1 + y_2$ is not a solution.

27. The graph of this equation is a parabola $x = -y^2$ with the vertex at the origin.
The parabola opens to the left.

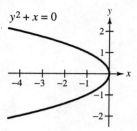

$y^2 + x = 0$

29. The graph of this equation is a hyperbola centered at the origin with transverse axis parallel to the x-axis.

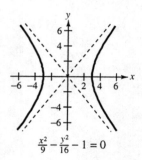

$\frac{x^2}{9} - \frac{y^2}{16} - 1 = 0$

31. First we complete the square to find the standard form.

$$(3x - 6)^2 + (5y - 5)^2 = 0$$

The graph of this equation is the single point (2, 1).

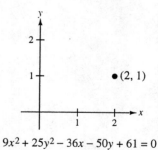

$9x^2 + 25y^2 - 36x - 50y + 61 = 0$

33. First we complete the square to find the standard form.

$$\frac{(x + 2)^2}{2^2} + \frac{(y + 4)^2}{1^2} = 1$$

We can now identify this as the equation of an ellipse centered at $(-2, -4)$ with major axis parallel to the x-axis.

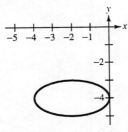

$x^2 + 4y^2 + 4x + 32y + 64 = 0$

35. First we complete the square to find the standard form.

$$(x + 2)^2 = 4\left(-\tfrac{3}{2}\right)(y - 1)$$

We see that this is the equation of a parabola centered at $(-2, 1)$ and opening downward.

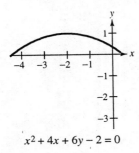

$x^2 + 4x + 6y - 2 = 0$

37. We begin by finding the rotation angle, θ, where

$$\cot 2\theta = \frac{a - c}{b} = \frac{0 - 0}{1} = 0, \text{ implying that } \theta = \frac{\pi}{4}.$$

Thus, $\sin \theta = 1/\sqrt{2}$ and $\cos \theta = 1/\sqrt{2}$. By substituting

$$x = x'\cos\theta - y'\sin\theta = \frac{1}{\sqrt{2}}(x' - y')$$

and

$$y = x'\sin\theta + y'\cos\theta = \frac{1}{\sqrt{2}}(x' + y')$$

into

$xy + 1 = 0$ and simplifying, we obtain

$(x')^2 - (y')^2 + 2 = 0.$

In standard form $\dfrac{(y')^2}{2} - \dfrac{(x')^2}{2} = 1.$

We can see that this is the equation of a hyperbola with a transverse axis parallel to the y'-axis.

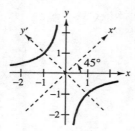

39. We begin by finding the rotation angle, θ, where

$$\cot 2\theta = \frac{5 - 5}{-2} = 0, \text{ implying that } \theta = \frac{\pi}{4}.$$

Thus, $\sin \theta = 1/\sqrt{2}$ and $\cos \theta = 1/\sqrt{2}$. By substituting

$$x = x' \cos \theta - y' \sin \theta = \frac{1}{\sqrt{2}}(x' - y')$$

and

$$y = x' \sin \theta + y' \cos \theta = \frac{1}{\sqrt{2}}(x' + y')$$

into

$5x^2 - 2xy + 5y^2 - 24 = 0$ and simplifying, we obtain

$4(x')^2 + 6(y')^2 - 24 = 0.$

In standard form $\dfrac{(x')^2}{6} - \dfrac{(y')^2}{4} = 1.$

We can see that this is the equation of an ellipse with major axis parallel to the x'-axis.

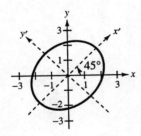

41. We begin by finding the rotation angle, θ, where

$$\cot 2\theta = \frac{a - c}{b} = \frac{13 - 7}{6\sqrt{3}} = \frac{1}{\sqrt{3}} \implies 2\theta = \frac{\pi}{3} \implies \theta = \frac{\pi}{6}.$$

Thus, $\sin \theta = \frac{1}{2}$ and $\cos \theta = \frac{\sqrt{3}}{2}$. By substituting

$$x = x' \cos \theta - y' \sin \theta = \frac{\sqrt{3}}{2} x' - \frac{1}{2} y'$$

and

$$y = x' \sin \theta + y' \cos \theta = \frac{1}{2} x' + \frac{\sqrt{3}}{2} y'$$

into $13x^2 + 6\sqrt{3}xy + 7y^2 - 16 = 0$ and simplifying, we obtain $(x')^2 + \frac{(y')^2}{4} = 1$, which is an ellipse.

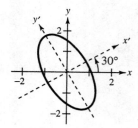

43. We begin by finding the rotation angle, θ, where

$$\cot 2\theta = \frac{1 - 3}{2\sqrt{3}} = -\frac{1}{\sqrt{3}},$$

implying that $\theta = \frac{\pi}{3}$. Thus,

$\sin \theta = \sqrt{3}/2$ and $\cos \theta = 1/2$.

By substituting $x = x' \cos \theta - y' \sin \theta = \frac{1}{2}(x' - \sqrt{3}y')$

and

$$y = x' \sin \theta + y' \cos \theta = \frac{1}{2}(\sqrt{3}x' + y')$$

into $x^2 + 2\sqrt{3}xy + 3y^2 - 2\sqrt{3}x + 2y + 16 = 0$ and simplifying, we obtain

$4(x')^2 + 4y' + 16 = 0.$

In standard form

$y' + 4 = -(x')^2.$

We can see that this is the equation of a parabola with axis parallel to the y'-axis.

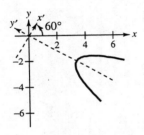

45. We begin by finding the rotation angle, θ, where

$$\cot 2\theta = \frac{1 - 1}{-2} = 0,$$

implying that $\theta = \dfrac{\pi}{4}$. Thus,

$$\sin \theta = 1/\sqrt{2} \text{ and } \cos \theta = 1/\sqrt{2}.$$

By substituting

$$x = x'\cos \theta - y'\sin \theta = \frac{1}{\sqrt{2}}(x' - y')$$

and

$$y = x'\sin \theta + y'\cos \theta = \frac{1}{\sqrt{2}}(x' + y')$$

into $x^2 - 2xy + y^2 = 0$ and simplifying, we obtain $2(y')^2 = 0$.

The graph of this equation is the line $y' = 0$.

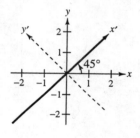

47. If $\theta = \dfrac{\pi}{4}$, then $\sin \theta = \dfrac{1}{\sqrt{2}}$ and $\cos \theta = \dfrac{1}{\sqrt{2}}$. Thus,

$$x = x'\cos \theta - y'\sin \theta = \frac{1}{\sqrt{2}}(x' - y') \text{ and}$$

$$y = x'\sin \theta - y'\cos \theta = \frac{1}{\sqrt{2}}(x' + y')$$

Substituting these expressions for x and y into $ax^2 + bxy + ay^2 + dx + ey + f = 0$, we obtain,

$$a\frac{1}{2}(x' - y')^2 + b\frac{1}{2}(x' - y')(x' + y') + a\frac{1}{2}(x' + y')^2 +$$

$$d\frac{1}{\sqrt{2}}(x' - y') + e\frac{1}{\sqrt{2}}(x' + y') + f = 0.$$

Expanding out the first three terms, we see that the $x'y'$-term has been eliminated.

49. Let A = $\begin{bmatrix} a & \frac{b}{2} \\ \frac{b}{2} & c \end{bmatrix}$ and assume $|A| = ac - \dfrac{b^2}{4} \neq 0$. If $a = 0$, then

$$ax^2 + bxy + cy^2 = bxy + cy^2 = y(cy + bx) = 0,$$

which implies that $y = 0$ or $y = \dfrac{-bx}{c}$, the equations of two intersecting lines.

On the other hand, if $a \neq 0$, then we can divide $ax^2 + bxy + cy^2 = 0$ through by a to obtain

$$x^2 + \frac{b}{a}xy + \frac{c}{a}y^2 = x^2 + \frac{b}{a}xy + \left(\frac{b}{2a}\right)^2 y^2 + \frac{c}{a}y^2 - \left(\frac{b}{2a}\right)^2 = 0 \quad \Rightarrow$$

$$\left(x + \frac{b}{2a}y\right)^2 = \left(\left(\frac{b}{2a}\right)^2 - \frac{c}{a}\right)y^2.$$

Since $4ac \neq b^2$, we see that this last equation represents two intersecting lines.

Chapter 4   Review Exercises

1. (a) $\mathbf{u} + \mathbf{v} = (-1, 2, 3) + (1, 0, 2) = (-1 + 1, 2 + 0, 3 + 2) = (0, 2, 5)$

    (b) $2\mathbf{v} = 2(1, 0, 2) = (2, 0, 4)$

    (c) $\mathbf{u} - \mathbf{v} = (-1, 2, 3) - (1, 0, 2) = (-1 - 1, 2 - 0, 3 - 2) = (-2, 2, 1)$

    (d) $3\mathbf{u} - 2\mathbf{v} = 3(-1, 2, 3) - 2(1, 0, 2) = (-3, 6, 9) - (2, 0, 4)$
    $$= (-3 - 2, 6 - 0, 9 - 4) = (-5, 6, 5)$$

3. (a) $\mathbf{u} + \mathbf{v} = (3, -1, 2, 3) + (0, 2, 2, 1) = (3, 1, 4, 4)$

    (b) $2\mathbf{v} = 2(0, 2, 2, 1) = (0, 4, 4, 2)$

    (c) $\mathbf{u} - \mathbf{v} = (3, -1, 2, 3) - (0, 2, 2, 1) = (3, -3, 0, 2)$

    (d) $3\mathbf{u} - 2\mathbf{v} = 3(3, -1, 2, 3) - 2(0, 2, 2, 1)$
    $$= (9, -3, 6, 9) - (0, 4, 4, 2) = (9, -7, 2, 7)$$

5. $x = \frac{1}{2}\mathbf{u} - \frac{3}{2}\mathbf{v} - \frac{1}{2}\mathbf{w}$
    $$= \frac{1}{2}(1, -1, 2) - \frac{3}{2}(0, 2, 3) - \frac{1}{2}(0, 1, 1)$$
    $$= (\tfrac{1}{2}, -4, -4)$$

7. To write $\mathbf{v}$ as a linear combination of $\mathbf{u}_1$, $\mathbf{u}_2$ and $\mathbf{u}_3$, we solve the equation

    $$c_1\mathbf{u}_1 + c_2\mathbf{u}_2 + c_3\mathbf{u}_3 = \mathbf{v}$$

    for c_1, c_2, and c_3. This vector equation corresponds to the system of linear equations

    $$
    \begin{aligned}
    c_1 - c_2 \phantom{{}+ c_3} &= 1 \\
    2c_1 - 2c_2 \phantom{{}+ c_3} &= 2 \\
    3c_1 - 3c_2 + c_3 &= 3 \\
    4c_1 + 4c_2 + c_3 &= 5.
    \end{aligned}
    $$

    The solution of this system is $c_1 = \frac{9}{8}$, $c_2 = \frac{1}{8}$, and $c_3 = 0$. Thus, $\mathbf{v} = \frac{9}{8}\mathbf{u}_1 + \frac{1}{8}\mathbf{u}_2$.

9. The zero vector is

    $$
    \begin{bmatrix}
    0 & 0 & 0 & 0 \\
    0 & 0 & 0 & 0 \\
    0 & 0 & 0 & 0
    \end{bmatrix}.
    $$

    The additive inverse of $\begin{bmatrix} a_{11} & a_{12} & a_{13} & a_{14} \\ a_{21} & a_{22} & a_{23} & a_{24} \\ a_{31} & a_{32} & a_{33} & a_{34} \end{bmatrix}$ is $\begin{bmatrix} -a_{11} & -a_{12} & -a_{13} & -a_{14} \\ -a_{21} & -a_{22} & -a_{23} & -a_{24} \\ -a_{31} & -a_{32} & -a_{33} & -a_{34} \end{bmatrix}$.

11. Since $W = \{(x, y) : x = 2y\}$ is nonempty and $W \subset R^2$, we need only check that W is closed under addition and scalar multiplication. Since

$$(2x_1, x_1) + (2x_2, x_2) = (2(x_1 + x_2), x_1 + x_2) \in W$$

and

$$c(2x_1, x_1) = (2cx_1, cx_1) \in W$$

We conclude that W is a subspace of R^2.

13. Since $W = \{(x, 2x, 3x) : x \text{ is a real number}\}$ is nonempty and $W \subset R^2$, we need only check that W is closed under addition and scalar multiplication. Since

$$(x_1, 2x_1, 3x_1) + (x_2, 2x_2, 3x_2) = ((x_1 + x_2), 2(x_1 + x_2), 3(x_1 + x_2)) \in W$$

and

$$c(x_1, 2x_1, 3x_1) = (cx_2, 2(cx_1), 3(cx_1)) \in W,$$

We conclude that W is a subspace of R^3.

15. W is not a subspace of $C[-1, 1]$. For instance, $f(x) = x - 1$ and $g(x) = -1$ are in W, but their sum $(f + g)(x) = x - 2$ is not in W, since $(f + g)(0) = -2 \neq -1$. Hence, W is not closed under addition (nor scalar multiplication).

17. (a) The only vector in W is the zero vector. Thus, W is nonempty and $W \subset R^3$. Furthermore, since W is closed under addition and scalar multiplication, it is a subspace of R^3.

   (b) W is not closed under addition or scalar multiplication, so it is not a subspace of R^3.
   For example, $(1, 0, 0) \in W$, and yet $2(1, 0, 0) = (2, 0, 0) \notin W$.

19. (a) To find the spanning set of S, we form the vector equation

$$c_1(1, -2, 7) + c_2(-5, 6, 4) + c_3(3, 6, -9) + c_4(5, 1, 2) = (u_1, u_2, u_3).$$

This yields the system of linear equations

$$\begin{aligned}
c_1 - 5c_2 + 3c_3 + 5c_4 &= u_1 \\
-2c_1 + 6c_2 + 6c_3 + c_4 &= u_2 \\
7c_1 + 4c_2 - 9c_3 + 2c_4 &= u_3
\end{aligned}$$

which has an infinite number of solutions. Thus, S spans R^3.

   (b) S is linearly dependent since the vector equation

$$c_1(1, -2, 7) + c_2(-5, 6, 4) + c_3(3, 6, -9) + c_4(5, 1, 2) = (0, 0, 0)$$

has infinitely many solutions [see part (a)].

   (c) S is not a basis for R^3 because it is not linearly independent.

21. (a) To find out whether S spans R^3, we form the vector equation

$$c_1(1, -5, 4) + c_2(11, 6, -1) + c_3(2, 3, 5) = (u_1, u_2, u_3).$$

This yields the system of linear equations

$$\begin{aligned} c_1 + 11c_2 + 2c_3 &= u_1 \\ -5c_1 + 6c_2 + 3c_3 &= u_2 \\ 4c_1 - c_2 + 5c_3 &= u_3. \end{aligned}$$

This system has a unique solution for every (u_1, u_2, u_3) since the determinant of the coefficient matrix is not zero. Thus, S spans R^3.

(b) Solving the same system in (a) with $(u_1, u_2, u_3) = (0, 0, 0)$ yields the trivial solution. Thus, S is linearly independent.

(c) Because S is linearly independent and S spans R^3, it is a basis for R^3.

23. (a) To find out whether S spans R^3, we form the vector equation

$$c_1\left(-\tfrac{1}{2}, \tfrac{3}{4}, -1\right) + c_2(5, 2, 3) + c_3(-4, 6, -8) = (u_1, u_2, u_3).$$

This yields the system

$$\begin{aligned} -\tfrac{1}{2}c_1 + 5c_2 - 4c_3 &= u_1 \\ \tfrac{3}{4}c_1 + 2c_2 + 6c_3 &= u_2 \\ -c_1 + 3c_2 - 8c_3 &= u_3. \end{aligned}$$

which is equivalent to the system

$$\begin{aligned} c_1 - 10c_2 + 8c_3 &= -2u_1 \\ 7c_2 &= 2u_1 - u_3 \\ 0 &= -17u_1 + 28u_2 + 38u_3. \end{aligned}$$

Thus, there are vectors (u_1, u_2, u_3) not spanned by S. For instance, $(0, 0, 1) \notin \text{span } (S)$.

(b) Solving the same system in (a) for $(u_1, u_2, u_3) = (0, 0, 0)$ yields nontrivial solutions. For instance, $c_1 = -8$, $c_2 = 0$ and $c_3 = 1$.

Thus, $-8\left(-\tfrac{1}{2}, \tfrac{3}{4}, -1\right) + 0(5, 2, 3) + 1(-4, 6, -8) = (0, 0, 0)$ and S is linearly dependent.

(c) S is not a basis because it does not span R^3 nor is it linearly independent.

25. S has four vectors, so we need only check that S is linearly independent.

We form the vector equation

$$c_1(1 - t) + c_2(2t + 3t^2) + c_3(t^2 - 2t^3) + c_4(2 + t^3) = 0 + 0t + 0t^2 + 0t^3$$

which yields the homogenous system of linear equations

$$
\begin{aligned}
c_1 \qquad\qquad\qquad + 2c_4 &= 0 \\
-c_1 + 2c_2 \qquad\qquad\quad &= 0 \\
3c_2 + \quad c_3 \qquad\quad &= 0 \\
-2c_3 + \quad c_4 &= 0.
\end{aligned}
$$

This system has only the trivial solution. Thus, S is linearly independent and S is a basis for P_3.

27. (a) This system has solutions of the form $(-2s - 3t, s, 4t, t)$, where s and t are any real numbers. A basis for the solution space is $\{(-2, 1, 0, 0), (-3, 0, 4, 1)\}$.

   (b) The dimension of the solution space is 2—the number of vectors in a basis for the solution space.

29. The system given by $A\mathbf{x} = \mathbf{0}$ has solutions of the form $(8t, 5t)$, where t is any real number. Thus, a basis for the solution space is $\{(8, 5)\}$. The rank of A is 1 (the number of nonzero row vectors in the reduced row-echelon matrix) and the nullity is 1. Note that rank (A) + nullity $(A) = 1 + 1 = 2 = n$.

31. The system given by $A\mathbf{x} = \mathbf{0}$ has solutions of the form $(3s - t, -2t, s, t)$, where s and t are any real numbers. Thus, a basis for the solution space of $A\mathbf{x} = \mathbf{0}$ is $\{(3, 0, 1, 0), (-1, -2, 0, 1)\}$. The rank of A is 2 (the number of row vectors in the reduced row-echelon matrix) and the nullity of A is 2. Note that rank (A) + nullity $(A) = 2 + 2 = 4 = n$.

33. (a) Using Gauss-Jordan elimination, the matrix reduces to

$$
\begin{bmatrix}
1 & 0 \\
0 & 1 \\
0 & 0
\end{bmatrix}.
$$

   Thus, the rank is 2.

   (b) A basis for the row space is $\{(1, 0), (0, 1)\}$.

35. (a) Using Gauss-Jordan elimination, the matrix reduces to

$$
\begin{bmatrix}
1 & 0 & 0 \\
0 & 1 & 0 \\
0 & 0 & 1
\end{bmatrix}.
$$

   Thus, the rank is 3.

   (b) A basis for the row space is $\{(1, 0, 0), (0, 1, 0), (0, 0, 1)\}$.

37. Because $[\mathbf{x}]_B = \begin{bmatrix} 3 \\ 5 \end{bmatrix}$, we can write $\mathbf{x}$ as

$$\mathbf{x} = 3(1, 1) + 5(-1, 1) = (-2, 8).$$

Since $(-2, 8) = -2(1, 0) + 8(0, 1)$, the coordinate vector of $\mathbf{x}$ relative to the standard basis is

$$[\mathbf{x}]_S = \begin{bmatrix} -2 \\ 8 \end{bmatrix}.$$

39. Because $[\mathbf{x}]_B = \begin{bmatrix} 2 \\ 0 \\ -1 \end{bmatrix}$, we can write $\mathbf{x}$ as

$$\mathbf{x} = 2(1, 0, 0) + 0(1, 1, 0) - 1(0, 1, 1) = (2, -1, -1).$$

Since $(2, -1, -1) = 2(1, 0, 0) - 1(0, 1, 0) - 1(0, 0, 1)$, the coordinate vector of $\mathbf{x}$ relative to the standard basis is

$$[\mathbf{x}]_S = \begin{bmatrix} 2 \\ -1 \\ -1 \end{bmatrix}.$$

41. To find $[\mathbf{x}]_{B'} = \begin{bmatrix} c_1 \\ c_2 \end{bmatrix}$, we solve the equation

$$c_1(5, 0) + c_2(0, -8) = (2, 2).$$

The resulting system of linear equations is

$$\begin{aligned} 5c_1 \quad\quad &= 2 \\ -8c_2 &= 2. \end{aligned}$$

Thus, $c_1 = \frac{2}{5}, c_2 = -\frac{1}{4}$, and we have

$$[\mathbf{x}]_{B'} = \begin{bmatrix} \frac{2}{5} \\ -\frac{1}{4} \end{bmatrix}.$$

43. To find $[\mathbf{x}]_{B'} = \begin{bmatrix} c_1 \\ c_2 \\ c_3 \\ c_4 \end{bmatrix}$, we solve the equation

$$c_1(9, -3, 15, 4) + c_2(-3, 0, 0, -1) + c_3(0, -5, 6, 8) + c_4(-3, 4, -2, 3) = (21, -5, 43, 14).$$

Forming the corresponding linear system, we find its solution to be
$c_1 = 3, c_2 = 1, c_3 = 0$ and $c_4 = 1$. Thus,

$$[\mathbf{x}]_{B'} = \begin{bmatrix} 3 \\ 1 \\ 0 \\ 1 \end{bmatrix}.$$

45. We begin by finding **x** relative to the standard basis

$$\mathbf{x} = 3(1, 1) + (-3)(-1, 1) = (6, 0).$$

Then we solve for $[\mathbf{x}]_{B'} = \begin{bmatrix} c_1 \\ c_2 \end{bmatrix}$

by forming the equation $c_1(0, 1) + c_2(1, 2) = (6, 0)$. The resulting system of linear equations is

$$\begin{aligned} c_2 &= 6 \\ c_1 + 2c_2 &= 0. \end{aligned}$$

The solution to this system is $c_1 = -12$ and $c_2 = 6$. Thus, we have

$$[\mathbf{x}]_{B'} = \begin{bmatrix} -12 \\ 6 \end{bmatrix}.$$

47. We begin by forming

$$[\, B' : B \,] = \begin{bmatrix} 1 & 0 & : & 1 & 3 \\ 0 & 1 & : & -1 & 1 \end{bmatrix}.$$

Since this matrix is already in the form $[\, I_2 : P^{-1} \,]$, we have

$$P^{-1} = \begin{bmatrix} 1 & 3 \\ -1 & 1 \end{bmatrix}.$$

49. We begin by forming

$$[\, B' : B \,] = \begin{bmatrix} 1 & -1 & : & 1 & 3 \\ 2 & 0 & : & -1 & 1 \end{bmatrix}.$$

We then use Gauss-Jordan elimination to obtain

$$[\, I_2 : P^{-1} \,] = \begin{bmatrix} 1 & 0 & : & -\frac{1}{2} & \frac{1}{2} \\ 0 & 1 & : & -\frac{3}{2} & -\frac{5}{2} \end{bmatrix}.$$

Thus,

$$P^{-1} = \begin{bmatrix} -\frac{1}{2} & \frac{1}{2} \\ -\frac{3}{2} & -\frac{5}{2} \end{bmatrix}.$$

51. We begin by finding a basis for W. The polynomials in W must have x as a factor. Consequently, a polynomial in W is of the form

$$\mathbf{p} = x(c_1 + c_2 x + c_3 x^2) = c_1 x + c_2 x^2 + c_3 x^3.$$

A basis for W is $\{x, x^2, x^3\}$. Similarly, the polynomials in U must have $(x - 1)$ as a factor. A polynomial in U is of the form

$$\mathbf{p} = (x - 1)(c_1 + c_2 x + c_3 x^2) = c_1(x - 1) + c_2(x^2 - x) + c_3(x^3 - x^2).$$

Thus, a basis for U is $\{x - 1, x^2 - x, x^3 - x^2\}$. The intersection of W and U contains polynomials with x and $(x - 1)$ as a factor. A polynomial in $W \cap U$ is of the form

$$\mathbf{p} = x(x - 1)(c_1 + c_2 x) = c_1(x^2 - x) + c_2(x^3 - x^2).$$

Thus, a basis for $W \cap U$ is $\{x^2 - x, x^3 - x^2\}$.

53. No. For example, the set

$$\{x^2 + x, x^2 - x, 1\}$$

is a basis for P_2.

55. Since W is a nonempty subset of V, we need only show that W is closed under addition and scalar multiplication. If $(x^3 + x)p(x)$ and $(x^3 + x)q(x)$ are in W, then $(x^3 + x)p(x) + (x^3 + x)q(x) = (x^3 + x)p(x) + q(x)) \in W$. Finally, $c(x^3 + x)p(x) = (x^3 + x)(cp(x)) \in W$. Hence, W is a subspace of P_5.

57. The row vectors of A are linearly dependent if and only if the rank of A is less than n, which is equivalent to the column vectors of A being linearly dependent.

59. (a) Consider the equation $c_1 f + c_2 g = c_1 x + c_2 |x| = 0$. If $x = \frac{1}{2}$, then $\frac{1}{2}c_1 + \frac{1}{2}c_2 = 0$, while if $x = -\frac{1}{2}$, we obtain $-\frac{1}{2}c_1 + \frac{1}{2}c_2 = 0$. This implies that $c_1 = c_2 = 0$, and f and g are linearly independent.

  (b) On the interval $[0, 1]$, $f = g = x$, and hence they are linearly dependent.

61. (a) Since $y' = 3e^{3x}$ and $y'' = 9e^{3x}$, we have
$$y'' - y' - 6y = 9e^{3x} - 3e^{3x} - 6(e^{3x}) = 0.$$
Therefore, e^{3x} is a solution.

  (b) Since $y' = 2e^{2x}$ and $y'' = 4e^{3x}$, we have
$$y'' - y' - 6y = 4e^{2x} - 2e^{2x} - 6(e^{2x}) = -4e^{2x} \neq 0.$$
Therefore, e^{2x} is *not* a solution.

  (c) Since $y' = -3e^{-3x}$ and $y'' = 9e^{-3x}$, we have
$$y'' - y', -6y = 9e^{-3x} - (-3e^{-3x}) - 6(e^{-3x}) = 6e^{-3x} \neq 0.$$
Therefore, e^{-3x} is *not* a solution.

  (d) Since $y' = -2e^{-2x}$ and $y'' = 4e^{-2x}$, we have
$$y'' - y' - 6y = 4e^{-2x} - (-2e^{-2x}) - 6(e^{-2x}) = 0.$$
Therefore, e^{-2x} is a solution.

63. $W(1, x, e^x) = \begin{vmatrix} 1 & x & e^x \\ 0 & 1 & e^x \\ 0 & 0 & e^x \end{vmatrix} = e^x$

65. The Wronskian of this set is

$$W\left(e^{-3x}, xe^{-3x}\right) = \begin{vmatrix} e^{-3x} & xe^{-3x} \\ -3e^{-3x} & (1-3x)e^{-3x} \end{vmatrix}$$

$$= (1 - 3x)e^{-6x} + 3xe^{-6x}$$

$$= e^{-6x}.$$

Since $W\left(e^{-3x}, xe^{-3x}\right) = e^{-6x} \neq 0$, the set is linearly independent.

67. The Wronskian of this set is

$$W\left(e^x, e^{2x}, e^x - e^{2x}\right) = \begin{vmatrix} e^x & e^{2x} & e^x - e^{2x} \\ e^x & 2e^{2x} & e^x - 2e^{2x} \\ e^x & 4e^{2x} & e^x - 4e^{2x} \end{vmatrix} = 0.$$

Since the third column is the difference of the first two columns, the set is linearly dependent.

69. We begin by completing the square.

$$\left(x^2 - 4x + 4\right) + \left(y^2 + 2y + 1\right) = 4 + 4 + 1$$
$$(x - 2)^2 + (y + 1)^2 = 9$$

This is the equation of a circle of radius

$\sqrt{9} = 3$, centered at $(2, -1)$.

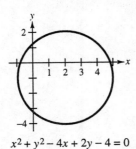

$x^2 + y^2 - 4x + 2y - 4 = 0$

71. We begin by completing the square.

$$2x^2 - 20x - y + 46 = 0$$
$$2(x^2 - 10x + 25) = y - 46 + 50$$
$$2(x - 5)^2 = y + 4$$

This is the equation of a parabola with vertex $(5, -4)$.

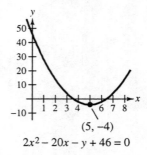

$$2x^2 - 20x - y + 46 = 0$$

73. From the equation

$$\cot 2\theta = \frac{a - c}{b} = \frac{0 - 0}{1} = 0$$

we find that the angle of rotation is $\theta = \frac{\pi}{4}$. Therefore, $\sin \theta = 1/\sqrt{2}$ and $\cos \theta = 1/\sqrt{2}$.
By substituting

$$x = x'\cos \theta - y'\sin \theta = \frac{1}{\sqrt{2}}(x' - y')$$

and

$$y = x'\sin \theta + y'\cos \theta = \frac{1}{\sqrt{2}}(x' + y')$$

into $xy = 3$, we obtain $\frac{1}{2}(x')^2 - \frac{1}{2}(y')^2 = 3$. In standard form,

$$\frac{(x')^2}{6} - \frac{(y')^2}{6} = 1$$

we recognize this to be the equation of a hyperbola whose transverse axis is the x'-axis.

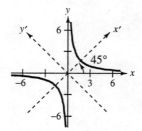

CHAPTER 5
Inner Product Spaces

Section 5.1   Length and Dot Product in R^n

1. $\|\mathbf{v}\| = \sqrt{4^2 + 3^2} = \sqrt{25} = 5$

3. $\|\mathbf{v}\| = \sqrt{1^2 + 0^2 + 0^2} = \sqrt{1} = 1$

5. $\|\mathbf{v}\| = \sqrt{0^2 + 0^2 + 0^2} = \sqrt{0} = 0$

7. $\|\mathbf{v}\| = \sqrt{4^2 + 0^2 + (-3)^2 + 5^2} = \sqrt{50} = 5\sqrt{2}$

9. (a) $\|\mathbf{u}\| = \sqrt{0^2 + 4^2 + 3^2} = \sqrt{25} = 5$

   (b) $\|\mathbf{v}\| = \sqrt{1^2 + (-2)^2 + 1^2} = \sqrt{6}$

   (c) $\|\mathbf{u} + \mathbf{v}\| = \|(1, 2, 4)\| = \sqrt{1^2 + 2^2 + 4^2} = \sqrt{21}$

11. (a) $\|\mathbf{u}\| = \sqrt{0^2 + 1^2 + (-1)^2 + 2^2} = \sqrt{6}$

    (b) $\|\mathbf{v}\| = \sqrt{1^2 + 1^2 + 3^2 + 0^2} = \sqrt{11}$

    (c) $\|\mathbf{u} + \mathbf{v}\| = \|(1, 2, 2, 2)\| = \sqrt{1^2 + 2^2 + 2^2 + 2^2} = \sqrt{13}$

13. (a) A unit vector $\mathbf{v}$ in the direction of $\mathbf{u}$ is given by

$$\mathbf{v} = \frac{\mathbf{u}}{\|\mathbf{u}\|} = \frac{1}{\sqrt{(-5)^2 + 12^2}}(-5, 12)$$

$$= \frac{1}{13}(-5, 12) = \left(-\frac{5}{13}, \frac{12}{13}\right).$$

   (b) A unit vector in the direction opposite that of $\mathbf{u}$ is given by

$$-\mathbf{v} = -\left(-\frac{5}{13}, \frac{12}{13}\right) = \left(\frac{5}{13}, -\frac{12}{13}\right).$$

15. (a) A unit vector $\mathbf{v}$ in the direction of $\mathbf{u}$ is given by

$$\mathbf{v} = \frac{\mathbf{u}}{\|\mathbf{u}\|} = \frac{1}{\sqrt{3^2 + 2^2 + (-5)^2}}(3, 2, -5)$$

$$= \frac{1}{\sqrt{38}}(3, 2, -5) = \left(\frac{3}{\sqrt{38}}, \frac{2}{\sqrt{38}}, -\frac{5}{\sqrt{38}}\right).$$

   (b) A unit vector in the direction opposite that of $\mathbf{u}$ is given by

$$-\mathbf{v} = -\left(\frac{3}{\sqrt{38}}, \frac{2}{\sqrt{38}}, -\frac{5}{\sqrt{38}}\right) = \left(-\frac{3}{\sqrt{38}}, -\frac{2}{\sqrt{38}}, \frac{5}{\sqrt{38}}\right).$$

17. We solve the equation for c as follows.

$$\|c(1, 2, 3)\| = 1$$

$$|c|\ \|(1, 2, 3)\| = 1$$

$$|c| = \frac{1}{\|(1, 2, 3)\|} = \frac{1}{\sqrt{14}}$$

$$c = \pm\frac{1}{\sqrt{14}}$$

19. First we find a unit vector in the direction of **u**.

$$\frac{\mathbf{u}}{\|\mathbf{u}\|} = \frac{1}{\sqrt{1^2 + 1^2}}(1, 1) = \left(\frac{1}{\sqrt{2}}, \frac{1}{\sqrt{2}}\right)$$

Then **v** is four times this vector.

$$\mathbf{v} = 4\frac{\mathbf{u}}{\|\mathbf{u}\|} = 4\left(\frac{1}{\sqrt{2}}, \frac{1}{\sqrt{2}}\right) = (2\sqrt{2}, 2\sqrt{2})$$

21. First we find a unit vector in the direction of **u**.

$$\frac{\mathbf{u}}{\|\mathbf{u}\|} = \frac{1}{\sqrt{3 + 9 + 0}}(\sqrt{3}, 3, 0) = \frac{1}{2\sqrt{3}}(\sqrt{3}, 3, 0) = \left(\frac{1}{2}, \frac{\sqrt{3}}{2}, 0\right)$$

Then **v** is twice this vector.

$$\mathbf{v} = 2\left(\frac{1}{2}, \frac{\sqrt{3}}{2}, 0\right) = (1, \sqrt{3}, 0)$$

23. (a) Since $\mathbf{v}/\|\mathbf{v}\|$ is a unit vector in the direction of **v**, we have

$$\mathbf{u} = \frac{\|\mathbf{v}\|}{2}\frac{\mathbf{v}}{\|\mathbf{v}\|} = \frac{1}{2}\mathbf{v} = \frac{1}{2}(8, 8, 6) = (4, 4, 3).$$

(b) Since $-\mathbf{v}/\|\mathbf{v}\|$ is a unit vector with direction opposite that of **v**, we have

$$\mathbf{u} = \frac{\|\mathbf{v}\|}{4}\left(-\frac{\mathbf{v}}{\|\mathbf{v}\|}\right) = \frac{-1}{4}\mathbf{v} = -\frac{1}{4}(8, 8, 6) = \left(-2, -2, -\frac{3}{2}\right).$$

25. $d(\mathbf{u}, \mathbf{v}) = \|\mathbf{u} - \mathbf{v}\| = \|(2, -2)\| = \sqrt{4 + 4} = 2\sqrt{2}$

27. $d(\mathbf{u}, \mathbf{v}) = \|\mathbf{u} - \mathbf{v}\| = \|(2, -2, 2)\|$
$$= \sqrt{2^2 + (-2)^2 + 2^2} = 2\sqrt{3}$$

29. (a) $\mathbf{u} \cdot \mathbf{v} = 3(2) + 4(-3) = 6 - 12 = -6$

(b) $\mathbf{u} \cdot \mathbf{u} = 3(3) + 4(4) = 9 + 16 = 25$

(c) $\|\mathbf{u}\|^2 = \mathbf{u} \cdot \mathbf{u} = 25$

(d) $(\mathbf{u} \cdot \mathbf{v})\mathbf{v} = -6(2, -3) = (-12, 18)$

(e) $\mathbf{u} \cdot (2\mathbf{v}) = 2(\mathbf{u} \cdot \mathbf{v}) = 2(-6) = -12$

31. (a) $\mathbf{u} \cdot \mathbf{v} = 2(1) + (-1)(0) + 1(-1) = 1$

(b) $\mathbf{u} \cdot \mathbf{u} = 2(2) + (-1)(-1) + 1(1) = 6$

(c) $\|\mathbf{u}\|^2 = \mathbf{u} \cdot \mathbf{u} = 6$

(d) $(\mathbf{u} \cdot \mathbf{v})\mathbf{v} = 1(1, 0, -1) = (1, 0, -1)$

(e) $\mathbf{u} \cdot (2\mathbf{v}) = 2(\mathbf{u} \cdot \mathbf{v}) = 2(1) = 2$

33. (a) $\mathbf{u} \cdot \mathbf{v} = 4(0) + 0(2) + (-3)5 + 5(4) = 5$

(b) $\mathbf{u} \cdot \mathbf{u} = 4(4) + 0(0) + (-3)(-3) + 5(5) = 50$

(c) $\|\mathbf{u}\|^2 = \mathbf{u} \cdot \mathbf{u} = 50$

(d) $(\mathbf{u} \cdot \mathbf{v})\mathbf{v} = 5(0, 2, 5, 4) = (0, 10, 25, 20)$

(e) $\mathbf{u} \cdot (2\mathbf{v}) = 2(5) = 10$

35. $(\mathbf{u} + \mathbf{v}) \cdot (2\mathbf{u} - \mathbf{v}) = \mathbf{u} \cdot (2\mathbf{u} - \mathbf{v}) + \mathbf{v} \cdot (2\mathbf{u} - \mathbf{v})$

$$= 2\mathbf{u} \cdot \mathbf{u} - \mathbf{u} \cdot \mathbf{v} + 2\mathbf{v} \cdot \mathbf{u} - \mathbf{v} \cdot \mathbf{v}$$

$$= 2(\mathbf{u} \cdot \mathbf{u}) + \mathbf{u} \cdot \mathbf{v} - \mathbf{v} \cdot \mathbf{v}$$

$$= 2(4) + (-5) - 10 = -7$$

37. We have

$$\mathbf{u} \cdot \mathbf{v} = 3(2) + 4(-3) = -6,$$

$$\|\mathbf{u}\| = \sqrt{3^2 + 4^2} = \sqrt{25} = 5, \text{ and}$$

$$\|\mathbf{v}\| = \sqrt{2^2 + (-3)^2} = \sqrt{13}. \text{ Thus,}$$

$$|\mathbf{u} \cdot \mathbf{v}| \le \|\mathbf{u}\| \, \|\mathbf{v}\|$$

$$|-6| = 6 \le 5\sqrt{13} \approx 18.03.$$

39. The cosine of the angle θ between $\mathbf{u}$ and $\mathbf{v}$ is given by

$$\cos \theta = \frac{\mathbf{u} \cdot \mathbf{v}}{\|\mathbf{u}\| \, \|\mathbf{v}\|} = \frac{1(2) + 1(-2)}{\sqrt{1^2 + 1^2} \, \sqrt{2^2 + (-2)^2}}$$

$$= \frac{0}{\sqrt{2} \, \sqrt{8}} = 0.$$

Thus, $\theta = \dfrac{\pi}{2}$ radians (90°).

41. The cosine of the angle θ between **u** and **v** is given by

$$\cos \theta = \frac{\mathbf{u} \cdot \mathbf{v}}{\|\mathbf{u}\| \, \|\mathbf{v}\|} = \frac{3(-2) + 1(4)}{\sqrt{3^2 + 1^2} \, \sqrt{(-2)^2 + 4^2}}$$

$$= -\frac{2}{10\sqrt{2}} = -\frac{\sqrt{2}}{10}.$$

Thus, $\theta = \cos^{-1}\left(-\frac{\sqrt{2}}{10}\right) \approx 1.713$ radians (98.13°).

43. The cosine of the angle θ between **u** and **v** is given by

$$\cos \theta = \frac{\mathbf{u} \cdot \mathbf{v}}{\|\mathbf{u}\| \, \|\mathbf{v}\|} = \frac{1(2) + 1(1) + 1(-1)}{\sqrt{1^2 + 1^2 + 1^2} \, \sqrt{2^2 + 1^2 + (-1)^2}}$$

$$= -\frac{2}{3\sqrt{2}} = -\frac{\sqrt{2}}{3}.$$

Thus, $\theta = \cos^{-1}\left(-\frac{\sqrt{2}}{3}\right) \approx 1.080$ radians (61.87°).

45. The cosine of the angle θ between **u** and **v** is given by

$$\cos \theta = \frac{\mathbf{u} \cdot \mathbf{v}}{\|\mathbf{u}\| \, \|\mathbf{v}\|} = \frac{0(3) + 1(3) + 0(3) + 1(3)}{\sqrt{0^2 + 1^2 + 0^2 + 1^2} \, \sqrt{3^2 + 3^2 + 3^2 + 3^2}}$$

$$= -\frac{6}{6\sqrt{2}} = -\frac{\sqrt{2}}{2}.$$

Thus, $\theta = \frac{\pi}{4}$.

47.
$$\mathbf{u} \cdot \mathbf{v} = 0$$
$$(0, 5) \cdot (v_1, v_2) = 0$$
$$0v_1 + 5v_2 = 0$$
$$v_2 = 0$$

Thus, $\mathbf{v} = (t, 0)$, where t is any real number.

49.
$$\mathbf{u} \cdot \mathbf{v} = 0$$
$$(-3, 2) \cdot (v_1, v_2) = 0$$
$$-3v_1 + 2v_2 = 0$$

Thus, $\mathbf{v} = (2t, 3t)$, where t is any real number.

51.
$$\mathbf{u} \cdot \mathbf{v} = 0$$
$$(4, -1, 0) \cdot (v_1, v_2, v_3) = 0$$
$$4v_1 + (-1)v_2 + 0v_2 = 0$$
$$4v_1 - v_3 = 0$$

Thus, $\mathbf{v} = (t, 4t, s)$, where s and t are any real numbers.

53. Since $\dfrac{\mathbf{u} \cdot \mathbf{v}}{\|\mathbf{u}\| \, \|\mathbf{v}\|} = \dfrac{4(1) + 0(1)}{\sqrt{4^2 + 0^2} \, \sqrt{1^2 + 1^2}}$

$$= -\frac{4}{4\sqrt{2}} = -\frac{\sqrt{2}}{2},$$

The angle between $\mathbf{u}$ and $\mathbf{v}$ is $\dfrac{\pi}{4}$ and $\mathbf{u}$ and $\mathbf{v}$ are neither orthogonal nor parallel.

55. Since $\dfrac{\mathbf{u} \cdot \mathbf{v}}{\|\mathbf{u}\| \, \|\mathbf{v}\|} = \dfrac{4\left(\frac{1}{2}\right) + 3\left(-\frac{2}{3}\right)}{\sqrt{4^2 + 3^2} \, \sqrt{\left(\frac{1}{2}\right)^2 + \left(-\frac{2}{3}\right)^2}}$

$$= \frac{0}{5\left(\frac{5}{6}\right)} = 0,$$

the vectors $\mathbf{u}$ and $\mathbf{v}$ are orthogonal.

57. Since $\dfrac{\mathbf{u} \cdot \mathbf{v}}{\|\mathbf{u}\| \, \|\mathbf{v}\|} = \dfrac{0(1) + 1(-2) + 6(-1)}{\sqrt{0^2 + 1^2 + 6^2} \, \sqrt{1^2 + (-2)^2 + (-1)^2}}$

$$= \frac{-8}{\sqrt{37} \, \sqrt{6}},$$

$\mathbf{u}$ and $\mathbf{v}$ are neither parallel nor orthogonal.

59. Since $\dfrac{\mathbf{u} \cdot \mathbf{v}}{\|\mathbf{u}\| \, \|\mathbf{v}\|} = \dfrac{\cos \theta \sin \theta + \sin \theta \, (-\cos \theta) + (-1)\,(0)}{\sqrt{\cos^2 \theta + \sin^2 \theta + 1} \, \sqrt{\sin^2 \theta + (-\cos \theta)^2 + 0^2}}$

$$= \frac{0}{\sqrt{2}} = 0,$$

the vectors $\mathbf{u}$ and $\mathbf{v}$ are orthogonal.

61. (a) $\|\mathbf{u} \cdot \mathbf{v}\|$ is meaningless because $\mathbf{u} \cdot \mathbf{v}$ is a scalar.

    (b) $\mathbf{u} + (\mathbf{u} \cdot \mathbf{v})$ is meaningless because $\mathbf{u}$ is a vector and $\mathbf{u} \cdot \mathbf{v}$ is a scalar.

63. Since $\mathbf{u} + \mathbf{v} = (4, 0) + (1, 1) = (5, 1)$, we have

$$\|\mathbf{u} + \mathbf{v}\| \le \|\mathbf{u}\| + \|\mathbf{v}\|$$

$$\| (5, 1) \| \le \| (4, 0) \| + \| (1, 1) \|$$

$$\sqrt{26} \le 4 + \sqrt{2}$$

65. First note that $\mathbf{u}$ and $\mathbf{v}$ are orthogonal, since $\mathbf{u} \cdot \mathbf{v} = (1, -1) \cdot (1, 1) = 0$.

On the other hand

$$\|\mathbf{u} + \mathbf{v}\|^2 = \|\mathbf{u}\|^2 + \|\mathbf{v}\|^2$$

$$\| (2, 0) \|^2 = \| (1, -1) \|^2 + \| (1, 1) \|^2$$

$$4 = 2 + 2$$

67. (a) If $\mathbf{u} \cdot \mathbf{v} = 0$, then

$$\frac{\mathbf{u} \cdot \mathbf{v}}{\|\mathbf{u}\| \, \|\mathbf{v}\|} = \frac{0}{\|\mathbf{u}\| \, \|\mathbf{v}\|}.$$

Thus, $\cos \theta = 0$ and $\theta = \dfrac{\pi}{2}$, provided $\mathbf{u} \neq \mathbf{0}$ and $\mathbf{v} \neq \mathbf{0}$.

(b) If $\mathbf{u} \cdot \mathbf{v} > 0$, then

$$\frac{\mathbf{u} \cdot \mathbf{v}}{\|\mathbf{u}\| \, \|\mathbf{v}\|} > 0.$$

Thus, $\cos \theta > 0$ and $0 \leq \theta < \dfrac{\pi}{2}$.

(c) If $\mathbf{u} \cdot \mathbf{v} < 0$, then

$$\frac{\mathbf{u} \cdot \mathbf{v}}{\|\mathbf{u}\| \, \|\mathbf{v}\|} < 0.$$

Thus, $\cos \theta < 0$, and $\dfrac{\pi}{2} < \theta \leq \pi$.

69. Let $t = $ length of side of cube. The diagonal of the cube can be represented by the vector $\mathbf{v} = (t, t, t)$, and one side by the vector $\mathbf{u} = (t, 0, 0)$. Thus,

$$\cos \theta = \frac{\mathbf{u} \cdot \mathbf{v}}{\|\mathbf{u}\| \, \|\mathbf{v}\|} = \frac{t^2}{t \sqrt{3} t} = \frac{1}{\sqrt{3}} \ \Rightarrow \ \theta = \cos^{-1}\left(\frac{1}{\sqrt{3}}\right) \approx 54.7°$$

71. $\begin{aligned}(\mathbf{u} + \mathbf{v}) \cdot \mathbf{w} &= \mathbf{w} \cdot (\mathbf{u} + \mathbf{v}) && \text{(Theorem 5.3, part 1)} \\ &= \mathbf{w} \cdot \mathbf{u} + \mathbf{w} \cdot \mathbf{v} && \text{(Theorem 5.3, part 2)} \\ &= \mathbf{u} \cdot \mathbf{w} + \mathbf{v} \cdot \mathbf{w} && \text{(Theorem 5.3, part 1)} \end{aligned}$

73. $\begin{aligned} \frac{1}{4}\|\mathbf{u} + \mathbf{v}\|^2 - \frac{1}{4}\|\mathbf{u} - \mathbf{v}\|^2 &= \frac{1}{4}\left[(\mathbf{u} + \mathbf{v}) \cdot (\mathbf{u} + \mathbf{v}) - (\mathbf{u} - \mathbf{v}) \cdot (\mathbf{u} - \mathbf{v}) \right] \\[2mm] &= \frac{1}{4}\left[\mathbf{u} \cdot \mathbf{u} + 2\mathbf{u} \cdot \mathbf{v} + \mathbf{v} \cdot \mathbf{v} - (\mathbf{u} \cdot \mathbf{u} - 2\mathbf{u} \cdot \mathbf{v} + \mathbf{v} \cdot \mathbf{v}) \right] \\[2mm] &= \frac{1}{4}\left[4\mathbf{u} \cdot \mathbf{v} \right] = \mathbf{u} \cdot \mathbf{v} \end{aligned}$

75. Let $\mathbf{u} = (\cos \theta)\mathbf{i} - (\sin \theta)\mathbf{j}$ and $\mathbf{v} = (\sin \theta)\mathbf{i} + (\cos \theta)\mathbf{j}$. Then

$$\|\mathbf{u}\| = \sqrt{\cos^2 \theta + \sin^2 \theta} = 1, \quad \|\mathbf{v}\| = \sqrt{\sin^2 \theta + \cos^2 \theta} = 1$$

and $\mathbf{u} \cdot \mathbf{v} = \cos \theta \sin \theta - \sin \theta \cos \theta = 0$. Hence, $\mathbf{u}$ and $\mathbf{v}$ are orthogonal unit vectors for any value of θ. If $\theta = \dfrac{\pi}{3}$, we have the following graph.

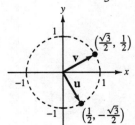

77. $\mathbf{u} \cdot \mathbf{v} = (3240, 1450, 2235) \cdot (2.22, 1.85, 3.25)$

   $= 17,139.05$

which represents the total amount for the three crops.

79. 1. $\mathbf{u} \cdot \mathbf{v} = \mathbf{u}^T \mathbf{v} = (\mathbf{u}^T \mathbf{v})^T = \mathbf{v}^T \mathbf{u} = \mathbf{v} \cdot \mathbf{u}$

   2. $\mathbf{u} \cdot (\mathbf{v} + \mathbf{w}) = \mathbf{u}^T (\mathbf{v} + \mathbf{w}) = \mathbf{u}^T \mathbf{v} + \mathbf{u}^T \mathbf{w} = \mathbf{u} \cdot \mathbf{v} + \mathbf{u} \cdot \mathbf{w}$

   3. $c(\mathbf{u} \cdot \mathbf{v}) = c(\mathbf{u}^T \mathbf{v}) = (c\mathbf{u})^T \mathbf{v} = (c\mathbf{u}) \cdot \mathbf{v}$ and $c(\mathbf{u} \cdot \mathbf{v}) = c(\mathbf{u}^T \mathbf{v}) = \mathbf{u}^T (c\mathbf{v}) = \mathbf{u} \cdot (c\mathbf{v})$.

Section 5.2   Inner Product Spaces

1. (a) $\langle \mathbf{u}, \mathbf{v} \rangle = \mathbf{u} \cdot \mathbf{v} = 3(5) + 4(-12) = -33$

   (b) $\|\mathbf{u}\| = \sqrt{\langle \mathbf{u}, \mathbf{u} \rangle} = \sqrt{\mathbf{u} \cdot \mathbf{u}} = \sqrt{3(3) + 4(4)} = 5$

   (c) $d(\mathbf{u}, \mathbf{v}) = \|\mathbf{u} - \mathbf{v}\| = \sqrt{\langle \mathbf{u} - \mathbf{v}, \mathbf{u} - \mathbf{v} \rangle} = \sqrt{(\mathbf{u} - \mathbf{v}) \cdot (\mathbf{u} - \mathbf{v})}$
   $$= \sqrt{(-2)(-2) + 16(16)} = 2\sqrt{65}$$

3. (a) $\langle \mathbf{u}, \mathbf{v} \rangle = 3(-4)(0) + 3(5) = 15$

   (b) $\|\mathbf{u}\| = \sqrt{\langle \mathbf{u}, \mathbf{u} \rangle} = \sqrt{3(-4)^2 + 3^2} = \sqrt{57}$

   (c) $d(\mathbf{u}, \mathbf{v}) = \|\mathbf{u} - \mathbf{v}\| = \sqrt{\langle \mathbf{u} - \mathbf{v}, \mathbf{u} - \mathbf{v} \rangle} = \sqrt{(3(-4)^2 + (-2)^2} = 2\sqrt{13}$

5. (a) $\langle \mathbf{u}, \mathbf{v} \rangle = \mathbf{u} \cdot \mathbf{v} = 0(9) + 9(-2) + 4(-4) = -34$

   (b) $\|\mathbf{u}\| = \sqrt{\langle \mathbf{u}, \mathbf{u} \rangle} = \sqrt{\mathbf{u} \cdot \mathbf{u}} = \sqrt{0 + 9^2 + 4^2} = \sqrt{97}$

   (c) $d(\mathbf{u}, \mathbf{v}) = \|\mathbf{u} - \mathbf{v}\| = \|(-9, 11, 8)\| = \sqrt{9^2 + 11^2 + 8^2} = \sqrt{266}$

7. (a) $\langle \mathbf{u}, \mathbf{v} \rangle = 2(8)(8) + 3(0)(3) + (-8)(16) = 0$

   (b) $\|\mathbf{u}\| = \sqrt{\langle \mathbf{u}, \mathbf{u} \rangle} = \sqrt{2(8)^2 + 3(0)^2 + (-8)^2} = \sqrt{192} = 8\sqrt{3}$

   (c) $d(\mathbf{u}, \mathbf{v}) = \|\mathbf{u} - \mathbf{v}\| = \|(0, -3, -24)\| = \sqrt{2(0)^2 + 3(-3)^2 + (-24)^2} = \sqrt{603} = 3\sqrt{67}$

9. (a) $\langle \mathbf{u}, \mathbf{v} \rangle = 8(-5) + 2(-3)(4) + (-1)(9) = -73$

   (b) $\|\mathbf{u}\| = \sqrt{\langle \mathbf{u}, \mathbf{u} \rangle} = \sqrt{8^2 + 2(-3)^2 + (-1)^2} = \sqrt{83}$

   (c) $d(\mathbf{u}, \mathbf{v}) = \|\mathbf{u} - \mathbf{v}\| = \sqrt{\langle \mathbf{u} - \mathbf{v}, \mathbf{u} - \mathbf{v} \rangle} = \sqrt{13^2 + 2(-7)^2 + (-10)^2} = \sqrt{367}$

11. (a) $<f, g> = \displaystyle\int_{-1}^{1} f(x)g(x)\,dx = \int_{-1}^{1} x^2(x^2 + 1)\,dx$

   $$= \int_{-1}^{1} (x^4 + x^2)\,dx = \frac{x^5}{5} + \frac{x^3}{3} \Big]_{-1}^{1}$$

   $$= \left(\frac{1}{5} + \frac{1}{3}\right) - \left(-\frac{1}{5} - \frac{1}{3}\right) = \frac{16}{15}$$

   (b) $\|f\|^2 = \langle f, f \rangle = \displaystyle\int_{-1}^{1} (x^2)^2\,dx = \frac{x^5}{5}\Big]_{-1}^{1} = \frac{2}{5}$

   $\|f\| = \sqrt{\frac{2}{5}} = \sqrt{10}/5$

   (c) We use the fact that $d(f, g) = \|f - g\|$. Since $f - g = x^2 - (x^2 + 1) = -1$, we have

   $$\langle f - g, f - g \rangle = \langle -1, -1 \rangle = \int_{-1}^{1} (-1)(-1)\,dx = x\Big]_{-1}^{1} = 2.$$

   Hence, $d(f, g) = \sqrt{\langle f - g, f - g \rangle} = \sqrt{2}$.

13. (a) $\langle \mathbf{f}, \mathbf{g} \rangle = \int_{-1}^{1} xe^x \, dx = (x-1)e^x \Big]_{-1}^{1} = 0 + 2e^{-1} = \dfrac{2}{e}$

     (b) $\| \mathbf{f} \|^2 = \langle \mathbf{f}, \mathbf{f} \rangle = \int_{-1}^{1} x^2 \, dx = \dfrac{x^3}{3}\Big]_{-1}^{1} = \dfrac{1}{3} + \dfrac{1}{3} = \dfrac{2}{3}$

          $\| \mathbf{f} \| = \dfrac{\sqrt{6}}{3}$

     (c) We use the fact that $d(\mathbf{f}, \mathbf{g}) = \| \mathbf{f} - \mathbf{g} \|$.

$$\langle \mathbf{f} - \mathbf{g}, \mathbf{f} - \mathbf{g} \rangle = \int_{-1}^{1} (x - e^x)^2 \, dx$$

$$= \int_{-1}^{1} (x^2 - 2xe^x + e^{2x}) \, dx$$

$$= \left[\dfrac{x^3}{3} - 2(x-1)e^x + \dfrac{e^{2x}}{2} \right]_{-1}^{1}$$

$$= \dfrac{2}{3} - \dfrac{4}{e} + \dfrac{e^2 - e^{-2}}{2}$$

$$= \dfrac{2}{3} - \dfrac{4}{e} + \dfrac{e^2}{2} - \dfrac{1}{2e^2}$$

$$d(\mathbf{f}, \mathbf{g}) = \sqrt{\langle \mathbf{f} - \mathbf{g}, \mathbf{f} - \mathbf{g} \rangle} = \sqrt{\dfrac{2}{3} - \dfrac{4}{e} + \dfrac{e^2}{2} - \dfrac{1}{2e^2}}$$

15. (a) $\langle A, B \rangle = 2(-1)(0) + 3(-2) + 4(1) + 2(-2)(1) = -6$

     (b) $\langle A, A \rangle = 2(-1)^2 + 3^2 + 4^2 + 2(-2)^2 = 35$

        $\|A\| = \sqrt{\langle A, A \rangle} = \sqrt{35}$

     (c) We use the fact that $d(A, B) = \| A - B \|$.

        $\langle A - B, A - B \rangle = 2(-1)^2 + 5^2 + 3^2 + 2(-3)^2 = 54$

           $d(A, B) = \sqrt{\langle A - B, A - B \rangle} = 3\sqrt{6}$

17. (a) $\langle \mathbf{p}, \mathbf{q} \rangle = 1(0) + (-1)(1) + 3(-1) = -4$

     (b) $\| \mathbf{p} \| = \sqrt{\langle \mathbf{p}, \mathbf{p} \rangle} = \sqrt{1^2 + (-1)^2 + 3^2} = \sqrt{11}$

     (c) $d(\mathbf{p}, \mathbf{q}) = \| \mathbf{p} - \mathbf{q} \| = \sqrt{\langle \mathbf{p} - \mathbf{q}, \mathbf{p} - \mathbf{q} \rangle} = \sqrt{1^2 + (-2)^2 + 4^2} = \sqrt{21}$

19. We verify that the function $\langle \mathbf{u}, \mathbf{v} \rangle = 3u_1v_1 + u_2v_2$ satisfies the four parts of the definition.

1. $\langle \mathbf{u}, \mathbf{v} \rangle = 3u_1v_1 + u_2v_2 = 3v_1u_1 + v_2u_2 = \langle \mathbf{v}, \mathbf{u} \rangle$

2. $\langle \mathbf{u}, \mathbf{v} + \mathbf{w} \rangle = 3u_1(v_1 + w_1) + u_2(v_2 + w_2) = 3u_1v_1 + u_2v_2 + 3u_1w_1 + u_2w_2$
    $$= \langle \mathbf{u}, \mathbf{v} \rangle + \langle \mathbf{u}, \mathbf{w} \rangle$$

3. $c\langle \mathbf{u}, \mathbf{v} \rangle = c(3u_1v_1 + u_2v_2) = 3(cu_1)v_1 + (cu_2)v_2 = \langle c\mathbf{u}, \mathbf{v} \rangle$

4. $\langle \mathbf{v}, \mathbf{v} \rangle = 3v_1^2 + v_2^2 \geq 0$ and $\langle \mathbf{v}, \mathbf{v} \rangle = 0$ if and only if $\mathbf{v} = (0, 0)$.

21. We verify that the function $\langle A, B \rangle = 2a_{11}b_{11} + a_{12}b_{12} + a_{21}b_{21} + 2a_{22}b_{22}$ satisfies the four parts of the definition.

1. $\langle A, B \rangle = 2a_{11}b_{11} + a_{12}b_{12} + a_{21}b_{21} + a_{22}b_{22} = 2b_{11}a_{11} + b_{12}a_{12} + b_{21}a_{21} + 2b_{22}a_{22}$
    $$= \langle B, A \rangle$$

2. $\langle A, B + C \rangle = 2a_{11}(b_{11} + c_{11}) + a_{12}(b_{12} + c_{12}) + a_{21}(b_{21} + c_{21}) + 2a_{22}(b_{22} + c_{22})$
    $$= 2a_{11}b_{11} + a_{12}b_{12} + a_{21}b_{21} + 2a_{22}b_{22} + 2a_{11}c_{11} + a_{12}c_{12} + a_{21}c_{21} + 2a_{22}c_{22}$$
    $$= \langle A, B \rangle + \langle A, C \rangle$$

3. $c\langle A, B \rangle = c(2a_{11}b_{11} + a_{12}b_{12} + a_{21}b_{21} + 2a_{22}b_{22})$
    $$= 2((ca_{11})b_{11} + (ca_{12})b_{12} + (ca_{21})b_{21} + 2(ca_{22})b_{22} = \langle cA, B \rangle$$

4. $\langle A, A \rangle = 2a_{11}^2 + a_{12}^2 + a_{21}^2 + 2a_{22}^2 \geq 0$, and

    $\langle A, A \rangle = 0$ if and only if

    $$A = \begin{bmatrix} 0 & 0 \\ 0 & 0 \end{bmatrix}.$$

23. The product $\langle \mathbf{u}, \mathbf{v} \rangle$ is not an inner product because nonzero vectors can have a norm of zero. For example, if $\mathbf{v} = (0, 1)$, then $\langle \mathbf{v}, \mathbf{v} \rangle = 0^2 = 0$.

25. The product $\langle \mathbf{u}, \mathbf{v} \rangle$ is not an inner product because it is not distributive over addition. For example, if $\mathbf{u} = (1, 0)$, $\mathbf{v} = (1, 0)$, and $\mathbf{w} = (1,0)$, then $\langle \mathbf{u}, \mathbf{v} + \mathbf{w} \rangle = 1^2(2)^2 + 0^2(0)^2 = 4$ and $\langle \mathbf{u}, \mathbf{v} \rangle + \langle \mathbf{u}, \mathbf{w} \rangle = 1^2(1)^2 + 0^2(0)^2 + 1^2(1)^2 + 0^2(0)^2 = 2$.

Thus, $\langle \mathbf{u}, \mathbf{v} + \mathbf{w} \rangle \neq \langle \mathbf{u}, \mathbf{v} \rangle + \langle \mathbf{u}, \mathbf{w} \rangle$.

27. Since

$$\frac{\langle \mathbf{u}, \mathbf{v} \rangle}{\| \mathbf{u} \| \, \| \mathbf{v} \|} = \frac{3(5) + 4(-12)}{\sqrt{3^2 + 4^2} \sqrt{5^2 + (-12)^2}} = \frac{-33}{5 \cdot 13} = \frac{-33}{65},$$

the angle between $\mathbf{u}$ and $\mathbf{v}$ is $\cos^{-1}\left(\dfrac{-33}{65}\right) \approx 2.103$ radians (120.51°).

29. Since

$$\langle \mathbf{u}, \mathbf{v} \rangle = 1(2) + 2(1)(-2) + 1(2) = 0,$$

The angle between $\mathbf{u}$ and $\mathbf{v}$ is $\dfrac{\pi}{2}$.

31. Since

$$\langle f, g \rangle = \int_{-1}^{1} x^3 \, dx = \frac{x^4}{4} \Big]_{-1}^{1} = 0,$$

The angle between **f** and **g** is $\frac{\pi}{2}$.

33. (a) To verify the Cauchy-Schwarz Inequality, we observe

$$| \langle \mathbf{u}, \mathbf{v} \rangle | \leq \| \mathbf{u} \| \, \| \mathbf{v} \|$$

$$| (5, 12) \cdot (3, 4) | \leq \| (5, 12) \| \, \| (3, 4) \|$$

$$63 \leq (13)(5) = 65.$$

(b) To verify the Triangle Inequality, we observe

$$\| \langle \mathbf{u} + \mathbf{v} \rangle \| \leq \| \mathbf{u} \| + \| \mathbf{v} \|$$

$$\| (8, 16) \| \leq 13 + 5$$

$$17.89 \leq 18.$$

35. (a) To verify the Cauchy-Schwarz Inequality, we observe

$$| \langle \mathbf{p}, \mathbf{q} \rangle | \leq \| \mathbf{p} \| \, \| \mathbf{q} \|$$

$$| 0(1) + 2(0) + 0(3) | \leq (2)\sqrt{10}$$

$$0 \leq 2\sqrt{10}.$$

(b) To verify the Triangle Inequality, we observe

$$\| \mathbf{p} + \mathbf{q} \| \leq \| \mathbf{p} \| + \| \mathbf{q} \|$$

$$\| 1 + 2x + 3x^2 \| \leq 2 + \sqrt{10}$$

$$\sqrt{14} \leq 2 + \sqrt{10}$$

$$3.742 \leq 5.162.$$

37. (a)   To verify the Cauchy-Schwarz Inequality, we compute

$$\langle f, g \rangle = \langle \sin x, \cos x \rangle = \int_{-\pi}^{\pi} \sin x \cos x \, dx = \frac{\sin^2 x}{2} \Bigg]_{-\pi}^{\pi} = 0$$

$$\| \mathbf{f} \|^2 = \langle \sin x, \sin x \rangle = \int_{-\pi}^{\pi} \sin^2 x \, dx = \int_{-\pi}^{\pi} \frac{1 - \cos 2x}{2} \, dx$$

$$= \frac{1}{2}x - \frac{\sin 2x}{4} \Bigg]_{-\pi}^{\pi} = \pi \implies \| \mathbf{f} \| = \sqrt{\pi}$$

$$\| \mathbf{g} \|^2 = \langle \cos x, \cos x \rangle = \int_{-\pi}^{\pi} \cos^2 x \, dx = \int_{-\pi}^{\pi} \frac{1 + \cos 2x}{2} \, dx$$

$$= \frac{1}{2}x - \frac{\sin 2x}{4} \Bigg]_{-\pi}^{\pi} = \pi \implies \| \mathbf{g} \| = \sqrt{\pi}$$

and observe that

$$| \langle \mathbf{f}, \mathbf{g} \rangle | \leq \| \mathbf{f} \| \, \| \mathbf{g} \|$$
$$0 \leq \sqrt{\pi} \sqrt{\pi}.$$

(b)   To verify the Triangle Inequality, we compute

$$\| \mathbf{f} + \mathbf{g} \| = \langle \sin x + \cos x, \sin x + \cos x \rangle = \int_{-\pi}^{\pi} (\sin x + \cos x)^2 dx$$

$$= \int_{-\pi}^{\pi} \sin^2 x \, dx + \int_{-\pi}^{\pi} \cos^2 x \, dx + 2 \int_{-\pi}^{\pi} \sin x \cos x \, dx$$

$$= \pi + \pi + 0 \implies \| \mathbf{f} + \mathbf{g} \| = \sqrt{2\pi}.$$

Hence, we see that $\| \mathbf{f} + \mathbf{g} \| \leq \| \mathbf{f} \| + \| \mathbf{g} \|$
$$\sqrt{2\pi} \leq \sqrt{\pi} + \sqrt{\pi}.$$

39. Since

$$\langle \mathbf{f}, \mathbf{g} \rangle = \int_{-\pi}^{\pi} \cos x \sin x \, dx = \frac{1}{2} \sin^2 x \Bigg]_{-\pi}^{\pi} = 0,$$

f and **g** are orthogonal.

41. The functions $\mathbf{f}(x) = x$ and $\mathbf{g}(x) = \frac{1}{2} \left(5x^3 - 3x \right)$ are orthogonal since

$$\langle \mathbf{f}, \mathbf{g} \rangle = \int_{-1}^{1} x \frac{1}{2} \left(5x^3 - 3x \right) dx = \frac{1}{2} \int_{-1}^{1} \left(5x^4 - 3x^2 \right) dx = \frac{1}{2} \left(x^5 - x^3 \right) \Bigg]_{-1}^{1} = 0.$$

43. (a) $\text{proj}_v \mathbf{u} = \dfrac{\langle \mathbf{u}, \mathbf{v} \rangle}{\langle \mathbf{v}, \mathbf{v} \rangle} \mathbf{v} = \dfrac{1(2) + 2(1)}{2^2 + 1^2} (2, 1) = \dfrac{4}{5} (2, 1) = \left(\dfrac{8}{5}, \dfrac{4}{5} \right)$

(b) $\text{proj}_\mathbf{u} \mathbf{v} = \dfrac{\langle \mathbf{v}, \mathbf{u} \rangle}{\langle \mathbf{u}, \mathbf{u} \rangle} \mathbf{u} = \dfrac{2(1) + 1(2)}{1^2 + 2^2} (1, 2) = \dfrac{4}{5} (1, 2) = \left(\dfrac{4}{5}, \dfrac{8}{5} \right)$

(c)

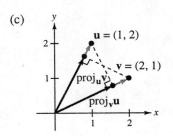

45. (a) $\text{proj}_v \mathbf{u} = \dfrac{\langle \mathbf{u}, \mathbf{v} \rangle}{\langle \mathbf{v}, \mathbf{v} \rangle} \mathbf{v} = \dfrac{1(0) + 3(-1) + (-2)(1)}{0^2 + (-1)^2 + 1^2} (0, -1, 1)$

$= \dfrac{-5}{2} (0, -1, 1) = \left(0, \dfrac{5}{2}, -\dfrac{5}{2} \right)$

(b) $\text{proj}_\mathbf{u} \mathbf{v} = \dfrac{\langle \mathbf{v}, \mathbf{u} \rangle}{\langle \mathbf{u}, \mathbf{u} \rangle} \mathbf{u} = \dfrac{0(1) + (-1)(3) + (-2)}{1^2 + 3^2 + (-2)^2} (1, 3, -2)$

$= \dfrac{-5}{14} (1, 3, -2) = \left(-\dfrac{5}{14}, -\dfrac{15}{14}, \dfrac{10}{14} \right)$

47. The inner products $\langle \mathbf{f}, \mathbf{g} \rangle$ and $\langle \mathbf{g}, \mathbf{g} \rangle$ are as follows.

$$\langle \mathbf{f}, \mathbf{g} \rangle = \int_{-1}^{1} x \, dx = \dfrac{x^2}{2} \bigg]_{-1}^{1} = 0$$

$$\langle \mathbf{g}, \mathbf{g} \rangle = \int_{-1}^{1} dx = x \bigg]_{-1}^{1} = 2$$

Thus, the projection of $\mathbf{f}$ onto $\mathbf{g}$ is

$$\text{proj}_\mathbf{g} \mathbf{f} = \dfrac{\langle \mathbf{f}, \mathbf{g} \rangle}{\langle \mathbf{g}, \mathbf{g} \rangle} \mathbf{g} = \dfrac{0}{2} 1 = 0.$$

49. The inner products $\langle \mathbf{f}, \mathbf{g} \rangle$ and $\langle \mathbf{g}, \mathbf{g} \rangle$ are as follows.

$$\langle \mathbf{f}, \mathbf{g} \rangle = \int_0^1 xe^x \, dx = \left[(x-1)e^x \right]_0^1 = 0 + 1 = 1$$

$$\langle \mathbf{g}, \mathbf{g} \rangle = \int_0^1 e^{2x} \, dx = \frac{1}{2} e^{2x} \Big]_0^1 = \frac{e^2 - 1}{2}$$

Thus, the projection of **f** onto g is

$$\text{proj}_{\mathbf{g}} \mathbf{f} = \frac{\langle \mathbf{f}, \mathbf{g} \rangle}{\langle \mathbf{g}, \mathbf{g} \rangle} \mathbf{g} = \frac{1}{(e^2 - 1)/2} e^x = \frac{2e^x}{e^2 - 1}.$$

51. The inner product $\langle \mathbf{f}, \mathbf{g} \rangle$ is

$$\langle \mathbf{f}, \mathbf{g} \rangle = \int_{-\pi}^{\pi} \sin 3x \, dx = -\frac{\cos 3x}{3} \Big]_{-\pi}^{\pi} = 0,$$

which implies that $\text{proj}_{\mathbf{g}} \mathbf{f} = 0$.

53. (a) $\langle \mathbf{u}, \mathbf{v} \rangle = 4(2) + 2(2)(-2) = 0 \implies \mathbf{u}$ and $\mathbf{v}$ are orthogonal.

(b) The vectors are not orthogonal in the Euclidean sense.

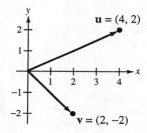

55. We verify the four parts of the definition for the function

$$\langle \mathbf{u}, \mathbf{v} \rangle = c_1 u_1 v_1 + \cdots + c_n u_n v_n = \sum_{i=1}^{n} c_i u_i v_i \,.$$

(1) $\langle \mathbf{u}, \mathbf{v} \rangle = \sum_{i=1}^{n} c_i u_i v_i = \sum_{i=1}^{n} c_i v_i u_i = \langle \mathbf{v}, \mathbf{u} \rangle$

(2) $\langle \mathbf{u}, \mathbf{v} + \mathbf{w} \rangle = \sum_{i=1}^{n} c_i u_i (v_i + w_i) = \sum_{i=1}^{n} c_i u_i v_i + \sum_{i=1}^{n} c_i v_i w_i$

$$= \langle \mathbf{u}, \mathbf{v} \rangle + \langle \mathbf{u}, \mathbf{w} \rangle$$

(3) $d\langle \mathbf{u}, \mathbf{v} \rangle = d \sum_{i=1}^{n} c_i u_i v_i = \sum_{i=1}^{n} c_i (du_i) v_i = \langle d\mathbf{u}, \mathbf{v} \rangle$

(4) $\langle \mathbf{v}, \mathbf{v} \rangle = \sum_{i=1}^{n} c_i v_i^2 \geq 0$, and $\langle \mathbf{v}, \mathbf{v} \rangle = 0$ if and only if $\mathbf{v} = \mathbf{0}$.

57. We have from the definition of inner product

$$\begin{aligned}
\langle \mathbf{u} + \mathbf{v}, \mathbf{w} \rangle &= \langle \mathbf{w}, \mathbf{u} + \mathbf{v} \rangle \\
&= \langle \mathbf{w}, \mathbf{u} \rangle + \langle \mathbf{w}, \mathbf{v} \rangle \\
&= \langle \mathbf{u}, \mathbf{w} \rangle + \langle \mathbf{v}, \mathbf{w} \rangle \,.
\end{aligned}$$

59. (a) $W^{\perp} = \{\mathbf{v} \in V : \langle \mathbf{v}, \mathbf{w} \rangle = 0 \text{ for all } \mathbf{w} \in W\}$ is nonempty because $\mathbf{0} \in W^{\perp}$.

Let $\mathbf{v}_1, \mathbf{v}_2 \in W^{\perp}$. Then $\langle \mathbf{v}_1, \mathbf{w} \rangle = \langle \mathbf{v}_2, \mathbf{w} \rangle = 0$ for all $\mathbf{w} \in W$.

Hence, $\langle \mathbf{v}_1 + \mathbf{v}_2, \mathbf{w} \rangle = \langle \mathbf{v}_1, \mathbf{w} \rangle + \langle \mathbf{v}_2, \mathbf{w} \rangle = 0 + 0 = 0$ for all $\mathbf{w} \in W \Rightarrow \mathbf{v}_1 + \mathbf{v}_2 \in W^{\perp}$.

Let $\mathbf{v} \in W^{\perp}$ and $c \in R$. Then, $\langle \mathbf{v}, \mathbf{w} \rangle = 0$ for all $\mathbf{w} \in W$, and $\langle c\mathbf{u}, \mathbf{w} \rangle = c \langle \mathbf{v}, \mathbf{w} \rangle = c0 = 0$ for all $\mathbf{w} \in W \Rightarrow c\mathbf{v} \in W^{\perp}$.

(b) If $(x, y, z) \in W^{\perp}$, then $(x, y, z) \cdot (1, 2, 3) = 0 \Rightarrow x + 2y + 3z = 0$. Letting y and z be free variables, $x = -2y - 3z$, and a basis for $W^{\perp}$ is $\{(-2, 1, 0), (-3, 0, 1)\}$. $W^{\perp}$ is the plane orthogonal to the vector $(1, 2, 3)$.

61. Let $(c, 2c, 0)$ be any scalar multiple of $\mathbf{v} = (1, 2, 0)$.

The distance from $(c, 2c, 0)$ to $\mathbf{u} = (6, 2, 4)$ is

$$\sqrt{(c - 6)^2 + (2c - 2)^2 + (0 - 4)^2}$$

To find the c that minimizes this expression, you can use calculus to minimize the function

$$f(c) = (c - 6)^2 + (2c - 2)^2 + 4^2.$$

$f'(c) = 2(c - 6) + 4(2c - 2) = 0 \Rightarrow 10c = 20 \Rightarrow c = 2$, which is the minimum.
Thus, $(2, 4, 0)$ is the vector closest to $\mathbf{u}$.

Section 5.3   Orthonormal Bases: Gram-Schmidt Process

1. The set is *not* orthogonal because

$$(-4, 6) \cdot (5, 0) = -4(5) + 6(0) = -20 \neq 0.$$

3. The set is orthogonal because

$$\left(\tfrac{3}{5}, \tfrac{4}{5}\right) \cdot \left(-\tfrac{4}{5}, \tfrac{3}{5}\right) = \tfrac{3}{5}\left(-\tfrac{4}{5}\right) + \tfrac{4}{5}\left(\tfrac{3}{5}\right) = -\tfrac{12}{25} + \tfrac{12}{25} = 0.$$

Furthermore, the set is orthonormal because

$$\left\| \left(\tfrac{3}{5}, \tfrac{4}{5}\right) \right\| = \sqrt{\left(\tfrac{3}{5}\right)^2 + \left(\tfrac{4}{5}\right)^2} = 1$$

$$\left\| \left(-\tfrac{4}{5}, \tfrac{3}{5}\right) \right\| = \sqrt{\left(-\tfrac{4}{5}\right)^2 + \left(\tfrac{3}{5}\right)^2} = 1.$$

5. The set is orthogonal because

$$(4, -1, 1) \cdot (-1, 0, 4) = -4 + 4 = 0$$

$$(4, -1, 1) \cdot (-4, -17, -1) = -16 + 17 - 1 = 0$$

$$(-1, 0, 4) \cdot (-4, -17, -1) = 4 - 4 = 0.$$

However, the set is *not* orthonormal because

$$\| (4, -1, 1) \| = \sqrt{(4)^2 + (-1)^2 + 1^2} = \sqrt{18} \neq 1.$$

7. The set is *not* orthogonal because

$$\left(\frac{\sqrt{2}}{3}, 0, -\frac{\sqrt{2}}{6}\right) \cdot \left(0, \frac{2\sqrt{5}}{5}, -\frac{\sqrt{5}}{5}\right) = \frac{\sqrt{10}}{30} \neq 0.$$

9. The set is orthogonal because

$$\left(\frac{\sqrt{2}}{2}, 0, 0, \frac{\sqrt{2}}{2}\right) \cdot \left(0, \frac{\sqrt{2}}{2}, \frac{\sqrt{2}}{2}, 0\right) = 0$$

$$\left(\frac{\sqrt{2}}{2}, 0, 0, \frac{\sqrt{2}}{2}\right) \cdot \left(-\frac{1}{2}, \frac{1}{2}, -\frac{1}{2}, \frac{1}{2}\right) = 0$$

$$\left(0, \frac{\sqrt{2}}{2}, \frac{\sqrt{2}}{2}, 0\right) \cdot \left(-\frac{1}{2}, \frac{1}{2}, -\frac{1}{2}, \frac{1}{2}\right) = 0.$$

Furthermore, the set is orthonormal because

$$\left\|\left(\frac{\sqrt{2}}{2}, 0, 0, \frac{\sqrt{2}}{2}\right)\right\| = \sqrt{\frac{1}{2} + 0 + 0 + \frac{1}{2}} = 1$$

$$\left\|\left(0, \frac{\sqrt{2}}{2}, \frac{\sqrt{2}}{2}, 0\right)\right\| = \sqrt{0 + \frac{1}{2} + \frac{1}{2} + 0} = 1$$

$$\left\|\left(-\frac{1}{2}, \frac{1}{2}, -\frac{1}{2}, \frac{1}{2}\right)\right\| = \sqrt{\frac{1}{4} + \frac{1}{4} + \frac{1}{4} + \frac{1}{4}} = 1.$$

11. The set $\{1, x, x^2, x^3\}$ is orthogonal because

$$\langle 1, x \rangle = 0, \langle 1, x^2 \rangle = 0, \langle 1, x^3 \rangle = 0$$

$$\langle x, x^2 \rangle = 0, \langle x, x^3 \rangle = 0, \langle x^2, x^3 \rangle = 0.$$

Furthermore, the set is orthonormal because

$$\|1\| = 1, \|x\| = 1, \|x^2\| = 1 \text{ and } \|x^3\| = 1.$$

Hence, $\{1, x, x^2, x^3\}$ is an orthonormal basis for P_3.

13. We use Theorem 5.11 to find the coordinates of $\mathbf{x} = (1, 2)$ relative to B.

$$(1, 2) \cdot \left(-\frac{2\sqrt{13}}{13}, \frac{3\sqrt{13}}{13}\right) = -\frac{2\sqrt{13}}{13} + \frac{6\sqrt{13}}{13} = \frac{4\sqrt{13}}{13}$$

$$(1, 2) \cdot \left(\frac{3\sqrt{13}}{13}, \frac{2\sqrt{13}}{13}\right) = \frac{3\sqrt{13}}{13} + \frac{4\sqrt{13}}{13} = \frac{7\sqrt{13}}{13}$$

Thus, $[\mathbf{x}]_B = \left[\dfrac{4\sqrt{13}}{13}, \dfrac{7\sqrt{13}}{13}\right]^T.$

15. We use Theorem 5.11 to find the coordinates of $\mathbf{x} = (2, -2, 1)$ relative to B.

$$(2, -2, 1) \cdot \left(\frac{\sqrt{10}}{10}, 0, \frac{3\sqrt{10}}{10} \right) = \frac{2\sqrt{10}}{10} + \frac{3\sqrt{10}}{10} = \frac{\sqrt{10}}{2}$$

$$(2, -2, 1) \cdot (0, 1, 0) \qquad = -2$$

$$(2, -2, 1) \cdot \left(-\frac{3\sqrt{10}}{10}, 0, \frac{\sqrt{10}}{10} \right) = -\frac{6\sqrt{10}}{10} + \frac{\sqrt{10}}{10} = -\frac{\sqrt{10}}{2}$$

Thus, $[\mathbf{x}]_B = \left[\dfrac{\sqrt{10}}{2}, -2, \dfrac{-\sqrt{10}}{2} \right]^T$.

17. We use Theorem 5.11 to find the coordinates of $\mathbf{x} = (5, 10, 15)$ relative to B.

$$(5, 10, 15) \cdot \left(\tfrac{3}{5}, \tfrac{4}{5}, 0 \right) = \quad 3 + 8 = 11$$
$$(5, 10, 15) \cdot \left(-\tfrac{4}{5}, \tfrac{3}{5}, 0 \right) = -4 + 6 = \quad 2$$
$$(5, 10, 15) \cdot \left(0, 0, 1 \right) = \quad 15$$

Thus, $[\mathbf{x}]_B = [11, 2, 15]^T$.

19. First, we orthogonalize each vector in B.

$$\mathbf{w}_1 = \mathbf{v}_1 = (3, 4)$$

$$\mathbf{w}_2 = \mathbf{v}_2 - \frac{\langle \mathbf{v}_2, \mathbf{w}_1 \rangle}{\langle \mathbf{w}_1, \mathbf{w}_1 \rangle} \mathbf{w}_1 = (1, 0) - \frac{1(3) + 0(4)}{3^2 + 4^2} (3, 4)$$

$$= (1, 0) - \tfrac{3}{25} (3, 4) = \left(\tfrac{16}{25}, -\tfrac{12}{25} \right)$$

Then, we normalize the vectors.

$$\mathbf{u}_1 = \frac{\mathbf{w}_1}{\|\mathbf{w}_1\|} = \frac{1}{\sqrt{3^2 + 4^2}} (3, 4) = \left(\tfrac{3}{5}, \tfrac{4}{5} \right)$$

$$\mathbf{u}_2 = \frac{\mathbf{w}_2}{\|\mathbf{w}_2\|} = \frac{1}{\sqrt{\left(\tfrac{16}{25} \right)^2 + \left(-\tfrac{12}{25} \right)^2}} \left(\tfrac{16}{25}, -\tfrac{12}{25} \right) = \left(\tfrac{4}{5}, -\tfrac{3}{5} \right)$$

Thus, the orthonormal basis is $B' = \left\{ \left(\tfrac{3}{5}, \tfrac{4}{5} \right), \left(\tfrac{4}{5}, -\tfrac{3}{5} \right) \right\}$.

21. First we orthogonalize each vector in B.

$$\mathbf{w}_1 = \mathbf{v}_1 = (1, -1)$$

$$\mathbf{w}_2 = \mathbf{v}_2 - \frac{\langle \mathbf{v}_2, \mathbf{w}_1 \rangle}{\langle \mathbf{w}_1, \mathbf{w}_1 \rangle} \mathbf{w}_1$$

$$= (1, 1) - \frac{1(1) + (-1)(1)}{1^2 + (-1)^2}(1, -1)$$

$$= (1, 1) - 0(1, -1) = (1, 1)$$

In other words, the vectors were already orthogonal!

Then, we normalize the vectors.

$$\mathbf{u}_1 = \frac{\mathbf{w}_1}{\|\mathbf{w}_1\|} = \frac{1}{\sqrt{2}}(1, -1) = \left(\frac{1}{\sqrt{2}}, -\frac{1}{\sqrt{2}} \right)$$

$$\mathbf{u}_2 = \frac{\mathbf{w}_2}{\|\mathbf{w}_2\|} = \frac{1}{\sqrt{2}}(1, 1) = \left(\frac{1}{\sqrt{2}}, \frac{1}{\sqrt{2}} \right)$$

Thus, the orthonormal basis is

$$\left\{ \left(\frac{1}{\sqrt{2}}, -\frac{1}{\sqrt{2}} \right), \left(\frac{1}{\sqrt{2}}, \frac{1}{\sqrt{2}} \right) \right\}.$$

23. First we orthogonalize each vector in B.

$$\mathbf{w}_1 = \mathbf{v}_1 = (4, -3, 0)$$

$$\mathbf{w}_2 = \mathbf{v}_2 - \frac{\langle \mathbf{v}_2, \mathbf{w}_1 \rangle}{\langle \mathbf{w}_1, \mathbf{w}_1 \rangle} \mathbf{w}_1 = (1, 2, 0) - \frac{-2}{25}(4, -3, 0) = \left(\frac{33}{25}, \frac{44}{25}, 0 \right)$$

$$\mathbf{w}_3 = \mathbf{v}_3 - \frac{\langle \mathbf{v}_3, \mathbf{w}_1 \rangle}{\langle \mathbf{w}_1, \mathbf{w}_1 \rangle} \mathbf{w}_1 - \frac{\langle \mathbf{v}_3, \mathbf{w}_2 \rangle}{\langle \mathbf{w}_2, \mathbf{w}_2 \rangle} \mathbf{w}_2$$

$$= (0, 0, 4) - 0(4, -3, 0) - 0\left(\frac{33}{25}, \frac{44}{25}, 0 \right) = (0, 0, 4)$$

Then, we normalize the vectors.

$$\mathbf{u}_1 = \frac{\mathbf{w}_1}{\|\mathbf{w}_1\|} = \frac{1}{5}(4, -3, 0) = \left(\frac{4}{5}, -\frac{3}{5}, 0 \right)$$

$$\mathbf{u}_2 = \frac{\mathbf{w}_2}{\|\mathbf{w}_2\|} = \frac{5}{11}\left(\frac{33}{25}, \frac{44}{25}, 0 \right) = \left(\frac{3}{5}, \frac{4}{5}, 0 \right)$$

$$\mathbf{u}_3 = \frac{\mathbf{w}_3}{\|\mathbf{w}_3\|} = \frac{1}{4}(0, 0, 4) = (0, 0, 1)$$

Thus, the orthonormal basis is

$$\left\{ \left(\tfrac{4}{5}, -\tfrac{3}{5}, 0 \right), \left(\tfrac{3}{5}, \tfrac{4}{5}, 0 \right), (0, 0, 1) \right\}.$$

25. First, we orthogonalize each vector in B.

$$\mathbf{w}_1 = \mathbf{v}_1 = (0, 1, 1)$$

$$\mathbf{w}_2 = \mathbf{v}_2 - \frac{\langle \mathbf{v}_2, \mathbf{w}_1 \rangle}{\langle \mathbf{w}_1, \mathbf{w}_1 \rangle} \mathbf{w}_1 = (1, 1, 0) - \frac{1(0) + 1(1) + 0(1)}{0^2 + 1^2 + 1^2}(0, 1, 1)$$

$$= (1, 1, 0) - \tfrac{1}{2}(0, 1, 1) = \left(1, \tfrac{1}{2}, -\tfrac{1}{2}\right)$$

$$\mathbf{w}_3 = \mathbf{v}_3 - \frac{\langle \mathbf{v}_3, \mathbf{w}_2 \rangle}{\langle \mathbf{w}_2, \mathbf{w}_2 \rangle} \mathbf{w}_2 - \frac{\langle \mathbf{v}_3, \mathbf{w}_1 \rangle}{\langle \mathbf{w}_1, \mathbf{w}_1 \rangle} \mathbf{w}_1$$

$$= (1, 0, 1) - \frac{1(1) + 0\left(\tfrac{1}{2}\right) + 1\left(-\tfrac{1}{2}\right)}{1^2 + \left(\tfrac{1}{2}\right)^2 + \left(-\tfrac{1}{2}\right)^2}\left(1, \tfrac{1}{2}, -\tfrac{1}{2}\right) - \frac{1(0) + 0(1) + 1(1)}{0^2 + 1^2 + 1^2}(0, 1, 1)$$

$$= (1, 0, 1) - \tfrac{1}{3}\left(1, \tfrac{1}{2}, -\tfrac{1}{2}\right) - \tfrac{1}{2}(0, 1, 1) = \left(\tfrac{2}{3}, -\tfrac{2}{3}, \tfrac{2}{3}\right)$$

Then, we normalize the vectors.

$$\mathbf{u}_1 = \frac{\mathbf{w}_1}{\|\mathbf{w}_1\|} = \frac{1}{\sqrt{0^2 + 1^2 + 1^2}}(0, 1, 1) = \left(0, \frac{\sqrt{2}}{2}, \frac{\sqrt{2}}{2}\right)$$

$$\mathbf{u}_2 = \frac{\mathbf{w}_2}{\|\mathbf{w}_2\|} = \frac{1}{\sqrt{1^2 + \left(\tfrac{1}{2}\right)^2 + \left(-\tfrac{1}{2}\right)^2}}\left(1, \tfrac{1}{2}, -\tfrac{1}{2}\right) = \left(\frac{\sqrt{6}}{3}, \frac{\sqrt{6}}{6}, -\frac{\sqrt{6}}{6}\right)$$

$$\mathbf{u}_3 = \frac{\mathbf{w}_3}{\|\mathbf{w}_3\|} = \frac{1}{\sqrt{\left(\tfrac{2}{3}\right)^2 + \left(-\tfrac{2}{3}\right)^2 + \left(\tfrac{2}{3}\right)^2}}\left(\tfrac{2}{3}, -\tfrac{2}{3}, \tfrac{2}{3}\right) = \left(\frac{\sqrt{3}}{3}, -\frac{\sqrt{3}}{3}, \frac{\sqrt{3}}{3}\right)$$

Thus, the orthonormal basis is $B' =$

$$\left\{\left(0, \frac{\sqrt{2}}{2}, \frac{\sqrt{2}}{2}\right), \left(\frac{\sqrt{6}}{3}, \frac{\sqrt{6}}{3}, -\frac{\sqrt{6}}{6}\right), \left(\frac{\sqrt{3}}{3}, -\frac{\sqrt{3}}{3}, \frac{\sqrt{3}}{3}\right)\right\}.$$

27. Since there is just one vector, we simply need to normalize it.

$$\mathbf{u}_1 = \frac{1}{\sqrt{(-8)^2 + 3^2 + 5^2}}(-8, 3, 5) = \left(-\frac{4\sqrt{2}}{7}, \frac{3\sqrt{2}}{14}, \frac{5\sqrt{2}}{14}\right)$$

Thus, the orthonormal basis is

$$B' = \left\{\left(-\frac{4\sqrt{2}}{7}, \frac{3\sqrt{2}}{14}, \frac{5\sqrt{2}}{14}\right)\right\}.$$

29. First we orthogonalize each vector in B.

$$\mathbf{w}_1 = \mathbf{v}_1 = (3, 4, 0)$$

$$\mathbf{w}_2 = \mathbf{v}_2 - \frac{\langle \mathbf{v}_2, \mathbf{w}_1 \rangle}{\langle \mathbf{w}_1, \mathbf{w}_1 \rangle} \mathbf{w}_1 = (1, 0, 0) - \tfrac{3}{25}(3, 4, 0) = \left(\tfrac{16}{25}, -\tfrac{12}{25}, 0\right)$$

Then, we normalize the vectors.

$$\mathbf{u}_1 = \frac{\mathbf{w}_1}{\|\mathbf{w}_1\|} = \tfrac{1}{5}(3, 4, 0) = \left(\tfrac{3}{5}, \tfrac{4}{5}, 0\right)$$

$$\mathbf{u}_2 = \frac{\mathbf{w}_2}{\|\mathbf{w}_2\|} = \tfrac{1}{4/5}\left(\tfrac{16}{25}, -\tfrac{12}{25}, 0\right) = \left(\tfrac{4}{5}, -\tfrac{3}{5}, 0\right)$$

Thus, the orthonormal basis is $\left\{\left(\tfrac{3}{5}, \tfrac{4}{5}, 0\right), \left(\tfrac{4}{5}, -\tfrac{3}{5}, 0\right)\right\}$.

31. First we orthogonalize each vector in B.

$$\mathbf{w}_1 = \mathbf{v}_1 = (1, 2, -1, 0)$$

$$\mathbf{w}_2 = \mathbf{v}_2 - \frac{\langle \mathbf{v}_2, \mathbf{w}_1 \rangle}{\langle \mathbf{w}_1, \mathbf{w}_1 \rangle} \mathbf{w}_1$$

$$= (2, 2, 0, 1) - \frac{2(1) + 2(2) + 0(-1) + 1(0)}{1^2 + 2^2 + (-1)^2 + 0^2}(1, 2, -1, 0)$$

$$= (2, 2, 0, 1) - (1, 2, -1, 0) = (1, 0, 1, 1)$$

Then, we normalize the vectors.

$$\mathbf{u}_1 = \frac{\mathbf{w}_1}{\|\mathbf{w}_1\|} = \frac{1}{\sqrt{1^2 + 2^2 + (-1)^2 + 0^2}}(1, 2, -1, 0) = \left(\frac{\sqrt{6}}{6}, \frac{\sqrt{6}}{3}, -\frac{\sqrt{6}}{6}, 0\right)$$

$$\mathbf{u}_2 = \frac{\mathbf{w}_2}{\|\mathbf{w}_2\|} = \frac{1}{\sqrt{1^2 + 0^2 + 1^2 + 1^2}}(1, 0, 1, 1) = \left(\frac{\sqrt{3}}{3}, 0, \frac{\sqrt{3}}{3}, \frac{\sqrt{3}}{3}\right).$$

Thus, the orthonormal basis is

$$B' = \left\{\left(\frac{\sqrt{6}}{6}, \frac{\sqrt{6}}{3}, -\frac{\sqrt{6}}{6}, 0\right), \left(\frac{\sqrt{3}}{3}, 0, \frac{\sqrt{3}}{3}, \frac{\sqrt{3}}{3}\right)\right\}.$$

33. $\langle x, 1 \rangle = \displaystyle\int_{-1}^{1} x\,dx = \left.\frac{x^2}{2}\right]_{-1}^{1} = \tfrac{1}{2} - \tfrac{1}{2} = 0$

35. $\langle x^2, 1 \rangle = \displaystyle\int_{-1}^{1} x^2\,dx = \left.\frac{x^3}{3}\right]_{-1}^{1} = \tfrac{1}{3} - \left(-\tfrac{1}{3}\right) = \tfrac{2}{3}$

37. The solutions of the homogenous system are of the form $(3s, -2t, s, t)$, where s and t are any real numbers. Thus, a basis for the solution space is

$$\{(3, 0, 1, 0), (0, -2, 0, 1)\}.$$

We orthogonalize this basis as follows.

$$\mathbf{w}_1 = (3, 0, 1, 0)$$

$$\mathbf{w}_2 = (0, -2, 0, 1) - \frac{0(3) + (-2)(0) + 0(1) + 1(0)}{3^2 + 0^2 + 1^2 + 0^2}(3, 0, 1, 0) = (0, -2, 0, 1)$$

Then, we normalize these vectors.

$$\mathbf{u}_1 = \frac{\mathbf{w}_1}{\|\mathbf{w}_1\|} = \frac{1}{\sqrt{3^2 + 0^2 + 1^2 + 0^2}}(3, 0, 1, 0) = \left(\frac{3\sqrt{10}}{10}, 0, \frac{\sqrt{10}}{10}, 0\right)$$

$$\mathbf{u}_2 = \frac{\mathbf{w}_2}{\|\mathbf{w}_2\|} = \frac{1}{\sqrt{0^2 + (-2)^2 + 0^2 + 1^2}}(0, -2, 0, 1) = \left(0, -\frac{2\sqrt{5}}{5}, 0, \frac{\sqrt{5}}{5}\right)$$

Thus, the orthonormal basis for the solution set is

$$B' = \left\{\left(\frac{3\sqrt{10}}{10}, 0, \frac{\sqrt{10}}{10}, 0\right), \left(0, -\frac{2\sqrt{5}}{5}, 0, \frac{\sqrt{5}}{5}\right)\right\}.$$

39. The solutions of the homogenous system are of the form $(s + t, 0, s, t)$, where s and t are any real numbers. Thus, a basis for the solution space is

$$\{(1, 0, 1, 0), (1, 0, 0, 1)\}.$$

We orthogonalize this basis as follows.

$$\mathbf{w}_1 = \mathbf{u}_1 = (1, 0, 1, 0)$$

$$\mathbf{w}_2 = \mathbf{u}_2 - \frac{\langle \mathbf{u}_2, \mathbf{w}_1 \rangle}{\langle \mathbf{w}_1, \mathbf{w}_1 \rangle}\mathbf{w}_1 = (1, 0, 0, 1) - \tfrac{1}{2}(1, 0, 1, 0) = \left(\tfrac{1}{2}, 0, -\tfrac{1}{2}, 1\right)$$

Then, we normalize these vectors.

$$\mathbf{u}_1 = \frac{\mathbf{w}_1}{\|\mathbf{w}_1\|} = \frac{1}{\sqrt{2}}(1, 0, 1, 0) = \left(\frac{1}{\sqrt{2}}, 0, \frac{1}{\sqrt{2}}, 0\right)$$

$$\mathbf{u}_2 = \frac{\mathbf{w}_2}{\|\mathbf{w}_2\|} = \frac{1}{\sqrt{6}/2}\left(\tfrac{1}{2}, 0, -\tfrac{1}{2}, 1\right) = \left(\frac{1}{\sqrt{6}}, 0, -\frac{1}{\sqrt{6}}, \frac{2}{\sqrt{6}}\right)$$

Thus, an orthonormal basis for the solution space is

$$\left\{\left(\frac{1}{\sqrt{2}}, 0, \frac{1}{\sqrt{2}}, 0\right), \left(\frac{1}{\sqrt{6}}, 0, -\frac{1}{\sqrt{6}}, \frac{2}{\sqrt{6}}\right)\right\}.$$

41. Let

$$p(x) = \frac{x^2 + 1}{\sqrt{2}} \quad \text{and} \quad q(x) = \frac{x^2 + x - 1}{\sqrt{3}}.$$

Then

$$\langle \mathbf{p}, \mathbf{q} \rangle = \frac{1}{\sqrt{2}} \left(-\frac{1}{\sqrt{3}} \right) + 0 \left(\frac{1}{\sqrt{3}} \right) + \frac{1}{\sqrt{2}} \left(\frac{1}{\sqrt{3}} \right) = 0. \text{ Furthermore,}$$

$$\|\mathbf{p}\| = \sqrt{\left(\frac{1}{\sqrt{2}} \right)^2 + 0^2 + \left(\frac{1}{\sqrt{2}} \right)^2} = 1$$

$$\|\mathbf{q}\| = \sqrt{\left(-\frac{1}{\sqrt{3}} \right)^2 + \left(\frac{1}{\sqrt{3}} \right)^2 + \left(\frac{1}{\sqrt{3}} \right)^2} = 1.$$

Thus, $\{\mathbf{p}, \mathbf{q}\}$ is an orthonormal set.

43. Let $\mathbf{p}_1(x) = x^2$, $\mathbf{p}_2(x) = x^2 + 2x$, and $\mathbf{p}_3(x) = x^2 + 2x + 1$.

Then, since $\langle \mathbf{p}_1, \mathbf{p}_2 \rangle = 0(0) + 0(2) + 1(1) = 1 \neq 0$, the set is not orthogonal. We orthogonalize the set as follows.

$$\mathbf{w}_1 = \mathbf{p}_1 = x^2$$

$$\mathbf{w}_2 = \mathbf{p}_2 - \frac{\langle \mathbf{p}_2, \mathbf{w}_1 \rangle}{\langle \mathbf{w}_1, \mathbf{w}_1 \rangle} \mathbf{w}_1 = x^2 + 2x - \frac{0(0) + 2(0) + 1(1)}{0^2 + 0^2 + 1^2} x^2 = 2x$$

$$\mathbf{w}_3 = \mathbf{p}_3 - \frac{\langle \mathbf{p}_3, \mathbf{w}_2 \rangle}{\langle \mathbf{w}_2, \mathbf{w}_2 \rangle} \mathbf{w}_2 - \frac{\langle \mathbf{p}_3, \mathbf{w}_1 \rangle}{\langle \mathbf{w}_1, \mathbf{w}_1 \rangle} \mathbf{w}_1$$

$$= x^2 + 2x + 1 - \frac{1(0) + 2(2) + 1(0)}{0^2 + 2^2 + 0^2} (2x) - \frac{1(0) + 2(0) + 1(1)}{0^2 + 0^2 + 1^2} x^2$$

$$= x^2 + 2x + 1 - 2x - x^2 = 1$$

Then, we normalize the vectors.

$$\mathbf{u}_1 = \frac{\mathbf{w}_1}{\|\mathbf{w}_1\|} = \frac{1}{\sqrt{0^2 + 0^2 + 1^2}} x^2 = x^2$$

$$\mathbf{u}_2 = \frac{\mathbf{w}_2}{\|\mathbf{w}_2\|} = \frac{1}{\sqrt{0^2 + 2^2 + 0^2}} (2x) = x$$

$$\mathbf{u}_3 = \frac{\mathbf{w}_3}{\|\mathbf{w}_3\|} = \frac{1}{\sqrt{1^2 + 0^2 + 0^2}} (1) = 1$$

Thus, the orthonormal set is $\{x^2, x, 1\}$.

45. Let $\mathbf{p}(x) = x^2 - 1$ and $\mathbf{q}(x) = x - 1$. Then, since $\langle \mathbf{p}, \mathbf{q} \rangle = 1 \neq 0$, the set is not orthogonal. We orthogonalize the set as follows.

$$\mathbf{w}_1 = \mathbf{p} = x^2 - 1$$

$$\mathbf{w}_2 = \mathbf{q} - \frac{\langle \mathbf{q}, \mathbf{w}_1 \rangle}{\langle \mathbf{w}_1, \mathbf{w}_1 \rangle} \mathbf{w}_1 = (x - 1) - \frac{1}{2}(x^2 - 1) = -\frac{1}{2}x^2 + x - \frac{1}{2}$$

Then, we normalize the vectors.

$$\mathbf{u}_1 = \frac{\mathbf{w}_1}{\|\mathbf{w}_1\|} = \frac{1}{\sqrt{2}}(x^2 - 1) = \frac{1}{\sqrt{2}}x^2 - \frac{1}{\sqrt{2}}$$

$$\mathbf{u}_2 = \frac{\mathbf{w}_2}{\|\mathbf{w}_2\|} = \frac{1}{\sqrt{6}/2}\left(-\frac{1}{2}x^2 + x - \frac{1}{2}\right) = -\frac{1}{\sqrt{6}}x^2 + \frac{2}{\sqrt{6}}x - \frac{1}{\sqrt{6}}$$

Thus, the orthonormal set is $\left\{ \frac{1}{\sqrt{2}}x^2 - \frac{1}{\sqrt{2}}, -\frac{1}{\sqrt{6}}x^2 + \frac{2}{\sqrt{6}}x - \frac{1}{\sqrt{6}} \right\}$

47. We begin by orthogonalizing the set.

$$\mathbf{w}_1 = (2, -1)$$

$$\mathbf{w}_2 = (-2, 10) - \frac{2(-2)(2) + 10(-1)}{2(2)^2 + (-1)^2}(2, -1) = (-2, 10) + 2(2, -1) = (2, 8)$$

Then, we normalize each vector.

$$\mathbf{u}_1 = \frac{\mathbf{w}_1}{\|\mathbf{w}_1\|} = \frac{1}{\sqrt{2(2)^2 + (-1)^2}}(2, -1) = \left(\frac{2}{3}, -\frac{1}{3} \right)$$

$$\mathbf{u}_2 = \frac{\mathbf{w}_2}{\|\mathbf{w}_2\|} = \frac{1}{\sqrt{2(2)^2 + 8^2}}(2, 8) = \left(\frac{\sqrt{2}}{6}, \frac{2\sqrt{2}}{3} \right)$$

Thus, an orthonormal basis, using the given inner product is

$$\left\{ \left(\frac{2}{3}, -\frac{1}{3} \right), \left(\frac{\sqrt{2}}{6}, \frac{2\sqrt{2}}{3} \right) \right\}.$$

49. Let $\mathbf{v} = c_1\mathbf{v}_1 + c_2\mathbf{v}_2 + \cdots + c_n\mathbf{v}_n$ be a linear combination of vectors in S. Then we have

$$\langle \mathbf{w}, c_1\mathbf{v}_1 + \cdots + c_n\mathbf{v}_n \rangle = \langle \mathbf{w}, c_1\mathbf{v}_1 \rangle + \cdots + \langle \mathbf{w}, c_n\mathbf{v}_n \rangle$$

$$= c_1 \langle \mathbf{w}, \mathbf{v}_1 \rangle + \cdots + c_n \langle \mathbf{w}, \mathbf{v}_n \rangle$$

$$= 0,$$

since $\langle \mathbf{w}, \mathbf{v}_1 \rangle = \langle \mathbf{w}, \mathbf{v}_2 \rangle = \cdots = \langle \mathbf{w}, \mathbf{v}_n \rangle = 0$.

51. We will first prove that condition (a) implies (b). If $P^{-1} = P^T$, consider $\mathbf{p}_i$ the ith row vector of P. Since $P P^T = I_n$, we have $\mathbf{p}_i \mathbf{p}_i = 1$ and $\mathbf{p}_i \cdot \mathbf{p}_j = 0$, for $i \neq j$. Hence the row vectors of P form an orthonormal basis for R^n.

($b \Rightarrow c$) if the row vectors of P form an orthonormal basis, then $P P^T = I_n \Rightarrow P^T P = I_n$, which implies that the column vectors of P form an orthonormal basis.

($c \Rightarrow a$) since the column vectors of P form an orthonormal basis, we have $P^T P = I_n$, which implies that $P^{-1} = P^T$.

53. We note that $\mathbf{v}_1$ and $\mathbf{v}_2$ are orthogonal unit vectors. Furthermore, a vector (c_1, c_2, c_3, c_4) orthogonal to $\mathbf{v}_1$ and $\mathbf{v}_2$ satisfies the homogenous system of linear equations

$$\frac{1}{\sqrt{2}} c_1 \qquad + \frac{1}{\sqrt{2}} c_3 \qquad = 0$$
$$-\frac{1}{\sqrt{2}} c_2 \qquad + \frac{1}{\sqrt{2}} c_4 = 0,$$

which has solutions of the form $(-s, t, s, t)$, where s and t are any real numbers. A basis for the solution set is $\{(1, 0, -1, 0), (0, 1, 0, 1)\}$. Since $(1, 0, -1, 0)$ and $(0, 1, 0, 1)$ are already orthogonal, we simply normalize them to yield $\left(\frac{1}{\sqrt{2}}, 0, -\frac{1}{\sqrt{2}}, 0\right)$ and $\left(0, \frac{1}{\sqrt{2}}, 0, \frac{1}{\sqrt{2}}\right)$. Thus,

$$\left\{ \left(\frac{1}{\sqrt{2}}, 0, \frac{1}{\sqrt{2}}, 0\right), \left(0, -\frac{1}{\sqrt{2}}, 0, \frac{1}{\sqrt{2}}\right), \left(\frac{1}{\sqrt{2}}, 0, -\frac{1}{\sqrt{2}}, 0\right), \left(0, \frac{1}{\sqrt{2}}, 0, \frac{1}{\sqrt{2}}\right) \right\}$$

is an orthonormal basis.

55. $A = \begin{bmatrix} 1 & 1 & -1 \\ 0 & 2 & 1 \\ 1 & 3 & 0 \end{bmatrix} \Rightarrow \begin{bmatrix} 2 & 0 & -3 \\ 0 & 2 & 1 \\ 0 & 0 & 0 \end{bmatrix}$

$A^T = \begin{bmatrix} 1 & 0 & 1 \\ 1 & 2 & 3 \\ -1 & 1 & 0 \end{bmatrix} \Rightarrow \begin{bmatrix} 1 & 0 & 1 \\ 0 & 1 & 1 \\ 0 & 0 & 0 \end{bmatrix}$

$N(A)$-basis: $\left\{ \begin{bmatrix} 3 \\ -1 \\ 2 \end{bmatrix} \right\}$

$N(A^T)$-basis: $\left\{ \begin{bmatrix} 1 \\ 1 \\ -1 \end{bmatrix} \right\}$

$R(A)$-basis: $\left\{ \begin{bmatrix} 1 \\ 0 \\ 1 \end{bmatrix}, \begin{bmatrix} 1 \\ 2 \\ 3 \end{bmatrix} \right\}$

$R(A^T)$-basis: $\left\{ \begin{bmatrix} 1 \\ 1 \\ -1 \end{bmatrix}, \begin{bmatrix} 0 \\ 2 \\ 1 \end{bmatrix} \right\}$

$N(A) = R(A^T)^{\perp}$ and $N(A^T) = R(A)^{\perp}$

57. $A = \begin{bmatrix} 1 & 0 & 1 \\ 1 & 1 & 1 \end{bmatrix} \Rightarrow \begin{bmatrix} 1 & 0 & 1 \\ 0 & 1 & 0 \end{bmatrix}$

$A^T = \begin{bmatrix} 1 & 1 \\ 0 & 1 \\ 1 & 1 \end{bmatrix} \Rightarrow \begin{bmatrix} 1 & 0 \\ 0 & 1 \\ 0 & 0 \end{bmatrix}$

$N(A)$-basis: $\left\{ \begin{bmatrix} -1 \\ 0 \\ 1 \end{bmatrix} \right\}$

$N(A^T) = \left\{ \begin{bmatrix} 0 \\ 0 \end{bmatrix} \right\}$

$R(A)$-basis: $\left\{ \begin{bmatrix} 1 \\ 1 \end{bmatrix}, \begin{bmatrix} 0 \\ 1 \end{bmatrix} \right\}$ $\quad (R(A) = R^2)$

$R(A^T)$-basis: $\left\{ \begin{bmatrix} 1 \\ 0 \\ 1 \end{bmatrix}, \begin{bmatrix} 1 \\ 1 \\ 1 \end{bmatrix} \right\}$

$N(A) = R(A^T)^\perp$ and $N(A^T) = R(A)^\perp$

59. (a) The row space of A is the column space of A^T, $R(A^T)$.

(b) Let $\mathbf{x} \in N(A) \Rightarrow A\mathbf{x} = \mathbf{0} \Rightarrow \mathbf{x}$ is orthogonal to all the rows of $A \Rightarrow \mathbf{x}$ is orthogonal to all the columns of $A^T \Rightarrow \mathbf{x} \in R(A^T)^\perp$.

(c) Let $\mathbf{x} \in R(A^T)^\perp \Rightarrow \mathbf{x}$ is orthogonal to each column vector of $A^T \Rightarrow A\mathbf{x} = \mathbf{0} \Rightarrow \mathbf{x} \in N(A)$. Combining this with part (b), $N(A) = R(A^T)^\perp$.

(d) Let $A = A^T$ and apply part (c).

Section 5.4   Mathematical Models and Least Squares Analysis

1. Not orthogonal: $\begin{bmatrix} 0 \\ 1 \\ 1 \end{bmatrix} \cdot \begin{bmatrix} -1 \\ 2 \\ 0 \end{bmatrix} = 2 \neq 0.$

3. Orthogonal: $\begin{bmatrix} 1 \\ 1 \\ 1 \\ 1 \end{bmatrix} \cdot \begin{bmatrix} -1 \\ 1 \\ -1 \\ 1 \end{bmatrix} = \begin{bmatrix} 1 \\ 1 \\ 1 \\ 1 \end{bmatrix} \cdot \begin{bmatrix} 0 \\ 2 \\ -2 \\ 0 \end{bmatrix} = 0$

5. $S = \text{span}\left(\begin{bmatrix} 1 \\ 0 \\ 0 \end{bmatrix}, \begin{bmatrix} 0 \\ 0 \\ 1 \end{bmatrix} \right) \Rightarrow S^\perp = \text{span}\left\{ \begin{bmatrix} 0 \\ 1 \\ 0 \end{bmatrix} \right\}$ (The *y*-axis)

7. $A^T = \begin{bmatrix} 1 & 2 & 0 & 0 \\ 0 & 1 & 0 & 1 \end{bmatrix} \Rightarrow \begin{bmatrix} 1 & 0 & 0 & -2 \\ 0 & 1 & 0 & 1 \end{bmatrix} \Rightarrow S^\perp\text{-basis is} \left\{ \begin{bmatrix} 0 \\ 0 \\ 1 \\ 0 \end{bmatrix}, \begin{bmatrix} 2 \\ -1 \\ 0 \\ 1 \end{bmatrix} \right\}$

9. The orthogonal complement of span $\left\{ \begin{bmatrix} 0 \\ 0 \\ 1 \\ 0 \end{bmatrix}, \begin{bmatrix} 2 \\ -1 \\ 0 \\ 1 \end{bmatrix} \right\} = S^\perp$

is $(S^\perp)^\perp = S = \text{span}\left(\begin{bmatrix} 1 \\ 2 \\ 0 \\ 0 \end{bmatrix}, \begin{bmatrix} 0 \\ 1 \\ 0 \\ 1 \end{bmatrix} \right).$

11. An orthonormal basis for *S* is $\left\{ \begin{bmatrix} 0 \\ 0 \\ -\frac{1}{\sqrt{2}} \\ \frac{1}{\sqrt{2}} \end{bmatrix}, \begin{bmatrix} 0 \\ \frac{1}{\sqrt{3}} \\ \frac{1}{\sqrt{3}} \\ \frac{1}{\sqrt{3}} \end{bmatrix} \right\}.$

$\text{proj}_S \mathbf{v} = (\mathbf{v} \cdot \mathbf{u}_1)\, \mathbf{u}_1 + (\mathbf{v} \cdot \mathbf{u}_2)\, \mathbf{u}_2 = 0\mathbf{u}_1 + \frac{2}{\sqrt{3}} \begin{bmatrix} 0 \\ \frac{1}{\sqrt{3}} \\ \frac{1}{\sqrt{3}} \\ \frac{1}{\sqrt{3}} \end{bmatrix} = \begin{bmatrix} 0 \\ \frac{2}{3} \\ \frac{2}{3} \\ \frac{2}{3} \end{bmatrix}$

13. We use Gram-Schmidt to construct an orthonormal basis for S.

$$\begin{bmatrix} 0 \\ 1 \\ 1 \end{bmatrix} - \frac{1}{2} \begin{bmatrix} 1 \\ 0 \\ 1 \end{bmatrix} = \begin{bmatrix} -\frac{1}{2} \\ 1 \\ \frac{1}{2} \end{bmatrix}$$

orthonormal basis: $\left\{ \begin{bmatrix} \frac{1}{\sqrt{2}} \\ 0 \\ \frac{1}{\sqrt{2}} \end{bmatrix}, \begin{bmatrix} -\frac{1}{\sqrt{6}} \\ \frac{2}{\sqrt{6}} \\ \frac{1}{\sqrt{6}} \end{bmatrix} \right\}.$

$$\text{proj}_S \mathbf{v} = (\mathbf{u}_1 \cdot \mathbf{v})\,\mathbf{u}_1 + (\mathbf{u}_2 \cdot \mathbf{v})\,\mathbf{u}_2 = \frac{6}{\sqrt{2}} \begin{bmatrix} \frac{1}{\sqrt{2}} \\ 0 \\ \frac{1}{\sqrt{2}} \end{bmatrix} + \frac{8}{\sqrt{6}} \begin{bmatrix} -\frac{1}{\sqrt{6}} \\ \frac{2}{\sqrt{6}} \\ \frac{1}{\sqrt{6}} \end{bmatrix} = \begin{bmatrix} 3 \\ 0 \\ 3 \end{bmatrix} + \begin{bmatrix} -\frac{4}{3} \\ \frac{8}{3} \\ \frac{4}{3} \end{bmatrix} = \begin{bmatrix} \frac{5}{3} \\ \frac{8}{3} \\ \frac{13}{3} \end{bmatrix}$$

15. We use Gram-Schmidt to construct an orthonormal basis for the column space of A.

$$\begin{bmatrix} 2 \\ 1 \\ 1 \end{bmatrix} - \frac{3}{2} \begin{bmatrix} 1 \\ 0 \\ 1 \end{bmatrix} = \begin{bmatrix} \frac{1}{2} \\ 1 \\ -\frac{1}{2} \end{bmatrix}$$

orthonormal basis: $\left\{ \begin{bmatrix} \frac{1}{\sqrt{2}} \\ 0 \\ \frac{1}{\sqrt{2}} \end{bmatrix}, \begin{bmatrix} \frac{1}{\sqrt{6}} \\ \frac{2}{\sqrt{6}} \\ -\frac{1}{\sqrt{6}} \end{bmatrix} \right\}$

$$\text{proj}_S \mathbf{b} = (\mathbf{u}_1 \cdot \mathbf{b})\,\mathbf{u}_1 + (\mathbf{u}_2 \cdot \mathbf{b})\,\mathbf{u}_2 = \frac{3}{\sqrt{2}} \begin{bmatrix} \frac{1}{\sqrt{2}} \\ 0 \\ \frac{1}{\sqrt{2}} \end{bmatrix} + \frac{-3}{\sqrt{6}} \begin{bmatrix} \frac{1}{\sqrt{6}} \\ \frac{2}{\sqrt{6}} \\ -\frac{1}{\sqrt{6}} \end{bmatrix} = \begin{bmatrix} \frac{3}{2} \\ 0 \\ \frac{3}{2} \end{bmatrix} + \begin{bmatrix} -\frac{1}{2} \\ -1 \\ \frac{1}{2} \end{bmatrix} = \begin{bmatrix} 1 \\ -1 \\ 2 \end{bmatrix}$$

17. $A = \begin{bmatrix} 1 & 2 & 3 \\ 0 & 1 & 0 \end{bmatrix} \Rightarrow \begin{bmatrix} 1 & 0 & 3 \\ 0 & 1 & 0 \end{bmatrix}$

$A^T = \begin{bmatrix} 1 & 0 \\ 2 & 1 \\ 3 & 0 \end{bmatrix} \Rightarrow \begin{bmatrix} 1 & 0 \\ 0 & 1 \\ 0 & 0 \end{bmatrix}$

$N(A)$-basis: $\left\{ \begin{bmatrix} -3 \\ 0 \\ 1 \end{bmatrix} \right\}$

$N(A^T) = \left\{ \begin{bmatrix} 0 \\ 0 \end{bmatrix} \right\}$

$R(A)$-basis: $\left\{ \begin{bmatrix} 1 \\ 0 \end{bmatrix}, \begin{bmatrix} 2 \\ 1 \end{bmatrix} \right\}$ $(R(A) = R^2)$

$R(A^T)$-basis: $\left\{ \begin{bmatrix} 1 \\ 2 \\ 3 \end{bmatrix}, \begin{bmatrix} 0 \\ 1 \\ 0 \end{bmatrix} \right\}$

19. $A = \begin{bmatrix} 1 & 0 & 0 & 1 \\ 0 & 1 & 1 & 1 \\ 1 & 1 & 1 & 2 \\ 1 & 2 & 2 & 3 \end{bmatrix} \Rightarrow \begin{bmatrix} 1 & 0 & 0 & 1 \\ 0 & 1 & 1 & 1 \\ 0 & 0 & 0 & 0 \\ 0 & 0 & 0 & 0 \end{bmatrix}$

$A^T = \begin{bmatrix} 1 & 0 & 1 & 1 \\ 0 & 1 & 1 & 2 \\ 0 & 1 & 1 & 2 \\ 1 & 1 & 2 & 3 \end{bmatrix} \Rightarrow \begin{bmatrix} 1 & 0 & 1 & 1 \\ 0 & 1 & 1 & 2 \\ 0 & 0 & 0 & 0 \\ 0 & 0 & 0 & 0 \end{bmatrix}$

$N(A)$-basis: $\left\{ \begin{bmatrix} -1 \\ -1 \\ 0 \\ 1 \end{bmatrix}, \begin{bmatrix} 0 \\ -1 \\ 1 \\ 0 \end{bmatrix} \right\}$

$N(A^T)$-basis: $\left\{ \begin{bmatrix} -1 \\ -1 \\ 1 \\ 0 \end{bmatrix}, \begin{bmatrix} -1 \\ -2 \\ 0 \\ 1 \end{bmatrix} \right\}$

$R(A)$-basis: $\left\{ \begin{bmatrix} 1 \\ 0 \\ 1 \\ 1 \end{bmatrix}, \begin{bmatrix} 0 \\ 1 \\ 1 \\ 2 \end{bmatrix} \right\}$

$R(A^T)$-basis: $\left\{ \begin{bmatrix} 1 \\ 0 \\ 0 \\ 1 \end{bmatrix}, \begin{bmatrix} 0 \\ 1 \\ 1 \\ 1 \end{bmatrix} \right\}$

21. $A^T A = \begin{bmatrix} 2 & 1 & 1 \\ 1 & 2 & 1 \end{bmatrix} \begin{bmatrix} 2 & 1 \\ 1 & 2 \\ 1 & 1 \end{bmatrix} = \begin{bmatrix} 6 & 5 \\ 5 & 6 \end{bmatrix}$

$A^T \mathbf{b} = \begin{bmatrix} 2 & 1 & 1 \\ 1 & 2 & 1 \end{bmatrix} \begin{bmatrix} 2 \\ 0 \\ -3 \end{bmatrix} = \begin{bmatrix} 1 \\ -1 \end{bmatrix}$

$\begin{bmatrix} 6 & 5 & 1 \\ 5 & 6 & -1 \end{bmatrix} \Rightarrow \begin{bmatrix} 1 & 0 & 1 \\ 0 & 1 & -1 \end{bmatrix} \Rightarrow \mathbf{x} = \begin{bmatrix} 1 \\ -1 \end{bmatrix}$

23. $A^T A = \begin{bmatrix} 1 & 1 & 0 & 1 \\ 0 & 1 & 1 & 1 \\ 1 & 1 & 1 & 0 \end{bmatrix} \begin{bmatrix} 1 & 0 & 1 \\ 1 & 1 & 1 \\ 0 & 1 & 1 \\ 1 & 1 & 0 \end{bmatrix} = \begin{bmatrix} 3 & 2 & 2 \\ 2 & 3 & 2 \\ 2 & 2 & 3 \end{bmatrix}$

$A^T \mathbf{b} = \begin{bmatrix} 1 & 1 & 0 & 1 \\ 0 & 1 & 1 & 1 \\ 1 & 1 & 1 & 0 \end{bmatrix} \begin{bmatrix} 4 \\ -1 \\ 0 \\ 1 \end{bmatrix} = \begin{bmatrix} 4 \\ 0 \\ 3 \end{bmatrix}$

$\begin{bmatrix} 3 & 2 & 2 & 4 \\ 2 & 3 & 2 & 0 \\ 2 & 2 & 3 & 3 \end{bmatrix} \Rightarrow \begin{bmatrix} 1 & 0 & 0 & 2 \\ 0 & 1 & 0 & -2 \\ 0 & 0 & 1 & 1 \end{bmatrix} \Rightarrow \mathbf{x} = \begin{bmatrix} 2 \\ -2 \\ 1 \end{bmatrix}$

25. $A^T A = \begin{bmatrix} 1 & 1 & 1 \\ -1 & 1 & 3 \end{bmatrix} \begin{bmatrix} 1 & -1 \\ 1 & 1 \\ 1 & 3 \end{bmatrix} = \begin{bmatrix} 3 & 3 \\ 3 & 11 \end{bmatrix}$

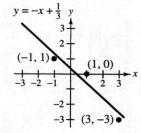

$A^T \mathbf{b} = \begin{bmatrix} 1 & 1 & 1 \\ -1 & 1 & 3 \end{bmatrix} \begin{bmatrix} 1 \\ 0 \\ -3 \end{bmatrix} = \begin{bmatrix} -2 \\ -10 \end{bmatrix}$

$\begin{bmatrix} 3 & 3 & -2 \\ 3 & 11 & -10 \end{bmatrix} \Rightarrow \begin{bmatrix} 1 & 0 & \frac{1}{3} \\ 0 & 1 & -1 \end{bmatrix} \Rightarrow \mathbf{x} = \begin{bmatrix} \frac{1}{3} \\ -1 \end{bmatrix}$

line: $y = \dfrac{1}{3} - x.$

27. $A^T A = \begin{bmatrix} 1 & 1 & 1 & 1 \\ -3 & -2 & 0 & 1 \end{bmatrix} \begin{bmatrix} 1 & -3 \\ 1 & -2 \\ 1 & 0 \\ 1 & 1 \end{bmatrix} = \begin{bmatrix} 4 & -4 \\ -4 & 14 \end{bmatrix}$

$A^T \mathbf{b} = \begin{bmatrix} 1 & 1 & 1 & 1 \\ -3 & -2 & 0 & 1 \end{bmatrix} \begin{bmatrix} -3 \\ -2 \\ 0 \\ 2 \end{bmatrix} = \begin{bmatrix} -3 \\ 15 \end{bmatrix}$

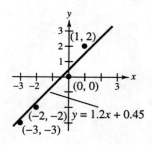

$\begin{bmatrix} 4 & -4 & -3 \\ -4 & 14 & 15 \end{bmatrix} \Rightarrow \begin{bmatrix} 1 & 0 & 0.45 \\ 0 & 1 & 1.2 \end{bmatrix} \Rightarrow \mathbf{x} = \begin{bmatrix} 0.45 \\ 1.2 \end{bmatrix}$

line: $y = 0.45 + 1.2\mathbf{x}$

29. $A^TA = \begin{bmatrix} 1 & 1 & 1 & 1 & 1 \\ -2 & -1 & 0 & 1 & 2 \\ 4 & 1 & 0 & 1 & 4 \end{bmatrix} \begin{bmatrix} 1 & -2 & 4 \\ 1 & -1 & 1 \\ 1 & 0 & 0 \\ 1 & 1 & 1 \\ 1 & 2 & 4 \end{bmatrix} = \begin{bmatrix} 5 & 0 & 10 \\ 0 & 10 & 0 \\ 10 & 0 & 34 \end{bmatrix}$

$A^Tb = \begin{bmatrix} 1 & 1 & 1 & 1 & 1 \\ -2 & -1 & 0 & 1 & 2 \\ 4 & 1 & 0 & 1 & 4 \end{bmatrix} \begin{bmatrix} 0 \\ 0 \\ 1 \\ 2 \\ 5 \end{bmatrix} = \begin{bmatrix} 8 \\ 12 \\ 22 \end{bmatrix}$

$\begin{bmatrix} 5 & 0 & 10 & 8 \\ 0 & 10 & 0 & 12 \\ 10 & 0 & 34 & 22 \end{bmatrix} \Rightarrow \begin{bmatrix} 1 & 0 & 0 & \frac{26}{35} \\ 0 & 1 & 0 & \frac{6}{5} \\ 0 & 0 & 1 & \frac{3}{7} \end{bmatrix}$

$\Rightarrow y = \dfrac{26}{35} + \dfrac{6}{5}x + \dfrac{3}{7}x^2$

31. Least squares quadratic polynomials seem appropriate for Kmart ($t = 5$ corresponds to 1985)

$$p(t) = 131.8t^2 - 67.9t + 19{,}494.6 \qquad 5 \le t \le 12$$
$$p(13) \approx 40{,}886.$$

For Wal-Mart,

$$p(t) = 749.0t^2 - 6248.4t + 21918.3 \qquad 5 \le t \le 12$$
$$p(13) \approx 67{,}270.$$

33. Let $\mathbf{v} \in S_1 \cap Sz$. Since $\mathbf{v} \in S_1$, $\mathbf{v} \cdot \mathbf{x}_2 = 0$ for all

$\mathbf{x}_2 \in S_2 \Rightarrow \mathbf{v} \cdot \mathbf{v} = 0$, since $\mathbf{v} \in S_2$

$\Rightarrow \mathbf{v} = \mathbf{0}.$

35. Let $\mathbf{v} \in R^n$, $\mathbf{v} = \mathbf{v}_1 + \mathbf{v}_2$, $\mathbf{v}_1 \in S$, $\mathbf{v}_2 \in S^\perp$.
Let $\{\mathbf{u}_1, \ldots, \mathbf{u}_t\}$ be an orthonormal basis for S.
Then

$\mathbf{v} = \mathbf{v}_1 + \mathbf{v}_2 = c_1\mathbf{u}_1 + \cdots + c_t\mathbf{u}_t + \mathbf{v}_2$, $c_i \in R$.

and

$\mathbf{v} \cdot \mathbf{u}_i = (c_1\mathbf{u}_1 + \cdots + c_t\mathbf{u}_t + \mathbf{v}_2) \cdot \mathbf{u}_i$
$= c_i(\mathbf{u}_i \cdot \mathbf{u}_i)$
$= c_i$

which shows that $\mathbf{v}_1 = \text{proj}_s\mathbf{v} = (\mathbf{v} \cdot \mathbf{u}_i)\mathbf{u}_1 + \cdots + (\mathbf{v} \cdot \mathbf{u}_z)\mathbf{u}_t$

37. If A has orthonormal columns, then $A^TA = I$ and the normal equations become

$A^TA\mathbf{x} = A^Tb$
$\mathbf{x} = A^Tb.$

Section 5.5   Applications of Inner Product Spaces

1. The cross product is

$$\mathbf{u} \times \mathbf{v} = \begin{vmatrix} \mathbf{i} & \mathbf{j} & \mathbf{k} \\ 1 & 0 & 0 \\ 0 & 1 & 0 \end{vmatrix} = \mathbf{k} = (0, 0, 1).$$

Furthermore, $\mathbf{u} \times \mathbf{v} = \mathbf{k}$ is orthogonal to both $(1, 0, 0)$ and $(0, 1, 0)$ because,

$$(1, 0, 0) \cdot (0, 0, 1) = 0 \quad \text{and} \quad (0, 1, 0) \cdot (0, 0, 1) = 0.$$

3. The cross product is

$$\mathbf{u} \times \mathbf{v} = \begin{vmatrix} \mathbf{i} & \mathbf{j} & \mathbf{k} \\ 0 & 1 & 0 \\ 0 & 0 & 1 \end{vmatrix} = \mathbf{i} = (1, 0, 0).$$

Furthermore, $\mathbf{u} \times \mathbf{v} = \mathbf{i}$ is orthogonal to both $\mathbf{u} = \mathbf{j}$ and $\mathbf{v} = \mathbf{k}$ because,

$$\mathbf{i} \cdot \mathbf{j} = 1(0) + 0(1) + 0(0) = 0$$

$$\mathbf{i} \cdot \mathbf{k} = 1(0) + 0(0) + 0(1) = 0.$$

5. The cross product is

$$\mathbf{u} \times \mathbf{v} = \begin{vmatrix} \mathbf{i} & \mathbf{j} & \mathbf{k} \\ 1 & 1 & 1 \\ 2 & 1 & -1 \end{vmatrix} = -2\mathbf{i} + 3\mathbf{j} - \mathbf{k} = (-2, 3, -1).$$

Furthermore, $\mathbf{u} \times \mathbf{v} = (-2, 3, -1)$ is orthogonal to both $(1, 1, 1)$ and $(2, 1, -1)$ because,

$$(-2, 3, -1) \cdot (1, 1, 1) = 0 \quad \text{and} \quad (-2, 3, -1) \cdot (2, 1, -1) = 0.$$

7. Since

$$\mathbf{u} \times \mathbf{v} = \begin{vmatrix} \mathbf{i} & \mathbf{j} & \mathbf{k} \\ 0 & 1 & 0 \\ 0 & 1 & 1 \end{vmatrix} = \mathbf{i},$$

the area of the parallelogram is

$$\|\mathbf{u} \times \mathbf{v}\| = \|\mathbf{i}\| = 1.$$

9. Since

$$\mathbf{u} \times \mathbf{v} = \begin{vmatrix} \mathbf{i} & \mathbf{j} & \mathbf{k} \\ 3 & 2 & -1 \\ 1 & 2 & 3 \end{vmatrix} = 8\mathbf{i} - 10\mathbf{j} + 4\mathbf{k} = (8, -10, 4),$$

the area of the parallelogram is

$$\|(8, -10, 4)\| = \sqrt{8^2 + (-10)^2 + 4^2} = \sqrt{180} = 6\sqrt{5}.$$

11. Since

$$\mathbf{v} \times \mathbf{w} = \begin{vmatrix} \mathbf{i} & \mathbf{j} & \mathbf{k} \\ 0 & 1 & 0 \\ 0 & 0 & 1 \end{vmatrix} = \mathbf{i},$$

the triple scalar product of **u, v,** and **w** is

$$\mathbf{u} \cdot (\mathbf{v} \times \mathbf{w}) = \mathbf{i} \cdot \mathbf{i} = 1.$$

13. Since

$$\mathbf{v} \times \mathbf{w} = \begin{vmatrix} \mathbf{i} & \mathbf{j} & \mathbf{k} \\ 0 & 3 & 0 \\ 0 & 0 & 1 \end{vmatrix} = 3\mathbf{i} = (3, 0, 0),$$

the triple scalar product is

$$\mathbf{u} \cdot (\mathbf{v} \times \mathbf{w}) = (2, 0, 1) \cdot (3, 0, 0) = 6.$$

15. Since

$$\mathbf{v} \times \mathbf{w} = \begin{vmatrix} \mathbf{i} & \mathbf{j} & \mathbf{k} \\ 0 & 1 & 1 \\ 1 & 0 & 2 \end{vmatrix} = (2, 1, -1),$$

the volume is given by

$$\|\mathbf{u} \cdot (\mathbf{v} \times \mathbf{w})\| = \|(1, 1, 0) \cdot (2, 1, -1)\| = 1(2) + 1(1) + 0(-1) = 3.$$

17. We have

$$c\mathbf{u} \times \mathbf{v} = \begin{vmatrix} \mathbf{i} & \mathbf{j} & \mathbf{k} \\ cu_1 & cu_2 & cu_3 \\ v_1 & v_2 & v_3 \end{vmatrix} = c \begin{vmatrix} \mathbf{i} & \mathbf{j} & \mathbf{k} \\ u_1 & u_2 & u_3 \\ v_1 & v_2 & v_3 \end{vmatrix} = c(\mathbf{u} \times \mathbf{v})$$

$$= \begin{vmatrix} \mathbf{i} & \mathbf{j} & \mathbf{k} \\ u_1 & u_2 & u_3 \\ cv_1 & cv_2 & cv_3 \end{vmatrix} = \mathbf{u} \times (c\mathbf{v}).$$

19. $\mathbf{u} \times \mathbf{0} = \begin{vmatrix} \mathbf{i} & \mathbf{j} & \mathbf{k} \\ u_1 & u_2 & u_3 \\ 0 & 0 & 0 \end{vmatrix} = \mathbf{0} = \begin{vmatrix} \mathbf{i} & \mathbf{j} & \mathbf{k} \\ 0 & 0 & 0 \\ u_1 & u_2 & u_3 \end{vmatrix} = \mathbf{0} \times \mathbf{u}$

21. $\mathbf{u} \cdot (\mathbf{v} \times \mathbf{w}) = \mathbf{u} \cdot \begin{vmatrix} \mathbf{i} & \mathbf{j} & \mathbf{k} \\ v_1 & v_2 & v_3 \\ w_1 & w_2 & w_3 \end{vmatrix}$

$$= (u_1, u_2, u_3) \cdot [(v_2 w_3 - v_3 w_2)\mathbf{i} - (v_1 w_3 - v_3 w_1)\mathbf{j} + (v_1 w_2 - v_2 w_1)\mathbf{k}]$$

$$= u_1 (v_2 w_3 - v_3 w_2) - u_2 (v_1 w_3 - v_3 w_1) + u_3 (v_1 w_2 - v_2 w_1)$$

$$= (u_2 v_3 - u_3 v_2)w_1 - (u_1 v_3 - v_1 u_3)w_2 + (u_1 v_2 - v_1 u_2)w_3$$

$$= \begin{vmatrix} \mathbf{i} & \mathbf{j} & \mathbf{k} \\ u_1 & u_2 & u_3 \\ v_1 & v_2 & v_3 \end{vmatrix} \cdot (w_1, w_2, w_3)$$

$$= (\mathbf{u} \times \mathbf{v}) \cdot \mathbf{w}$$

23. $\|\mathbf{u}\| \, \|\mathbf{v}\| \sin \theta = \|\mathbf{u}\| \, \|\mathbf{v}\| \sqrt{1 - \cos^2 \theta}$

$$= \|\mathbf{u}\| \, \|\mathbf{v}\| \sqrt{1 - \frac{(\mathbf{u} \cdot \mathbf{v})^2}{\|\mathbf{u}\|^2 \, \|\mathbf{v}\|^2}}$$

$$= \sqrt{\|\mathbf{u}\|^2 \, \|\mathbf{v}\|^2 - (\mathbf{u} \cdot \mathbf{v})^2}$$

$$= \sqrt{(u_1^2 + u_2^2 + u_3^2)(v_1^2 + v_2^2 + v_3^2) - (u_1 v_1 + u_2 v_2 + u_3 v_3)^2}$$

$$= \sqrt{(u_2 v_3 - u_3 v_2)^2 - (u_3 v_1 - u_1 v_3)^2 + (u_1 v_2 - u_2 v_1)^2}$$

$$= \|\mathbf{u} \times \mathbf{v}\|$$

25. $\|\mathbf{u} \times \mathbf{v}\|^2 = \|\mathbf{u}\|^2 \, \|\mathbf{v}\|^2 \sin^2 \theta$

$$= \|\mathbf{u}\|^2 \, \|\mathbf{v}\|^2 (1 - \cos^2 \theta)$$

$$= \|\mathbf{u}\|^2 \, \|\mathbf{v}\|^2 \left(1 - \frac{(\mathbf{u} \cdot \mathbf{v})^2}{\|\mathbf{u}\|^2 \, \|\mathbf{v}\|^2}\right)$$

$$= \|\mathbf{u}\|^2 \, \|\mathbf{v}\|^2 - (\mathbf{u} \cdot \mathbf{v})^2$$

27. (a) The standard basis for P_1 is $\{1, x\}$. Applying the Gram-Schmidt orthonormalization process produces the orthonormal basis

$$B = \{\mathbf{w}_1, \mathbf{w}_2\} = \{1, \sqrt{3}\,(2x - 1)\}.$$

The least squares approximating function is then given by

$$g(x) = \langle \mathbf{f}, \mathbf{w}_1 \rangle \mathbf{w}_1 + \langle \mathbf{f}, \mathbf{w}_2 \rangle \mathbf{w}_2.$$

Thus, we find the inner products

$$\langle \mathbf{f}, \mathbf{w}_1 \rangle = \int_0^1 (x^2)\,(1)\,dx = \frac{1}{3}x^3 \Big]_0^1 = \frac{1}{3}$$

$$\langle \mathbf{f}, \mathbf{w}_2 \rangle = \int_0^1 (x^2)\,[\sqrt{3}(2x - 1)]\,dx = \sqrt{3}\left(\frac{1}{2}x^4 - \frac{1}{3}x^3\right)\Big]_0^1 = \frac{\sqrt{3}}{6}$$

and conclude that $\mathbf{g}$ is given by

$$g(x) = \langle \mathbf{f}, \mathbf{w}_1 \rangle \mathbf{w}_1 + \langle \mathbf{f}, \mathbf{w}_2 \rangle \mathbf{w}_2$$

$$= \frac{1}{3}(1) + \frac{\sqrt{3}}{6}[\sqrt{3}\,(2x - 1)]$$

$$= \frac{1}{3} + x - \frac{1}{2}$$

$$= x - \frac{1}{6}.$$

(b)

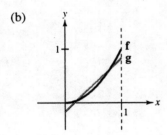

29. (a) The standard basis for P_1 is $\{1, x\}$. Applying the Gram-Schmidt orthonormalization process produces the orthonormal basis

$$B = \{\mathbf{w}_1, \mathbf{w}_2\} = \{1, \sqrt{3}\,(2x - 1)\}.$$

The least squares approximating function is then given by

$$g(x) = \langle f, \mathbf{w}_1 \rangle \mathbf{w}_1 + \langle f, \mathbf{w}_2 \rangle \mathbf{w}_2.$$

Thus, we find the inner products

$$\langle f, \mathbf{w}_1 \rangle = \int_0^1 e^{2x}\, dx = \frac{1}{2} e^{2x} \Big]_0^1 = \frac{1}{2}\left(e^2 - 1\right)$$

$$\langle f, \mathbf{w}_2 \rangle = \int_0^1 e^{2x} \sqrt{3}\,(2x - 1)\, dx = \sqrt{3}\,(x - 1)e^{2x} \Big]_0^1 = \sqrt{3}$$

and conclude that

$$g(x) = \langle f, \mathbf{w}_1 \rangle \mathbf{w}_1 + \langle f, \mathbf{w}_2 \rangle \mathbf{w}_2$$

$$= \frac{1}{2}\left(e^2 - 1\right) + \sqrt{3}\left(\sqrt{3}\,(2x - 1)\right)$$

$$= 6x + \frac{1}{2}\left(e^2 - 7\right) \quad (\approx 6x + 0.1945)$$

(b)

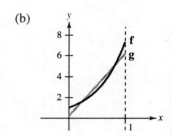

31. (a) The standard basis for P_1 is $\{1, x\}$. Applying the Gram-Schmidt orthonormalization process produces the orthonormal basis

$$B = \{\mathbf{w}_1, \mathbf{w}_2\} = \left\{ \frac{\sqrt{2\pi}}{\pi}, \frac{\sqrt{6\pi}}{\pi^2}(4x - \pi) \right\}.$$

The least squares approximating function is then given by

$$g(x) = \langle \mathbf{f}, \mathbf{w}_1 \rangle \mathbf{w}_1 + \langle \mathbf{f}, \mathbf{w}_2 \rangle \mathbf{w}_2.$$

Thus, we find the inner products

$$\langle \mathbf{f}, \mathbf{w}_1 \rangle = \int_0^{\pi/2} (\sin x)\left(\frac{\sqrt{2\pi}}{\pi}\right) dx = -\frac{\sqrt{2\pi}}{\pi}\cos x \Big]_0^{\pi/2} = \frac{\sqrt{2\pi}}{\pi}$$

$$\langle \mathbf{f}, \mathbf{w}_2 \rangle = \int_0^{\pi/2} (\sin x)\left[\frac{\sqrt{6\pi}}{\pi^2}(4x - \pi)\right] dx$$

$$= \frac{\sqrt{6\pi}}{\pi^2}\Big[-4x\cos x + 4\sin x + \pi\cos x\Big]_0^{\pi/2}$$

$$= \frac{\sqrt{6\pi}}{\pi^2}(4 - \pi)$$

and conclude that **g** is given by

$$g(x) = \langle \mathbf{f}, \mathbf{w}_1 \rangle \mathbf{w}_1 + \langle \mathbf{f}, \mathbf{w}_2 \rangle \mathbf{w}_2$$

$$= \frac{\sqrt{2\pi}}{\pi}\left(\frac{\sqrt{2\pi}}{\pi}\right) + \frac{\sqrt{6\pi}}{\pi^2}(4 - \pi)\left[\frac{\sqrt{6\pi}}{\pi^2}(4x - \pi)\right]$$

$$= \frac{2}{\pi} + \frac{6}{\pi^3}(4 - \pi)(4x - \pi)$$

$$= \frac{24(4 - \pi)}{\pi^3}x - \frac{8(3 - \pi)}{\pi^2} \approx 0.6644x + 0.1148.$$

(b)

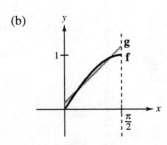

33. (a) The standard basis for P_2 is $\{1, x, x^2\}$. Applying the Gram-Schmidt orthonormalization process produces the orthonormal basis

$$B = \{\mathbf{w}_1, \mathbf{w}_2, \mathbf{w}_3\} = \{1, \sqrt{3}\,(2x - 1), \sqrt{5}\,(6x^2 - 6x + 1)\}.$$

The least squares approximating function for $\mathbf{f}$ is given by

$$g(x) = \langle \mathbf{f}, \mathbf{w}_1 \rangle \mathbf{w}_1 + \langle \mathbf{f}, \mathbf{w}_2 \rangle \mathbf{w}_2 + \langle \mathbf{f}, \mathbf{w}_3 \rangle \mathbf{w}_3.$$

Thus, we find the inner products

$$\langle \mathbf{f}, \mathbf{w}_1 \rangle = \int_0^1 x^3\,(1)\,dx = \frac{1}{4}x^4\Big]_0^1 = \frac{1}{4}$$

$$\langle \mathbf{f}, \mathbf{w}_2 \rangle = \int_0^1 x^3\,[\sqrt{3}\,(2x - 1)]\,dx = \sqrt{3}\left[\frac{2}{5}x^5 - \frac{1}{4}x^4\right]_0^1 = \frac{3\sqrt{3}}{20}$$

$$\langle \mathbf{f}, \mathbf{w}_3 \rangle = \int_0^1 x^3\,[\sqrt{5}\,(6x^2 - 6x + 1)]\,dx = \sqrt{5}\left[x^6 - \frac{6}{5}x^5 + \frac{1}{4}x^4\right]_0^1 = \frac{\sqrt{5}}{20}$$

and conclude that $\mathbf{g}$ is given by

$$g(x) = \langle \mathbf{f}, \mathbf{w}_1 \rangle \mathbf{w}_1 + \langle \mathbf{f}, \mathbf{w}_2 \rangle \mathbf{w}_2 + \langle \mathbf{f}, \mathbf{w}_3 \rangle \mathbf{w}_3$$

$$= \frac{1}{4}\,(1) + \frac{3\sqrt{3}}{20}[\sqrt{3}\,(2x - 1)] + \frac{\sqrt{5}}{20}[\sqrt{5}\,(6x^2 - 6x + 1)]$$

$$= \frac{3}{2}x^2 - \frac{3}{5}x + \frac{1}{20}.$$

(b)

35. (a) The standard basis for P_2 is $\{1, x, x^2\}$. Applying the Gram-Schmidt orthonormalization process produces the orthonormal basis

$$B = \{\mathbf{w}_1, \mathbf{w}_2, \mathbf{w}_3\} = \left\{\frac{1}{\sqrt{\pi}}, \frac{\sqrt{3}}{\pi\sqrt{\pi}}(2x - \pi), \frac{\sqrt{5}}{\pi^2\sqrt{\pi}}(6x^2 - 6\pi x + \pi^2)\right\}.$$

The least squares approximating function for $\mathbf{f}$ is given by

$$g(x) = \langle \mathbf{f}, \mathbf{w}_1\rangle\mathbf{w}_1 + \langle \mathbf{f}, \mathbf{w}_2\rangle\mathbf{w}_2 + \langle \mathbf{f}, \mathbf{w}_3\rangle\mathbf{w}_3.$$

Thus, we find the inner products

$$\langle \mathbf{f}, \mathbf{w}_1\rangle = \int_0^{\pi}(\sin x)\left(\frac{1}{\sqrt{\pi}}\right)dx = -\frac{1}{\sqrt{\pi}}\cos x\Big]_0^{\pi} = \frac{2}{\sqrt{\pi}}$$

$$\langle \mathbf{f}, \mathbf{w}_2\rangle = \int_0^{\pi}(\sin x)\left[\frac{\sqrt{3}}{\pi\sqrt{\pi}}(2x - \pi)\right]dx$$

$$= \frac{\sqrt{3}}{\pi\sqrt{\pi}}\left[-2x\cos x + 2\sin x + \pi\cos x\right]_0^{\pi} = 0$$

$$\langle \mathbf{f}, \mathbf{w}_3\rangle = \int_0^{\pi}(\sin x)\left[\frac{\sqrt{5}}{\pi^2\sqrt{\pi}}(6x^2 - 6\pi x + \pi^2)\right]dx$$

$$= \frac{\sqrt{5}}{\pi^2\sqrt{\pi}}\left[(12x - 6\pi)\sin x - (6x^2 - 6\pi x - 12 + \pi^2)\cos x\right]_0^{\pi}$$

$$= \frac{2\sqrt{5}\,(\pi^2 - 12)}{\pi^2\sqrt{\pi}}$$

and conclude that $\mathbf{g}$ is given by

$$g(x) = \frac{2}{\sqrt{\pi}}\left(\frac{1}{\sqrt{\pi}}\right) + \frac{2\sqrt{5}\,(\pi^2 - 12)}{\pi^2\sqrt{\pi}}\left[\frac{\sqrt{5}}{\pi^2\sqrt{\pi}}(6x^2 - 6\pi x + \pi^2)\right]$$

$$= \frac{12\,(\pi^2 - 10)}{\pi^3} - \frac{60\,(\pi^2 - 12)}{\pi^4}x + \frac{60\,(\pi^2 - 12)}{\pi^5}x^2$$

$$\approx -0.0505 + 1.3122x - 0.4177x^2.$$

(b)

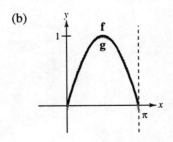

37. We find the coefficients as follows.

$$a_0 = \frac{1}{\pi} \int_0^{2\pi} f(x)\, dx = \frac{1}{\pi} \int_0^{2\pi} (\pi - x)\, dx = -\frac{1}{2\pi} (\pi - x)^2 \Big]_0^{2\pi} = 0$$

$$a_j = \frac{1}{\pi} \int_0^{2\pi} f(x) \cos jx\, dx$$

$$= \frac{1}{\pi} \int_0^{2\pi} (\pi - x) \cos jx\, dx$$

$$= \left[-\frac{1}{j\pi} x \sin jx - \frac{1}{j^2 \pi} \cos jx + \frac{1}{j} \sin jx \right]_0^{2\pi}$$

$$= 0, \quad j = 1, 2, 3$$

$$b_j = \frac{1}{\pi} \int_0^{2\pi} f(x) \sin jx\, dx$$

$$= \frac{1}{\pi} \int_0^{2\pi} (\pi - x) \sin jx\, dx$$

$$= \left[-\frac{1}{j\pi} x \cos jx - \frac{1}{j^2 \pi} \sin jx + \frac{1}{j} \cos jx \right]_0^{2\pi}$$

$$= \frac{2}{j}, \quad j = 1, 2, 3$$

Thus, the approximation is

$$g(x) = b_1 \sin x + b_2 \sin 2x + b_3 \sin 3x$$

$$= 2 \sin x + \sin 2x + \tfrac{2}{3} \sin 3x.$$

39. We find the coefficients as follows.

$$a_0 = \frac{1}{\pi} \int_0^{2\pi} f(x)\, dx = \frac{1}{\pi} \int_0^{2\pi} (x - \pi)^2\, dx = \frac{1}{3\pi} (x - \pi)^3 \Big]_0^{2\pi} = \frac{2\pi^2}{3}$$

$$a_j = \frac{1}{\pi} \int_0^{2\pi} f(x) \cos jx\, dx$$

$$= \frac{1}{\pi} \int_0^{2\pi} (\pi - x)^2 \cos jx\, dx$$

$$= \left[\frac{\pi}{j} \sin jx - \frac{2}{j} x \sin jx + \frac{2}{j^2 \pi} x \cos jx + \frac{1}{j\pi} x^2 \sin jx - \frac{2}{j^3 \pi} \sin jx - \frac{2}{j^2} \cos jx \right]_0^{2\pi}$$

$$= \frac{4}{j^2}, \quad j = 1, 2, 3$$

$$b_j = \frac{1}{\pi} \int_0^{2\pi} f(x) \sin jx\, dx$$

$$= \frac{1}{\pi} \int_0^{2\pi} (x - \pi)^2 \sin jx\, dx$$

$$= \left[-\frac{\pi}{j} \cos jx + \frac{2}{j} x \cos jx + \frac{2}{j^2 \pi} x \sin jx - \frac{1}{j\pi} x^2 \cos jx + \frac{2}{j^3 \pi} \cos jx - \frac{2}{j^2} \sin jx \right]_0^{2\pi}$$

$$= 0, \quad j = 1, 2, 3$$

Thus, the approximation is

$$g(x) = \frac{a_0}{2} + a_1 \cos x + a_2 \cos 2x + a_3 \cos 3x$$

$$= \frac{\pi^2}{3} + 4 \cos x + \cos 2x + \frac{4}{9} \cos 3x.$$

41. We find the coefficients as follows.

$$a_0 = \frac{1}{\pi} \int_0^{2\pi} f(x)\, dx = \frac{1}{\pi} \int_0^{2\pi} e^{-x}\, dx = -\frac{1}{\pi} e^{-x} \bigg]_0^{2\pi} = \frac{1 - e^{-2\pi}}{\pi}$$

$$a_1 = \frac{1}{\pi} \int_0^{2\pi} f(x) \cos x\, dx$$

$$= \frac{1}{\pi} \int_0^{2\pi} e^{-x} \cos x\, dx$$

$$= \left[-\frac{1}{2\pi} e^{-x} \cos x + \frac{1}{2\pi} e^{-x} \sin x \right]_0^{2\pi}$$

$$= \frac{1 - e^{-2\pi}}{2\pi}$$

$$b_1 = \frac{1}{\pi} \int_0^{2\pi} f(x) \sin x\, dx$$

$$= \frac{1}{\pi} \int_0^{2\pi} e^{-x} \sin x\, dx$$

$$= \left[-\frac{1}{2\pi} e^{-x} \cos x - \frac{1}{2\pi} e^{-x} \sin x \right]_0^{2\pi}$$

$$= \frac{1 - e^{-2\pi}}{2\pi}$$

Thus, the approximation is

$$g(x) = \frac{a_0}{2} + a_1 \cos x + b_1 \sin x$$

$$= \frac{1}{2\pi} (1 - e^{-2\pi}) (1 + \cos x + \sin x).$$

43. The third order Fourier approximation of $f(x) = 1 + x$ is of the form

$$g(x) = \frac{a_0}{2} + a_1 \cos x + b_1 \sin x + a_2 \cos 2x + b_2 \sin 2x + a_3 \cos 3x + b_3 \sin 3x.$$

We find the coefficients as follows.

$$a_0 = \frac{1}{\pi} \int_0^{2\pi} f(x)\, dx = \frac{1}{\pi} \int_0^{2\pi} (1 + x)\, dx = \frac{1}{\pi} \left(x + \frac{x^2}{2} \right) \Big]_0^{2\pi} = 2 + 2\pi$$

$$a_j = \frac{1}{\pi} \int_0^{2\pi} f(x) \cos (jx)\, dx = \frac{1}{\pi} \int_0^{2\pi} (1 + x) \cos (jx)\, dx$$

$$= \frac{1}{\pi} \left[\frac{1 + x}{j} \sin (jx) + \frac{1}{j^2} \cos (jx) \right]_0^{2\pi} = 0$$

$$b_j = \frac{1}{\pi} \int_0^{2\pi} f(x) \sin (jx)\, dx = \frac{1}{\pi} \int_0^{2\pi} (1 + x) \sin (jx)\, dx$$

$$= \frac{1}{\pi} \left[\frac{-(1 + x)}{j} \cos (jx) + \frac{1}{j^2} \sin (jx) \right]_0^{2\pi} = \frac{-2}{j}$$

Thus, the approximation is

$$g(x) = (1 + \pi) - 2 \sin x - \sin 2x - \frac{2}{3} \sin 3x.$$

45. Since $f(x) = 2 \sin x \cos x = \sin 2x$, we see that the fourth order Fourier approximation is simply

$$g(x) = \sin 2x.$$

47. Since

$$a_0 = 0,\ a_j = 0\ (j = 1, 2, 3, \ldots, n),$$

and

$$b_j = \frac{2}{j}\ (j = 1, 2, 3, \ldots, n)$$

the nth-order Fourier approximation is

$$g(x) = 2 \sin x + \sin 2x + \frac{2}{3} \sin 3x + \cdots + \frac{2}{n} \sin nx = \sum_{j=1}^{n} \frac{2}{j} \sin jx.$$

Chapter 5   Review Exercises

1. (a) $\|\mathbf{u}\| = \sqrt{1^2 + 2^2} = \sqrt{5}$

   (b) $\|\mathbf{v}\| = \sqrt{4^2 + 1^2} = \sqrt{17}$

   (c) $\mathbf{u} \cdot \mathbf{v} = 1(4) + 2(1) = 6$

   (d) $d(\mathbf{u}, \mathbf{v}) = \|\mathbf{u} - \mathbf{v}\| = \|(-3, 1)\| = \sqrt{(-3)^2 + 1^2} = \sqrt{10}$

3. (a) $\|\mathbf{u}\| = \sqrt{1^2 + (-1)^2 + 2^2} = \sqrt{6}$

   (b) $\|\mathbf{v}\| = \sqrt{2^2 + 3^2 + 1^2} = \sqrt{14}$

   (c) $\mathbf{u} \cdot \mathbf{v} = 1(2) + (-1)(3) + 2(1) = 1$

   (d) $d(\mathbf{u}, \mathbf{v}) = \|\mathbf{u} - \mathbf{v}\| = \sqrt{(1 - 2)^2 + (-1 - 3)^2 + (2 - 1)^2} = 3\sqrt{2}$

5. (a) $\|\mathbf{u}\| = \sqrt{1^2 + (-2)^2 + 2^2 + 0^2} = \sqrt{9} = 3$

   (b) $\|\mathbf{v}\| = \sqrt{2^2 + (-1)^2 + 0^2 + 2^2} = \sqrt{9} = 3$

   (c) $\mathbf{u} \cdot \mathbf{v} = 1(2) + (-2)(-1) + 2(0) + (0)(2) = 4$

   (d) $d(\mathbf{u}, \mathbf{v}) = \|\mathbf{u} - \mathbf{v}\| = \|(-1, -1, 2, -2)\| = \sqrt{(-1)^2 + (-1)^2 + 2^2 + (-2)^2} = \sqrt{10}$

7. The norm of $\mathbf{v}$ is

$$\|\mathbf{v}\| = \sqrt{5^2 + 3^2 + (-2)^2} = \sqrt{38}.$$

Thus, a unit vector in the direction of $\mathbf{v}$ is

$$\|\mathbf{v}\| = \frac{1}{\|\mathbf{v}\|}\,\mathbf{v} = \frac{1}{\sqrt{38}}\,(5, 3, -2) = \left(\frac{5}{\sqrt{38}}, \frac{3}{\sqrt{38}}, -\frac{2}{\sqrt{38}}\right).$$

9. The cosine of the angle θ between $\mathbf{u}$ and $\mathbf{v}$ is given by

$$\cos \theta = \frac{\mathbf{u} \cdot \mathbf{v}}{\|\mathbf{u}\|\,\|\mathbf{v}\|} = \frac{1(3) + 5(6)}{\sqrt{1^2 + 5^2}\,\sqrt{3^2 + 6^2}} = \frac{33}{3\sqrt{130}} = \frac{11}{\sqrt{130}}.$$

Thus, $\theta = \cos^{-1}(11/\sqrt{130}) \approx 0.2663$ radians (15.26°).

11. The cosine of the angle θ between $\mathbf{u}$ and $\mathbf{v}$ is given by

$$\cos \theta = \frac{\mathbf{u} \cdot \mathbf{v}}{\|\mathbf{u}\|\,\|\mathbf{v}\|} = \frac{12 - 2 - 10}{\sqrt{40}\,\sqrt{17}} = 0.$$

Thus, $\theta = \dfrac{\pi}{2}$ radians (90°).

13. The cosine of the angle θ between $\mathbf{u}$ and $\mathbf{v}$ is given by

$$\cos \theta = \frac{\mathbf{u} \cdot \mathbf{v}}{\|\mathbf{u}\|\,\|\mathbf{v}\|} = \frac{-20 - 5 - 45}{\sqrt{350}\,\sqrt{14}} = \frac{-70}{70} - 1.$$

Thus, $\theta = \pi$ radians (180°).

15. The projection of **u** onto **v** is given by

$$\text{proj}_\mathbf{v}\mathbf{u} = \frac{\mathbf{u} \cdot \mathbf{v}}{\mathbf{v} \cdot \mathbf{v}}\mathbf{v} = \frac{2 - 20}{1 + 25}(1, -5) = -\frac{9}{13}(1, -5) = \left(-\frac{9}{13}, \frac{45}{13}\right).$$

17. The projection of **u** onto **v** is given by

$$\text{proj}_\mathbf{v}\mathbf{u} = \frac{\mathbf{u} \cdot \mathbf{v}}{\mathbf{v} \cdot \mathbf{v}}\mathbf{v} = \frac{0(3) + (-1)(2) + 2(4)}{3^2 + 2^2 + 4^2}(3, 2, 4) = \left(\frac{18}{29}, \frac{12}{29}, \frac{24}{29}\right).$$

19. (a) $\langle \mathbf{u}, \mathbf{v} \rangle = 2\left(\frac{3}{2}\right) + 2\left(-\frac{1}{2}\right)(2) + 3(1)(-1) = -2$

  (b) $d(\mathbf{u}, \mathbf{v}) = \|\mathbf{u} - \mathbf{v}\| = \sqrt{\langle \mathbf{u} - \mathbf{v}, \mathbf{u} - \mathbf{v} \rangle}$

$$= \sqrt{\left(2 - \frac{3}{2}\right)^2 + 2\left(-\frac{1}{2} - 2\right)^2 + 3(1 - (-1))^2}$$

$$= \frac{3}{2}\sqrt{11}$$

21. We verify the Triangle Inequality as follows.

$$\|\mathbf{u} + \mathbf{v}\| \leq \|\mathbf{u}\| + \|\mathbf{v}\|$$

$$\left\|\left(\frac{7}{2}, \frac{3}{2}, 0\right)\right\| \leq \sqrt{2^2 + 2\left(-\frac{1}{2}\right)^2 + 3(1)^2} + \sqrt{\left(\frac{3}{2}\right)^2 + 2(2)^2 + 3(-1)^2}$$

$$\sqrt{\left(\frac{7}{2}\right)^2 + 2\left(\frac{3}{2}\right)^2 + 0} \leq \sqrt{\frac{15}{2}} + \frac{\sqrt{53}}{2}$$

$$\frac{\sqrt{67}}{2} \leq \frac{\sqrt{30}}{2} + \frac{\sqrt{53}}{2}$$

$$4.093 \leq 6.379.$$

We verify the Cauchy-Schwarz Inequality as follows.

$$|\langle \mathbf{u}, \mathbf{v} \rangle| \leq \|\mathbf{u}\|\|\mathbf{v}\|$$

$$2 \leq \frac{\sqrt{30}}{2}\frac{\sqrt{53}}{2}$$

$$2 \leq 9.969.$$

23. A vector $\mathbf{v} = (v_1, v_2, v_3)$ that is orthogonal to **u** must satisfy the equation

$$\mathbf{u} \cdot \mathbf{v} = 0v_1 - 4v_2 + 3v_3 = 0.$$

This equation has solutions of the form $\mathbf{v} = (s, 3t, 4t)$, where s and t are any real numbers.

25. First we orthogonalize the vectors in B.

$$\mathbf{w}_1 = (1, 1)$$

$$\mathbf{w}_2 = (0, 1) - \tfrac{1}{2}(1, 1) = (-\tfrac{1}{2}, \tfrac{1}{2})$$

Then we normalize each vector.

$$\mathbf{u}_1 = \frac{1}{\|\mathbf{w}_1\|} \mathbf{w}_1 = \frac{1}{\sqrt{2}}(1, 1) = \left(\frac{1}{\sqrt{2}}, \frac{1}{\sqrt{2}}\right)$$

$$\mathbf{u}_2 = \frac{1}{\|\mathbf{w}_2\|} \mathbf{w}_2 = \sqrt{2}\left(-\frac{1}{2}, \frac{1}{2}\right) = \left(-\frac{1}{\sqrt{2}}, \frac{1}{\sqrt{2}}\right)$$

Thus, an orthonormal basis for R^2 is $\left\{\left(\dfrac{1}{\sqrt{2}}, \dfrac{1}{\sqrt{2}}\right), \left(-\dfrac{1}{\sqrt{2}}, \dfrac{1}{\sqrt{2}}\right)\right\}$.

27. $\mathbf{w}_1 = (0, 3, 4)$

$$\mathbf{w}_2 = (1, 0, 0) - \frac{1(0) + 0(3) + 0(4)}{0^2 + 3^2 + 4^2}(0, 3, 4)$$

$$= (1, 0, 0)$$

$$\mathbf{w}_3 = (1, 1, 0) - \frac{1(1) + 1(0) + 0(0)}{1^2 + 0^2 + 0^2}(1, 0, 0) - \frac{1(0) + 1(3) + 0(4)}{0^2 + 3^2 + 4^2}(0, 3, 4)$$

$$= \left(0, \frac{16}{25}, -\frac{12}{25}\right)$$

Then, we normalize each vector.

$$\mathbf{u}_1 = \frac{1}{\|\mathbf{w}_1\|} \mathbf{w}_1 = \tfrac{1}{5}(0, 3, 4) = \left(0, \tfrac{3}{5}, \tfrac{4}{5}\right)$$

$$\mathbf{u}_2 = \frac{1}{\|\mathbf{w}_2\|} \mathbf{w}_2 = 1(1, 0, 0) = (1, 0, 0)$$

$$\mathbf{u}_3 = \frac{1}{\|\mathbf{w}_3\|} \mathbf{w}_3 = \tfrac{5}{4}\left(0, \tfrac{16}{25}, -\tfrac{12}{25}\right) = \left(0, \tfrac{4}{5}, -\tfrac{3}{5}\right)$$

Thus, an orthonormal basis for R^3 is

$$\left\{\left(0, \tfrac{3}{5}, \tfrac{4}{5}\right), (1, 0, 0), \left(0, \tfrac{4}{5} -\tfrac{3}{5}\right)\right\}.$$

29. (a) To find **x** as a linear combination of the vectors in B, we solve the vector equation

$$c_1(0, 2, -2) + c_2(1, 0, -2) = (-1, 4, -2).$$

This produces the system of linear equations

$$
\begin{aligned}
c_2 &= -1 \\
2c_1 \quad\;\; &= \;\;\; 4 \\
-2c_1 - 2c_2 &= -2
\end{aligned}
$$

which has the solution $c_1 = 2$ and $c_2 = -1$. Thus, $[\mathbf{x}]_B = (2, -1)$, and we can write

$$(-1, 4, -2) = 2(0, 2, -2) - (1, 0, -2).$$

(b) To apply the Gram-Schmidt orthonormalization process, we first orthogonalize each vector in B.

$$\mathbf{w}_1 = (0, 2, -2)$$

$$\mathbf{w}_2 = (1, 0, -2) - \frac{1(0) + 0(2) + (-2)(-2)}{0^2 + 2^2 + (-2)^2}(0, 2, -2) = (1, -1, -1).$$

Then we normalize $\mathbf{w}_1$ and $\mathbf{w}_2$ as follows.

$$\mathbf{u}_1 = \frac{1}{\|\mathbf{w}_1\|}\mathbf{w}_1 = \frac{1}{2\sqrt{2}}(0, 2, -2) = \left(0, \frac{1}{\sqrt{2}}, -\frac{1}{\sqrt{2}}\right)$$

$$\mathbf{u}_2 = \frac{1}{\|\mathbf{w}_2\|}\mathbf{w}_2 = \frac{1}{\sqrt{3}}(1, -1, -1) = \left(\frac{1}{\sqrt{3}}, -\frac{1}{\sqrt{3}}, -\frac{1}{\sqrt{3}}\right)$$

Thus, $B' = \left\{\left(0, \frac{1}{\sqrt{2}}, -\frac{1}{\sqrt{2}}\right), \left(\frac{1}{\sqrt{3}}, -\frac{1}{\sqrt{3}}, -\frac{1}{\sqrt{3}}\right)\right\}$.

(c) To find **x** as a linear combination of the vectors in B', we solve the vector equation

$$c_1\left(0, \frac{1}{\sqrt{2}}, -\frac{1}{\sqrt{2}}\right) + c_2\left(\frac{1}{\sqrt{3}}, -\frac{1}{\sqrt{3}}, -\frac{1}{\sqrt{3}}\right) = (-1, 4, -2).$$

This produces the system of linear equations

$$\frac{1}{\sqrt{3}}c_2 = -1$$

$$\frac{1}{\sqrt{2}}c_1 - \frac{1}{\sqrt{3}}c_2 = \;\;\; 4$$

$$\frac{1}{\sqrt{2}}c_1 - \frac{1}{\sqrt{3}}c_2 = -2$$

which has the solution $c_1 = 3\sqrt{2}$ and $c_2 = -\sqrt{3}$. Thus, $[\mathbf{x}]_{B'} = (3\sqrt{2}, -\sqrt{3})$, and we can write

$$(-1, 4, -2) = 3\sqrt{2}\left(0, \frac{1}{\sqrt{2}}, -\frac{1}{\sqrt{2}}\right) - \sqrt{3}\left(\frac{1}{\sqrt{3}}, -\frac{1}{\sqrt{3}}, -\frac{1}{\sqrt{3}}\right).$$

31. (a) $\langle \mathbf{f}, \mathbf{g} \rangle = \int_0^1 f(x)g(x)\, dx = \int_0^1 x^3\, dx = \frac{1}{4}x^4 \Big]_0^1 = \frac{1}{4}$

(b) Since

$$\langle \mathbf{g}, \mathbf{g} \rangle = \int_0^1 g(x)g(x)\, dx = \int_0^1 x^4\, dx = \frac{1}{5}x^5 \Big]_0^1 = \frac{1}{5}$$

the norm of $\mathbf{g}$ is

$$\|\mathbf{g}\| = \sqrt{\langle \mathbf{g}, \mathbf{g} \rangle} = \sqrt{\frac{1}{5}} = \frac{1}{\sqrt{5}}.$$

(c) Since

$$\langle \mathbf{f} - \mathbf{g}, \mathbf{f} - \mathbf{g} \rangle = \int_0^1 (x - x^2)^2\, dx = \left[\frac{1}{3}x^3 - \frac{1}{2}x^4 + \frac{1}{5}x^5 \right]_0^1 = \frac{1}{30}$$

the distance between $\mathbf{f}$ and $\mathbf{g}$ is

$$d(\mathbf{f}, \mathbf{g}) = \|\mathbf{f} - \mathbf{g}\| = \sqrt{\langle \mathbf{f} - \mathbf{g}, \mathbf{f} - \mathbf{g} \rangle} = \sqrt{\frac{1}{30}} = \frac{1}{\sqrt{30}}.$$

(d) First we orthogonalize the vectors.

$$\mathbf{w}_1 = \mathbf{f} = x$$

$$\mathbf{w}_2 = \mathbf{g} - \frac{\langle \mathbf{g}, \mathbf{w}_1 \rangle}{\langle \mathbf{w}_1, \mathbf{w}_1 \rangle} \mathbf{w}_1 = x^2 - \frac{\int_0^1 x^3\, dx}{\int_0^1 x^2\, dx}\, x = x^2 - \frac{3}{4}x$$

Then, we normalize each vector. Since

$$\langle \mathbf{w}_1, \mathbf{w}_1 \rangle = \int_0^1 x^2\, dx = \frac{1}{3}x^3 \Big]_0^1 = \frac{1}{3}$$

$$\langle \mathbf{w}_2, \mathbf{w}_2 \rangle = \int_0^1 \left(x^2 - \frac{3}{4}x \right)^2 dx = \left[\frac{1}{5}x^5 - \frac{3}{8}x^4 + \frac{3}{16}x^3 \right]_0^1 = \frac{1}{80}$$

we have

$$\mathbf{u}_1 = \frac{1}{\|\mathbf{w}_1\|}\, \mathbf{w}_1 = \sqrt{3}x$$

$$\mathbf{u}_2 = \frac{1}{\|\mathbf{w}_2\|}\, \mathbf{w}_2 = 4\sqrt{5}x^2 - 3\sqrt{5}x = \sqrt{5}\,(4x^2 - 3x).$$

The orthonormal set is $B' = \{\sqrt{3}x, \sqrt{5}\,(4x^2 - 3x)\}$.

33. These functions are orthogonal because

$$\langle f, g \rangle = \int_{-1}^{1} \sqrt{1 - x^2}\, 2x\, \sqrt{1 - x^2}\, dx$$

$$= \int_{-1}^{1} (2x - 2x^3)\, dx = x^2 - \frac{x^4}{2} \Big]_{-1}^{1} = 0.$$

35. Vectors in W are of the form $(-s - t, s, t)$ where s and t are any real numbers. Thus, a basis for W is $\{(-1, 0, 1), (-1, 1, 0)\}$. We orthogonalize these vectors as follows.

$$\mathbf{w}_1 = (-1, 0, 1)$$

$$\mathbf{w}_2 = (-1, 1, 0) - \frac{-1(-1) + 1(0) + 0(1)}{(-1)^2 + 0^2 + 1^2} (-1, 0, 1) = \left(-\tfrac{1}{2}, 1, -\tfrac{1}{2}\right)$$

Finally, we normalize $\mathbf{w}_1$ and $\mathbf{w}_2$ to obtain

$$\mathbf{u}_1 = \frac{1}{\|\mathbf{w}_1\|} \mathbf{w}_1 = \frac{1}{\sqrt{2}} (-1, 0, 1) = \left(-\frac{1}{\sqrt{2}}, 0, \frac{1}{\sqrt{2}}\right)$$

$$\mathbf{u}_2 = \frac{1}{\|\mathbf{w}_2\|} \mathbf{w}_2 = \frac{2}{\sqrt{6}} \left(-\tfrac{1}{2}, 1, -\tfrac{1}{2}\right) = \left(-\frac{1}{\sqrt{6}}, \frac{2}{\sqrt{6}}, -\frac{1}{\sqrt{6}}\right)$$

Thus, $W' = \left\{ \left(-\frac{1}{\sqrt{2}}, 0, \frac{1}{\sqrt{2}}\right), \left(-\frac{1}{\sqrt{6}}, \frac{2}{\sqrt{6}}, -\frac{1}{\sqrt{6}}\right) \right\}$.

37. (a) $\langle f, g \rangle = \int_{-1}^{1} x \frac{1}{x^2 + 1}\, dx = \frac{1}{2} \ln (x^2 + 1) \Big]_{-1}^{1}$

$$= \frac{1}{2} \ln 2 - \frac{1}{2} \ln 2 = 0$$

(b) The vectors are orthogonal.

(c) Since $\langle f, g \rangle = 0$, we immediately verify that $|\langle f, g \rangle| \le \|f\| \, \|g\|$.

39. If $\|\mathbf{u}\| \le 1$ and $\|\mathbf{v}\| \le 1$, then the Cauchy-Schwarz Inequality implies that $|\langle \mathbf{u}, \mathbf{v} \rangle| \le \|\mathbf{u}\| \, \|\mathbf{v}\| \le 1$.

41. Let $\{\mathbf{v}_1, \ldots, \mathbf{v}_m\}$ be a basis for V. We can extend this basis to one for R^n.

$$B = \{\mathbf{v}_1, \ldots, \mathbf{v}_m, \mathbf{w}_{m+1}, \ldots, \mathbf{w}_n\}$$

We now apply the Gram-Schmidt orthonormalization process to this basis, which results in the following basis for R^n.

$$B' = \{\mathbf{u}_1, \ldots, \mathbf{u}_m, \mathbf{z}_{m+1}, \ldots, \mathbf{z}_n\}$$

The first m vectors of B' still span V. Hence, any vector $\mathbf{u} \in R^n$ is of the form

$$\mathbf{u} = c_1 \mathbf{u}_1 + \cdots + c_m \mathbf{u}_m + c_{m+1} \mathbf{z}_{m+1} + \cdots + c_n \mathbf{z}_n$$
$$= \mathbf{v} + \mathbf{w}$$

where $\mathbf{v} \in V$ and $\mathbf{w}$ is orthogonal to every vector in V.

43. First we extend the set $\{\mathbf{u}_1, \ldots, \mathbf{u}_m\}$ to an orthonormal basis for R^n.

$$B = \{\mathbf{u}_1, \ldots, \mathbf{u}_m, \mathbf{u}_{m+1}, \ldots, \mathbf{u}_n\}$$

If $\mathbf{v}$ is any vector in R^n, we have

$$\mathbf{v} = \sum_{i=1}^{n} (\mathbf{v} \cdot \mathbf{u}_i)\, \mathbf{u}_i$$

which implies that

$$\|\mathbf{v}\|^2 = \langle \mathbf{v}, \mathbf{v} \rangle = \sum_{i=1}^{n} (\mathbf{v} \cdot \mathbf{u}_i)^2 \, \|\mathbf{u}_i\|^2 \geq \sum_{i=1}^{m} (\mathbf{v} \cdot \mathbf{u}_i)^2.$$

45. If $\mathbf{u}$ and $\mathbf{v}$ are orthogonal, then $\|\mathbf{u}\| + \|\mathbf{v}\| = \|\mathbf{u} + \mathbf{v}\|$ by the Pythagorean Theorem. Furthermore,

$$\|\mathbf{u}\| + \|-\mathbf{v}\| = \|\mathbf{u}\| + \|\mathbf{v}\| = \|\mathbf{u} - \mathbf{v}\|,$$

which gives us

$$\|\mathbf{u}\| + \|\mathbf{v}\| = \|\mathbf{u} - \mathbf{v}\|.$$

On the other hand, if $\|\mathbf{u} + \mathbf{v}\| = \|\mathbf{u} - \mathbf{v}\|$, then $\langle \mathbf{u} + \mathbf{v}, \mathbf{u} + \mathbf{v} \rangle^2 = \langle \mathbf{u} - \mathbf{v}, \mathbf{u} - \mathbf{v} \rangle^2$ which implies that $\|\mathbf{u}\| + \|\mathbf{v}\|^2 + 2\langle \mathbf{u}, \mathbf{v} \rangle = \|\mathbf{u}\|^2 + \|\mathbf{v}\|^2 - 2\langle \mathbf{u}, \mathbf{v} \rangle$, or $\langle \mathbf{u}, \mathbf{v} \rangle = 0$, and $\mathbf{u}$ and $\mathbf{v}$ are orthogonal.

47. $S^\perp = N(A^T)$, the orthogonal complement of S is the nullspace of A^T.

$$\begin{bmatrix} 1 & 2 & 0 \\ 2 & 1 & -1 \end{bmatrix} \Rightarrow \begin{bmatrix} 1 & 2 & 0 \\ 0 & -3 & -1 \end{bmatrix} \Rightarrow \begin{bmatrix} 1 & 0 & -\frac{2}{3} \\ 0 & 1 & \frac{1}{3} \end{bmatrix}$$

Hence, $S^\perp$ is spanned by $\mathbf{u} = \begin{bmatrix} 2 \\ -1 \\ 3 \end{bmatrix}$.

49. $\begin{bmatrix} 0 & 1 & 0 \\ 0 & -3 & 0 \\ 1 & 0 & 1 \end{bmatrix} \Rightarrow \begin{bmatrix} 1 & 0 & 1 \\ 0 & 1 & 0 \\ 0 & 0 & 0 \end{bmatrix}$ $R(A) = \text{span}\left\{ \begin{bmatrix} 0 \\ 0 \\ 1 \end{bmatrix}, \begin{bmatrix} 1 \\ -3 \\ 0 \end{bmatrix} \right\}$

$R(A^T) = \text{span}\left\{ \begin{bmatrix} 0 \\ 1 \\ 0 \end{bmatrix}, \begin{bmatrix} 1 \\ 0 \\ 1 \end{bmatrix} \right\}$ $N(A) = \text{span}\left\{ \begin{bmatrix} 1 \\ 0 \\ -1 \end{bmatrix} \right\}$ $N(A^T) = \left\{ \begin{bmatrix} 3 \\ 1 \\ 0 \end{bmatrix} \right\}$

51. The cross product is

$$\mathbf{u} \times \mathbf{v} = \begin{vmatrix} \mathbf{i} & \mathbf{j} & \mathbf{k} \\ 1 & 1 & 1 \\ 1 & 0 & 0 \end{vmatrix} = \mathbf{j} - \mathbf{k} = (0, 1, -1).$$

Furthermore, $\mathbf{u} \times \mathbf{v}$ is orthogonal to both $\mathbf{u}$ and $\mathbf{v}$ because,

$$\mathbf{u} \cdot (\mathbf{u} \times \mathbf{v}) = 1(0) + 1(1) + 1(-1) = 0$$

and

$$\mathbf{v} \cdot (\mathbf{u} \times \mathbf{v}) = 1(0) + 0(1) + 0(-1) = 0.$$

53. The cross product is

$$\mathbf{u} \times \mathbf{v} = \begin{vmatrix} \mathbf{i} & \mathbf{j} & \mathbf{k} \\ 1 & 3 & 0 \\ -1 & 0 & 2 \end{vmatrix} = 6\mathbf{i} - 2\mathbf{j} + 3\mathbf{k} = (6, -2, 3),$$

the area of the parallelogram is

$$\|\mathbf{u} \times \mathbf{v}\| = \sqrt{6^2 + (-2)^2 + 3^2} = 7.$$

55. Since

$$\mathbf{v} \times \mathbf{w} = \begin{vmatrix} \mathbf{i} & \mathbf{j} & \mathbf{k} \\ 0 & 0 & 1 \\ 0 & 1 & 0 \end{vmatrix} = -\mathbf{i} = (-1, 0, 0),$$

the volume is

$$\|\mathbf{u} \cdot (\mathbf{v} \times \mathbf{w})\| = \|1(-1) + 0(0) + 0(0)\| = 1.$$

57. The standard basis for P_1 is $\{1, x\}$. In $C[-1, 1]$, the Gram-Schmidt orthonormalization process yields the orthonormal basis $\left\{ \dfrac{\sqrt{2}}{2}, \dfrac{\sqrt{6}}{2} x \right\}$. The linear least squares approximating function is given by

$$g(x) = \langle \mathbf{f}, \mathbf{w}_1 \rangle \mathbf{w}_1 + \langle \mathbf{f}, \mathbf{w}_2 \rangle \mathbf{w}_2.$$

Since

$$\langle \mathbf{f}, \mathbf{w}_1 \rangle = \int_{-1}^{1} \frac{\sqrt{2}}{2} x^3 \, dx = \frac{\sqrt{2}}{8} x^4 \Big]_{-1}^{1} = 0$$

$$\langle \mathbf{f}, \mathbf{w}_2 \rangle = \int_{-1}^{1} \frac{\sqrt{6}}{2} x^4 \, dx = \frac{\sqrt{6}}{10} x^5 \Big]_{-1}^{1} = \frac{\sqrt{6}}{5}$$

$\mathbf{g}$ is given by

$$g(x) = 0 \left(\frac{\sqrt{2}}{2} \right) + \frac{\sqrt{6}}{5} \left(\frac{\sqrt{6}}{2} x \right) = \frac{3}{5} x.$$

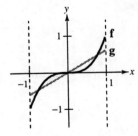

59. The standard basis for P_1 is $\{1, x\}$. In $C[0, \frac{\pi}{2}]$, the Gram-Schmidt orthonormalization process yields the orthonormal basis $\left\{ \sqrt{\frac{2}{\pi}}, \frac{\sqrt{6\pi}}{\pi^2} (4x - \pi) \right\}$.

Since

$$\langle f, \mathbf{w}_1 \rangle = \int_0^{\frac{\pi}{2}} sin(2x) \sqrt{\frac{2}{\pi}}\, dx = \sqrt{\frac{2}{\pi}}$$

$$\langle f, \mathbf{w}_2 \rangle = \int_0^{\frac{\pi}{2}} sin(2x) \left(\frac{\sqrt{6\pi}}{\pi^2} \right) (4x - \pi)\, dx = 0,$$

g is given by

$$g(x) = \langle f, \mathbf{w}_1 \rangle \mathbf{w}_1 + \langle f, \mathbf{w}_2 \rangle \mathbf{w}_2 = \sqrt{\frac{2}{\pi}} \sqrt{\frac{2}{\pi}} = \frac{2}{\pi}.$$

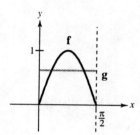

61. The standard basis for P_2 is $\{1, x, x^2\}$. In $C[0, 1]$, the Gram-Schmidt orthonormalization process yields the orthonormal basis $\{1, \sqrt{3}\,(2x - 1), \sqrt{5}\,(6x^2 - 6x + 1)\}$.

Since

$$\langle f, \mathbf{w}_1 \rangle = \int_0^1 \sqrt{x}\, dx = \frac{2}{3}$$

$$\langle f, \mathbf{w}_2 \rangle = \int_0^1 \sqrt{x}\, \sqrt{3}\,(2x - 1)\, dx = \sqrt{3} \int_0^1 (2x^{3/2} - x^{1/2})\, dx$$

$$= \sqrt{3} \left(\frac{4}{5} x^{5/2} - \frac{2}{3} x^{3/2} \right) \Big]_0^1 = \frac{2}{15} \sqrt{3}$$

$$\langle f, \mathbf{w}_3 \rangle = \int_0^1 \sqrt{x}\, \sqrt{5}\,(6x^2 - 6x + 1)\, dx$$

$$= \sqrt{5} \int_0^1 (6x^{5/2} - 6x^{3/2} + x^{1/2})\, dx$$

$$= \sqrt{5} \left(\frac{12}{7} x^{7/2} - \frac{12}{5} x^{5/2} + \frac{2}{3} x^{3/2} \right) \Big]_0^1 = \frac{-2\sqrt{5}}{105},$$

g is given by

$$g(x) = \langle f, \mathbf{w}_1 \rangle \mathbf{w}_1 + \langle f, \mathbf{w}_2 \rangle \mathbf{w}_2 + \langle f, \mathbf{w}_3 \rangle \mathbf{w}_3$$

$$= \frac{2}{3} (1) + \frac{2}{15} \sqrt{3}\,(\sqrt{3})\,(2x - 1) + \frac{-2\sqrt{5}}{105} \sqrt{5}\,(6x^2 - 6x + 1)$$

$$= -\frac{4}{7} x^2 + \frac{48}{35} x + \frac{6}{35}$$

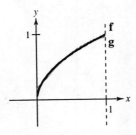

63. We find the coefficients as follows.

$$a_0 = \frac{1}{\pi} \int_{-\pi}^{\pi} f(x)\, dx = \frac{1}{\pi} \int_{-\pi}^{\pi} x^2 dx = \frac{1}{3\pi} x^3 \Big]_{-\pi}^{\pi} = \frac{2\pi^2}{3}$$

$$a_1 = \frac{1}{\pi} \int_{-\pi}^{\pi} f(x) \cos x\, dx$$

$$= \frac{1}{\pi} \int_{-\pi}^{\pi} x^2 \cos x\, dx$$

$$= \frac{1}{\pi} \left(x^2 \sin x + 2x \cos x - 2 \sin x \right) \Big]_{-\pi}^{\pi}$$

$$= -4$$

$$b_1 = \frac{1}{\pi} \int_{-\pi}^{\pi} f(x) \sin x\, dx$$

$$= \frac{1}{\pi} \int_{-\pi}^{\pi} x^2 \sin x\, dx$$

$$= \frac{1}{\pi} \left(-x^2 \cos x + 2x \sin x + 2 \cos x \right) \Big]_{-\pi}^{\pi}$$

$$= 0$$

Thus, the approximation is

$$g(x) = \frac{\pi^2}{3} - 4 \cos x.$$

Chapters 4-5   Solutions — Cumulative Test

1. (a) $(-1, 2) + (3, -1) = (2, 1)$

(b) $(-3, 6)$

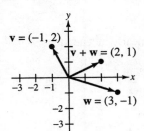

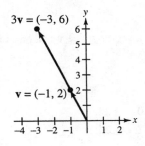

(c) $2\mathbf{v} - 4\mathbf{w} = (-2, 4) - (12, -4) = (-14, 8)$

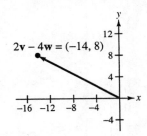

2. $\begin{pmatrix} 1 & -1 & 0 & 3 \\ 2 & 0 & 3 & 2 \\ 0 & 1 & 0 & 1 \end{pmatrix} \Rightarrow \begin{pmatrix} 1 & 0 & 0 & 4 \\ 0 & 1 & 0 & 1 \\ 0 & 0 & 1 & -2 \end{pmatrix}$

$4(1, 2, 0) + 1(-1, 0, 1) - 2(0, 3, 0) = (3, 2, 1)$

3. Not closed under addition: $\begin{pmatrix} 1 & 0 \\ 0 & 0 \end{pmatrix} + \begin{pmatrix} 0 & 0 \\ 0 & 1 \end{pmatrix} = \begin{pmatrix} 1 & 0 \\ 0 & 1 \end{pmatrix}$

4. Yes.

5. No: $(1, 1, 1) + (1, 1, 1) = (2, 2, 2)$

6. Yet, since $\begin{pmatrix} 1 & 2 & -1 & 0 \\ 1 & 3 & 0 & 2 \\ 0 & 0 & 1 & -1 \\ 1 & 0 & 0 & 1 \end{pmatrix}$ row reduces to I.

7. (a) See definition page 185.

(b) linearly dependent

8. $B = \left\{ \begin{pmatrix} 1 & 0 & 0 \\ 0 & 0 & 0 \\ 0 & 0 & 0 \end{pmatrix}, \begin{pmatrix} 0 & 1 & 0 \\ 1 & 0 & 0 \\ 0 & 0 & 0 \end{pmatrix}, \begin{pmatrix} 0 & 0 & 1 \\ 0 & 0 & 0 \\ 1 & 0 & 0 \end{pmatrix}, \begin{pmatrix} 0 & 0 & 0 \\ 0 & 1 & 0 \\ 0 & 0 & 0 \end{pmatrix}, \begin{pmatrix} 0 & 0 & 0 \\ 0 & 0 & 1 \\ 0 & 1 & 0 \end{pmatrix}, \begin{pmatrix} 0 & 0 & 0 \\ 0 & 0 & 0 \\ 0 & 0 & 1 \end{pmatrix} \right\}$

Dimension 6

9. (a) A set of vectors $\{v_1, \ldots, v_n\}$ in a vector space v is a basis for v if the set is linearly independent and spans v.

   (b) Yes.

10. $A = \begin{bmatrix} -1 & 0 & 2 \\ 1 & 1 & 0 \end{bmatrix} \Rightarrow \begin{bmatrix} 1 & 0 & -2 \\ 0 & 1 & 2 \end{bmatrix}$

    (a) rank = 2

    (b) row space $\{(1 \quad 0 \quad -2), (0, 1, 2)\}$

    (c) column space $\left\{ \begin{pmatrix} 1 \\ 0 \end{pmatrix}, \begin{pmatrix} 0 \\ 1 \end{pmatrix} \right\}$

11. $\begin{bmatrix} 1 & 1 & 0 & 0 \\ -2 & -2 & 0 & 0 \\ 0 & 0 & 1 & 1 \\ -1 & -1 & 0 & 0 \end{bmatrix} \Rightarrow \begin{bmatrix} 1 & 1 & 0 & 0 \\ 0 & 0 & 1 & 1 \\ 0 & 0 & 0 & 0 \\ 0 & 0 & 0 & 0 \end{bmatrix} \begin{matrix} x_1 = -s \\ x_2 = s \\ x_3 = -t \\ x_4 = t \end{matrix}$ basis $\left\{ \begin{pmatrix} -1 \\ 1 \\ 0 \\ 0 \end{pmatrix}, \begin{pmatrix} 0 \\ 0 \\ -1 \\ 1 \end{pmatrix} \right\}$

12. $\begin{pmatrix} 0 & 1 & 1 & 1 \\ 1 & 1 & 0 & 2 \\ 1 & 0 & 1 & -3 \end{pmatrix} \Rightarrow \begin{pmatrix} 1 & 0 & 0 & | & -1 \\ 0 & 1 & 0 & | & 3 \\ 0 & 0 & 1 & | & -2 \end{pmatrix}$ $[v]_B = \begin{bmatrix} -1 \\ 3 \\ -2 \end{bmatrix}$

13. $[B' \vdots B] \Rightarrow [I \vdots P^{-1}] \begin{bmatrix} 1 & 1 & 0 & | & 2 & 1 & 0 \\ 0 & 1 & 1 & | & 1 & 0 & 1 \\ 2 & 1 & 3 & | & 0 & 0 & 1 \end{bmatrix} \Rightarrow \begin{bmatrix} 1 & 0 & 0 & | & \frac{1}{4} & \frac{1}{2} & -\frac{1}{2} \\ 0 & 1 & 0 & | & \frac{7}{4} & \frac{1}{2} & \frac{1}{2} \\ 0 & 0 & 1 & | & -\frac{3}{4} & -\frac{1}{2} & \frac{1}{2} \end{bmatrix}$

14. (a) $\|u\| = \sqrt{5}$

    (b) $\|u - v\| = \| (3, -1, -1) \| = \sqrt{11}$

    (c) $u \cdot v = -2 + 6 = 4$

15. $\int_0^1 x^2(x - 2)dx = \frac{x^4}{4} - \frac{2x^3}{3} \Big]_0^1 = \frac{1}{4} - \frac{2}{3} = \frac{-5}{12}$

16. $\left\{ (1, 0, 0), \left(0, \frac{\sqrt{2}}{2}, \frac{\sqrt{2}}{2} \right), \left(0, \frac{-\sqrt{2}}{2}, \frac{\sqrt{2}}{2} \right) \right\}$

17. $\text{proj}_v \mathbf{u} = \dfrac{\mathbf{u} \cdot \mathbf{v}}{\mathbf{v} \cdot \mathbf{v}} \mathbf{v} = \dfrac{1}{13}(-3, 2)$

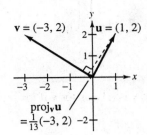

18. $\begin{bmatrix} 0 & 1 & 1 & 0 \\ -1 & 0 & 0 & 1 \\ 1 & 1 & 1 & 1 \end{bmatrix} \Rightarrow \begin{bmatrix} 1 & 0 & 0 & 0 \\ 0 & 1 & 1 & 0 \\ 0 & 0 & 0 & 1 \end{bmatrix}$

$R(A) = \text{column space of } A = R^3$

$N(A) = \text{span}\begin{pmatrix} 0 \\ 1 \\ -1 \\ 0 \end{pmatrix}$

$R(A^T) \Rightarrow \begin{bmatrix} 1 & 0 & 0 \\ 0 & 1 & 0 \\ 0 & 0 & 1 \\ 0 & 0 & 0 \end{bmatrix} \Rightarrow \text{span}\left\{ \begin{pmatrix} 0 \\ 1 \\ 1 \\ 0 \end{pmatrix}, \begin{pmatrix} -1 \\ 0 \\ 0 \\ 1 \end{pmatrix}, \begin{pmatrix} 1 \\ 1 \\ 1 \\ 1 \end{pmatrix} \right\}$

$N(A^T) = \{\mathbf{0}\}$

19. $S^\perp = N(A^T); \begin{pmatrix} 1 & 0 & 1 \\ -1 & 1 & 0 \end{pmatrix} \Rightarrow \begin{pmatrix} 1 & 0 & 1 \\ 0 & 1 & 1 \end{pmatrix} \Rightarrow S^\perp = \text{span} \begin{pmatrix} -1 \\ -1 \\ -1 \end{pmatrix}$

20.
$$0\mathbf{v} = (0 + 0)\mathbf{v} = 0\mathbf{v} + 0\mathbf{v}$$
$$-0\mathbf{v} + 0\mathbf{v} = (-0\mathbf{v} + 0\mathbf{v}) + 0\mathbf{v}$$
$$\mathbf{0} = 0\mathbf{v}$$

21. Suppose $c_1\mathbf{x}_1 + \cdots + c_n\mathbf{x}_n + c_\mathbf{y} = \mathbf{0}$

If $c = 0$, then $c_1\mathbf{x}_1 + \ldots + c_n\mathbf{x}_n = \mathbf{0}$ and $\mathbf{x}_i$ independent $\Rightarrow c_i = 0$

If $c \neq 0$, then $\mathbf{y} = -c_1/c\, \mathbf{x}_1 + \cdots + -c_n/c\, \mathbf{x}_n$, a contradiction.

22. Let $\mathbf{v}_1, \mathbf{v}_2 \in W^\perp$. $\langle \mathbf{v}_1, \mathbf{w} \rangle = 0, \langle \mathbf{v}_2, \mathbf{w} \rangle = 0, \forall \mathbf{w} \Rightarrow \mathbf{v}_1 + \mathbf{v}_2 \in W^\perp$

and, $\langle c\mathbf{v}, \mathbf{w} \rangle = 0 \Rightarrow c\mathbf{v} \in W^\perp$.

Since $W^\perp$ is nonempty, it is a subspace.

23. $A = \begin{pmatrix} 1 & 1 \\ 1 & 3 \\ 1 & 5 \end{pmatrix}$ $A^T A = \begin{pmatrix} 3 & 9 \\ 9 & 35 \end{pmatrix}$ $y = \dfrac{7}{3} - x$

$$A^T \mathbf{b} = \begin{pmatrix} -2 \\ -14 \end{pmatrix}$$

$$\mathbf{x} = \begin{pmatrix} 7/3 \\ -1 \end{pmatrix}$$

24. (a) rank $A = 3$

(b) first 3 rows of A

(c) columns 1, 3, 4, 5 of A

(d) $\begin{aligned} x_1 &= 2r - 3s - 2t \\ x_2 &= r \\ x_3 &= 5s + 3t \\ x_4 &= -s - 7t \\ x_5 &= s \\ x_6 &= t \end{aligned}$ $\left\{ \begin{pmatrix} 2 \\ 1 \\ 0 \\ 0 \\ 0 \\ 0 \end{pmatrix} \begin{pmatrix} -3 \\ 0 \\ 5 \\ -1 \\ 1 \\ 0 \end{pmatrix} \begin{pmatrix} -2 \\ 0 \\ 3 \\ -7 \\ 0 \\ 1 \end{pmatrix} \right\}$

(e) no

(f) no

(g) yes

(h) no

25. $\|\mathbf{u} + \mathbf{v}\| = \|\mathbf{u} - \mathbf{v}\| \iff \|\mathbf{u} + \mathbf{v}\|^2 = \|\mathbf{u} - \mathbf{v}\|^2$

$$\iff (\mathbf{u} + \mathbf{v}) \cdot (\mathbf{u} + \mathbf{v}) = (\mathbf{u} - \mathbf{v}) \cdot (\mathbf{u} - \mathbf{v})$$

$$\iff \mathbf{u} \cdot \mathbf{u} + 2\mathbf{u} \cdot \mathbf{v} + \mathbf{v} \cdot \mathbf{v} = \mathbf{u} \cdot \mathbf{u} - 2\mathbf{u} \cdot \mathbf{v} + \mathbf{v} \cdot \mathbf{v}$$

$$\iff 2\mathbf{u} \cdot \mathbf{v} = -2\mathbf{u} \cdot \mathbf{v}$$

$$\iff \mathbf{u} \cdot \mathbf{v} = 0$$

CHAPTER 6
Linear Transformations

Section 6.1   Introduction to Linear Transformations

1. (a) The image of $\mathbf{v}$ is

$$T(3, -4) = \big(3 + (-4), 3 - (-4)\big) = (-1, 7).$$

(b) If $T(v_1, v_2) = (v_1 + v_2, v_1 - v_2) = (3, 19)$, then

$$v_1 + v_2 = 3$$
$$v_1 - v_2 = 19,$$

which implies that $v_1 = 11$ and $v_2 = -8$. Thus, the preimage of $\mathbf{w}$ is $(11, -8)$.

3. (a) The image of $\mathbf{v}$ is

$$T(2, 3, 0) = (3 - 2, 2 + 3, 2(2)) = (1, 5, 4).$$

(b) If $T(v_1, v_2, v_3) = (v_2 - v_1, v_1 + v_2, 2v_1) = (-11, -1, 10)$, then

$$v_2 - v_1 = -11$$
$$v_1 + v_2 = -1$$
$$2v_1 = 10$$

which implies that $v_1 = 5$ and $v_2 = -6$. Thus, the preimage of $\mathbf{w}$ is $(5, -6, t)$, where t is any real number.

5. (a) The image of $\mathbf{v}$ is

$$T(2, -3, -1) = \big(4(-3) - 2, 4(2) + 5(-3)\big) = (-14, -7).$$

(b) If $T(v_1, v_2, v_3) = (4v_2 - v_1, 4v_1 + 5v_2) = (3, 9)$, then

$$-v_1 + 4v_2 = 3$$
$$4v_1 + 5v_2 = 9,$$

which implies that $v_1 = 1$, $v_2 = 1$, and $v_3 = t$, where t is any real number.
Thus, the preimage of $\mathbf{w}$ is $\{(1, 1, t) : t \text{ is any real number}\}$.

7. T is *not* a linear transformation because it does not preserve addition nor scalar multiplication.
For example,

$$T(1, 1) + T(1, 1) = (1, 1) + (1, 1) = (2, 2) \neq (2, 1) = T(2, 2).$$

9. T is *not* a linear transformation because it does not preserve addition nor scalar multiplication.
For example,

$$T(0, 1) + T(1, 0) = (3, 1) + (4, 0) = (7, 1) \neq (4, 1) = T(1, 1).$$

11. T is *not* a linear transformation because it does not preserve addition. For example,

$$T\left(\begin{bmatrix} -1 & 0 \\ 0 & -1 \end{bmatrix}\right) + T\left(\begin{bmatrix} 1 & 0 \\ 0 & 1 \end{bmatrix}\right) = 2 \neq 0 = T\left(\begin{bmatrix} -1 & 0 \\ 0 & -1 \end{bmatrix} + \begin{bmatrix} 1 & 0 \\ 0 & 1 \end{bmatrix}\right) = T\left(\begin{bmatrix} 0 & 0 \\ 0 & 0 \end{bmatrix}\right).$$

13. T preserves addition.

$$T(A_1 + A_2) = (A_1 + A_2) B = A_1B + A_2B = T(A_1) + T(A_2).$$

T preserves scalar multiplication.

$$T(cA) = (cA)B = c(AB) = cT(A).$$

Therefore, T *is* a linear transformation.

15. T preserves addition.

$$T\left(a_0 + a_1x + a_2x^2\right) + T\left(b_0 + b_1x + b_2x^2\right)$$

$$= (a_0 + a_1 + a_2) + (a_1 + a_2)x + a_2x^2 + (b_0 + b_1 + b_2) + (b_1 + b_2)x + b_2x^2$$

$$= (a_0 + b_0) + (a_1 + b_1) + (a_2 + b_2) + [(a_1 + b_1) + (a_2 + b_2)]x + (a_2 + b_2)x^2$$

$$= T\left((a_0 + b_0) + (a_1 + b_1)x + (a_2 + b_2)x^2\right)$$

T preserves scalar multiplication.

$$T\left(ca_0 + ca_1x + ca_2x^2\right) = (ca_0 + ca_1 + ca_2) + (ca_1 + ca_2)x + ca_2x^2$$

$$= c[(a_0 + a_1 + a_2) + (a_1 + a_2)x + a_2x^2]$$

$$= cT\left(a_0 + a_1 + a_2x^2\right)$$

Therefore, T *is* a linear transformation.

17. Since the matrix has four columns, the dimension of R^n is 4. Since the matrix has three rows, the dimension of R^m is 3. Thus, $T : R^4 \rightarrow R^3$.

19. Since the matrix has two columns, the dimension of R^n is 2. Since the matrix has three rows, the dimension of R^m is 3. Thus, $T : R^2 \rightarrow R^3$.

21. Since the matrix has four columns, the dimension of R^n is 4. Since the matrix has four rows, the dimension of R^m is 4. Thus, $T : R^4 \rightarrow R^4$.

23. (a) $T(1, 0, 2, 3) = \begin{bmatrix} 0 & 1 & -2 & 1 \\ -1 & 4 & 5 & 0 \\ 0 & 1 & 3 & -1 \end{bmatrix} \begin{bmatrix} 1 \\ 0 \\ 2 \\ 3 \end{bmatrix} = \begin{bmatrix} -1 \\ 9 \\ 3 \end{bmatrix} = (-1, 9, 3).$

(b) The preimage of $(0, 0, 0)$ is determined by solving the equation

$$T(v_1, v_2, v_3, v_4) = \begin{bmatrix} 0 & 1 & -2 & 1 \\ -1 & 4 & 5 & 0 \\ 0 & 1 & 3 & -1 \end{bmatrix} \begin{bmatrix} v_1 \\ v_2 \\ v_3 \\ v_4 \end{bmatrix} = \begin{bmatrix} 0 \\ 0 \\ 0 \end{bmatrix}$$

for (v_1, v_2, v_3, v_4). The equivalent system of linear equations has the solution $v_1 = 6t$, $v_2 = -t$, $v_3 = 2t$, and $v_4 = 5t$, where t is any real number. Thus, the preimage is given by the set of vectors

$$\{(6t, -t, 2t, 5t) \mid t \text{ is any real number}\}.$$

25. (a) $T(2, 4) = \begin{bmatrix} 1 & 2 \\ -2 & 4 \\ -2 & 2 \end{bmatrix} \begin{bmatrix} 2 \\ 4 \end{bmatrix} = \begin{bmatrix} 10 \\ 12 \\ 4 \end{bmatrix} = (10, 12, 4)$

(b) The preimage of $(-1, 2, 2)$ is given by solving the equation

$$T(v_1, v_2) = \begin{bmatrix} 1 & 2 \\ -2 & 4 \\ -2 & 2 \end{bmatrix} \begin{bmatrix} v_1 \\ v_2 \end{bmatrix} = \begin{bmatrix} -1 \\ 2 \\ 2 \end{bmatrix}$$

for $\mathbf{v} = (v_1, v_2)$. The equivalent system of linear equations

$$\begin{aligned} v_1 + 2v_2 &= -1 \\ -2v_1 + 4v_2 &= 2 \\ -2v_1 + 2v_2 &= 2 \end{aligned}$$

has the solution $v_1 = -1$ and $v_2 = 0$. Thus, $(-1, 0)$ is the preimage of $(-1, 2, 2)$ under T. Since the system of linear equations represented by the equation

$$\begin{bmatrix} 1 & 2 \\ -2 & 4 \\ -2 & 2 \end{bmatrix} \begin{bmatrix} v_1 \\ v_2 \end{bmatrix} = \begin{bmatrix} 1 \\ 1 \\ 1 \end{bmatrix}$$

has no solution, $(1, 1, 1)$ has no preimage under T.

27. (a) $T(1, 1, 1, 1) = \begin{bmatrix} -1 & 0 & 0 & 0 \\ 0 & 1 & 0 & 0 \\ 0 & 0 & 2 & 0 \\ 0 & 0 & 0 & 1 \end{bmatrix} \begin{bmatrix} 1 \\ 1 \\ 1 \\ 1 \end{bmatrix} = \begin{bmatrix} -1 \\ 1 \\ 2 \\ 1 \end{bmatrix} = (-1, 1, 2, 1).$

(b) The preimage of $(1, 1, 1, 1)$ is determined by solving the equation

$$T(v_1, v_2, v_3, v_4) = \begin{bmatrix} -1 & 0 & 0 & 0 \\ 0 & 1 & 0 & 0 \\ 0 & 0 & 2 & 0 \\ 0 & 0 & 0 & 1 \end{bmatrix} \begin{bmatrix} v_1 \\ v_2 \\ v_3 \\ v_4 \end{bmatrix} = \begin{bmatrix} 1 \\ 1 \\ 1 \\ 1 \end{bmatrix}$$

for $\mathbf{v} = (v_1, v_2, v_3, v_4)$. The equivalent system of linear equations has solution $v_1 = -1, v_2 = 1, v_3 = \frac{1}{2}, v_4 = 1$. Thus, the preimage is $\left(-1, 1, \frac{1}{2}, 1\right)$.

29. (a) When $\theta = 45°$, $\cos \theta = \sin \theta = \frac{1}{\sqrt{2}}$, so

$$T(4, 4) = \left(4\left(\frac{1}{\sqrt{2}}\right) - 4\left(\frac{1}{\sqrt{2}}\right), 4\left(\frac{1}{\sqrt{2}}\right) + 4\left(\frac{1}{\sqrt{2}}\right)\right) = (0, 4\sqrt{2}).$$

(b) When $\theta = 30°$, $\cos \theta = \frac{\sqrt{3}}{2}$ and $\sin \theta = \frac{1}{2}$, so

$$T(4, 4) = \left(4\left(\frac{\sqrt{3}}{2}\right) - 4\left(\frac{1}{2}\right), 4\left(\frac{1}{2}\right) + 4\left(\frac{\sqrt{3}}{2}\right)\right) = (2\sqrt{3} - 2, 2\sqrt{3} + 2).$$

(c) When $\theta = 120°$, $\cos \theta = -\frac{1}{2}$ and $\sin \theta = \frac{\sqrt{3}}{2}$, so

$$T(5, 0) = \left(5\left(-\frac{1}{2}\right) - 0\left(\frac{\sqrt{3}}{2}\right), 5\left(\frac{\sqrt{3}}{2}\right) - 0\left(-\frac{1}{2}\right)\right) = \left(-\frac{5}{2}, \frac{5\sqrt{3}}{2}\right).$$

31. (a) This statement is true because D_x is a linear transformation and thus preserves addition and scalar multiplication.

(b) This statement is true because D_x is a linear transformation and thus preserves addition and scalar multiplication.

(c) This statement is false because $\sin 2x \neq 2 \sin x$ for all x.

33. (a) $T(3x^2 - 2) = \int_0^1 (3x^2 - 2) \, dx = \left[x^3 - 2x\right]_0^1 = -1$

(b) $T(x^3 - x^5) = \int_0^1 (x^3 - x^5) \, dx = \left[\frac{1}{4}x^4 - \frac{1}{6}x^6\right]_0^1 = \frac{1}{12}$

(c) $T(4x - 6) = \int_0^1 (4x - 6) \, dx = \left[2x^2 - 6x\right]_0^1 = -4$

35. We first express $(1, 0)$ in terms of $(1, 1)$ and $(1, -1)$: $(1, 0) = \frac{1}{2}(1, 1) + \frac{1}{2}(1, -1)$. Then

$$
\begin{aligned}
T(1, 0) &= T\left[\tfrac{1}{2}(1, 1) + \tfrac{1}{2}(1, -1)\right] \\
&= \tfrac{1}{2}T(1, 1) + \tfrac{1}{2}T(1, -1) \\
&= \tfrac{1}{2}(1, 0) + \tfrac{1}{2}(0, 1) \\
&= \left(\tfrac{1}{2}, \tfrac{1}{2}\right).
\end{aligned}
$$

Similarly, we express $(0, 2) = 1(1, 1) - 1(1, -1)$, and compute

$$T(0, 2) = T[(1, 1) - (1, -1)] = T(1, 1) - T(1, -1) = (1, 0) - (0, 1) = (1, -1).$$

37.

$$
\begin{aligned}
T\left(2 - 6x + x^2\right) &= 2T(1) - 6T(x) + T\left(x^2\right) \\
&= 2x - 6(1 + x) + \left(1 + x + x^2\right) \\
&= -5 - 3x + x^2
\end{aligned}
$$

39. (a) $T(x, y) = T\left[x(1, 0) + y(0, 1)\right] = xT(1, 0) + yT(0, 1) = x(1, 0) + y(0, 0) = (x, 0)$.

(b) T is the projection onto the x-axis.

41. Since

$$\text{proj}_{\mathbf{v}}\mathbf{u} = \frac{\mathbf{u} \cdot \mathbf{v}}{\mathbf{v} \cdot \mathbf{v}}\mathbf{v}$$

and $T(\mathbf{u}) = \text{proj}_{\mathbf{v}}\mathbf{u}$, we have

$$T(x, y) = \frac{x(1) + y(1)}{1^2 + 1^2}(1, 1) = \left(\frac{x + y}{2}, \frac{x + y}{2}\right).$$

43. From the result of Exercise 41,

$$
\begin{aligned}
T(\mathbf{u} + \mathbf{w}) &= T\left[(x_1, y_1) + (x_2, y_2)\right] = T(x_1 + x_2, y_1 + y_2) \\
&= \left(\frac{x_1 + x_2 + y_1 + y_2}{2}, \frac{x_1 + x_2 + y_1 + y_2}{2}\right) \\
&= \left(\frac{x_1 + y_1}{2}, \frac{x_1 + y_1}{2}\right), \left(\frac{x_2 + y_2}{2}, \frac{x_2 + y_2}{2}\right) \\
&= T(x_1, y_1) + T(x_2, y_2) \\
&= T(\mathbf{u}) + T(\mathbf{v}).
\end{aligned}
$$

45. We use the result of Exercise 41 as follows.

$$T(3, 4) = \left(\frac{3 + 4}{2}, \frac{3 + 4}{2}\right) = \left(\frac{7}{2}, \frac{7}{2}\right)$$

$$T(T(3, 4)) = T\left(\frac{7}{2}, \frac{7}{2}\right) = \left(\frac{1}{2}\left(\frac{7}{2} + \frac{7}{2}\right), \frac{1}{2}\left(\frac{7}{2} + \frac{7}{2}\right)\right) = \left(\frac{7}{2}, \frac{7}{2}\right).$$

T is a projection onto the line $y = x$.

47. Since $T(\mathbf{0}) = \mathbf{0}$ for any linear transformation T, $\mathbf{0}$ is a fixed point of T.

49. A vector $\mathbf{u}$ is a fixed point if $T(\mathbf{u}) = \mathbf{u}$. Since $T(x, y) = (x, 2y) = (x, y)$ has solutions $x = t$ and $y = 0$, the set of all fixed points of T is $\{(t, 0) : t \text{ is any real number.}\}$.

51. Since $T(0, 0) = (-h, -k) \neq (0, 0)$, a translation cannot be a linear transformation.

53. Since $T(x, y) = (x - h, y - k) = (x, y)$ implies $x - h = x$ and $y - k = y$, a translation has no fixed points.

55. There are many possible examples. For instance, let $T : R^3 \to R^3$ be given by $T(x, y, z) = (0, 0, 0)$. Then if $\{v_1, v_2, v_3\}$ is any set of linearly independent vectors, their images $T(v_1), T(v_2), T(v_3)$ form a dependent set.

57. Let $T(\mathbf{v}) = \mathbf{v}$ be the identity transformation. Since $T(\mathbf{u} + \mathbf{v}) = \mathbf{u} + \mathbf{v} = T(\mathbf{u}) + T(\mathbf{v})$ and $T(c\mathbf{u}) = c\mathbf{u} = cT(\mathbf{u}), T$ is a linear transformation.

59. T is a linear transformation because

$$
\begin{aligned}
T(A + B) &= (a_{11} + b_{11}) + \cdots + (a_{nn} + b_{nn}) \\
&= (a_{11} + \cdots + a_{nn}) + (b_{11} + \cdots + b_{nn}) \\
&= T(A) + T(B)
\end{aligned}
$$

and

$$
\begin{aligned}
T(cA) &= ca_{11} + \cdots + ca_{nn} \\
&= c(a_{11} + \cdots + a_{nn}) \\
&= cT(A).
\end{aligned}
$$

61. Let $\mathbf{v} = c_1\mathbf{v}_1 + \ldots + c_n\mathbf{v}_n$ be an arbitrary vector in $\mathbf{v}$. Then

$$
\begin{aligned}
T(\mathbf{v}) &= T(c_1\mathbf{v}_1 + \cdots + c_n\mathbf{v}_n) \\
&= (c_1T(\mathbf{v}_1) + \cdots + c_nT(\mathbf{v}_n)) \\
&= \mathbf{0} + \cdots + \mathbf{0} \\
&= \mathbf{0}
\end{aligned}
$$

Section 6.2   The Kernel and Range of a Linear Transformation

1. Since T sends every vector in R^3 to the zero vector, the kernel is R^3.

3. Solving the equation $T(a_0 + a_1x + a_2x^2 + a_3x^3) = a_0 = 0$ yields solutions of the form $a_0 = 0$ and $a_1, a_2,$ and a_3 are any real numbers. Thus,

$$\ker(T) = \{a_1x + a_2x^2 + a_3x^3 : a_1, a_2, a_3 \in R\}.$$

5. Solving the equation $T(x, y) = (x + 2y, y - x) = (0, 0)$ yields the trivial solution $x = y = 0$. Thus,

$$\ker(T) = \{(0, 0)\}.$$

7. (a) Since

$$T(\mathbf{v}) = \begin{bmatrix} 1 & 2 \\ 3 & 4 \end{bmatrix} \begin{bmatrix} v_1 \\ v_2 \end{bmatrix} = \begin{bmatrix} 0 \\ 0 \end{bmatrix}$$

has only the trivial solution $v_1 = v_2 = 0$, the kernel is $\{(0, 0)\}$.

(b) We transpose A and find the equivalent reduced row-echelon form.

$$A^T = \begin{bmatrix} 1 & 3 \\ 2 & 4 \end{bmatrix} \Rightarrow \begin{bmatrix} 1 & 0 \\ 0 & 1 \end{bmatrix}$$

Thus, a basis for the range is $\{(1, 0), (0, 1)\}$.

9. (a) Since

$$T(\mathbf{v}) = \begin{bmatrix} 1 & -1 & 2 \\ 0 & 1 & 2 \end{bmatrix} \begin{bmatrix} v_1 \\ v_2 \\ v_3 \end{bmatrix} = \begin{bmatrix} 0 \\ 0 \end{bmatrix}$$

has solutions of the form $(-4t, -2t, t)$, where t is any real number, a basis for $\ker(T)$ is $\{(-4, -2, 1)\}$.

(b) We transpose A and find the equivalent reduced row-echelon form.

$$A^T = \begin{bmatrix} 1 & 0 \\ -1 & 1 \\ 2 & 2 \end{bmatrix} \Rightarrow \begin{bmatrix} 1 & 0 \\ 0 & 1 \\ 0 & 0 \end{bmatrix}$$

Thus, a basis for the range(T) is $\{(1, 0), (0, 1)\}$.

11. (a) Since

$$T(\mathbf{v}) = \begin{bmatrix} 1 & 2 & -1 & 4 \\ 3 & 1 & 2 & -1 \\ -4 & -3 & -1 & -3 \\ -1 & -2 & 1 & 1 \end{bmatrix} \begin{bmatrix} v_1 \\ v_2 \\ v_3 \\ v_4 \end{bmatrix} = \begin{bmatrix} 0 \\ 0 \\ 0 \\ 0 \end{bmatrix}$$

has solutions of the form $(-t, t, t, 0)$, where t is any real number, a basis for $\ker(T)$ is $\{(-1, 1, 1, 0)\}$.

(b) We transpose A and find the equivalent reduced row-echelon form.

$$A^T = \begin{bmatrix} 1 & 3 & -4 & -1 \\ 2 & 1 & -3 & -2 \\ -1 & 2 & -1 & 1 \\ 4 & -1 & -3 & 1 \end{bmatrix} \Rightarrow \begin{bmatrix} 1 & 0 & -1 & 0 \\ 0 & 1 & -1 & 0 \\ 0 & 0 & 0 & 1 \\ 0 & 0 & 0 & 0 \end{bmatrix}$$

Thus, a basis for the $\text{range}(T)$ is $\{(1, 0, -1, 0), (0, 1, -1, 0), (0, 0, 0, 1)\}$.

Equivalently, you could use columns 1, 2 and 4 of the original matrix.

13. (a) Since $T(\mathbf{x}) = \mathbf{0}$ has only the trivial solution $\mathbf{x} = (0, 0)$, the kernel of T is $\{(0, 0)\}$.

(b) $\text{nullity}(T) = \dim\big(\ker(T)\big) = 0$

(c) We transpose A and find the equivalent reduced row-echelon form.

$$A^T = \begin{bmatrix} 1 & 1 \\ 1 & -1 \end{bmatrix} \Rightarrow \begin{bmatrix} 1 & 0 \\ 0 & 1 \end{bmatrix}$$

Thus, $\text{range}(T) = R^2$.

(d) $\text{rank}(T) = \dim\big(\text{range}(T)\big) = 2$.

15. (a) Since $T(\mathbf{x}) = \mathbf{0}$ has only the trivial solution $\mathbf{x} = (0, 0)$, the kernel of T is $\{(0, 0)\}$.

(b) $\text{nullity}(T) = \dim\big(\ker(T)\big) = 0$.

(c) We transpose A and find the equivalent reduced row-echelon form.

$$A^T = \begin{bmatrix} 5 & 1 & 1 \\ -3 & 1 & -1 \end{bmatrix} \Rightarrow \begin{bmatrix} 1 & 0 & \frac{1}{4} \\ 0 & 1 & -\frac{1}{4} \end{bmatrix}$$

Thus, $\text{range}(T) = \{(4s, 4t, s - t) \mid s, t \in R\}$.

(d) $\text{rank}(T) = \dim\big(\text{range}(T)\big) = 2$.

17. (a) The kernel of T is given by the solution to the equation $T(\mathbf{x}) = \mathbf{0}$.
Thus, $\ker(T) = \{(-11t, 6t, 4t) : t \text{ is any real number}\}$.

(b) $\text{nullity}(T) = \dim\big(\ker(T)\big) = 1$

(c) We transpose A and find the equivalent reduced row-echelon form.

$$A^T = \begin{bmatrix} 0 & 4 \\ -2 & 0 \\ 3 & 11 \end{bmatrix} \Rightarrow \begin{bmatrix} 1 & 0 \\ 0 & 1 \\ 0 & 0 \end{bmatrix}$$

Thus, range $(T) = R^2$.

(d) $\text{rank}(T) = \dim\big(\text{range}(T)\big) = 2$.

19. (a) The kernel of T is given by the solution to the equation $T(\mathbf{x}) = \mathbf{0}$.
Thus, $\ker(T) = \{(t, -3t)\,|\,t \in R\}$.

(b) $\text{nullity}(T) = \dim\big(\ker(T)\big) = 1$

(c) We transpose A and find its equivalent row-echelon form.

$$A^T = \begin{bmatrix} \frac{9}{10} & \frac{3}{10} \\ \frac{3}{10} & \frac{1}{10} \end{bmatrix} \Rightarrow \begin{bmatrix} 3 & 1 \\ 0 & 0 \end{bmatrix}$$

Thus, $\text{range}(T) = \{(3t, t)\,|\,t \in R\}$.

(d) $\text{rank}(T) = \dim\big(\text{range}(T)\big) = 1$.

21. (a) The kernel of T is given by the solution to the equation $T(\mathbf{x}) = \mathbf{0}$.
Thus, $\ker(T) = \{(2t - s, s, 4t, -5t, t)\,|\,s, t \in R\}$.

(b) $\text{nullity}(T) = \dim\big(\ker(T)\big) = 2$

(c) We transpose A and find its equivalent row-echelon form.

$$A^T = \begin{matrix} 2 & 1 & 3 & 6 \\ 2 & 1 & 3 & 6 \\ -3 & 1 & -5 & -2 \\ 1 & 1 & 0 & 4 \\ 13 & -1 & 14 & 16 \end{matrix} \Rightarrow \begin{matrix} 7 & 0 & 0 & 8 \\ 0 & 7 & 0 & 20 \\ 0 & 0 & 7 & 2 \\ 0 & 0 & 0 & 0 \\ 0 & 0 & 0 & 0 \end{matrix}$$

Thus, $\text{range}(T) = \{(7r, 7s, 7t, 8r + 20s + 2t)\,|\,r, s, t \in R\}$.

Equivalently, the range of T is spanned by columns 1, 3 and 4 of A.

(d) $\text{rank}(T) = \dim\big(\text{range}(T)\big) = 3$

23. (a) The kernel of T is given by the solution to the equation $T(\mathbf{x}) = \mathbf{0}$.
Thus, $\ker(T) = \{(s + t, s, -2t) : s \text{ and } t \text{ are real numbers}\}$.

(b) $\text{nullity}(T) = \dim\big(\ker(T)\big) = 2$

(c) We transpose A and find the equivalent reduced row-eschelon form.

$$A^T = \begin{bmatrix} \frac{4}{9} & -\frac{4}{9} & \frac{2}{9} \\ -\frac{4}{9} & \frac{4}{9} & -\frac{2}{9} \\ \frac{2}{9} & -\frac{2}{9} & \frac{1}{9} \end{bmatrix} \Rightarrow \begin{bmatrix} 1 & -1 & \frac{1}{2} \\ 0 & 0 & 0 \\ 0 & 0 & 0 \end{bmatrix}$$

Thus, $\text{range}(T) = \{(2t, -2t, t) : t \text{ is any real number}\}$.

(d) $\text{rank}(T) = \dim\big(\text{range}(T)\big) = 1$

25. We use Theorem 6.5 to find nullity(T).

$$\text{rank}(T) + \text{nullity}(T) = \dim(R^3)$$

$$\text{nullity}(T) = 3 - 2 = 1$$

Since $\text{nullity}(T) = \dim\big(\ker(T)\big) = 1$, the kernel of T is a line in space.
Furthermore, since $\text{rank}(T) = \dim\big(\text{range}(T)\big) = 2$, the range of T is a plane in space.

27. Since $\text{rank}(T) + \text{nullity}(T) = 3$, and we are given $\text{rank}(T) = 0$, then $\text{nullity}(T) = 3$.
Hence, the kernel of T is all of R^3, and the range is the single point $\{0, 0, 0)\}$.

29. The preimage of $(0, 0, 0)$ is

$\{(0, 0, 0)\}$.

Thus, $\text{nullity}(T) = 0$, and the rank of T is determined as follows.

$$\text{rank}(T) + \text{nullity}(T) = \dim(R^3)$$

$$\text{rank}(T) = 3 - 0 = 3$$

The kernel of T is the single point $(0, 0, 0)$. Since $\text{rank}(T) = \dim\big(\text{range}(T)\big) = 3$,
the range of T is R^3.

31. The kernel of T is determined by solving $T(x, y, z) = \frac{x + 2y + 2z}{9}(1, 2, 2) = (0, 0, 0)$, which
implies that $x + 2y + 2z = 0$. Hence, the nullity of T is 2, and the kernel is a plane. The range of
T is found by observing that $\text{rank}(T) + \text{nullity}(T) = 3$. That is, the range of T is 1-dimensional, a
line in $R^3 : \text{range}(T) = \{(t, 2t, 2t) \mid t \in R\}$.

33. $\text{rank}T + \text{nullity}(T) = \dim R^4 \Rightarrow \text{nullity}(T) = 4 - 1 = 3$

35. $\text{rank}T + \text{nullity}(T) = \dim R^5 \Rightarrow \text{nullity}(T) = 5 - 0 = 5$

37.   **Zero**   **Standard Basis**

(a) $(0, 0, 0, 0)$ $\{(1, 0, 0, 0), (0, 1, 0, 0), (0, 0, 1, 0), (0, 0, 0, 1)\}$

(b) $\begin{bmatrix} 0 \\ 0 \\ 0 \\ 0 \end{bmatrix}$ $\left\{ \begin{bmatrix} 1 \\ 0 \\ 0 \\ 0 \end{bmatrix}, \begin{bmatrix} 0 \\ 1 \\ 0 \\ 0 \end{bmatrix}, \begin{bmatrix} 0 \\ 0 \\ 1 \\ 0 \end{bmatrix}, \begin{bmatrix} 0 \\ 0 \\ 0 \\ 1 \end{bmatrix} \right\}$

(c) $\begin{bmatrix} 0 & 0 \\ 0 & 0 \end{bmatrix}$ $\left\{ \begin{bmatrix} 1 & 0 \\ 0 & 0 \end{bmatrix}, \begin{bmatrix} 0 & 1 \\ 0 & 0 \end{bmatrix}, \begin{bmatrix} 0 & 0 \\ 1 & 0 \end{bmatrix}, \begin{bmatrix} 0 & 0 \\ 0 & 1 \end{bmatrix} \right\}$

(d) $p(x) = 0$ $\{1, x, x^2, x^3\}$

(e) $(0, 0, 0, 0, 0)$ $\{(1, 0, 0, 0, 0), (0, 1, 0, 0, 0), (0, 0, 1, 0, 0), (0, 0, 0, 1, 0)\}$

39. We solve the equation

$$T(\overline{\mathbf{p}}) = \frac{d}{dx}\left(a_0 + a_1 x + a_2 x^2 + a_3 x^3 + a_4 x^4\right) = 0$$

yielding $\mathbf{p} = a_0$. Thus, $\ker(T) = \{p(x) = a_0 : a_0 \text{ is a real number}\}$. (The constant polynomials)

41. We first compute $T(\mathbf{u}) = \text{proj}_\mathbf{v}\mathbf{u}$, for $\mathbf{u} = (x, y, z)$.

$$T(\mathbf{u}) = \text{proj}_\mathbf{v}\mathbf{u} = \frac{(x, y, z) \cdot (2, -1, 1)}{(2, -1, 1) \cdot (2, -1, 1)}(2, -1, 1) = \frac{2x - y + z}{6}(2, -1, 1)$$

(a)   Setting $T(\mathbf{u}) = \mathbf{0}$, we have $2x - y + z = 0$, and hence nullity$(T) = 2$.
      Thus, rank$(T) = 3 - 2 = 1$.

(b)   A basis for the kernel of T is obtained by solving $2x - y + z = 0$.
      Letting $t = z$ and $s = y$, we have $x = \frac{1}{2}(y - z) = \frac{1}{2}s - \frac{1}{2}t$.
      Thus, a basis for $\ker(T)$ is

$$\left\{ \left(\tfrac{1}{2}, 1, 0\right), \left(-\tfrac{1}{2}, 0, 1\right) \right\}, \text{ or } \{(1, 2, 0), (1, 0, -2)\}.$$

43. Since $|A| = -1 \neq 0$, the homogenous equation $A\mathbf{x} = \mathbf{0}$ has only the trivial solution.
Thus, $\ker(T) = \{(0, 0)\}$ and T is one-to-one (by Theorem 6.6). Furthermore, since

$$\text{rank}(T) = \dim(R^2) - \text{nullity}(T) = 2 - 0 = 2 = \dim(R^2)$$

T is onto (by Theorem 6.7).

45. Since $|A| = -1 \neq 0$, the homogenous equation $A\mathbf{x} = \mathbf{0}$ has only the trivial solution.
Thus, $\ker(T) = \{(0, 0, 0)\}$ and T is one-to-one (by Theorem 6.6). Furthermore, since

$$\text{rank}(T) = \dim R^3 - \text{nullity}(T) = 3 - 0 = 3 = \dim(R^3)$$

T is onto (by Theorem 6.7).

47. (a) A is an $n \times n$ matrix and $\det(A) = \det(A^T) \neq 0$. Thus, the reduced row-echelon matrix equivalent to A^T has n nonzero rows and we conclude that $\text{rank}(T) = n$.

   (b) A is an $n \times n$ matrix and $\det(A) = \det(A^T) = 0$. Thus, the reduced row-echelon matrix equivalent to A^T has at least one row of zeros and we conclude that $\text{rank}(T) < n$.

49. Theorem 6.9 tells us that if $M_{m,n}$ and $M_{j,k}$ are of the same dimension then they are isomorphic. Thus, we conclude that $mn = jk$.

51. From Theorem 6.5, $\text{rank}(T) + \text{nullity}(T) = n = $ dimension of V. T is one-to-one if and only if $\text{nullity}(T) = 0$ if and only if $\text{rank}(T) = $ dimension of V.

53. Although they are not the same, they have the same dimension (4) and are isomorphic.

Section 6.3   Matrices for Linear Transformations

1. Since

$$T\left(\begin{bmatrix}1\\0\end{bmatrix}\right) = \begin{bmatrix}1\\1\end{bmatrix} \quad \text{and} \quad T\left(\begin{bmatrix}0\\1\end{bmatrix}\right) = \begin{bmatrix}1\\-1\end{bmatrix}$$

the standard matrix for T is

$$\begin{bmatrix}1 & 1\\1 & -1\end{bmatrix}.$$

3. Since

$$T\left(\begin{bmatrix}1\\0\end{bmatrix}\right) = \begin{bmatrix}5\\1\\-4\end{bmatrix} \quad \text{and} \quad T\left(\begin{bmatrix}0\\1\end{bmatrix}\right) = \begin{bmatrix}-3\\1\\1\end{bmatrix}$$

the standard matrix for T is

$$\begin{bmatrix}5 & -3\\1 & 1\\-4 & 1\end{bmatrix}.$$

5. Since

$$T\left(\begin{bmatrix}1\\0\\0\end{bmatrix}\right) = \begin{bmatrix}1\\1\\0\end{bmatrix}, \quad T\left(\begin{bmatrix}0\\1\\0\end{bmatrix}\right) = \begin{bmatrix}1\\-1\\0\end{bmatrix}, \quad \text{and} \quad T\left(\begin{bmatrix}0\\0\\1\end{bmatrix}\right) = \begin{bmatrix}0\\0\\1\end{bmatrix}$$

the standard matrix for T is

$$A = \begin{bmatrix}1 & 1 & 0\\1 & -1 & 0\\0 & 0 & 1\end{bmatrix}.$$

7. Since

$$T\left(\begin{bmatrix}1\\0\\0\end{bmatrix}\right) = \begin{bmatrix}0\\4\end{bmatrix}, \quad T\left(\begin{bmatrix}0\\1\\0\end{bmatrix}\right) = \begin{bmatrix}-2\\0\end{bmatrix}, \quad \text{and} \quad T\left(\begin{bmatrix}0\\0\\1\end{bmatrix}\right) = \begin{bmatrix}3\\11\end{bmatrix}$$

the standard matrix for T is

$$A = \begin{bmatrix}0 & -2 & 3\\4 & 0 & 11\end{bmatrix}.$$

9. Since

$$T\left(\begin{bmatrix}1\\0\\0\end{bmatrix}\right) = \begin{bmatrix}13\\6\end{bmatrix}, \quad T\left(\begin{bmatrix}0\\1\\0\end{bmatrix}\right) = \begin{bmatrix}-9\\5\end{bmatrix}, \quad \text{and} \quad T\left(\begin{bmatrix}0\\0\\1\end{bmatrix}\right) = \begin{bmatrix}4\\-3\end{bmatrix}$$

the standard matrix for T is

$$A = \begin{bmatrix}13 & -9 & 4\\6 & 5 & -3\end{bmatrix}.$$

Hence $T(\mathbf{v}) = \begin{bmatrix}13 & -9 & 4\\6 & 5 & -3\end{bmatrix}\begin{bmatrix}1\\-2\\1\end{bmatrix} = \begin{bmatrix}35\\-7\end{bmatrix}$

and $T(1, -2, 1) = (35, -7)$

11. Since

$$T\left(\begin{bmatrix}1\\0\\0\\0\end{bmatrix}\right) = \begin{bmatrix}1\\0\end{bmatrix}, \quad T\left(\begin{bmatrix}0\\1\\0\\0\end{bmatrix}\right) = \begin{bmatrix}1\\0\end{bmatrix}, \quad T\left(\begin{bmatrix}0\\0\\1\\0\end{bmatrix}\right) = \begin{bmatrix}0\\1\end{bmatrix}, \quad \text{and}$$

$$T\left(\begin{bmatrix}0\\0\\0\\1\end{bmatrix}\right) = \begin{bmatrix}0\\1\end{bmatrix}$$

the standard matrix for T is

$$\begin{bmatrix}1 & 1 & 0 & 0\\0 & 0 & 1 & 1\end{bmatrix}.$$

Hence $T(\mathbf{v}) = \begin{bmatrix}1 & 1 & 0 & 0\\0 & 0 & 1 & 1\end{bmatrix}\begin{bmatrix}1\\-1\\1\\-1\end{bmatrix} = \begin{bmatrix}0\\0\end{bmatrix}$

and $T(1, -1, 1, -1) = (0, 0)$

13. (a) The matrix of the reflection through the origin, $T(x, y) = (-x, -y)$, is given by

$$A = [\, T(1, 0) \,\vdots\, T(0, 1) \,] = \begin{bmatrix} -1 & 0 \\ 0 & -1 \end{bmatrix}.$$

(b) The image of $\mathbf{v} = (3, 4)$ is given by

$$A\mathbf{v} = \begin{bmatrix} -1 & 0 \\ 0 & -1 \end{bmatrix} \begin{bmatrix} 3 \\ 4 \end{bmatrix} = \begin{bmatrix} -3 \\ -4 \end{bmatrix}.$$

Thus, $T(3, 4) = (-3, -4)$.

(c)

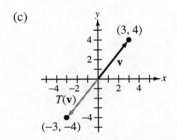

15. (a) The counterclockwise rotation of $135°$ in R^2 is given by

$$T(x, y) = \left(-\frac{\sqrt{2}}{2}x - \frac{\sqrt{2}}{2}y, \frac{\sqrt{2}}{2}x - \frac{\sqrt{2}}{2}y \right). \text{ Thus,}$$

$$A = [T(1, 0) \,\vdots\, T(0, 1)] = \begin{bmatrix} -\frac{\sqrt{2}}{2} & -\frac{\sqrt{2}}{2} \\ \frac{\sqrt{2}}{2} & -\frac{\sqrt{2}}{2} \end{bmatrix}.$$

(b) The image of $\mathbf{v}$ is given by

$$A\mathbf{v} = \begin{bmatrix} -\frac{\sqrt{2}}{2} & -\frac{\sqrt{2}}{2} \\ \frac{\sqrt{2}}{2} & -\frac{\sqrt{2}}{2} \end{bmatrix} \begin{bmatrix} 4 \\ 4 \end{bmatrix} = \begin{bmatrix} -4\sqrt{2} \\ 0 \end{bmatrix}.$$

Thus, $T(4, 4) = \left(-4\sqrt{2}, 0 \right)$.

(c)

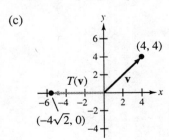

17. (a) The standard matrix for T is

$$A = [T(1, 0, 0) \vdots T(0, 1, 0) \vdots T(0, 0, 1)] = \begin{bmatrix} 1 & 0 & 0 \\ 0 & 1 & 0 \\ 0 & 0 & -1 \end{bmatrix}.$$

(b) The image of **v** is

$$A\mathbf{v} = \begin{bmatrix} 1 & 0 & 0 \\ 0 & 1 & 0 \\ 0 & 0 & -1 \end{bmatrix} \begin{bmatrix} 3 \\ 2 \\ 2 \end{bmatrix} = \begin{bmatrix} 3 \\ 2 \\ -2 \end{bmatrix}.$$

Thus, $T(3, 2, 2) = (3, 2, -2)$.

(c)

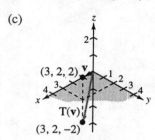

19. (a) The standard matrix for T is

$$A = [T(1, 0) \vdots T(0, 1)] = \begin{bmatrix} -1 & 0 \\ 0 & -1 \end{bmatrix}.$$

(b) The image of $\mathbf{v} = (1, 2)$ is given by

$$A\mathbf{v} = \begin{bmatrix} -1 & 0 \\ 0 & -1 \end{bmatrix} \begin{bmatrix} 1 \\ 2 \end{bmatrix} = \begin{bmatrix} -1 \\ -2 \end{bmatrix}.$$

Thus, $T(1, 2) = (-1, -2)$.

(c)

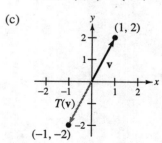

21. (a) The projection onto the vector $\mathbf{w} = (3, 1)$ is given by

$$T(\mathbf{v}) = \text{proj}_{\mathbf{w}}\mathbf{v} = \frac{3x + y}{10}(3, 1) = \left(\tfrac{3}{10}(3x + y), \tfrac{1}{10}(3x + y)\right).$$

Thus, the matrix is

$$A = [T(1, 0) \;\vdots\; T(0, 1)] = \begin{bmatrix} \frac{9}{10} & \frac{3}{10} \\ \frac{3}{10} & \frac{1}{10} \end{bmatrix}.$$

(b) The image of $\mathbf{v} = (1, 4)$ is given by

$$A\mathbf{v} = \begin{bmatrix} \frac{9}{10} & \frac{3}{10} \\ \frac{3}{10} & \frac{1}{10} \end{bmatrix} \begin{bmatrix} 1 \\ 4 \end{bmatrix} = \begin{bmatrix} 21/10 \\ 7/10 \end{bmatrix}.$$

Thus, $T(1, 4) = (21/10, 7/10)$.

(c)

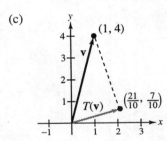

23. (a) The reflection of a vector **v** through **w** is given by

$$T(\mathbf{v}) = 2 \operatorname{proj}_{\mathbf{w}} \mathbf{v} - \mathbf{v}$$

$$T(x, y) = 2 \frac{3x + y}{10} (3, 1) - (x, y)$$

$$= \left(\frac{4}{5} x + \frac{3}{5} y, \frac{3}{5} x - \frac{4}{5} y \right).$$

The standard matrix for T is

$$A = [T(1, 0) \vdots T(0, 1)] = \begin{bmatrix} \frac{4}{5} & \frac{3}{5} \\ \frac{3}{5} & -\frac{4}{5} \end{bmatrix}.$$

(b) The image of **v** is

$$A\mathbf{v} = \begin{bmatrix} \frac{4}{5} & \frac{3}{5} \\ \frac{3}{5} & -\frac{4}{5} \end{bmatrix} \begin{bmatrix} 1 \\ 4 \end{bmatrix} = \begin{bmatrix} \frac{16}{5} \\ -\frac{13}{5} \end{bmatrix}.$$

Thus, $T(1, 4) = \left(\frac{16}{5}, -\frac{13}{5} \right)$.

(c)

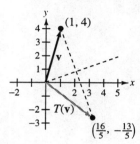

25. The standard matrices for T_1 and T_2 are

$$A_1 = \begin{bmatrix} 1 & -2 \\ 2 & 3 \end{bmatrix} \quad \text{and} \quad A_2 = \begin{bmatrix} 2 & 0 \\ 1 & -1 \end{bmatrix}.$$

The standard matrix for $T = T_2 \circ T_1$ is

$$A_2 A_1 = \begin{bmatrix} 2 & 0 \\ 1 & -1 \end{bmatrix} \begin{bmatrix} 1 & -2 \\ 2 & 3 \end{bmatrix} = \begin{bmatrix} 2 & -4 \\ -1 & -5 \end{bmatrix}$$

and the standard matrix for $T' = T_1 \circ T_2$ is

$$A_1 A_2 = \begin{bmatrix} 1 & -2 \\ 2 & 3 \end{bmatrix} \begin{bmatrix} 2 & 0 \\ 1 & -1 \end{bmatrix} = \begin{bmatrix} 0 & 2 \\ 7 & -3 \end{bmatrix}.$$

27. The standard matrices for T_1 and T_2 are

$$A_1 = \begin{bmatrix} 1 & 0 & 0 \\ 0 & 1 & 0 \\ 0 & 0 & 1 \end{bmatrix} \quad \text{and} \quad A_2 = \begin{bmatrix} 0 & 0 & 0 \\ 1 & 0 & 0 \\ 0 & 0 & 0 \end{bmatrix}.$$

The standard matrix for $T = T_2 \circ T_1$ is

$$A_2 A_1 = \begin{bmatrix} 0 & 0 & 0 \\ 1 & 0 & 0 \\ 0 & 0 & 0 \end{bmatrix} \begin{bmatrix} 1 & 0 & 0 \\ 0 & 1 & 0 \\ 0 & 0 & 1 \end{bmatrix} = \begin{bmatrix} 0 & 0 & 0 \\ 1 & 0 & 0 \\ 0 & 0 & 0 \end{bmatrix} = A_2$$

and the standard matrix for $T' = T_1 \circ T_2$ is

$$A_1 A_2 = \begin{bmatrix} 1 & 0 & 0 \\ 0 & 1 & 0 \\ 0 & 0 & 1 \end{bmatrix} \begin{bmatrix} 0 & 0 & 0 \\ 1 & 0 & 0 \\ 0 & 0 & 0 \end{bmatrix} = \begin{bmatrix} 0 & 0 & 0 \\ 1 & 0 & 0 \\ 0 & 0 & 0 \end{bmatrix} = A_2.$$

29. The standard matrices for T_1 and T_2 are

$$A_1 = \begin{bmatrix} -1 & 2 \\ 1 & 1 \\ 1 & -1 \end{bmatrix} \quad \text{and} \quad A_2 = \begin{bmatrix} 1 & -3 & 0 \\ 3 & 0 & 1 \end{bmatrix}.$$

The standard matrix for $T = T_2 \circ T_1$ is

$$A_2 A_1 = \begin{bmatrix} 1 & -3 & 0 \\ 3 & 0 & 1 \end{bmatrix} \begin{bmatrix} -1 & 2 \\ 1 & 1 \\ 1 & -1 \end{bmatrix} = \begin{bmatrix} -4 & -1 \\ -2 & 5 \end{bmatrix}$$

and the standard matrix for $T' = T_1 \circ T_2$ is

$$A_1 A_2 = \begin{bmatrix} -1 & 2 \\ 1 & 1 \\ 1 & -1 \end{bmatrix} \begin{bmatrix} 1 & -3 & 0 \\ 3 & 0 & 1 \end{bmatrix} = \begin{bmatrix} 5 & 3 & 2 \\ 4 & -3 & 1 \\ -2 & -3 & -1 \end{bmatrix}.$$

31. The standard matrices for T is

$$A = \begin{bmatrix} 1 & 1 \\ 1 & -1 \end{bmatrix}.$$

Since $|A| = -2 \neq 0$, A is invertible.

$$A^{-1} = -\frac{1}{2} \begin{bmatrix} -1 & -1 \\ -1 & 1 \end{bmatrix} = \begin{bmatrix} \frac{1}{2} & \frac{1}{2} \\ \frac{1}{2} & -\frac{1}{2} \end{bmatrix}$$

Thus, $T^{-1}(x, y) = \left(\frac{1}{2} x + \frac{1}{2} y, \frac{1}{2} x - \frac{1}{2} y \right)$.

33. The standard matrix for T is

$$A = \begin{bmatrix} 2 & 0 \\ 0 & 0 \end{bmatrix}.$$

Since $|A| = 0$, A is not invertible and hence, T is not invertible.

35. The standard matrices for T is

$$A = \begin{bmatrix} 5 & 0 \\ 0 & 5 \end{bmatrix}.$$

Since $|A| = 25 \neq 0$, A is invertible. We have

$$A^{-1} = \begin{bmatrix} \frac{1}{5} & 0 \\ 0 & \frac{1}{5} \end{bmatrix}$$

and hence $T^{-1}(x, y) = \left(\frac{x}{5}, \frac{y}{5} \right)$.

37. (a) The standard matrix for T is

$$A' = \begin{bmatrix} 1 & 1 \\ 1 & 0 \\ 0 & 1 \end{bmatrix}$$

and the image of **v** under T is

$$A'\mathbf{v} = \begin{bmatrix} 1 & 1 \\ 1 & 0 \\ 0 & 1 \end{bmatrix} \begin{bmatrix} 5 \\ 4 \end{bmatrix} = \begin{bmatrix} 9 \\ 5 \\ 4 \end{bmatrix}.$$

Thus, $T(\mathbf{v}) = (9, 5, 4)$.

(b) The image of each vector in B is as follows.

$$T(1, -1) = (0, 1, -1) = (1, 1, 0) + 0(0, 1, 1) - (1, 0, 1)$$
$$T(0, 1) = (1, 0, 1) = 0(1, 1, 0) + 0(0, 1, 1) + (1, 0, 1)$$

Thus, we have

$$[T(1, -1)]_{B'} = \begin{bmatrix} 1 \\ 0 \\ -1 \end{bmatrix} \quad \text{and} \quad [T(0, 1)]_{B'} = \begin{bmatrix} 0 \\ 0 \\ 1 \end{bmatrix}$$

which implies that

$$A = \begin{bmatrix} 1 & 0 \\ 0 & 0 \\ -1 & 1 \end{bmatrix}.$$

Then, since

$$[\mathbf{v}]_B = \begin{bmatrix} 5 \\ 9 \end{bmatrix},$$

we have

$$[T(\mathbf{v})]_{B'} = A[\mathbf{v}]_B = \begin{bmatrix} 1 & 0 \\ 0 & 0 \\ -1 & 1 \end{bmatrix} \begin{bmatrix} 5 \\ 9 \end{bmatrix} = \begin{bmatrix} 5 \\ 0 \\ 4 \end{bmatrix}.$$

Thus, $T(\mathbf{v}) = 5(1, 1, 0) + 4(1, 0, 1) = (9, 5, 4)$.

39. (a) The standard matrix for T is

$$A' = \begin{bmatrix} 1 & -1 & 0 \\ 0 & 1 & -1 \end{bmatrix}$$

and the image of $\mathbf{v}$ under T is

$$A'\mathbf{v} = \begin{bmatrix} 1 & -1 & 0 \\ 0 & 1 & -1 \end{bmatrix} \begin{bmatrix} 1 \\ 2 \\ -3 \end{bmatrix} = \begin{bmatrix} -1 \\ 5 \end{bmatrix}.$$

Thus, $T(\mathbf{v}) = (-1, 5)$.

(b) The image of each vector in B is as follows.

$$T(1, 1, 1) = (0, 0) = 0(1, 2) + 0(1, 1)$$
$$T(1, 1, 0) = (0, 1) = (1, 2) - (1, 1)$$
$$T(0, 1, 1) = (-1, 0) = (1, 2) - 2(1, 1)$$

Thus, we have

$$[T(1, 1, 1)]_{B'} = \begin{bmatrix} 0 \\ 0 \end{bmatrix}, \quad [T(1, 1, 0)]_{B'} = \begin{bmatrix} 1 \\ -1 \end{bmatrix},$$

and

$$[T(0, 1, 1)]_{B'} = \begin{bmatrix} 1 \\ -2 \end{bmatrix},$$

which implies that

$$A = \begin{bmatrix} 0 & 1 & 1 \\ 0 & -1 & -2 \end{bmatrix}.$$

Then, since

$$[\mathbf{v}]_B = \begin{bmatrix} -4 \\ 5 \\ 1 \end{bmatrix},$$

we have

$$[T(\mathbf{v})]_{B'} = A[\mathbf{v}]_B = \begin{bmatrix} 0 & 1 & 1 \\ 0 & -1 & -2 \end{bmatrix} \begin{bmatrix} -4 \\ 5 \\ 1 \end{bmatrix} = \begin{bmatrix} 6 \\ -7 \end{bmatrix}.$$

Thus, $T(\mathbf{v}) = 6(1, 2) - 7(1, 1) = (-1, 5)$.

41. (a) The standard matrix for T is

$$A' = \begin{bmatrix} 2 & 0 & 0 \\ 1 & 1 & 0 \\ 0 & 1 & 1 \\ 1 & 0 & 1 \end{bmatrix}$$

and the image of $\mathbf{v} = (1, -5, 2)$ under T is

$$A'\mathbf{v} = \begin{bmatrix} 2 & 0 & 0 \\ 1 & 1 & 0 \\ 0 & 1 & 1 \\ 1 & 0 & 1 \end{bmatrix} \begin{bmatrix} 1 \\ -5 \\ 2 \end{bmatrix} = \begin{bmatrix} 2 \\ -4 \\ -3 \\ 3 \end{bmatrix} \Rightarrow T(\mathbf{v}) = (2, -4, -3, 3).$$

(b) Since

$$T(2, 0, 1) = (4, 2, 1, 3)$$

$$= 2(1, 0, 0, 1) + (0, 1, 0, 1) + (1, 0, 1, 0) + (1, 1, 0, 0)$$

$$T(0, 2, 1) = (0, 2, 3, 1)$$

$$= -2(1, 0, 0, 1) + 3(0, 1, 0, 1) + 3(1, 0, 1, 0) - (1, 1, 0, 0)$$

$$T(1, 2, 1) = (2, 3, 3, 2)$$

$$= -(1, 0, 0, 1) + 3(0, 1, 0, 1) + 3(0, 0, 1, 0)$$

the matrix for T relative to B and B' is

$$A = \begin{bmatrix} 2 & -2 & -1 \\ 1 & 3 & 3 \\ 1 & 3 & 3 \\ 1 & -1 & 0 \end{bmatrix}.$$

Since $\mathbf{v} = (1, -5, 2) = \frac{9}{2}(2, 0, 1) + \frac{11}{2}(0, 2, 1) - 8(1, 2, 1)$

$$[T(\mathbf{v})]_{B'} = A[\mathbf{v}]_B = \begin{bmatrix} 2 & -2 & -1 \\ 1 & 3 & 3 \\ 1 & 3 & 3 \\ 1 & -1 & 0 \end{bmatrix} \begin{bmatrix} 9/2 \\ 11/2 \\ -8 \end{bmatrix} = \begin{bmatrix} 6 \\ -3 \\ -3 \\ -1 \end{bmatrix}.$$

Thus,

$$T(1, -5, 2) = 6(1, 0, 0, 1) - 3(0, 1, 0, 1) - 3(1, 0, 1, 0) - (1, 1, 0, 0)$$

$$= (2, -4, -3, 3).$$

43. (a) The standard matrix for T is

$$A' = \begin{bmatrix} 1 & 1 & 1 \\ -1 & 0 & 2 \\ 0 & 2 & -1 \end{bmatrix}$$

and the image of $\mathbf{v} = (4, -5, 10)$ under T is

$$A'\mathbf{v} = \begin{bmatrix} 1 & 1 & 1 \\ -1 & 0 & 2 \\ 0 & 2 & -1 \end{bmatrix} \begin{bmatrix} 4 \\ -5 \\ 10 \end{bmatrix} = \begin{bmatrix} 9 \\ 16 \\ -20 \end{bmatrix} \Rightarrow T(\mathbf{v}) = (9, 16, -20).$$

(b) Since

$$T(2, 0, 1) = (3, 0, -1) = 2(1, 1, 1) + 1(1, 1, 0) - 3(0, 1, 1)$$
$$T(0, 2, 1) = (3, 2, \quad 3) = 4(1, 1, 1) \quad -(1, 1, 0) \quad -(0, 1, 1)$$
$$T(1, 2, 1) = (4, 1, \quad 3) = 6(1, 1, 1) - 2(1, 1, 0) - 3(0, 1, 1)$$

the matrix for T relative to B and B' is

$$A = \begin{bmatrix} 2 & 4 & 6 \\ 1 & -1 & -2 \\ -3 & -1 & -3 \end{bmatrix}.$$

Since $\mathbf{v} = (4, -5, 10) = \frac{25}{2}(2, 0, 1) + \frac{37}{2}(0, 2, 1) - 21(1, 2, 1)$, we have

$$[T(\mathbf{v})]_{B'} = A[\mathbf{v}]_B = \begin{bmatrix} 2 & 4 & 6 \\ 1 & -1 & -2 \\ -3 & -1 & -3 \end{bmatrix} \begin{bmatrix} 25/2 \\ 37/2 \\ -21 \end{bmatrix} = \begin{bmatrix} -27 \\ 36 \\ 7 \end{bmatrix}.$$

Thus, $T(\mathbf{v}) = -27(1, 1, 1) + 36(1, 1, 0) + 7(0, 1, 1) = (9, 16, -20).$

45. The image of each vector in B is as follows.

$$T(1) = x, \quad T(x) = x^2, \quad T(x^2) = x^3.$$

Thus, the matrix of T relative to B and B' is

$$A = \begin{bmatrix} 0 & 0 & 0 \\ 1 & 0 & 0 \\ 0 & 1 & 0 \\ 0 & 0 & 1 \end{bmatrix}.$$

47. The image of each vector in B is as follows.

$$D_x(1) = 0 = 0(1) + 0x + 0e^x + 0xe^x$$

$$D_x(x) = 1 = 1 + 0x + 0e^x + 0xe^x$$

$$D_x(e^x) = e^x = 0(1) + 0x + e^x + 0xe^x$$

$$D_x(xe^x) = e^x + xe^x = 0(1) + 0x + e^x + xe^x$$

Thus, we have

$$[D_x(1)]_B = \begin{bmatrix} 0 \\ 0 \\ 0 \\ 0 \end{bmatrix}, \quad [D_x(x)]_B = \begin{bmatrix} 1 \\ 0 \\ 0 \\ 0 \end{bmatrix}$$

$$[D_x(e^x)]_B = \begin{bmatrix} 0 \\ 0 \\ 1 \\ 0 \end{bmatrix}, \quad [D_x(xe^x)]_B = \begin{bmatrix} 0 \\ 0 \\ 1 \\ 1 \end{bmatrix}$$

which implies that

$$A = \begin{bmatrix} 0 & 1 & 0 & 0 \\ 0 & 0 & 0 & 0 \\ 0 & 0 & 1 & 1 \\ 0 & 0 & 0 & 1 \end{bmatrix}.$$

49. Since $3x - 2xe^x = 0(1) + 3(x) + 0(e^x) - 2(xe^x)$, we have

$$A[\mathbf{v}]_B = \begin{bmatrix} 0 & 1 & 0 & 0 \\ 0 & 0 & 0 & 0 \\ 0 & 0 & 1 & 1 \\ 0 & 0 & 0 & 1 \end{bmatrix} \begin{bmatrix} 0 \\ 3 \\ 0 \\ -2 \end{bmatrix} = \begin{bmatrix} 3 \\ 0 \\ -2 \\ -2 \end{bmatrix} \Rightarrow D_x(3x - 2xe^x) = 3 - 2e^x - 2xe^x.$$

51. (a) The image of each vector in B is as follows.

$$T(1) = \int_0^x dt = x = 0(1) + x + 0x^2 + 0x^3 + 0x^4$$

$$T(x) = \int_0^x t\, dt = \tfrac{1}{2}x^2 = 0(1) + 0x + \tfrac{1}{2}x^2 + 0x^3 + 0x^4$$

$$T(x^2) = \int_0^x t^2\, dt = \tfrac{1}{3}x^3 = 0(1) + 0x + 0x^2 + \tfrac{1}{3}x^3 + 0x^4$$

$$T(x^3) = \int_0^x t^3\, dt = \tfrac{1}{4}x^4 = 0(1) + 0(x) + 0x^2 + 0x^3 + \tfrac{1}{4}x^4$$

Thus, we have

$$A = \begin{bmatrix} 0 & 0 & 0 & 0 \\ 1 & 0 & 0 & 0 \\ 0 & \tfrac{1}{2} & 0 & 0 \\ 0 & 0 & \tfrac{1}{3} & 0 \\ 0 & 0 & 0 & \tfrac{1}{4} \end{bmatrix}.$$

(b) The image of $p(x) = 6 - 2x + 3x^3$ under T relative to the basis of B' is given by

$$A[\mathbf{p}]_B = \begin{bmatrix} 0 & 0 & 0 & 0 \\ 1 & 0 & 0 & 0 \\ 0 & \tfrac{1}{2} & 0 & 0 \\ 0 & 0 & \tfrac{1}{3} & 0 \\ 0 & 0 & 0 & \tfrac{1}{4} \end{bmatrix} \begin{bmatrix} 6 \\ -2 \\ 0 \\ 3 \end{bmatrix} = \begin{bmatrix} 0 \\ 6 \\ -1 \\ 0 \\ \tfrac{3}{4} \end{bmatrix}.$$

Thus, we have

$$T(\mathbf{p}) = 0(1) + 6x - x^2 + 0x^3 + \tfrac{3}{4}x^4$$

$$= 6x - x^2 + \tfrac{3}{4}x^4$$

$$= \int_0^x p(t)\, dt.$$

53. The standard basis for $M_{2,3}$ is

$$B = \left\{ \begin{bmatrix} 1 & 0 & 0 \\ 0 & 0 & 0 \end{bmatrix}, \begin{bmatrix} 0 & 1 & 0 \\ 0 & 0 & 0 \end{bmatrix}, \begin{bmatrix} 0 & 0 & 1 \\ 0 & 0 & 0 \end{bmatrix}, \right.$$

$$\left. \begin{bmatrix} 0 & 0 & 0 \\ 1 & 0 & 0 \end{bmatrix}, \begin{bmatrix} 0 & 0 & 0 \\ 0 & 1 & 0 \end{bmatrix}, \begin{bmatrix} 0 & 0 & 0 \\ 0 & 0 & 1 \end{bmatrix} \right\}$$

and the standard basis for $M_{3,2}$ is

$$B' = \left\{ \begin{bmatrix} 1 & 0 \\ 0 & 0 \\ 0 & 0 \end{bmatrix}, \begin{bmatrix} 0 & 1 \\ 0 & 0 \\ 0 & 0 \end{bmatrix}, \begin{bmatrix} 0 & 0 \\ 1 & 0 \\ 0 & 0 \end{bmatrix}, \right.$$

$$\left. \begin{bmatrix} 0 & 0 \\ 0 & 1 \\ 0 & 0 \end{bmatrix}, \begin{bmatrix} 0 & 0 \\ 0 & 0 \\ 1 & 0 \end{bmatrix}, \begin{bmatrix} 0 & 0 \\ 0 & 0 \\ 0 & 1 \end{bmatrix} \right\}.$$

By finding the image of each vector in B we can find A.

$$T\left(\begin{bmatrix} 1 & 0 & 0 \\ 0 & 0 & 0 \end{bmatrix} \right) = \begin{bmatrix} 1 & 0 \\ 0 & 0 \\ 0 & 0 \end{bmatrix}, \quad T\left(\begin{bmatrix} 0 & 1 & 0 \\ 0 & 0 & 0 \end{bmatrix} \right) = \begin{bmatrix} 0 & 0 \\ 1 & 0 \\ 0 & 0 \end{bmatrix},$$

$$T\left(\begin{bmatrix} 0 & 0 & 1 \\ 0 & 0 & 0 \end{bmatrix} \right) = \begin{bmatrix} 0 & 0 \\ 0 & 0 \\ 1 & 0 \end{bmatrix}, \quad T\left(\begin{bmatrix} 0 & 0 & 0 \\ 1 & 0 & 0 \end{bmatrix} \right) = \begin{bmatrix} 0 & 1 \\ 0 & 0 \\ 0 & 0 \end{bmatrix},$$

$$T\left(\begin{bmatrix} 0 & 0 & 0 \\ 0 & 1 & 0 \end{bmatrix} \right) = \begin{bmatrix} 0 & 0 \\ 0 & 1 \\ 0 & 0 \end{bmatrix}, \quad T\left(\begin{bmatrix} 0 & 0 & 0 \\ 0 & 0 & 1 \end{bmatrix} \right) = \begin{bmatrix} 0 & 0 \\ 0 & 0 \\ 0 & 1 \end{bmatrix},$$

Thus,

$$A = \begin{bmatrix} 1 & 0 & 0 & 0 & 0 & 0 \\ 0 & 0 & 0 & 1 & 0 & 0 \\ 0 & 1 & 0 & 0 & 0 & 0 \\ 0 & 0 & 0 & 0 & 1 & 0 \\ 0 & 0 & 1 & 0 & 0 & 0 \\ 0 & 0 & 0 & 0 & 0 & 1 \end{bmatrix}.$$

55. Let $(T_2 \circ T_1)(\mathbf{v}_1) = (T_2 \circ T_1)(\mathbf{v}_2)$

$$T_2(T_1(\mathbf{v}_1)) = T_2(T_1(\mathbf{v}_2))$$

$$(T_1(\mathbf{v}_1)) = T_1(\mathbf{v}_2) \qquad \text{since } T_2 \text{ one-to-one}$$

$$\mathbf{v}_1 = \mathbf{v}_2 \qquad \text{since } T_1 \text{ one-to-one}$$

Since $T_2 \circ T_1$ is one-to-one from V to V, it is also onto. The inverse is $T_1^{-1} \circ T_2^{-1}$ because

$$(T_2 \circ T_1) \circ (T_1^{-1} \circ T_2^{-1}) = T_2 \circ I \circ T_2^{-1} = I.$$

57. Sometimes it is preferable to use a nonstandard basis. For example, some linear transformations have diagonal matrix representations relative to a nonstandard basis.

Section 6.4   Transition Matrices and Similarity

1. (a) The standard matrix for T is

$$A = \begin{bmatrix} 2 & -1 \\ -1 & 1 \end{bmatrix}.$$

Furthermore, the transition matrix from B' to the standard basis $B = \{(1, 0), (0, 1)\}$ is

$$P = \begin{bmatrix} 1 & 0 \\ -2 & 3 \end{bmatrix}$$

and its inverse is

$$P^{-1} = \begin{bmatrix} 1 & 0 \\ \frac{2}{3} & \frac{1}{3} \end{bmatrix}.$$

Therefore, the matrix for T relative to B' is

$$A' = P^{-1} AP = \begin{bmatrix} 1 & 0 \\ \frac{2}{3} & \frac{1}{3} \end{bmatrix} \begin{bmatrix} 2 & -1 \\ -1 & 1 \end{bmatrix} \begin{bmatrix} 1 & 0 \\ -2 & 3 \end{bmatrix} = \begin{bmatrix} 4 & -3 \\ \frac{5}{3} & -1 \end{bmatrix}.$$

(b) Since $A' = P^{-1} AP$, it follows that A and A' are similar.

3. (a) The standard matrix for T is

$$A = \begin{bmatrix} 0 & 1 \\ 1 & 0 \end{bmatrix}.$$

Furthermore, the transition matrix from B' to the standard basis $B = \{(1, 0), (0, 1)\}$ is

$$P = \begin{bmatrix} 1 & 1 \\ -1 & 1 \end{bmatrix}$$

and its inverse is

$$P^{-1} = \begin{bmatrix} \frac{1}{2} & -\frac{1}{2} \\ \frac{1}{2} & \frac{1}{2} \end{bmatrix}.$$

Therefore, the matrix for T relative to B' is

$$A' = P^{-1} AP = \begin{bmatrix} \frac{1}{2} & -\frac{1}{2} \\ \frac{1}{2} & \frac{1}{2} \end{bmatrix} \begin{bmatrix} 0 & 1 \\ 1 & 0 \end{bmatrix} \begin{bmatrix} 1 & 1 \\ -1 & 1 \end{bmatrix} = \begin{bmatrix} -1 & 0 \\ 0 & 1 \end{bmatrix}.$$

(b) Since $A' = P^{-1} AP$, it follows that A and A' are similar.

5. (a) The standard matrix for T is

$$A = \begin{bmatrix} 1 & 0 & 0 \\ 0 & 1 & 0 \\ 0 & 0 & 1 \end{bmatrix}.$$

Furthermore, the transition matrix from B' to the standard basis

$$B = \{(1, 0, 0), (0, 1, 0), (0, 0, 1)\} \text{ is}$$

$$P = \begin{bmatrix} 1 & 1 & 0 \\ 1 & 0 & 1 \\ 0 & 1 & 1 \end{bmatrix}$$

and its inverse is

$$P^{-1} = \begin{bmatrix} \frac{1}{2} & \frac{1}{2} & -\frac{1}{2} \\ \frac{1}{2} & -\frac{1}{2} & \frac{1}{2} \\ -\frac{1}{2} & \frac{1}{2} & \frac{1}{2} \end{bmatrix}.$$

Therefore, the matrix for T relative to B' is

$$A' = P^{-1}AP = \begin{bmatrix} \frac{1}{2} & \frac{1}{2} & -\frac{1}{2} \\ \frac{1}{2} & -\frac{1}{2} & \frac{1}{2} \\ -\frac{1}{2} & \frac{1}{2} & \frac{1}{2} \end{bmatrix} \begin{bmatrix} 1 & 0 & 0 \\ 0 & 1 & 0 \\ 0 & 0 & 1 \end{bmatrix} \begin{bmatrix} 1 & 1 & 0 \\ 1 & 0 & 1 \\ 0 & 1 & 1 \end{bmatrix} = \begin{bmatrix} 1 & 0 & 0 \\ 0 & 1 & 0 \\ 0 & 0 & 1 \end{bmatrix}.$$

(b) Since $A' = P^{-1}AP$, it follows that A and A' are similar.

7. (a) The standard matrix for T is

$$A = \begin{bmatrix} 1 & -1 & 2 \\ 2 & 1 & -1 \\ 1 & 2 & 1 \end{bmatrix}.$$

Furthermore, the transition matrix P from B' to the standard basis B, and its inverse, are

$$P = \begin{bmatrix} 1 & 0 & 1 \\ 0 & 2 & 2 \\ 1 & 2 & 0 \end{bmatrix} \text{ and } P^{-1} = \begin{bmatrix} \frac{2}{3} & -\frac{1}{3} & \frac{1}{3} \\ -\frac{1}{3} & \frac{1}{6} & \frac{1}{3} \\ \frac{1}{3} & \frac{1}{3} & -\frac{1}{3} \end{bmatrix}.$$

Therefore, the matrix for T relative to B' is

$$A' = P^{-1}AP = \begin{bmatrix} \frac{2}{3} & -\frac{1}{3} & \frac{1}{3} \\ -\frac{1}{3} & \frac{1}{6} & \frac{1}{3} \\ \frac{1}{3} & \frac{1}{3} & -\frac{1}{3} \end{bmatrix} \begin{bmatrix} 1 & -1 & 2 \\ 2 & 1 & -1 \\ 1 & 2 & 1 \end{bmatrix} \begin{bmatrix} 1 & 0 & 1 \\ 0 & 2 & 2 \\ 1 & 2 & 0 \end{bmatrix}$$

$$= \begin{bmatrix} \frac{7}{3} & \frac{10}{3} & -\frac{1}{3} \\ -\frac{1}{6} & \frac{4}{3} & \frac{8}{3} \\ \frac{2}{3} & -\frac{4}{3} & -\frac{2}{3} \end{bmatrix}.$$

(b) Since $A' = P^{-1}AP$, it follows that A and A' are similar.

9. (a) The transition matrix P from B' to B is found by row-reducing $[B \vdots B']$ to $[I \vdots P]$.

$$[B \vdots B'] = \begin{bmatrix} 1 & -2 & \vdots & -12 & -4 \\ 3 & -2 & \vdots & 0 & 4 \end{bmatrix} \implies [I \vdots P] = \begin{bmatrix} 1 & 0 & \vdots & 6 & 4 \\ 0 & 1 & \vdots & 9 & 4 \end{bmatrix}$$

Thus,

$$P = \begin{bmatrix} 6 & 4 \\ 9 & 4 \end{bmatrix}.$$

(b) The coordinate matrix for **v** relative to B is

$$[\mathbf{v}]_B = P[\mathbf{v}]_{B'} = \begin{bmatrix} 6 & 4 \\ 9 & 4 \end{bmatrix} \begin{bmatrix} -1 \\ 2 \end{bmatrix} = \begin{bmatrix} 2 \\ -1 \end{bmatrix}.$$

Furthermore, the image of **v** under T relative to B is

$$[T(\mathbf{v})]_B = A[\mathbf{v}]_B = \begin{bmatrix} 3 & 2 \\ 0 & 4 \end{bmatrix} \begin{bmatrix} 2 \\ -1 \end{bmatrix} = \begin{bmatrix} 4 \\ -4 \end{bmatrix}.$$

(c) The inverse of P is

$$P^{-1} = \begin{bmatrix} -\frac{1}{3} & \frac{1}{3} \\ \frac{3}{4} & -\frac{1}{2} \end{bmatrix}.$$

The matrix of T relative to B' is then

$$A' = P^{-1}AP = \begin{bmatrix} -\frac{1}{3} & \frac{1}{3} \\ \frac{3}{4} & -\frac{1}{2} \end{bmatrix} \begin{bmatrix} 3 & 2 \\ 0 & 4 \end{bmatrix} \begin{bmatrix} 6 & 4 \\ 9 & 4 \end{bmatrix} = \begin{bmatrix} 0 & -\frac{4}{3} \\ 9 & 7 \end{bmatrix}.$$

(d) The image of **v** under T relative to B' is

$$P^{-1}[T(\mathbf{v})]_B = \begin{bmatrix} -\frac{1}{3} & \frac{1}{3} \\ \frac{3}{4} & -\frac{1}{2} \end{bmatrix} \begin{bmatrix} 4 \\ -4 \end{bmatrix} = \begin{bmatrix} -\frac{8}{3} \\ 5 \end{bmatrix}.$$

We can also find the image of **v** under T relative to B' by

$$A'[\mathbf{v}]_{B'} = \begin{bmatrix} 0 & -\frac{4}{3} \\ 9 & 7 \end{bmatrix} \begin{bmatrix} -1 \\ 2 \end{bmatrix} = \begin{bmatrix} -\frac{8}{3} \\ 5 \end{bmatrix}.$$

11. (a) The transition matrix P from B' to B is found by row-reducing $[B \vdots B']$ to $[I \vdots P]$.

$$[B \vdots B'] = \begin{bmatrix} 1 & 1 & 0 & \vdots & 1 & 0 & 0 \\ 1 & 0 & 1 & \vdots & 0 & 1 & 0 \\ 0 & 1 & 1 & \vdots & 0 & 0 & 1 \end{bmatrix} \Rightarrow [I \vdots P] = \begin{bmatrix} 1 & 0 & 0 & \vdots & \frac{1}{2} & \frac{1}{2} & -\frac{1}{2} \\ 0 & 1 & 0 & \vdots & \frac{1}{2} & -\frac{1}{2} & \frac{1}{2} \\ 0 & 0 & 1 & \vdots & -\frac{1}{2} & \frac{1}{2} & \frac{1}{2} \end{bmatrix}$$

Thus,

$$P = \frac{1}{2} \begin{bmatrix} 1 & 1 & -1 \\ 1 & -1 & 1 \\ -1 & 1 & 1 \end{bmatrix}.$$

(b) The coordinate matrix for $\mathbf{v}$ relative to B is

$$[\mathbf{v}]_B = P[\mathbf{v}]_{B'} = \frac{1}{2} \begin{bmatrix} 1 & 1 & -1 \\ 1 & -1 & 1 \\ -1 & 1 & 1 \end{bmatrix} \begin{bmatrix} 1 \\ 0 \\ -1 \end{bmatrix} = \begin{bmatrix} 1 \\ 0 \\ -1 \end{bmatrix}.$$

Furthermore, the image of $\mathbf{v}$ under T relative to B is

$$[T(\mathbf{v})]_B = A[\mathbf{v}]_B = \begin{bmatrix} \frac{3}{2} & -1 & -\frac{1}{2} \\ -\frac{1}{2} & 2 & \frac{1}{2} \\ \frac{1}{2} & 1 & \frac{5}{2} \end{bmatrix} \begin{bmatrix} 1 \\ 0 \\ -1 \end{bmatrix} = \begin{bmatrix} 2 \\ -1 \\ -2 \end{bmatrix}.$$

(c) The matrix of T relative to B' is

$$A' = P^{-1}AP = \begin{bmatrix} 1 & 1 & 0 \\ 1 & 0 & 1 \\ 0 & 1 & 1 \end{bmatrix} \begin{bmatrix} \frac{3}{2} & -1 & -\frac{1}{2} \\ -\frac{1}{2} & 2 & \frac{1}{2} \\ \frac{1}{2} & 1 & \frac{5}{2} \end{bmatrix} \begin{bmatrix} \frac{1}{2} & \frac{1}{2} & -\frac{1}{2} \\ \frac{1}{2} & -\frac{1}{2} & \frac{1}{2} \\ -\frac{1}{2} & \frac{1}{2} & \frac{1}{2} \end{bmatrix} = \begin{bmatrix} 1 & 0 & 0 \\ 0 & 2 & 0 \\ 0 & 0 & 3 \end{bmatrix}.$$

(d) The image of $\mathbf{v}$ under T relative to B' is

$$P^{-1}[T(\mathbf{v})]_B = \begin{bmatrix} 1 & 1 & 0 \\ 1 & 0 & 1 \\ 0 & 1 & 1 \end{bmatrix} \begin{bmatrix} 2 \\ -1 \\ -2 \end{bmatrix} = \begin{bmatrix} 1 \\ 0 \\ -3 \end{bmatrix}.$$

We can also find the image of $\mathbf{v}$ under T relative to B' by

$$A'[\mathbf{v}]_{B'} = \begin{bmatrix} 1 & 0 & 0 \\ 0 & 2 & 0 \\ 0 & 0 & 3 \end{bmatrix} \begin{bmatrix} 1 \\ 0 \\ -1 \end{bmatrix} = \begin{bmatrix} 1 \\ 0 \\ -3 \end{bmatrix}.$$

13. If A and B are similar, then $B = P^{-1}AP$, for some nonsingular matrix P. Hence,

$$|B| = |P^{-1}AP| = |P^{-1}|\,|A|\,|P| = |A|\frac{1}{|P|}|P| = |A|.$$

No, the converse is not true.

For example, $\begin{vmatrix} 1 & 1 \\ 0 & 1 \end{vmatrix} = \begin{vmatrix} 1 & 0 \\ 0 & 1 \end{vmatrix}$,

but these matrices are not similar.

15. (a) $B = P^{-1}AP \Rightarrow B^T = (P^{-1}AP)^T = P^TA^T(P^{-1})^T = P^TA^T(P^T)^{-1}$,

which shows that A^T and B^T are similar.

(b) If A is nonsingular, then so is $P^{-1}AP = B$, and we have

$$B = P^{-1}AP$$

$$B^{-1} = (P^{-1}AP)^{-1} = P^{-1}A^{-1}(P^{-1})^{-1} = P^{-1}A^{-1}P$$

which shows that A^{-1} and B^{-1} are similar.

(c) $B = P^{-1}AP \Rightarrow$

$$B^K = (P^{-1}AP)^K = (P^{-1}AP)(P^{-1}AP) \cdots (P^{-1}AP) \qquad (K \text{ times})$$

$$= P^{-1}A^KP.$$

17. Let A be an $n \times n$ matrix similar to I_n. Then there exists an invertible matrix P such that

$$A = P^{-1}I_nP = P^{-1}P = I_n.$$

Thus, I_n is similar only to itself.

19. If $A^2 = 0$ and $B = P^{-1}AP$, then

$$B^2 = (P^{-1}AP)^2 = (P^{-1}AP)(P^{-1}AP) = P^{-1}A^2P = P^{-1}0P = 0.$$

21. If A is similar to B, then $B = P^{-1}AP$. If B is similar to C, then $C = Q^{-1}BQ$.
Hence, $C = Q^{-1}BQ = Q^{-1}(P^{-1}AP)Q = (PQ)^{-1}A(PQ)$, which shows that A is similar to C.

23. Since $B = P^{-1}AP$, we have

$$B^2 = (P^{-1}AP)^2 = (P^{-1}AP)(P^{-1}AP) = P^{-1}A^2P$$

which shows that A^2 is similar to B^2.

25. If $A = CD$ and C is nonsingular, then $C^{-1}A = D \Rightarrow C^{-1}AC = DC$, which shows that DC is similar to A.

27. The matrix of I relative to B and B' is the square matrix whose columns are the coordinates of $\mathbf{v}_1, \ldots \mathbf{v}_n$ relative to the standard basis. The matrix of I relative to B, or relative to B', is the identity matrix.

Section 6.5   Applications of Linear Transformations

1. The standard matrix for T is

$$A = \begin{bmatrix} 1 & 0 \\ 0 & -1 \end{bmatrix}.$$

   (a) $\begin{bmatrix} 1 & 0 \\ 0 & -1 \end{bmatrix}\begin{bmatrix} 3 \\ 5 \end{bmatrix} = \begin{bmatrix} 3 \\ -5 \end{bmatrix}$ $\Rightarrow$ $T(3, 5) = (3, -5)$

   (b) $\begin{bmatrix} 1 & 0 \\ 0 & -1 \end{bmatrix}\begin{bmatrix} 2 \\ -1 \end{bmatrix} = \begin{bmatrix} 2 \\ 1 \end{bmatrix}$ $\Rightarrow$ $T(2, -1) = (2, 1)$

   (c) $\begin{bmatrix} 1 & 0 \\ 0 & -1 \end{bmatrix}\begin{bmatrix} a \\ 0 \end{bmatrix} = \begin{bmatrix} a \\ 0 \end{bmatrix}$ $\Rightarrow$ $T(a, 0) = (a, 0)$

   (d) $\begin{bmatrix} 1 & 0 \\ 0 & -1 \end{bmatrix}\begin{bmatrix} 0 \\ b \end{bmatrix} = \begin{bmatrix} 0 \\ -b \end{bmatrix}$ $\Rightarrow$ $T(0, b) = (0, -b)$

3. (a) $T(x, y) = xT(1, 0) + yT(0, 1) = x(0, 1) + y(1, 0) = (y, x)$

   (b) T is a reflection in the line $y = x$.

5. (a) We can identify T as a vertical contraction from its standard matrix.

$$A = \begin{bmatrix} 1 & 0 \\ 0 & \frac{1}{2} \end{bmatrix}$$

   (b)

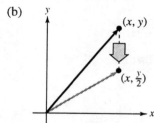

7. (a) We can identify T as a horizontal shear from its matrix.

$$A = \begin{bmatrix} 1 & 3 \\ 0 & 1 \end{bmatrix}.$$

   (b)

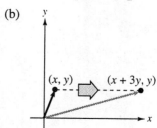

9. The reflection in the y-axis is given by $T(x, y) = (-x, y)$. If (x, y) is a fixed point, then $T(x, y) = (x, y) = (-x, y)$ which implies that $x = 0$. Hence the set of fixed points is $\{(0, t) \mid t \in R\}$.

11. A vertical contraction has the standard matrix ($k \neq 1$)

$$\begin{bmatrix} 1 & 0 \\ 0 & k \end{bmatrix}.$$

A fixed point of T satisfies the equation

$$T(\mathbf{v}) = \begin{bmatrix} 1 & 0 \\ 0 & k \end{bmatrix} \begin{bmatrix} v_1 \\ v_2 \end{bmatrix} = \begin{bmatrix} v_1 \\ kv_2 \end{bmatrix} = \begin{bmatrix} v_1 \\ v_2 \end{bmatrix} = \mathbf{v}.$$

Thus, the fixed points of T are $\{\mathbf{v} = (t, 0) : t$ is a real number$\}$.

13. We find the image of each vertex under $T(x, y) = (x, -y)$

$$T(0, 0) = (0, 0), \qquad T(1, 0) = (1, 0),$$
$$T(1, 1) = (1, -1) \qquad T(0, 1) = (0, -1).$$

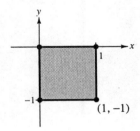

15. We find the image of each vertex under T.

$$T(0, 0) = (0, 0), \qquad T(1, 0) = \left(\tfrac{1}{2}, 0\right)$$
$$T(1, 1) = \left(\tfrac{1}{2}, 1\right), \qquad T(0, 1) = (0, 1)$$

The image of the unit square under T is shown in the following figure.

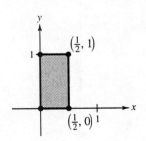

17. We find the image of each vertex under *T*.

$$T(0, 0) = (0, 0), \qquad T(1, 0) = (1, 0)$$

$$T(1, 1) = (3, 1), \qquad T(0, 1) = (2, 1)$$

The image of the unit square under *T* is shown in the following figure.

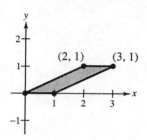

19. The standard matrix for *T* is

$$\begin{bmatrix} -1 & 0 \\ 0 & 1 \end{bmatrix}.$$

Thus, $T(x, y) = (-x, y)$. The image of each vertex under *T* is as follows.

$$T(0, 0) = (0, 0), \qquad T(0, 2) = (0, 2)$$

$$T(1, 2) = (-1, 2), \qquad T(1, 0) = (-1, 0)$$

The image of the rectangle is shown in the following figure.

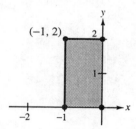

21. We find the image of each vertex under $T(x, y) = (x, y/2)$.

$$T(0, 0) = (0, 0), \qquad T(0, 2) = (0, 1),$$

$$T(1, 2) = (1, 1), \qquad T(1, 0) = (1, 0)$$

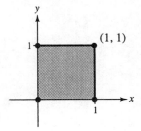

23. We find the image of each vertex under $T(x, y) = (x + y, y)$.

$$T(0, 0) = (0, 0), \qquad T(0, 2) = (2, 2),$$

$$T(1, 2) = (3, 2), \qquad T(1, 0) = (1, 0)$$

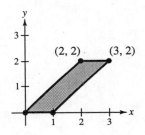

25. The images of the given vectors are as follows.

$$T(1, 0) = \begin{bmatrix} 2 & 0 \\ 0 & 3 \end{bmatrix} \begin{bmatrix} 1 \\ 0 \end{bmatrix} = \begin{bmatrix} 2 \\ 0 \end{bmatrix} = (2, 0)$$

$$T(0, 1) = \begin{bmatrix} 2 & 0 \\ 0 & 3 \end{bmatrix} \begin{bmatrix} 0 \\ 1 \end{bmatrix} = \begin{bmatrix} 0 \\ 3 \end{bmatrix} = (0, 3)$$

$$T(2, 2) = \begin{bmatrix} 2 & 0 \\ 0 & 3 \end{bmatrix} \begin{bmatrix} 2 \\ 2 \end{bmatrix} = \begin{bmatrix} 4 \\ 6 \end{bmatrix} = (4, 6)$$

The two triangles are shown in the following figure.

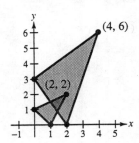

27. The linear transformation defined by A is a horizontal expansion.

29. The linear transformation defined by A is a reflection in the line $y = x$.

31. Since

$$\begin{bmatrix} 1 & 0 \\ 2 & 1 \end{bmatrix}$$

represents a vertical shear and

$$\begin{bmatrix} 2 & 0 \\ 0 & 1 \end{bmatrix}$$

represents a horizontal expansion, A is a vertical shear *followed* by a horizontal expansion.

33. A rotation of $30°$ about the z-axis is given by the matrix

$$A = \begin{bmatrix} \cos 30° & -\sin 30° & 0 \\ \sin 30° & \cos 30° & 0 \\ 0 & 0 & 1 \end{bmatrix} = \begin{bmatrix} \frac{\sqrt{3}}{2} & -\frac{1}{2} & 0 \\ \frac{1}{2} & \frac{\sqrt{3}}{2} & 0 \\ 0 & 0 & 1 \end{bmatrix}.$$

35. A rotation about the y-axis of $\theta = 60°$ is given by the matrix

$$A = \begin{bmatrix} \cos \theta & 0 & \sin \theta \\ 0 & 1 & 0 \\ -\sin \theta & 0 & \cos \theta \end{bmatrix} = \begin{bmatrix} \frac{1}{2} & 0 & \frac{\sqrt{3}}{2} \\ 0 & 1 & 0 \\ -\frac{\sqrt{3}}{2} & 0 & \frac{1}{2} \end{bmatrix}.$$

37. Using the matrix obtained in Exercise 33, we find

$$T(1, 1, 1) = \begin{bmatrix} \frac{\sqrt{3}}{2} & -\frac{1}{2} & 0 \\ \frac{1}{2} & \frac{\sqrt{3}}{2} & 0 \\ 0 & 0 & 1 \end{bmatrix} \begin{bmatrix} 1 \\ 1 \\ 1 \end{bmatrix} = \begin{bmatrix} (\sqrt{3} - 1)/2 \\ (1 + \sqrt{3})/2 \\ 1 \end{bmatrix}.$$

39. Using the matrix obtained in Exercise 35, we find

$$T(1, 1, 1) = \begin{bmatrix} \frac{1}{2} & 0 & \frac{\sqrt{3}}{2} \\ 0 & 1 & 0 \\ -\frac{\sqrt{3}}{2} & 0 & \frac{1}{2} \end{bmatrix} \begin{bmatrix} 1 \\ 1 \\ 1 \end{bmatrix} = \begin{bmatrix} \frac{1 + \sqrt{3}}{2} \\ 1 \\ \frac{1 - \sqrt{3}}{2} \end{bmatrix}.$$

41. The indicated tetrahedron is produced by a $90°$ rotation about the x-axis.

43. The indicated tetrahedron is produced by a $180°$ rotation about the y-axis.

45. The indicated tetrahedron is produced by a $90°$ rotation about the z-axis.

Chapter 6   Review Exercises

1. (a) $T(v) = T(2, -3) = (2, -4)$

(b) The preimage of **w** is given by solving the equation

$$T(v_1, v_2) = (v_1, v_1 + 2v_2) = (4, 12).$$

The resulting system of linear equations

$$v_1 \qquad = 4$$
$$v_1 + 2v_2 = 12$$

has the solution $v_1 = v_2 = 4$. Thus, the preimage of **w** is $(4, 4)$.

3. (a) $T(\mathbf{v}) = T(0, 1, 1) = (1, 1, 1)$

(b) The preimage of **w** is given by solving the equation

$$T(v_1, v_2, v_3) = (v_2, v_1 + v_2, v_3) = (4, 4, 4).$$

the resulting system of linear equations has the solution $v_1 = 0$, $v_2 = 4$ and $v_3 = 4$. Thus, the preimage of **w** is $(0, 4, 4)$.

5. T preserves addition.

$$T(x_1, x_2) + T(y_1, y_2) = (x_1 + 2x_2, -x_1 - x_2) + (y_1 + 2y_2, -y_1 - y_2)$$
$$= (x_1 + 2x_2 + y_1 + 2y_2, -x_1 - x_2 - y_1 - y_2)$$
$$= ((x_1 + y_1) + 2(x_1 + y_1), -(x_1 + y_1) - (x_2 + y_2))$$
$$= T(x_1 + y_1, x_2 + y_2)$$

T preserves scalar multiplication.

$$cT(x_1, x_2) = c(x_1 + 2x_2, -x_1 - x_2)$$
$$= (cx_1 + 2(cx_2), -cx_1 - cx_2)$$
$$= T(cx_1, cx_2)$$

Thus, T is a linear transformation with standard matrix

$$A = \begin{bmatrix} 1 & 2 \\ -1 & -1 \end{bmatrix}.$$

7. T does not preserve addition or scalar multiplication, thus, T is *not* a linear transformation. A counterexample is

$$T(1, 0) + T(0, 1) = (1 + h, k) + (h, 1 + k)$$
$$= (1 + 2h, 1 + 2k)$$
$$\neq T(1 + h, 1 + k)$$
$$= T(1, 1).$$

9. T preserves addition.

$$T(a_1, a_2) + T(b_1, b_2) = (a_2, a_2, a_1) + (b_2, b_2, b_1)$$
$$= (a_2 + b_2, a_2 + b_2, a_1 + b_1).$$
$$= T(a_1 + b_1, a_2 + b_2)$$

T preserves scalar multiplication.

$$cT(x_1, x_2) = c(x_2, x_2, x_1)$$
$$= (cx_2, cx_2, cx_1)$$
$$= T(cx_1, cx_2)$$

Thus, T is a linear transformation with standard matrix

$$A = \begin{bmatrix} 0 & 1 \\ 0 & 1 \\ 1 & 0 \end{bmatrix}.$$

11. T preserves addition.

$$T(x_1, x_2, x_3) + T(y_1, y_2, y_3)$$
$$= (x_1 - x_2, x_2 - x_3, x_3 - x_1) + (y_1 - y_2, y_2 - y_3, y_3 - y_1)$$
$$= (x_1 - x_2 + y_1 - y_2, x_2 - x_3 + y_2 - y_3, x_3 - x_1 + y_3 - y_1)$$
$$= ((x_1 + y_1) - (x_2 + y_2), (x_2 + y_2) - (x_3 + y_3), (x_3 + y_3) + (x_1 + y_1))$$
$$= T(x_1 + y_1, x_2 + y_2, x_3 + y_3)$$

T preserves scalar multiplication.

$$cT(x_1, x_2, x_3) = c(x_1 - x_2, x_2 - x_3, x_3 - x_1)$$
$$= (c(x_1 - x_2), c(x_2 - x_3), c(x_3 - x_1))$$
$$= (cx_1 - cx_2, cx_2 - cx_3, cx_3 - cx_1)$$
$$= T(cx_1, cx_2, cx_3)$$

Thus, T is a linear transformation with standard matrix

$$\begin{bmatrix} 1 & -1 & 0 \\ 0 & 1 & -1 \\ -1 & 0 & 1 \end{bmatrix}.$$

13. Since $(1, 1) = \frac{1}{2}(2, 0) + \frac{1}{3}(0, 3)$, we have

$$
\begin{aligned}
T(1, 1) &= \tfrac{1}{2}T(2, 0) + \tfrac{1}{3}T(0, 3) \\
&= \tfrac{1}{2}(1, 1) + \tfrac{1}{3}(3, 3) \\
&= \left(\tfrac{3}{2}, \tfrac{3}{2}\right).
\end{aligned}
$$

Since $(0, 1) = \frac{1}{3}(0, 3)$, we have

$$
\begin{aligned}
T(0, 1) &= \tfrac{1}{3}T(0, 3) \\
&= \tfrac{1}{3}(3, 3) \\
&= (1, 1).
\end{aligned}
$$

15. The standard matrix for T is

$$
A = \begin{bmatrix} 1 & 0 & 0 \\ 0 & 1 & 0 \\ 0 & 0 & -1 \end{bmatrix}.
$$

Therefore, we have

$$
A^2 = \begin{bmatrix} 1^2 & 0 & 0 \\ 0 & 1^2 & 0 \\ 0 & 0 & (-1)^2 \end{bmatrix} = \begin{bmatrix} 1 & 0 & 0 \\ 0 & 1 & 0 \\ 0 & 0 & 1 \end{bmatrix} = I_3.
$$

17. The standard matrix for T is

$$
A = \begin{bmatrix} \cos\theta & -\sin\theta \\ \sin\theta & \cos\theta \end{bmatrix}.
$$

Therefore, we have

$$
A^3 = \begin{bmatrix} \cos 3\theta & -\sin 3\theta \\ \sin 3\theta & \cos 3\theta \end{bmatrix}.
$$

19. (a) Since A is a 2×3 matrix, it maps R^3 into R^2, ($n = 3$, $m = 2$).

(b) Since $T(\mathbf{v}) = A\mathbf{v}$ and

$$
A\mathbf{v} = \begin{bmatrix} 0 & 1 & 2 \\ -2 & 0 & 0 \end{bmatrix} \begin{bmatrix} 6 \\ 1 \\ 1 \end{bmatrix} = \begin{bmatrix} 3 \\ -12 \end{bmatrix}
$$

it follows that $T(6, 1, 1) = (3, -12)$.

(c) The preimage of $\mathbf{w}$ is given by the solution to the equation

$$
T(v_1, v_2, v_3) = \mathbf{w} = (3, 5).
$$

The equivalent system of linear equations

$$
\begin{aligned}
v_2 + 2v_3 &= 3 \\
-2v_1 \qquad\quad &= 5
\end{aligned}
$$

has the solution $\left\{\left(-\tfrac{5}{2}, 3 - 2t, t\right) : t \text{ is a real number}\right\}$.

21. (a) Since A is a 3×3 matrix, it maps R^3 into R^3 ($n = 3, m = 3$).

(b) Since $T(\mathbf{v}) = A\mathbf{v}$ and

$$A\mathbf{v} = \begin{bmatrix} 1 & 1 & 1 \\ 0 & 1 & 1 \\ 0 & 0 & 1 \end{bmatrix} \begin{bmatrix} 2 \\ 1 \\ -5 \end{bmatrix} = \begin{bmatrix} -2 \\ -4 \\ -5 \end{bmatrix},$$

it follows that $T(2, 1, -5) = (-2, -4, -5)$.

(c) The preimage of $\mathbf{w} = (6, 4, 2)$ is given by the solution to the equation

$$T(v_1, v_2, v_3) = (6, 4, 2) = \mathbf{w}.$$

The equivalent system of linear equations has the solution $v_1 = v_2 = v_3 = 2$.
Thus, the preimage is $(2, 2, 2)$.

23. (a) The standard matrix for T is

$$A = \begin{bmatrix} 2 & 4 & 6 & 5 \\ -1 & -2 & 2 & 0 \\ 0 & 0 & 8 & 4 \end{bmatrix}.$$

Solving $A\mathbf{v} = 0$ yields the solution $\{(-2s + 2t, s, t, -2t) : s \text{ and } t \text{ are real numbers}\}$.
Thus, a basis for ker(T) is $\{(-2, 1, 0, 0), (2, 0, 1, -2)\}$.

(b) We use Gauss-Jordan elimination to reduce A^T as follows.

$$A^T = \begin{bmatrix} 2 & -1 & 0 \\ 4 & -2 & 0 \\ 6 & 2 & 8 \\ 5 & 0 & 4 \end{bmatrix} \Rightarrow \begin{bmatrix} 1 & 0 & \frac{4}{5} \\ 0 & 1 & \frac{8}{5} \\ 0 & 0 & 0 \\ 0 & 0 & 0 \end{bmatrix}$$

The nonzero row vectors form a basis for the range of T, $\left\{ \left(1, 0, \frac{4}{5}\right), \left(0, 1, \frac{8}{5}\right) \right\}$.

25. (a) To find the kernel of T, we row-reduce A,

$$A = \begin{bmatrix} 1 & 2 \\ -1 & 0 \\ 1 & 1 \end{bmatrix} \Rightarrow \begin{bmatrix} 1 & 0 \\ 0 & 1 \\ 0 & 0 \end{bmatrix}$$

which shows that ker(T) = $\{(0, 0)\}$.

(b) The range of T can be found by row-reducing the transpose of A.

$$A^T = \begin{bmatrix} 1 & -1 & 1 \\ 2 & 0 & 1 \end{bmatrix} \Rightarrow \begin{bmatrix} 1 & 0 & \frac{1}{2} \\ 0 & 1 & -\frac{1}{2} \end{bmatrix}$$

Thus, a basis for range (T) is $\left\{ \left(1, 0, \frac{1}{2}\right), \left(0, 1, -\frac{1}{2}\right) \right\}$.

Or, use the 2 columns of A, $\{(1, -1, 1), (2, 0, 1)\}$.

(c) dim(range(T)) = rank(T) = 2 and nullity(T) = 0.

27. Rank(T) = dim R^5 $-$ nullity(T) = 5 $-$ 2 = 3.

29. nullity(T) = dim(P_4) $-$ rank(T) = 5 $-$ 4 = 1.

31. The standard matrix for T is

$$A = \begin{bmatrix} 0 & 1 \\ 1 & 0 \end{bmatrix}.$$

Since A is invertible, T is invertible, and the standard matrix for T^{-1} is

$$A^{-1} = \begin{bmatrix} 0 & 1 \\ 1 & 0 \end{bmatrix}.$$

33. The standard matrix for T is

$$A = \begin{bmatrix} 1 & 0 \\ k & 1 \end{bmatrix}.$$

Since A is invertible, T is invertible, and the standard matrix for T^{-1} is

$$A^{-1} = \begin{bmatrix} 1 & 0 \\ -k & 1 \end{bmatrix}.$$

35. The standard matrix for T is

$$A = \begin{bmatrix} 1 & 0 & 0 \\ 0 & 1 & 0 \\ 0 & 0 & 0 \end{bmatrix}.$$

Since A is *not* invertible, T has no inverse.

37. The standard matrices for T_1 and T_2 are

$$A_1 = \begin{bmatrix} 1 & 0 \\ 1 & 1 \\ 0 & 1 \end{bmatrix} \quad \text{and} \quad A_2 = \begin{bmatrix} 0 & 0 & 0 \\ 0 & 1 & 0 \end{bmatrix}.$$

The standard matrix for $T = T_1 \circ T_2$ is

$$A = A_1 A_2 = \begin{bmatrix} 1 & 0 \\ 1 & 1 \\ 0 & 1 \end{bmatrix} \begin{bmatrix} 0 & 0 & 0 \\ 0 & 1 & 0 \end{bmatrix} = \begin{bmatrix} 0 & 0 & 0 \\ 0 & 1 & 0 \\ 0 & 1 & 0 \end{bmatrix}$$

and the standard matrix for $T' = T_2 \circ T_1$ is

$$A' = A_2 A_1 = \begin{bmatrix} 0 & 0 & 0 \\ 0 & 1 & 0 \end{bmatrix} \begin{bmatrix} 1 & 0 \\ 1 & 1 \\ 0 & 1 \end{bmatrix} = \begin{bmatrix} 0 & 0 \\ 1 & 1 \end{bmatrix}.$$

39. The standard matrix for the 90° counterclockwise notation is

$$A = \begin{bmatrix} \cos 90° & -\sin 90° \\ \sin 90° & \cos 90° \end{bmatrix} = \begin{bmatrix} 0 & -1 \\ 1 & 0 \end{bmatrix}.$$

Calculating the image of the three vertices,

$$\begin{bmatrix} 0 & -1 \\ 1 & 0 \end{bmatrix}\begin{bmatrix} 3 \\ 5 \end{bmatrix} = \begin{bmatrix} -5 \\ 3 \end{bmatrix}, \begin{bmatrix} 0 & -1 \\ 1 & 0 \end{bmatrix}\begin{bmatrix} 5 \\ 3 \end{bmatrix} = \begin{bmatrix} -3 \\ 5 \end{bmatrix}, \begin{bmatrix} 0 & -1 \\ 1 & 0 \end{bmatrix}\begin{bmatrix} 3 \\ 0 \end{bmatrix} = \begin{bmatrix} 0 \\ 3 \end{bmatrix}$$

we have the following graph.

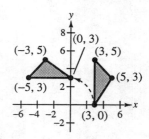

41. (a) Since $|A| = 6 \neq 0$, $\ker(T) = \{(0, 0)\}$ and the transformation is one-to-one.

(b) Since the nullity of T is 0, the rank of T equals the dimension of the domain and the transformation is onto.

(c) The transformation is one-to-one and onto (an isomorphism) and is thus invertible.

43. (a) Since $|A| = 1 \neq 0$, $\ker(T) = \{(0, 0)\}$ and T is one-to-one.

(b) Since rank$(A) = 2$, T is onto.

(c) The transformation is one-to-one and onto, and is thus invertible.

45. (a) The standard matrix for T is

$$A = \begin{bmatrix} -1 & 0 \\ 0 & 1 \\ 1 & 1 \end{bmatrix}$$

so it follows that

$$T(\mathbf{v}) = A(\mathbf{v}) = \begin{bmatrix} -1 & 0 \\ 0 & 1 \\ 1 & 1 \end{bmatrix} \begin{bmatrix} 0 \\ 1 \end{bmatrix} = \begin{bmatrix} 0 \\ 1 \\ 1 \end{bmatrix} = (0, 1, 1).$$

(b) The image of each vector in B is as follows.

$$T(1, 1) = (-1, 1, 2) = (0, 1, 0) + 2(0, 0, 1) - (1, 0, 0)$$

$$T(1, -1) = (-1, -1, 0) = -(0, 1, 0) + 0(0, 0, 1) - (1, 0, 0)$$

Therefore, we have

$$[T(1, 1)]_{B'} = [1, 2, -1]^T \quad \text{and} \quad [T(1, -1)]_{B'} = [-1, 0, -1]^T$$

and

$$A' = \begin{bmatrix} 1 & -1 \\ 2 & 0 \\ -1 & -1 \end{bmatrix}.$$

Since

$$[\mathbf{v}]_B = \begin{bmatrix} \frac{1}{2} \\ -\frac{1}{2} \end{bmatrix},$$

the image of $\mathbf{v}$ under T relative to B' is

$$[T(\mathbf{v})]_{B'} = A'[\mathbf{v}]_B = \begin{bmatrix} 1 & -1 \\ 2 & 0 \\ -1 & -1 \end{bmatrix} \begin{bmatrix} \frac{1}{2} \\ -\frac{1}{2} \end{bmatrix} = \begin{bmatrix} 1 \\ 1 \\ 0 \end{bmatrix}.$$

Thus, $T(\mathbf{v}) = (0, 1, 0) + (0, 0, 1) + 0(1, 0, 0) = (0, 1, 1)$.

47. The standard matrix for T is

$$A = \begin{bmatrix} 1 & -3 \\ -1 & 1 \end{bmatrix}.$$

The transformation matrix from B' to the standard basis $B = \{(1, 0), (0, 1)\}$ is

$$P = \begin{bmatrix} 1 & 1 \\ -1 & 1 \end{bmatrix}.$$

The matrix A' for T relative to B' is

$$A' = P^{-1}AP = \begin{bmatrix} \frac{1}{2} & -\frac{1}{2} \\ \frac{1}{2} & \frac{1}{2} \end{bmatrix} \begin{bmatrix} 1 & -3 \\ -1 & 1 \end{bmatrix} \begin{bmatrix} 1 & 1 \\ -1 & 1 \end{bmatrix} = \begin{bmatrix} 3 & -1 \\ 1 & -1 \end{bmatrix}.$$

Since $A' = P^{-1}AP$, it follows that A and A' are similar.

49. (a) Since $T(\mathbf{v}) = T(x, y, z) = \text{proj}_{\mathbf{u}}\mathbf{v}$ where $\mathbf{u} = (0, 1, 2)$, we have

$$T(\mathbf{v}) = \frac{y + 2z}{5}(0, 1, 2).$$

Thus,

$$T(1, 0, 0) = (0, 0, 0), \; T(0, 1, 0) = \left(0, \tfrac{1}{5}, \tfrac{2}{5}\right), \; T(0, 0, 1) = \left(0, \tfrac{2}{5}, \tfrac{4}{5}\right)$$

and the standard matrix for T is

$$A = \begin{bmatrix} 0 & 0 & 0 \\ 0 & \frac{1}{5} & \frac{2}{5} \\ 0 & \frac{2}{5} & \frac{4}{5} \end{bmatrix}.$$

(b) $S = I - A$ satisfies $S(\mathbf{u}) = 0$. Letting $\mathbf{w}_1 = (1, 0, 0)$ and $\mathbf{w}_2 = (0, 2, -1)$ be two vectors orthogonal to $\mathbf{u}$, we have

$$\text{proj}_{\mathbf{w}_1}\mathbf{v} = \frac{x}{1}(1, 0, 0) \implies P_1 = \begin{bmatrix} 1 & 0 & 0 \\ 0 & 0 & 0 \\ 0 & 0 & 0 \end{bmatrix}$$

$$\text{proj}_{\mathbf{w}_2}\mathbf{v} = \frac{2y - z}{5}(0, 2, -1) \implies P_2 = \begin{bmatrix} 0 & 0 & 0 \\ 0 & \frac{4}{5} & -\frac{2}{5} \\ 0 & -\frac{2}{5} & \frac{1}{5} \end{bmatrix}.$$

Hence,

$$S = I - A = \begin{bmatrix} 1 & 0 & 0 \\ 0 & \frac{4}{5} & -\frac{2}{5} \\ 0 & -\frac{2}{5} & \frac{1}{5} \end{bmatrix} = P_1 + P_2$$

verifying that $S(\mathbf{v}) = \text{proj}_{\mathbf{w}_1}\mathbf{v} + \text{proj}_{\mathbf{w}_2}\mathbf{v}$.

(c) The kernel of T has basis $\{(1, 0, 0), (0, 2, -1)\}$, which is precisely the column space of S.

51. $S + T$ preserves addition.

$$(S + T)(\mathbf{v} + \mathbf{w}) = S(\mathbf{v} + \mathbf{w}) + T(\mathbf{v} + \mathbf{w})$$
$$= S(\mathbf{v}) + S(\mathbf{w}) + T(\mathbf{v}) + T(\mathbf{w})$$
$$= S(\mathbf{v}) + T(\mathbf{v}) + S(\mathbf{w}) + T(\mathbf{w})$$
$$= (S + T)\mathbf{v} + (S + T)(\mathbf{w})$$

$S + T$ preserves scalar multiplication.

$$(S + T)(c\mathbf{v}) = S(c\mathbf{v}) + T(c\mathbf{v})$$
$$= cS(\mathbf{v}) + cT(\mathbf{v})$$
$$= c(S(\mathbf{v}) + T(\mathbf{v}))$$
$$= c(S + T)(\mathbf{v})$$

kT preserves addition.

$$(kT)(\mathbf{v} + \mathbf{w}) = kT(\mathbf{v} + \mathbf{w}) = k(T(\mathbf{v}) + T(\mathbf{w}))$$
$$= kT(\mathbf{v}) + kT(\mathbf{w})$$
$$= (kT)(\mathbf{v}) + (kT)(\mathbf{w})$$

kT preserves scalar multiplication.

$$(kT)(c\mathbf{v}) = kT(c\mathbf{v}) = kcT(\mathbf{v}) = ckT(\mathbf{v}) = c(kT)(\mathbf{v}).$$

53. Let $\mathbf{w}$ be in the range of $S + T$. Then there exists $\mathbf{v} \in V$ such that $(S + T)(\mathbf{v}) = \mathbf{w}$, or $S(\mathbf{v}) + T(\mathbf{v}) = \mathbf{w}$. Hence, $\mathbf{w} \in \text{range}(S) + \text{range}(T)$. That is, $\text{range}(S + T) \subseteq \text{range}(S) + \text{range}(T) \Rightarrow \text{rank}(S + T) \leq \text{rank}(S) + \text{rank}(T)$.

55. (a) T preserves addition.

$$T[(a_0 + a_1 x + a_2 x^2 + a_3 x^3) + (b_0 + b_1 x + b_2 x^2 + b_3 x^3)]$$
$$= T[(a_0 + b_0) + (a_1 + b_1)x + (a_2 + b_2)x^2 + (a_3 + b_3)x^3]$$
$$= (a_0 + b_0) + (a_1 + b_1) + (a_2 + b_2) + (a_3 + b_3)$$
$$= (a_0 + a_1 + a_2 + a_3) + (b_0 + b_1 + b_2 + b_3)$$
$$= T(a_0 + a_1 x + a_2 x^2 + a_3 x^3) + T(b_0 + b_1 x + b_2 x^2 + b_3 x^3)$$

T preserves scalar multiplication.

$$T(c(a_0 + a_1 x + a_2 x^2 + a_3 x^3))$$
$$= T(ca_0 + ca_1 x + ca_2 x^2 + ca_3 x^3)$$
$$= ca_0 + ca_1 + ca_2 + ca_3$$
$$= c(a_0 + a_1 + a_2 + a_3)$$
$$= cT(a_0 + a_1 x + a_2 x^2 + a_3 x^3)$$

(b) Since the range of T is R, $\text{rank}(T) = 1$. Hence, $\text{nullity}(T) = 4 - 1 = 3$.

(c) A basis for the kernel of T is obtained by solving

$$T(a_0 + a_1 x + a_2 x^2 + a_3 x^3) = a_0 + a_1 + a_2 + a_3 = 0.$$

Letting $a_3 = t, a_2 = s, a_1 = r$ be the free variables, $a_0 = -t - s - r$ and a basis is

$$\{-1 + x^3, -1 + x^2, -1 + x\}.$$

57. Let B be a basis for V and let $[\mathbf{v}_0]_B = [a_1, a_2, \ldots, a_n]^T$, where at least one $a_i \neq 0$ for $i = 1, \ldots, n$. Then for $[\mathbf{v}]_B = [v_1, v_2, \ldots, v_n]^T$ we have

$$[T(\mathbf{v})]_B = \langle \mathbf{v}, \mathbf{v}_0 \rangle = a_1 v_1 + a_2 v_2 + \cdots + a_n v_n.$$

The matrix for T relative to B is then

$$A = [a_1 \quad a_2 \quad \ldots \quad a_n].$$

Since A^T row-reduces to one nonzero row, the range of T is $\{t : t \in R\} = R$.
Thus, the rank of T is 1 and nullity$(T) = n - 1$. Finally, $\ker(T) = \{\mathbf{v} : \langle \mathbf{v}, \mathbf{v}_0 \rangle = 0\}$.

59. $M_{m,n}$ and $M_{p,q}$ will be isomorphic if they are of the same dimension. That is, $mn = pq$. Any function taking the standard basis of $M_{m,n}$ to the standard basis of $M_{p,q}$ will be an isomorphism.

61. (a) T is a vertical expansion.

(b)

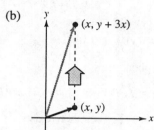

63.   (a) T is a vertical shear.

(b)

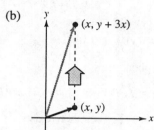

65. (a) The image of each vertex is $T(0, 0) = (0, 0)$, $T(1, 0) = (1, 0)$, $T(0, 1) = (0, -1)$.
A sketch of the triangle and its image follows.

(b)

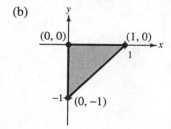

67. (a) The image of each vertex is $T(0, 0) = (0, 0)$, $T(1, 0) = (1, 0)$, and $T(0, 1) = (3, 1)$.
A sketch of the triangle and its image follows.

(b)

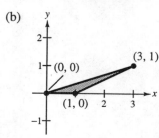

69. The transformation is a reflection is the line $y = x$

$$\begin{bmatrix} 0 & 1 \\ 1 & 0 \end{bmatrix}$$

followed by a horizontal expansion $\begin{bmatrix} 2 & 0 \\ 0 & 1 \end{bmatrix}$.

71. A rotation of 45° about the z-axis is given by

$$A = \begin{bmatrix} \cos 45° & -\sin 45° & 0 \\ \sin 45° & \cos 45° & 0 \\ 0 & 0 & 1 \end{bmatrix} = \begin{bmatrix} \frac{\sqrt{2}}{2} & -\frac{\sqrt{2}}{2} & 0 \\ \frac{\sqrt{2}}{2} & \frac{\sqrt{2}}{2} & 0 \\ 0 & 0 & 1 \end{bmatrix}.$$

Since

$$A\mathbf{v} = \begin{bmatrix} \frac{\sqrt{2}}{2} & -\frac{\sqrt{2}}{2} & 0 \\ \frac{\sqrt{2}}{2} & \frac{\sqrt{2}}{2} & 0 \\ 0 & 0 & 1 \end{bmatrix} \begin{bmatrix} 1 \\ -1 \\ 1 \end{bmatrix} = \begin{bmatrix} \sqrt{2} \\ 0 \\ 1 \end{bmatrix}$$

the image of $(1, -1, 1)$ is $\left(\sqrt{2}, 0, 1\right)$.

73. A rotation of 60° about the x-axis has the standard matrix

$$\begin{bmatrix} 1 & 0 & 0 \\ 0 & \cos 60° & -\sin 60° \\ 0 & \sin 60° & \cos 60° \end{bmatrix} = \begin{bmatrix} 1 & 0 & 0 \\ 0 & \frac{1}{2} & -\frac{\sqrt{3}}{2} \\ 0 & \frac{\sqrt{3}}{2} & \frac{1}{2} \end{bmatrix},$$

while a rotation of 30° about the z-axis has the standard matrix

$$\begin{bmatrix} \cos 30° & -\sin 30° & 0 \\ \sin 30° & \cos 30° & 0 \\ 0 & 0 & 1 \end{bmatrix} = \begin{bmatrix} \frac{\sqrt{3}}{2} & -\frac{1}{2} & 0 \\ \frac{1}{2} & \frac{\sqrt{3}}{2} & 0 \\ 0 & 0 & 1 \end{bmatrix}.$$

Thus, the pair of rotations is given by

$$\begin{bmatrix} \frac{\sqrt{3}}{2} & -\frac{1}{2} & 0 \\ \frac{1}{2} & \frac{\sqrt{3}}{2} & 0 \\ 0 & 0 & 1 \end{bmatrix} \begin{bmatrix} 1 & 0 & 0 \\ 0 & \frac{1}{2} & -\frac{\sqrt{3}}{2} \\ 0 & \frac{\sqrt{3}}{2} & \frac{1}{2} \end{bmatrix} = \begin{bmatrix} \frac{\sqrt{3}}{2} & -\frac{1}{4} & \frac{\sqrt{3}}{4} \\ \frac{1}{2} & \frac{\sqrt{3}}{4} & -\frac{3}{4} \\ 0 & \frac{\sqrt{3}}{2} & \frac{1}{2} \end{bmatrix}.$$

75. The standard matrix for T is

$$\begin{bmatrix} \cos 45° & -\sin 45° & 0 \\ \sin 45° & \cos 45° & 0 \\ 0 & 0 & 1 \end{bmatrix} = \begin{bmatrix} \frac{\sqrt{2}}{2} & -\frac{\sqrt{2}}{2} & 0 \\ \frac{\sqrt{2}}{2} & \frac{\sqrt{2}}{2} & 0 \\ 0 & 0 & 1 \end{bmatrix}.$$

Therefore, T is given by

$$T(x, y, z) = \left(\tfrac{\sqrt{2}}{2}x - \tfrac{\sqrt{2}}{2}y, \tfrac{\sqrt{2}}{2}x + \tfrac{\sqrt{2}}{2}y, z\right).$$

The image of each vertex is as follows.

$$T(0, 0, 0) = (0, 0, 0)$$

$$T(1, 0, 0) = \left(\tfrac{\sqrt{2}}{2}, \tfrac{\sqrt{2}}{2}, 0\right)$$

$$T(1, 1, 0) = \left(0, \sqrt{2}, 0\right)$$

$$T(0, 1, 0) = \left(-\tfrac{\sqrt{2}}{2}, \tfrac{\sqrt{2}}{2}, 0\right)$$

$$T(0, 0, 1) = (0, 0, 1)$$

$$T(1, 0, 1) = \left(\tfrac{\sqrt{2}}{2}, \tfrac{\sqrt{2}}{2}, 1\right)$$

$$T(1, 1, 1) = \left(0, \sqrt{2}, 1\right)$$

$$T(0, 1, 1) = \left(-\tfrac{\sqrt{2}}{2}, \tfrac{\sqrt{2}}{2}, 1\right)$$

CHAPTER 7
Eigenvalues and Eigenvectors

Section 7.1   Eigenvalues and Eigenvectors

1. $A\mathbf{x}_1 = \begin{bmatrix} 0 & 1 \\ 1 & 0 \end{bmatrix} \begin{bmatrix} 1 \\ 1 \end{bmatrix} = \begin{bmatrix} 1 \\ 1 \end{bmatrix} = 1 \begin{bmatrix} 1 \\ 1 \end{bmatrix} = \lambda_1 \mathbf{x}_1$

$A\mathbf{x}_2 = \begin{bmatrix} 0 & 1 \\ 1 & 0 \end{bmatrix} \begin{bmatrix} 1 \\ -1 \end{bmatrix} = \begin{bmatrix} -1 \\ 1 \end{bmatrix} = -1 \begin{bmatrix} 1 \\ -1 \end{bmatrix} = \lambda_2 \mathbf{x}_2$

3. $A\mathbf{x}_1 = \begin{bmatrix} 1 & k \\ 0 & -1 \end{bmatrix} \begin{bmatrix} 1 \\ 0 \end{bmatrix} = \begin{bmatrix} 1 \\ 0 \end{bmatrix} = 1 \begin{bmatrix} 1 \\ 0 \end{bmatrix} = \lambda_1 \mathbf{x}_1$

5. $A\mathbf{x}_1 = \begin{bmatrix} 1 & 1 \\ 1 & 1 \end{bmatrix} \begin{bmatrix} 1 \\ -1 \end{bmatrix} = \begin{bmatrix} 0 \\ 0 \end{bmatrix} = 0 \begin{bmatrix} 1 \\ -1 \end{bmatrix} = \lambda_1 \mathbf{x}_1$

$A\mathbf{x}_2 = \begin{bmatrix} 1 & 1 \\ 1 & 1 \end{bmatrix} \begin{bmatrix} 1 \\ 1 \end{bmatrix} = \begin{bmatrix} 2 \\ 2 \end{bmatrix} = 2 \begin{bmatrix} 1 \\ 1 \end{bmatrix} = \lambda_2 \mathbf{x}_2$

7. $A\mathbf{x}_1 = \begin{bmatrix} -2 & 2 & -3 \\ 2 & 1 & -6 \\ -1 & -2 & 0 \end{bmatrix} \begin{bmatrix} 1 \\ 2 \\ -1 \end{bmatrix} = \begin{bmatrix} 5 \\ 10 \\ -5 \end{bmatrix} = 5 \begin{bmatrix} 1 \\ 2 \\ -1 \end{bmatrix} = \lambda_1 \mathbf{x}_1$

$A\mathbf{x}_2 = \begin{bmatrix} -2 & 2 & -3 \\ 2 & 1 & -6 \\ -1 & -2 & 0 \end{bmatrix} \begin{bmatrix} -2 \\ 1 \\ 0 \end{bmatrix} = \begin{bmatrix} 6 \\ -3 \\ 0 \end{bmatrix} = -3 \begin{bmatrix} -2 \\ 1 \\ 0 \end{bmatrix} = \lambda_2 \mathbf{x}_2$

$A\mathbf{x}_3 = \begin{bmatrix} -2 & 2 & -3 \\ 2 & 1 & -6 \\ -1 & -2 & 0 \end{bmatrix} \begin{bmatrix} 3 \\ 0 \\ 1 \end{bmatrix} = \begin{bmatrix} -9 \\ 0 \\ -3 \end{bmatrix} = -3 \begin{bmatrix} 3 \\ 0 \\ 1 \end{bmatrix} = \lambda_3 \mathbf{x}_3$

9. (a) $A(c\mathbf{x}_1) = \begin{bmatrix} 1 & 1 \\ 1 & 1 \end{bmatrix} \begin{bmatrix} c \\ -c \end{bmatrix} = \begin{bmatrix} 0 \\ 0 \end{bmatrix} = 0 \begin{bmatrix} c \\ -c \end{bmatrix} = 0(c\mathbf{x}_1)$

(b) $A(c\mathbf{x}_2) = \begin{bmatrix} 1 & 1 \\ 1 & 1 \end{bmatrix} \begin{bmatrix} c \\ c \end{bmatrix} = \begin{bmatrix} 2c \\ 2c \end{bmatrix} = 2 \begin{bmatrix} c \\ c \end{bmatrix} = 2(c\mathbf{x}_2)$

11. (a) Since

$$Ax = \begin{bmatrix} 7 & 2 \\ 2 & 4 \end{bmatrix} \begin{bmatrix} 1 \\ 2 \end{bmatrix} = \begin{bmatrix} 11 \\ 10 \end{bmatrix} \neq \lambda \begin{bmatrix} 1 \\ 2 \end{bmatrix}$$

x is *not* an eigenvector of *A*.

(b) Since

$$Ax = \begin{bmatrix} 7 & 2 \\ 2 & 4 \end{bmatrix} \begin{bmatrix} 2 \\ 1 \end{bmatrix} = \begin{bmatrix} 16 \\ 8 \end{bmatrix} = 8 \begin{bmatrix} 2 \\ 1 \end{bmatrix}$$

x *is* an eigenvector of *A* (with a corresponding eigenvalue 8).

(c) Since

$$Ax = \begin{bmatrix} 7 & 2 \\ 2 & 4 \end{bmatrix} \begin{bmatrix} 1 \\ -2 \end{bmatrix} = \begin{bmatrix} 3 \\ -6 \end{bmatrix} = 3 \begin{bmatrix} 1 \\ -2 \end{bmatrix}$$

x *is* an eigenvector of *A* (with a corresponding eigenvalue 3).

(d) Since

$$Ax = \begin{bmatrix} 7 & 2 \\ 2 & 4 \end{bmatrix} \begin{bmatrix} -1 \\ 0 \end{bmatrix} = \begin{bmatrix} -7 \\ -2 \end{bmatrix} \neq \lambda \begin{bmatrix} -1 \\ 0 \end{bmatrix}$$

x is *not* an eigenvector of *A*.

13. (a) Since

$$Ax = \begin{bmatrix} -1 & -1 & 1 \\ -2 & 0 & -2 \\ 3 & -3 & 1 \end{bmatrix} \begin{bmatrix} 2 \\ -4 \\ 6 \end{bmatrix} = \begin{bmatrix} 8 \\ -16 \\ 24 \end{bmatrix} = 4 \begin{bmatrix} 2 \\ -4 \\ 6 \end{bmatrix}$$

x *is* an eigenvector of *A* (with a corresponding eigenvalue 4).

(b) Since

$$Ax = \begin{bmatrix} -1 & -1 & 1 \\ -2 & 0 & -2 \\ 3 & -3 & 1 \end{bmatrix} \begin{bmatrix} 2 \\ 0 \\ 6 \end{bmatrix} = \begin{bmatrix} 4 \\ -16 \\ 12 \end{bmatrix} \neq \lambda \begin{bmatrix} 2 \\ 0 \\ 6 \end{bmatrix}$$

x is *not* an eigenvector of *A*.

(c) Since

$$Ax = \begin{bmatrix} -1 & -1 & 1 \\ -2 & 0 & -2 \\ 3 & -3 & 1 \end{bmatrix} \begin{bmatrix} 2 \\ 2 \\ 0 \end{bmatrix} = \begin{bmatrix} -4 \\ -4 \\ 0 \end{bmatrix} = -2 \begin{bmatrix} 2 \\ 2 \\ 0 \end{bmatrix}$$

x *is* an eigenvector of *A* (with a corresponding eigenvalue −2).

(d) Since

$$Ax = \begin{bmatrix} -1 & -1 & 1 \\ -2 & 0 & -2 \\ 3 & -3 & 1 \end{bmatrix} \begin{bmatrix} -1 \\ 0 \\ 1 \end{bmatrix} = \begin{bmatrix} 2 \\ 0 \\ -2 \end{bmatrix} = -2 \begin{bmatrix} -1 \\ 0 \\ 1 \end{bmatrix}$$

x *is* an eigenvector of *A* (with a corresponding eigenvalue −2).

15. (a) The characteristic equation is

$$|\lambda I - A| = \begin{vmatrix} \lambda - 2 & -1 \\ 0 & \lambda - 3 \end{vmatrix} = (\lambda - 2)(\lambda - 3) = 0.$$

(b) The eigenvalues are $\lambda_1 = 2$ and $\lambda_2 = 3$. For $\lambda_1 = 2$, we have

$$\begin{bmatrix} \lambda_1 - 2 & -1 \\ 0 & \lambda_1 - 3 \end{bmatrix} \begin{bmatrix} x_1 \\ x_2 \end{bmatrix} = \begin{bmatrix} 0 \\ 0 \end{bmatrix} \Rightarrow \begin{bmatrix} 0 & -1 \\ 0 & -1 \end{bmatrix} \begin{bmatrix} x_1 \\ x_2 \end{bmatrix} = \begin{bmatrix} 0 \\ 0 \end{bmatrix}.$$

The solution is $\{(t, 0) : t \in R\}$. Thus, an eigenvector corresponding to $\lambda_1 = 2$ is $(1, 0)$. For $\lambda_2 = 3$, we have

$$\begin{bmatrix} \lambda_2 - 2 & -1 \\ 0 & \lambda_2 - 3 \end{bmatrix} \begin{bmatrix} x_1 \\ x_2 \end{bmatrix} = \begin{bmatrix} 0 \\ 0 \end{bmatrix} \Rightarrow \begin{bmatrix} 1 & -1 \\ 0 & 0 \end{bmatrix} \begin{bmatrix} x_1 \\ x_2 \end{bmatrix} = \begin{bmatrix} 0 \\ 0 \end{bmatrix}.$$

The solution is $\{(t, t) : t \in R\}$. Thus, an eigenvector corresponding to $\lambda_2 = 3$ is $(1, 1)$.

17. (a) The characteristic equation is

$$|\lambda I - A| = \begin{vmatrix} \lambda - 6 & 3 \\ 2 & \lambda - 1 \end{vmatrix} = \lambda^2 - 7\lambda = \lambda(\lambda - 7) = 0.$$

(b) The eigenvalues are $\lambda_1 = 0$ and $\lambda_2 = 7$. For $\lambda_1 = 0$, we have

$$\begin{bmatrix} \lambda_1 - 6 & 3 \\ 2 & \lambda_1 - 1 \end{bmatrix} \begin{bmatrix} x_1 \\ x_2 \end{bmatrix} = \begin{bmatrix} 0 \\ 0 \end{bmatrix} \Rightarrow \begin{bmatrix} 2 & -1 \\ 0 & 0 \end{bmatrix} \begin{bmatrix} x_1 \\ x_2 \end{bmatrix} = \begin{bmatrix} 0 \\ 0 \end{bmatrix}.$$

The solution is $\{(t, 2t) : t \in R\}$. Thus, an eigenvector corresponding to $\lambda_1 = 0$ is $(1, 2)$. For $\lambda_2 = 7$, we have

$$\begin{bmatrix} \lambda_1 - 6 & 3 \\ 2 & \lambda_1 - 1 \end{bmatrix} \begin{bmatrix} x_1 \\ x_2 \end{bmatrix} = \begin{bmatrix} 0 \\ 0 \end{bmatrix} \Rightarrow \begin{bmatrix} 1 & 3 \\ 0 & 0 \end{bmatrix} \begin{bmatrix} x_1 \\ x_2 \end{bmatrix} = \begin{bmatrix} 0 \\ 0 \end{bmatrix}.$$

The solution is $\{(-3t, t) : t \in R\}$. Thus, an eigenvector corresponding to $\lambda_2 = 7$ is $(-3, 1)$.

19. (a) The characteristic equation is

$$|\lambda I - A| = \begin{vmatrix} \lambda - 2 & -3 \\ -1 & \lambda - 4 \end{vmatrix} = \lambda^2 - 6\lambda + 5 = 0.$$

(b) The eigenvalues are $\lambda_1 = 1$ and $\lambda_2 = 5$. For $\lambda_1 = 1$, we have

$$\begin{bmatrix} \lambda_1 - 2 & -3 \\ -1 & \lambda_1 - 4 \end{bmatrix} \begin{bmatrix} x_1 \\ x_2 \end{bmatrix} = \begin{bmatrix} 0 \\ 0 \end{bmatrix} \Rightarrow \begin{bmatrix} -1 & -3 \\ -1 & -3 \end{bmatrix} \begin{bmatrix} x_1 \\ x_2 \end{bmatrix} = \begin{bmatrix} 0 \\ 0 \end{bmatrix}.$$

The solution is $\{(-3t, t) : t \in R\}$. Thus, an eigenvector corresponding to $\lambda_1 = 1$ is $(-3, 1)$. For $\lambda_2 = 5$, we have

$$\begin{bmatrix} \lambda_2 - 2 & -3 \\ -1 & \lambda_2 - 4 \end{bmatrix} \begin{bmatrix} x_1 \\ x_2 \end{bmatrix} = \begin{bmatrix} 0 \\ 0 \end{bmatrix} \Rightarrow \begin{bmatrix} 3 & -3 \\ -1 & 1 \end{bmatrix} \begin{bmatrix} x_1 \\ x_2 \end{bmatrix} = \begin{bmatrix} 0 \\ 0 \end{bmatrix}.$$

The solution is $\{(t, t) : t \in R\}$. Thus, an eigenvector corresponding to $\lambda_2 = 5$ is $(1, 1)$.

21. (a) The characteristic equation is

$$|\lambda I - A| = \begin{vmatrix} \lambda - 2 & 0 & -1 \\ 0 & \lambda - 3 & -4 \\ 0 & 0 & \lambda - 1 \end{vmatrix} = (\lambda - 2)(\lambda - 3)(\lambda - 1) = 0.$$

(b) The eigenvalues are $\lambda_1 = 2$, $\lambda_2 = 3$ and $\lambda_3 = 1$. For $\lambda_1 = 2$, we have

$$\begin{bmatrix} \lambda_1 - 2 & 0 & -1 \\ 0 & \lambda_1 - 3 & -4 \\ 0 & 0 & \lambda_1 - 1 \end{bmatrix} \begin{bmatrix} x_1 \\ x_2 \\ x_3 \end{bmatrix} = \begin{bmatrix} 0 \\ 0 \\ 0 \end{bmatrix} \Rightarrow \begin{bmatrix} 0 & 1 & 0 \\ 0 & 0 & 1 \\ 0 & 0 & 0 \end{bmatrix} \begin{bmatrix} x_1 \\ x_2 \\ x_3 \end{bmatrix} = \begin{bmatrix} 0 \\ 0 \\ 0 \end{bmatrix}.$$

The solution is $\{(t, 0, 0) : t \in R\}$. Thus, an eigenvector corresponding to $\lambda_1 = 2$ is $(1, 0, 0)$. For $\lambda_2 = 3$, we have

$$\begin{bmatrix} \lambda_2 - 2 & 0 & -1 \\ 0 & \lambda_2 - 3 & -4 \\ 0 & 0 & \lambda_2 - 1 \end{bmatrix} \begin{bmatrix} x_1 \\ x_2 \\ x_3 \end{bmatrix} = \begin{bmatrix} 0 \\ 0 \\ 0 \end{bmatrix} \Rightarrow \begin{bmatrix} 1 & 0 & 0 \\ 0 & 0 & 1 \\ 0 & 0 & 0 \end{bmatrix} \begin{bmatrix} x_1 \\ x_2 \\ x_3 \end{bmatrix} = \begin{bmatrix} 0 \\ 0 \\ 0 \end{bmatrix}.$$

The solution is $\{(0, t, 0) : t \in R\}$. Thus, an eigenvector corresponding to $\lambda_2 = 3$ is $(0, 1, 0)$. For $\lambda_3 = 1$, we have

$$\begin{bmatrix} \lambda_3 - 2 & 0 & -1 \\ 0 & \lambda_3 - 3 & -4 \\ 0 & 0 & \lambda_3 - 1 \end{bmatrix} \begin{bmatrix} x_1 \\ x_2 \\ x_3 \end{bmatrix} = \begin{bmatrix} 0 \\ 0 \\ 0 \end{bmatrix} \Rightarrow \begin{bmatrix} 1 & 0 & 1 \\ 0 & 1 & 2 \\ 0 & 0 & 0 \end{bmatrix} \begin{bmatrix} x_1 \\ x_2 \\ x_3 \end{bmatrix} = \begin{bmatrix} 0 \\ 0 \\ 0 \end{bmatrix}.$$

The solution is $\{(-t, -2t, t) : t \in R\}$. Thus, an eigenvector corresponding to $\lambda_3 = 1$ is $(-1, -2, 1)$.

23. (a) The characteristic equation is

$$|\lambda I - A| = \begin{vmatrix} \lambda - 1 & -2 & 2 \\ 2 & \lambda - 5 & 2 \\ 6 & -6 & \lambda + 3 \end{vmatrix} = \lambda^3 - 3\lambda^2 - 9\lambda + 27 = 0.$$

(b) The eigenvalues are $\lambda_1 = -3$ and $\lambda_2 = 3$ (repeated). For $\lambda_1 = -3$, we have

$$\begin{bmatrix} \lambda_1 - 1 & -2 & 2 \\ 2 & \lambda_1 - 5 & 2 \\ 6 & -6 & \lambda_1 + 3 \end{bmatrix} \begin{bmatrix} x_1 \\ x_2 \\ x_3 \end{bmatrix} = \begin{bmatrix} 0 \\ 0 \\ 0 \end{bmatrix} \Rightarrow \begin{bmatrix} -4 & -2 & 2 \\ 2 & -8 & 2 \\ 6 & -6 & 0 \end{bmatrix} \begin{bmatrix} x_1 \\ x_2 \\ x_3 \end{bmatrix} = \begin{bmatrix} 0 \\ 0 \\ 0 \end{bmatrix}.$$

The solution is $\{(t, t, 3t) : t \in R\}$. Thus, an eigenvector corresponding to $\lambda_1 = -3$ is $(1, 1, 3)$. For $\lambda_2 = 3$, we have

$$\begin{bmatrix} \lambda_2 - 1 & -2 & 2 \\ 2 & \lambda_2 - 5 & 2 \\ 6 & -6 & \lambda_2 + 3 \end{bmatrix} \begin{bmatrix} x_1 \\ x_2 \\ x_3 \end{bmatrix} = \begin{bmatrix} 0 \\ 0 \\ 0 \end{bmatrix} \Rightarrow \begin{bmatrix} 2 & -2 & 2 \\ 2 & -2 & 2 \\ 6 & -6 & 6 \end{bmatrix} \begin{bmatrix} x_1 \\ x_2 \\ x_3 \end{bmatrix} = \begin{bmatrix} 0 \\ 0 \\ 0 \end{bmatrix}.$$

The solution is $\{(s - t, s, t) : s, t \in R\}$. Thus, two eigenvectors corresponding to $\lambda_2 = 3$ are $(1, 1, 0)$ and $(1, 0, -1)$.

25. (a) The characteristic equation is

$$|\lambda I - A| = \begin{vmatrix} \lambda - 1 & 2 & -1 \\ 0 & \lambda - 1 & -4 \\ 0 & 0 & \lambda - 2 \end{vmatrix} = (\lambda - 1)^2 (\lambda - 2) = 0.$$

(b) The eigenvalues are $\lambda_1 = 1$ (repeated) and $\lambda_2 = 2$. For $\lambda_1 = 1$, we have

$$\begin{bmatrix} \lambda_1 - 1 & 2 & -1 \\ 0 & \lambda_1 - 1 & -4 \\ 0 & 0 & \lambda_1 - 2 \end{bmatrix} \begin{bmatrix} x_1 \\ x_2 \\ x_3 \end{bmatrix} = \begin{bmatrix} 0 \\ 0 \\ 0 \end{bmatrix} \Rightarrow \begin{bmatrix} 0 & 1 & 0 \\ 0 & 0 & 1 \\ 0 & 0 & 0 \end{bmatrix} \begin{bmatrix} x_1 \\ x_2 \\ x_3 \end{bmatrix} = \begin{bmatrix} 0 \\ 0 \\ 0 \end{bmatrix}.$$

The solution is $\{(t, 0, 0) : t \in R\}$. Thus, an eigenvector corresponding to $\lambda_1 = 1$ is $(1, 0, 0)$. For $\lambda_2 = 2$, we have

$$\begin{bmatrix} \lambda_2 - 1 & 2 & -1 \\ 0 & \lambda_2 - 1 & -4 \\ 0 & 0 & \lambda_2 - 2 \end{bmatrix} \begin{bmatrix} x_1 \\ x_2 \\ x_3 \end{bmatrix} = \begin{bmatrix} 0 \\ 0 \\ 0 \end{bmatrix} \Rightarrow \begin{bmatrix} 1 & 0 & 7 \\ 0 & 1 & -4 \\ 0 & 0 & 0 \end{bmatrix} \begin{bmatrix} x_1 \\ x_2 \\ x_3 \end{bmatrix} = \begin{bmatrix} 0 \\ 0 \\ 0 \end{bmatrix}.$$

The solution is $\{(-7t, 4t, t) : t \in R\}$. Thus, an eigenvector corresponding to $\lambda_2 = 2$ is $(-7, 4, 1)$.

27. (a) The characteristic equation is

$$|\lambda I - A| = \begin{vmatrix} \lambda & 3 & -5 \\ 4 & \lambda - 4 & 10 \\ 0 & 0 & \lambda - 4 \end{vmatrix} = (\lambda - 4)\left(\lambda^2 - 4\lambda - 12\right)$$

$$= (\lambda - 4)(\lambda - 6)(\lambda + 2) = 0.$$

(b) The eigenvalues are $\lambda_1 = 4$, $\lambda_2 = 6$ and $\lambda_3 = -2$. For $\lambda_1 = 4$, we have

$$\begin{bmatrix} \lambda_1 & 3 & -5 \\ 4 & \lambda_1 - 4 & 10 \\ 0 & 0 & \lambda_1 - 4 \end{bmatrix} \begin{bmatrix} x_1 \\ x_2 \\ x_3 \end{bmatrix} = \begin{bmatrix} 0 \\ 0 \\ 0 \end{bmatrix} \Rightarrow \begin{bmatrix} 2 & 0 & 5 \\ 0 & 1 & -5 \\ 0 & 0 & 0 \end{bmatrix} \begin{bmatrix} x_1 \\ x_2 \\ x_3 \end{bmatrix} = \begin{bmatrix} 0 \\ 0 \\ 0 \end{bmatrix}.$$

The solution is $\{(-5t, 10t, 2t) : t \in R\}$. Thus, an eigenvector corresponding to $\lambda_1 = 4$ is $(-5, 10, 2)$. For $\lambda_2 = 6$, we have

$$\begin{bmatrix} \lambda_2 & 3 & -5 \\ 4 & \lambda_2 - 4 & 10 \\ 0 & 0 & \lambda_2 - 4 \end{bmatrix} \begin{bmatrix} x_1 \\ x_2 \\ x_3 \end{bmatrix} = \begin{bmatrix} 0 \\ 0 \\ 0 \end{bmatrix} \Rightarrow \begin{bmatrix} 2 & 1 & 0 \\ 0 & 0 & 1 \\ 0 & 0 & 0 \end{bmatrix} \begin{bmatrix} x_1 \\ x_2 \\ x_3 \end{bmatrix} = \begin{bmatrix} 0 \\ 0 \\ 0 \end{bmatrix}.$$

The solution is $\{(t, -2t, 0) : t \in R\}$. Thus, an eigenvector corresponding to $\lambda_2 = 6$ is $(1, -2, 0)$. For $\lambda_3 = -2$, we have

$$\begin{bmatrix} \lambda_3 & 3 & -5 \\ 4 & \lambda_3 - 4 & 10 \\ 0 & 0 & \lambda_3 - 4 \end{bmatrix} \begin{bmatrix} x_1 \\ x_2 \\ x_3 \end{bmatrix} = \begin{bmatrix} 0 \\ 0 \\ 0 \end{bmatrix} \Rightarrow \begin{bmatrix} 2 & -3 & 0 \\ 0 & 0 & 1 \\ 0 & 0 & 0 \end{bmatrix} \begin{bmatrix} x_1 \\ x_2 \\ x_3 \end{bmatrix} = \begin{bmatrix} 0 \\ 0 \\ 0 \end{bmatrix}.$$

The solution is $\{(3t, 2t, 0) : t \in R\}$. Thus, an eigenvector corresponding to $\lambda_3 = -2$ is $(3, 2, 0)$.

29. (a) The characteristic equation is

$$|\lambda I - A| = \begin{vmatrix} \lambda - 1 & 0 & 1 & -1 \\ 0 & \lambda - 1 & 0 & -1 \\ 2 & 0 & \lambda - 2 & 2 \\ 0 & -2 & 0 & \lambda - 2 \end{vmatrix} = \lambda^2(\lambda - 3)^2 = 0.$$

(b) The eigenvalues are $\lambda_1 = 0$ and $\lambda_2 = 3$. We solve

$$\begin{bmatrix} \lambda_i - 1 & 0 & 1 & -1 \\ 0 & \lambda_i - 1 & 0 & -1 \\ 2 & 0 & \lambda_i - 2 & 2 \\ 0 & -2 & 0 & \lambda_i - 2 \end{bmatrix} \begin{bmatrix} x_1 \\ x_2 \\ x_3 \\ x_4 \end{bmatrix} = \begin{bmatrix} 0 \\ 0 \\ 0 \\ 0 \end{bmatrix}$$

for each eigenvalue. For $\lambda_1 = 0$, two corresponding eigenvectors are $\mathbf{x}_1 = (1, 0, 1, 0)$ and $\mathbf{x}_2 = (1, 1, 0, -1)$. For $\lambda_2 = 3$, a corresponding eigenvector is $\mathbf{x}_3 = (1, 0, -2, 0)$.

31. The characteristic equation is

$$|\lambda I - A| = \begin{vmatrix} \lambda - 4 & 0 \\ 3 & \lambda - 2 \end{vmatrix} = (\lambda - 2)(\lambda - 4) = \lambda^2 - 6\lambda + 8 = 0.$$

Since

$$A^2 - 6A + 8I = \begin{bmatrix} 4 & 0 \\ -3 & 2 \end{bmatrix}^2 - 6\begin{bmatrix} 4 & 0 \\ -3 & 2 \end{bmatrix} + 8\begin{bmatrix} 1 & 0 \\ 0 & 1 \end{bmatrix}$$

$$= \begin{bmatrix} 16 & 0 \\ -18 & 4 \end{bmatrix} - \begin{bmatrix} 24 & 0 \\ -18 & 12 \end{bmatrix} + \begin{bmatrix} 8 & 0 \\ 0 & 8 \end{bmatrix}$$

$$= \begin{bmatrix} 0 & 0 \\ 0 & 0 \end{bmatrix}$$

the theorem holds for this matrix.

33. The characteristic equation is

$$|\lambda I - A| = \begin{vmatrix} \lambda - 1 & 0 & 4 \\ 0 & \lambda - 3 & -1 \\ -2 & 0 & \lambda - 1 \end{vmatrix} = \lambda^3 - 5\lambda^2 + 15\lambda - 27 = 0.$$

Since

$$A^3 - 5A^2 + 15A - 27I$$

$$= \begin{bmatrix} 1 & 0 & -4 \\ 0 & 3 & 1 \\ 2 & 0 & 1 \end{bmatrix}^3 - 5\begin{bmatrix} 1 & 0 & -4 \\ 0 & 3 & 1 \\ 2 & 0 & 1 \end{bmatrix}^{-2} + 15\begin{bmatrix} 1 & 0 & -4 \\ 0 & 3 & 1 \\ 2 & 0 & 1 \end{bmatrix} - 27\begin{bmatrix} 1 & 0 & 0 \\ 0 & 1 & 0 \\ 0 & 0 & 1 \end{bmatrix}$$

$$= \begin{bmatrix} -23 & 0 & 20 \\ 10 & 27 & 5 \\ -10 & 0 & -23 \end{bmatrix} - 5\begin{bmatrix} -7 & 0 & -8 \\ 2 & 9 & 4 \\ 4 & 0 & -7 \end{bmatrix} + 15\begin{bmatrix} 1 & 0 & -4 \\ 0 & 3 & 1 \\ 2 & 0 & 1 \end{bmatrix} - \begin{bmatrix} 27 & 0 & 0 \\ 0 & 27 & 0 \\ 0 & 0 & 27 \end{bmatrix}$$

$$= \begin{bmatrix} 0 & 0 & 0 \\ 0 & 0 & 0 \\ 0 & 0 & 0 \end{bmatrix}$$

the theorem holds for this matrix.

35.

Exercise	Trace of A	Determinant of A	Eigenvalues of A
15	5	6	2, 3
16	9	0	0, 9
17	7	0	0, 7
18	1	-6	3, -2
19	6	5	1, 5
20	0	-16	4, -4
21	6	6	1, 2, 3
22	5	-105	$-5, 3, 7$
23	3	-27	$-3, 3, 3$
24	4	0	0, 2, 2
25	4	2	1, 1, 2
26	0	2	$-1, -1, 2$
27	8	-48	$-2, 4, 6$
28	$\dfrac{31}{2}$	$\dfrac{29}{8}$	$\dfrac{1}{2}, \dfrac{1}{2}, \dfrac{29}{2}$
29	6	0	0, 0, 3, 3
30	6	0	0, 1, 1, 4

37. If $A\mathbf{x} = \lambda\mathbf{x}$, then $A^{-1}A\mathbf{x} = A^{-1}\lambda\mathbf{x}$ and $\mathbf{x} = \lambda A^{-1}\mathbf{x}$. Thus, $A^{-1}\mathbf{x} = \frac{1}{\lambda}\mathbf{x}$, which shows that $\mathbf{x}$ is an eigenvector of A^{-1} with eigenvalue $1/\lambda$. The eigenvectors of A and A^{-1} are the same.

39. The characteristic polynomial of A is $|\lambda I - A|$. The constant term of this polynomial (in λ) is obtained by setting $\lambda = 0$. Thus, the constant term is $|0I - A| = |-A| = \pm |A|$.

41. Let A be a triangular matrix. Since the eigenvalues of A are its diagonal entries, A is nonsingular if and only if 0 is not an eigenvalue of A if and only if the eigenvalues are real and nonzero.

43. The characteristic equation of A is

$$\begin{vmatrix} \lambda - a & -b \\ 0 & \lambda - d \end{vmatrix} = (\lambda - a)(\lambda - d) = \lambda^2 + (a + d)\lambda + ad = 0.$$

Since the given eigenvalues indicate a characteristic equation of $\lambda(\lambda - 1) = \lambda^2 - \lambda$, we have

$$\lambda^2 - (a + d)\lambda + ad = \lambda^2 - \lambda.$$

Thus, $a = 0$ and $d = 1$, or $a = 1$ and $d = 0$.

45. Substituting the value $\lambda - 3$ yields the system

$$\begin{bmatrix} \lambda - 3 & 0 & 0 \\ 0 & \lambda - 3 & 0 \\ 0 & 0 & \lambda - 3 \end{bmatrix} \begin{bmatrix} x_1 \\ x_2 \\ x_3 \end{bmatrix} = \begin{bmatrix} 0 \\ 0 \\ 0 \end{bmatrix} \Rightarrow \begin{bmatrix} 0 & 0 & 0 \\ 0 & 0 & 0 \\ 0 & 0 & 0 \end{bmatrix} \begin{bmatrix} x_1 \\ x_2 \\ x_3 \end{bmatrix} = \begin{bmatrix} 0 \\ 0 \\ 0 \end{bmatrix}.$$

Thus, 3 has three linearly independent eigenvectors and the dimension of the eigenspace is 3.

47. Substituting the value $\lambda - 3$ yields the system

$$\begin{bmatrix} \lambda - 3 & 1 & 0 \\ 0 & \lambda - 3 & 1 \\ 0 & 0 & \lambda - 3 \end{bmatrix} \begin{bmatrix} x_1 \\ x_2 \\ x_3 \end{bmatrix} = \begin{bmatrix} 0 \\ 0 \\ 0 \end{bmatrix} \Rightarrow \begin{bmatrix} 0 & -1 & 0 \\ 0 & 0 & -1 \\ 0 & 0 & 0 \end{bmatrix} \begin{bmatrix} x_1 \\ x_2 \\ x_3 \end{bmatrix} = \begin{bmatrix} 0 \\ 0 \\ 0 \end{bmatrix}.$$

Thus, 3 has one linearly independent eigenvector, and the dimension of the eigenspace is 1.

49. $T(e^x) = \dfrac{d}{dx}[e^x] = e^x = 1(e^x)$

Therefore, $\lambda = 1$ is an eigenvalue.

51. The standard matrix for T is

$$A = \begin{bmatrix} 0 & -3 & 5 \\ -4 & 4 & -10 \\ 0 & 0 & 4 \end{bmatrix}.$$

The characteristic equation of A is

$$\begin{vmatrix} \lambda & 3 & -5 \\ 4 & \lambda - 4 & 10 \\ 0 & 0 & \lambda - 4 \end{vmatrix} = (\lambda + 2)(\lambda - 4)(\lambda - 6) = 0.$$

The eigenvalues of A are $\lambda_1 = -2$, $\lambda_2 = 4$, and $\lambda_3 = 6$. The corresponding eigenvectors are found by solving

$$\begin{bmatrix} \lambda_i & 3 & -5 \\ 4 & \lambda_i - 4 & 10 \\ 0 & 0 & \lambda_i - 4 \end{bmatrix} \begin{bmatrix} x_1 \\ x_2 \\ x_3 \end{bmatrix} = \begin{bmatrix} 0 \\ 0 \\ 0 \end{bmatrix}$$

for each λ_i. Thus, $\mathbf{p}_1 = 3 + 2x$, $\mathbf{p}_2 = -5 + 10x + 2x^2$ and $\mathbf{p}_3 = -1 + 2x$ are eigenvectors corresponding to λ_1, λ_2, and λ_3.

53. The standard matrix for T is

$$A = \begin{bmatrix} 1 & 0 & -1 & 1 \\ 0 & 1 & 0 & 1 \\ -2 & 0 & 2 & -2 \\ 0 & 2 & 0 & 2 \end{bmatrix}.$$

Since the standard matrix is the same as that in Exercise 29, we know the eigenvalues are $\lambda_1 = 0$ and $\lambda_2 = 3$. Thus, two eigenvectors corresponding to $\lambda_1 = 0$ are

$$\mathbf{x}_1 = \begin{bmatrix} 1 & 0 \\ 1 & 0 \end{bmatrix} \quad \text{and} \quad \mathbf{x}_2 = \begin{bmatrix} 1 & 1 \\ 0 & -1 \end{bmatrix}$$

and an eigenvector corresponding to $\lambda_2 = 3$ is

$$\mathbf{x}_3 = \begin{bmatrix} 1 & 0 \\ -2 & 0 \end{bmatrix}.$$

55. 0 is the only eigenvalue of a nilpotent matrix. For if $A\mathbf{x} = \lambda\mathbf{x}$, then $A^2\mathbf{x} = A\lambda\mathbf{x} = \lambda^2\mathbf{x}$. Thus,

$$A^k\mathbf{x} = \lambda^k\mathbf{x} = \mathbf{0} \implies \lambda^k = 0 \implies \lambda = 0$$

57. Let $\mathbf{x} = \begin{bmatrix} 1 \\ 1 \\ \vdots \\ 1 \end{bmatrix}$. Then $A\mathbf{x} = \begin{bmatrix} r \\ r \\ \vdots \\ r \end{bmatrix} = r\mathbf{x}$,

which shows that r is an eigenvalue of A with eigenvetor $\mathbf{x}$.

For example, let $A = \begin{bmatrix} 1 & 2 \\ 3 & 0 \end{bmatrix}$.

Then $\begin{bmatrix} 1 & 2 \\ 3 & 0 \end{bmatrix} \begin{bmatrix} 1 \\ 1 \end{bmatrix} = \begin{bmatrix} 3 \\ 3 \end{bmatrix} = 3\begin{bmatrix} 1 \\ 1 \end{bmatrix}$.

Section 7.2   Diagonalization

1. $P^{-1} = \begin{bmatrix} 1 & -4 \\ -1 & 3 \end{bmatrix}$

$$P^{-1}AP = \begin{bmatrix} 1 & -4 \\ -1 & 3 \end{bmatrix} \begin{bmatrix} -11 & 36 \\ -3 & 10 \end{bmatrix} \begin{bmatrix} -3 & -4 \\ -1 & -1 \end{bmatrix} = \begin{bmatrix} 1 & 0 \\ 0 & -2 \end{bmatrix}$$

3. $P^{-1} = \begin{bmatrix} \frac{2}{3} & -\frac{2}{3} & 1 \\ 0 & \frac{1}{4} & 0 \\ -\frac{1}{3} & \frac{1}{12} & 0 \end{bmatrix}$ and

$$P^{-1}AP = \begin{bmatrix} \frac{2}{3} & -\frac{2}{3} & 1 \\ 0 & \frac{1}{4} & 0 \\ -\frac{1}{3} & \frac{1}{12} & 0 \end{bmatrix} \begin{bmatrix} -1 & 1 & 0 \\ 0 & 3 & 0 \\ 4 & -2 & 5 \end{bmatrix} \begin{bmatrix} 0 & 1 & -3 \\ 0 & 4 & 0 \\ 1 & 2 & 2 \end{bmatrix} = \begin{bmatrix} 5 & 0 & 0 \\ 0 & 3 & 0 \\ 0 & 0 & -1 \end{bmatrix}$$

5. A has only one eigenvalue, $\lambda = 0$, and a basis for the eigenspace is $\{(0, 1)\}$. Thus, A does not satisfy Theorem 7.5 (it does not have two linearly independent eigenvectors) and is not diagonalizable.

7.   From Exercise 25, Section 7.1, we know that A has only two linearly independent eigenvectors. Thus, A does not satisfy Theorem 7.5 and is not diagonalizable.

9.   From Exercise 29, Section 7.1, we know that A has only three linearly independent eigenvectors. Thus, A does not satisfy Theorem 7.5 and is not diagonalizable.

11.   The eigenvalues of A are $\lambda_1 = 0$ and $\lambda_2 = 2$. Since A has two distinct eigenvalues, it is diagonalizable (by Theorem 7.6).

13.   The eigenvalues of A are $\lambda = 0$ and $\lambda = 2$ (repeated). Since A does not have three <u>distinct</u> eigenvalues, Theorem 7.6 does not guarantee that A is diagonalizable.

15.   The eigenvalues of A are $\lambda_1 = -1$ and $\lambda_2 = 1$. The corresponding eigenvectors $(1, -1)$ and $(1, 1)$ are used to form the columns of P. Thus,

$$P = \begin{bmatrix} 1 & 1 \\ -1 & 1 \end{bmatrix} \quad \Rightarrow \quad P^{-1} = \begin{bmatrix} \frac{1}{2} & -\frac{1}{2} \\ \frac{1}{2} & \frac{1}{2} \end{bmatrix}$$

and

$$P^{-1}AP = \begin{bmatrix} \frac{1}{2} & -\frac{1}{2} \\ \frac{1}{2} & \frac{1}{2} \end{bmatrix} \begin{bmatrix} 0 & 1 \\ 1 & 0 \end{bmatrix} \begin{bmatrix} 1 & 1 \\ -1 & 1 \end{bmatrix} = \begin{bmatrix} -1 & 0 \\ 0 & 1 \end{bmatrix}.$$

17. The eigenvalues of A are $\lambda_1 = 1$ and $\lambda_2 = 5$ (see Exercise 19, Section 7.1). The corresponding eigenvectors $(-3, 1)$ and $(1, 1)$ are used to form the columns of P. Thus,

$$P = \begin{bmatrix} -3 & 1 \\ 1 & 1 \end{bmatrix}$$

and

$$P^{-1}AP = \begin{bmatrix} -\frac{1}{4} & -\frac{1}{4} \\ \frac{1}{4} & \frac{3}{4} \end{bmatrix} \begin{bmatrix} 2 & 3 \\ 1 & 4 \end{bmatrix} \begin{bmatrix} -3 & 1 \\ 1 & 1 \end{bmatrix} = \begin{bmatrix} 1 & 0 \\ 0 & 5 \end{bmatrix}.$$

19. The eigenvalues of A are $\lambda_1 = 2$, $\lambda_2 = 3$ and $\lambda_3 = 1$ (see Exercise 21, Section 7.1). The corresponding eigenvectors $(1, 0, 0)$, $(0, 1, 0)$ and $(-1, -2, 1)$ are used to form the columns of P. Thus,

$$P = \begin{bmatrix} 1 & 0 & -1 \\ 0 & 1 & -2 \\ 0 & 0 & 1 \end{bmatrix} \implies P^{-1} = \begin{bmatrix} 1 & 0 & 1 \\ 0 & 1 & 2 \\ 0 & 0 & 1 \end{bmatrix}$$

and

$$P^{-1}AP = \begin{bmatrix} 1 & 0 & 1 \\ 0 & 1 & 2 \\ 0 & 0 & 1 \end{bmatrix} \begin{bmatrix} 2 & 0 & 1 \\ 0 & 3 & 4 \\ 0 & 0 & 1 \end{bmatrix} \begin{bmatrix} 1 & 0 & -1 \\ 0 & 1 & -2 \\ 0 & 0 & 1 \end{bmatrix} = \begin{bmatrix} 2 & 0 & 0 \\ 0 & 3 & 0 \\ 0 & 0 & 1 \end{bmatrix}.$$

21. The eigenvalues of A are $\lambda_1 = -3$ and $\lambda_2 = 3$ (repeated) (see Exercise 23, Section 7.1). The corresponding eigenvectors $(1, 1, 3)$, $(1, 1, 0)$, and $(1, 0, -1)$ are used to form the columns of P. Thus, we have

$$P = \begin{bmatrix} 1 & 1 & 1 \\ 1 & 1 & 0 \\ 3 & 0 & -1 \end{bmatrix}$$

and

$$P^{-1}AP = \begin{bmatrix} \frac{1}{3} & -\frac{1}{3} & \frac{1}{3} \\ -\frac{1}{3} & \frac{4}{3} & -\frac{1}{3} \\ 1 & -1 & 0 \end{bmatrix} \begin{bmatrix} 1 & 2 & -2 \\ -2 & 5 & -2 \\ -6 & 6 & -3 \end{bmatrix} \begin{bmatrix} 1 & 1 & 1 \\ 1 & 1 & 0 \\ 3 & 0 & -1 \end{bmatrix} = \begin{bmatrix} -3 & 0 & 0 \\ 0 & 3 & 0 \\ 0 & 0 & 3 \end{bmatrix}.$$

23. The eigenvalues of A are $\lambda_1 = -2$, $\lambda_2 = 6$ and $\lambda_3 = 4$ (see Exercise 27, Section 7.1). The corresponding eigenvectors $(3, 2, 0)$, $(-1, 2, 0)$ and $(-5, 10, 2)$ are used to form the columns of P. Thus,

$$P = \begin{bmatrix} 3 & -1 & -5 \\ 2 & 2 & 10 \\ 0 & 0 & 2 \end{bmatrix} \implies P^{-1} = \begin{bmatrix} \frac{1}{4} & \frac{1}{8} & 0 \\ -\frac{1}{4} & \frac{3}{8} & -\frac{5}{2} \\ 0 & 0 & \frac{1}{2} \end{bmatrix}$$

and

$$P^{-1}AP = \begin{bmatrix} \frac{1}{4} & \frac{1}{8} & 0 \\ -\frac{1}{4} & \frac{3}{8} & -\frac{5}{8} \\ 0 & 0 & \frac{1}{2} \end{bmatrix} \begin{bmatrix} 0 & -3 & 5 \\ -4 & 4 & -10 \\ 0 & 0 & 4 \end{bmatrix} \begin{bmatrix} 3 & -1 & -5 \\ 2 & 2 & 10 \\ 0 & 0 & 2 \end{bmatrix} = \begin{bmatrix} -2 & 0 & 0 \\ 0 & 6 & 0 \\ 0 & 0 & 4 \end{bmatrix}.$$

25. The eigenvalues of A are $\lambda_1 = 1$ and $\lambda_2 = 2$. Furthermore, there are just two linearly independent eigenvectors of A, $\mathbf{x}_1 = (-1, 0, 1)$ and $\mathbf{x}_2 = (0, 1, 0)$. Thus, A is not diagonalizable.

27. The eigenvalues of A are $\lambda_1 = 2$, $\lambda_2 = 1$, $\lambda_3 = -1$ and $\lambda_4 = -2$. The corresponding eigenvectors $(4, 4, 4, 1)$, $(0, 0, 3, 1)$, $(0, -2, 1, 1)$ and $((0, 0, 0, 1)$ are used to form the columns of P. Thus,

$$P = \begin{bmatrix} 4 & 0 & 0 & 0 \\ 4 & 0 & -2 & 0 \\ 4 & 3 & 1 & 0 \\ 1 & 1 & 1 & 1 \end{bmatrix} \implies P^{-1} = \begin{bmatrix} \frac{1}{4} & 0 & 0 & 0 \\ -\frac{1}{2} & \frac{1}{6} & \frac{1}{3} & 0 \\ \frac{1}{2} & -\frac{1}{2} & 0 & 0 \\ -\frac{1}{4} & \frac{1}{3} & -\frac{1}{3} & 1 \end{bmatrix}$$

and

$$P^{-1}AP = \begin{bmatrix} \frac{1}{4} & 0 & 0 & 0 \\ -\frac{1}{2} & \frac{1}{6} & \frac{1}{3} & 0 \\ \frac{1}{2} & -\frac{1}{2} & 0 & 0 \\ -\frac{1}{4} & \frac{1}{3} & -\frac{1}{3} & 1 \end{bmatrix} \begin{bmatrix} 2 & 0 & 0 & 0 \\ 3 & -1 & 0 & 0 \\ 0 & 1 & 1 & 0 \\ 0 & 0 & 1 & -2 \end{bmatrix} \begin{bmatrix} 4 & 0 & 0 & 0 \\ 4 & 0 & -2 & 0 \\ 4 & 3 & 1 & 0 \\ 1 & 1 & 1 & 1 \end{bmatrix}$$

$$\begin{bmatrix} 2 & 0 & 0 & 0 \\ 0 & 1 & 0 & 0 \\ 0 & 0 & -1 & 0 \\ 0 & 0 & 0 & -2 \end{bmatrix}.$$

29. The standard matrix for T is

$$A = \begin{bmatrix} 1 & 1 \\ 1 & 1 \end{bmatrix}$$

which has eigenvalues $\lambda_1 = 0$ and $\lambda_2 = 2$ and corresponding eigenvectors $(1, -1)$ and $(1, 1)$. We let $B = \{(1, -1), (1, 1)\}$ and find the image of each vector in B.

$$[T(1, -1)]_B = [(0, 0)]_B = (0, 0)$$

$$[T(1, 1)]_B = [(2, 2)]_B = (0, 2)$$

The matrix for T relative to B is then

$$A' = \begin{bmatrix} 0 & 0 \\ 0 & 2 \end{bmatrix}.$$

31. The standard matrix for T is

$$A = \begin{bmatrix} 1 & 0 \\ 1 & 2 \end{bmatrix}$$

which has eigenvalues $\lambda_1 = 1$ and $\lambda_2 = 2$ and corresponding eigenvectors $-1 + x$ and x. We let $B = \{-1 + x, x\}$ and find the image of each vector in B.

$$[T(-1 + x)]_B = [-1 + x]_B = (1, 0)$$

$$[T(x)]_B = [2x]_B = (0, 2)$$

The matrix for T relative to B is then

$$A' = \begin{bmatrix} 1 & 0 \\ 0 & 2 \end{bmatrix}.$$

33. (a) $B^k = \left(P^{-1}AP\right)^k = \left(P^{-1}AP\right)\left(P^{-1}AP\right)\ldots\left(P^{-1}AP\right)$ (k times)

$$= P^{-1}A^k P$$

(b) $B = P^{-1}AP \implies A = PBP^{-1} \implies A^k = PB^k P^{-1}$ from part (a).

35. The eigenvalues and corresponding eigenvectors of A are $\lambda_1 = -2$, $\lambda_2 = 1$, $\mathbf{x}_1 = \left(-\frac{3}{2}, 1\right)$, and $\mathbf{x}_2 = (-2, 1)$. We construct a nonsingular matrix P from the eigenvectors of A,

$$P = \begin{bmatrix} -\frac{3}{2} & -2 \\ 1 & 1 \end{bmatrix}$$

and find a diagonal matrix B similar to A.

$$B = P^{-1}AP = \begin{bmatrix} 2 & 4 \\ -2 & -3 \end{bmatrix}\begin{bmatrix} 10 & 28 \\ -6 & -11 \end{bmatrix}\begin{bmatrix} -\frac{3}{2} & -2 \\ 1 & 1 \end{bmatrix} = \begin{bmatrix} -2 & 0 \\ 0 & 1 \end{bmatrix}$$

Then

$$A^6 = PB^6 P^{-1} = \begin{bmatrix} -\frac{3}{2} & -2 \\ 1 & 1 \end{bmatrix}\begin{bmatrix} 64 & 0 \\ 0 & 1 \end{bmatrix}\begin{bmatrix} 2 & 4 \\ -2 & -3 \end{bmatrix} = \begin{bmatrix} -188 & -378 \\ 126 & 253 \end{bmatrix}.$$

37. The eigenvalues and corresponding eigenvectors of A are $\lambda_1 = 0$, $\lambda_2 = 2$ (repeated), $\mathbf{x}_1 = (-1, 3, 1)$, $\mathbf{x}_2 = (3, 0, 1)$ and $\mathbf{x}_3 = (-2, 1, 0)$. We construct a nonsingular matrix P from the eigenvectors of A.

$$P = \begin{bmatrix} -1 & 3 & -2 \\ 3 & 0 & 1 \\ 1 & 1 & 0 \end{bmatrix}$$

and find a diagonal matrix B similar to A.

$$B = P^{-1}AP = \begin{bmatrix} \frac{1}{2} & 1 & -\frac{3}{2} \\ -\frac{1}{2} & -1 & \frac{5}{2} \\ -\frac{3}{2} & -2 & \frac{9}{2} \end{bmatrix} \begin{bmatrix} 3 & 2 & -3 \\ -3 & -4 & 9 \\ -1 & -2 & 5 \end{bmatrix} \begin{bmatrix} -1 & 3 & -2 \\ 3 & 0 & 1 \\ 1 & 1 & 0 \end{bmatrix}$$

$$= \begin{bmatrix} 0 & 0 & 0 \\ 0 & 2 & 0 \\ 0 & 0 & 2 \end{bmatrix}$$

Then,

$$A^8 = PB^8 P^{-1} = P \begin{bmatrix} 0 & 0 & 0 \\ 0 & 256 & 0 \\ 0 & 0 & 256 \end{bmatrix} P^{-1} = \begin{bmatrix} 384 & 256 & -384 \\ -384 & -512 & 1152 \\ -128 & -256 & 640 \end{bmatrix}.$$

39. Yes, the order of the elements on the main diagonal may change. For instance,

$$\begin{bmatrix} 1 & 0 \\ 0 & 2 \end{bmatrix} \text{ and } \begin{bmatrix} 2 & 0 \\ 0 & 1 \end{bmatrix} \text{ are similar.}$$

41. Assume that A is diagonalizable, $P^{-1}AP = D$, where D is diagonal. Then

$$D^T = \left(P^{-1}AP\right)^T = P^T A^T \left(P^{-1}\right)^T = P^T A^T (P^T)^{-1}$$

is diagonal, which shows that A^T is diagonalizable.

43. Assume that A is diagonalizable with n real eigenvalues $\lambda_1, \ldots, \lambda_n$. Then if $PAP^{-1} = D$ is diagonal,

$$|A| = |P^{-1}AP| = \begin{vmatrix} \lambda_1 & 0 & \cdots & 0 \\ 0 & \lambda_2 & & \vdots \\ \vdots & & & 0 \\ 0 & \cdots & 0 & \lambda_n \end{vmatrix} = \lambda_1 \lambda_2 \ldots \lambda_n.$$

45. Let the eigenvalues of the diagonalizable matrix A be all ± 1. Then there exists an invertible matrix P such that

$$P^{-1}AP = D$$

where D is diagonal with ± 1 along the main diagonal. Thus $A = PDP^{-1}$ and because $D^{-1} = D$, we have

$$A^{-1} = (PDP^{-1})^{-1} = (P^{-1})^{-1} D^{-1}P^{-1} = PDP^{-1} = A.$$

47. Given that $P^{-1}AP = D$, where D is diagonal, we have

$$A = PDP^{-1}$$

and

$$A^{-1} = (PDP^{-1})^{-1} = (P^{-1})^{-1}D^{-1}P^{-1} = PD^{-1}P^{-1} \implies P^{-1}A^{-1}P = D^{-1},$$

which shows that A' is diagonalizable.

Section 7.3   Symmetric Matrices and Orthogonal Diagonalization

1. Since

$$\begin{bmatrix} 1 & -1 \\ -1 & 4 \end{bmatrix}^T = \begin{bmatrix} 1 & -1 \\ -1 & 4 \end{bmatrix}$$

the matrix *is* symmetric.

3. Since

$$\begin{bmatrix} 4 & -2 & 1 \\ 3 & 1 & 2 \\ 1 & 2 & 1 \end{bmatrix}^T = \begin{bmatrix} 4 & 3 & 1 \\ -2 & 1 & 2 \\ 1 & 2 & 1 \end{bmatrix}$$

the matrix is *not* symmetric.

5. Since

$$\begin{bmatrix} 0 & 1 & 2 \\ 1 & 0 & -3 \\ 2 & -3 & 0 \end{bmatrix}^T = \begin{bmatrix} 0 & 1 & 2 \\ 1 & 0 & -3 \\ 2 & -3 & 0 \end{bmatrix}$$

the matrix *is* symmetric.

7. The characteristic equation of A is

$$|\lambda I - A| = \begin{vmatrix} \lambda - 1 & -2 \\ -2 & \lambda - 1 \end{vmatrix} = (\lambda + 1)(\lambda - 3) = 0.$$

Therefore, the eigenvalues of A are $\lambda_1 = -1$ and $\lambda_2 = 3$. The dimension of the corresponding eigenspace of each eigenvalue is 1 (by Theorem 7.7).

9. The characteristic equation of A is

$$|\lambda I - A| = \begin{vmatrix} \lambda - 3 & 0 & 0 \\ 0 & \lambda - 2 & 0 \\ 0 & 0 & \lambda - 2 \end{vmatrix} = (\lambda - 3)(\lambda - 2)^2 = 0.$$

Therefore, the eigenvalues of A are $\lambda_1 = 3$ and $\lambda_2 = 2$. The dimension of the eigenspace corresponding $\lambda_1 = 3$ is 1. The multiplicity of $\lambda_2 = 2$ is 2, so the dimension of the corresponding eigenspace is 2 (by Theorem 7.7).

11. The characteristic equation of A is

$$|\lambda I - A| = \begin{vmatrix} \lambda & -2 & -2 \\ -2 & \lambda & -2 \\ -2 & -2 & \lambda \end{vmatrix} = (\lambda + 2)^2 (\lambda - 4) = 0.$$

The eigenvalues of A are $\lambda_1 = -2$ and $\lambda_2 = 4$. The multiplicity of $\lambda_1 = -2$ is 2, so the dimension of the corresponding eigenspace is 2 (by Theorem 7.7). The dimension for the eigenspace coresponding to $\lambda_2 = 4$ is 1.

13. Because the column vectors of the matrix form an orthonormal set, the matrix *is* orthogonal.

15. Because the column vectors of the matrix do not form an orthonormal set $[(-4, 0, 3)$ and $(3, 0, 4)$ are not unit vectors], the matrix is *not* orthogonal.

17. Because the column vectors of the matrix form an orthonormal set, the matrix *is* orthogonal.

19. Because the column vectors of the matrix form an orthonormal set, the matrix *is* orthogonal.

21. The eigenvalues of A are $\lambda_1 = 0$ and $\lambda_2 = 2$, with corresponding eigenvectors $(1, -1)$ and $(1, 1)$, respectively. We normalize each eigenvector to form the columns of P. Then

$$P = \begin{bmatrix} \frac{\sqrt{2}}{2} & \frac{\sqrt{2}}{2} \\ -\frac{\sqrt{2}}{2} & \frac{\sqrt{2}}{2} \end{bmatrix}$$

and

$$P^T A P = \begin{bmatrix} \frac{\sqrt{2}}{2} & -\frac{\sqrt{2}}{2} \\ \frac{\sqrt{2}}{2} & \frac{\sqrt{2}}{2} \end{bmatrix} \begin{bmatrix} 1 & 1 \\ 1 & 1 \end{bmatrix} \begin{bmatrix} \frac{\sqrt{2}}{2} & \frac{\sqrt{2}}{2} \\ -\frac{\sqrt{2}}{2} & \frac{\sqrt{2}}{2} \end{bmatrix} = \begin{bmatrix} 0 & 0 \\ 0 & 2 \end{bmatrix}.$$

23. The eigenvalues of A are $\lambda_1 = 0$ and $\lambda_2 = 3$, with corresponding eigenvectors $\left(\frac{\sqrt{2}}{2}, -1\right)$ and $(\sqrt{2}, 1)$, respectively. We normalize each eigenvector to form the columns of P. Then

$$P = \begin{bmatrix} \frac{\sqrt{3}}{3} & \frac{\sqrt{6}}{3} \\ -\frac{\sqrt{6}}{3} & \frac{\sqrt{3}}{3} \end{bmatrix}$$

and

$$P^T A P = \begin{bmatrix} \frac{\sqrt{3}}{3} & -\frac{\sqrt{6}}{3} \\ \frac{\sqrt{6}}{3} & \frac{\sqrt{3}}{3} \end{bmatrix} \begin{bmatrix} 2 & \sqrt{2} \\ \sqrt{2} & 1 \end{bmatrix} \begin{bmatrix} \frac{\sqrt{3}}{3} & \frac{\sqrt{6}}{3} \\ -\frac{\sqrt{6}}{3} & \frac{\sqrt{3}}{3} \end{bmatrix} = \begin{bmatrix} 0 & 0 \\ 0 & 3 \end{bmatrix}.$$

25. The eigenvalues of A are $\lambda_1 = -15$ and $\lambda_2 = 0$, and $\lambda_3 = 15$, with corresponding eigenvectors $(-2, 1, 2)$, $(-1, 2, -2)$ and $(2, 2, 1)$, respectively. We normalize each eigenvector to form the columns of P. Then

$$P = \begin{bmatrix} -\frac{2}{3} & -\frac{1}{3} & \frac{2}{3} \\ \frac{1}{3} & \frac{2}{3} & \frac{2}{3} \\ \frac{2}{3} & -\frac{2}{3} & \frac{1}{3} \end{bmatrix}$$

and

$$P^T A P = \begin{bmatrix} -\frac{2}{3} & \frac{1}{3} & \frac{2}{3} \\ -\frac{1}{3} & \frac{2}{3} & -\frac{2}{3} \\ \frac{2}{3} & \frac{2}{3} & \frac{1}{3} \end{bmatrix} \begin{bmatrix} 0 & 10 & 10 \\ 10 & 5 & 0 \\ 10 & 0 & -5 \end{bmatrix} \begin{bmatrix} -\frac{2}{3} & -\frac{1}{3} & \frac{2}{3} \\ \frac{1}{3} & \frac{2}{3} & \frac{2}{3} \\ \frac{2}{3} & -\frac{2}{3} & \frac{1}{3} \end{bmatrix}$$

$$\begin{bmatrix} -15 & 0 & 0 \\ 0 & 0 & 0 \\ 0 & 0 & 15 \end{bmatrix}.$$

27. The eigenvalues of A are $\lambda_1 = 2$ and $\lambda_2 = 6$, with corresponding eigenvectors $(1, -1, 0, 0)$ and $(0, 0, 1, -1)$ for λ_1 and $(1, 1, 0, 0)$ and $(0, 0, 1, 1)$ for λ_2. We normalize each eigenvector to form the columns of P. Then

$$
P = \begin{bmatrix}
\frac{\sqrt{2}}{2} & 0 & \frac{\sqrt{2}}{2} & 0 \\
-\frac{\sqrt{2}}{2} & 0 & \frac{\sqrt{2}}{2} & 0 \\
0 & \frac{\sqrt{2}}{2} & 0 & \frac{\sqrt{2}}{2} \\
0 & -\frac{\sqrt{2}}{2} & 0 & \frac{\sqrt{2}}{2}
\end{bmatrix}
$$

and

$$
P^T A P = \begin{bmatrix}
\frac{\sqrt{2}}{2} & -\frac{\sqrt{2}}{2} & 0 & 0 \\
0 & 0 & \frac{\sqrt{2}}{2} & -\frac{\sqrt{2}}{2} \\
\frac{\sqrt{2}}{2} & \frac{\sqrt{2}}{2} & 0 & 0 \\
0 & 0 & \frac{\sqrt{2}}{2} & \frac{\sqrt{2}}{2}
\end{bmatrix}
\begin{bmatrix}
4 & 2 & 0 & 0 \\
2 & 4 & 0 & 0 \\
0 & 0 & 4 & 2 \\
0 & 0 & 2 & 4
\end{bmatrix}
\begin{bmatrix}
\frac{\sqrt{2}}{2} & 0 & \frac{\sqrt{2}}{2} & 0 \\
-\frac{\sqrt{2}}{2} & 0 & \frac{\sqrt{2}}{2} & 0 \\
0 & \frac{\sqrt{2}}{2} & 0 & \frac{\sqrt{2}}{2} \\
0 & -\frac{\sqrt{2}}{2} & 0 & \frac{\sqrt{2}}{2}
\end{bmatrix}
$$

$$
= \begin{bmatrix}
2 & 0 & 0 & 0 \\
0 & 2 & 0 & 0 \\
0 & 0 & 6 & 0 \\
0 & 0 & 0 & 6
\end{bmatrix}.
$$

29. $\left(A^T A\right)^T = A^T \left(A^T\right)^T = A^T A \implies A^T A$ is symmetric.

$\left(A A^T\right)^T = \left(A^T\right)^T A^T = A A^T \implies A A^T$ is symmetric.

31. If A is orthogonal, then $A A^T = I$. Hence,

$$
1 = |A A^T| = |A|\,|A^T| = |A|^2 \implies |A| = \pm 1.
$$

33. We observe that A is orthogonal since

$$
A^{-1} = \begin{bmatrix} \cos\theta & \sin\theta \\ -\sin\theta & \cos\theta \end{bmatrix} \frac{1}{\cos^2\theta + \sin^2\theta} = A^T.
$$

35. Let A be orthogonal, $A^{-1} = A^T$.

Then $\left(A^T\right)^{-1} = \left(A^{-1}\right)^{-1} = A = \left(A^T\right)^T \implies A^T$ is orthogonal. Furthermore,

$\left(A^{-1}\right)^{-1} = \left(A^T\right)^{-1} = \left(A^{-1}\right)^T \implies A^{-1}$ is orthogonal.

Section 7.4 Applications of Eigenvalues and Eigenvectors

1. $\mathbf{x}_2 = A\mathbf{x}_1 = \begin{bmatrix} 0 & 2 \\ \frac{1}{2} & 0 \end{bmatrix} \begin{bmatrix} 10 \\ 10 \end{bmatrix} = \begin{bmatrix} 20 \\ 5 \end{bmatrix}$

   $\mathbf{x}_3 = A\mathbf{x}_2 = \begin{bmatrix} 0 & 2 \\ \frac{1}{2} & 0 \end{bmatrix} \begin{bmatrix} 20 \\ 5 \end{bmatrix} = \begin{bmatrix} 10 \\ 10 \end{bmatrix}$

3. $\mathbf{x}_2 = A\mathbf{x}_1 = \begin{bmatrix} 0 & 3 & 4 \\ 1 & 0 & 0 \\ 0 & \frac{1}{2} & 0 \end{bmatrix} \begin{bmatrix} 12 \\ 12 \\ 12 \end{bmatrix} = \begin{bmatrix} 84 \\ 12 \\ 6 \end{bmatrix}$

   $\mathbf{x}_3 = A\mathbf{x}_2 = \begin{bmatrix} 0 & 3 & 4 \\ 1 & 0 & 0 \\ 0 & \frac{1}{2} & 0 \end{bmatrix} \begin{bmatrix} 84 \\ 12 \\ 6 \end{bmatrix} = \begin{bmatrix} 60 \\ 84 \\ 6 \end{bmatrix}$

5. The eigenvalues are 1 and -1. Choosing the positive eigenvalue, $\lambda = 1$, we find the corresponding eigenvector by row-reducing $\lambda I - A = I - A$.

   $$\begin{bmatrix} 1 & -2 \\ -\frac{1}{2} & 1 \end{bmatrix} \Rightarrow \begin{bmatrix} 1 & -2 \\ 0 & 0 \end{bmatrix}$$

   Thus, an eigenvector is (2, 1), and this represents a stable age distribution.

7. The eigenvalues of A are -1 and 2. Choosing the positive eigenvalue, we let $\lambda = 2$. An eigenvector corresponding to $\lambda = 2$ is found by row-reducing $2I - A$.

   $$\begin{bmatrix} 2 & -3 & -4 \\ -1 & 2 & 0 \\ 0 & -\frac{1}{2} & 2 \end{bmatrix} \Rightarrow \begin{bmatrix} 1 & 0 & -8 \\ 0 & 1 & -4 \\ 0 & 0 & 0 \end{bmatrix}$$

   Thus, an eigenvector is (8, 4, 1) and this represents a stable age distribution.

9. We use the information given above to construct the age transition matrix.

$$A = \begin{bmatrix} 2 & 4 & 2 \\ 0.75 & 0 & 0 \\ 0 & 0.25 & 0 \end{bmatrix}$$

The current age distribution vector is

$$\mathbf{x}_1 = \begin{bmatrix} 120 \\ 120 \\ 120 \end{bmatrix}.$$

In one year the age distribution vector will be

$$\mathbf{x}_2 = A\mathbf{x}_1 = \begin{bmatrix} 2 & 4 & 2 \\ 0.75 & 0 & 0 \\ 0 & 0.25 & 0 \end{bmatrix} \begin{bmatrix} 120 \\ 120 \\ 120 \end{bmatrix} = \begin{bmatrix} 960 \\ 90 \\ 30 \end{bmatrix}.$$

In two years the age distribution vector will be

$$\mathbf{x}_3 = A\mathbf{x}_2 = \begin{bmatrix} 2 & 4 & 2 \\ 0.75 & 0 & 0 \\ 0 & 0.25 & 0 \end{bmatrix} \begin{bmatrix} 960 \\ 90 \\ 30 \end{bmatrix} = \begin{bmatrix} 2340 \\ 720 \\ 22.5 \end{bmatrix}.$$

11. The solution to the differential equation $y' = ky$ is $y = Ce^{kt}$. Thus, $y_1 = C_1 e^{2t}$ and $y_2 = C_2 e^{t}$.

13. The solution to the differential equation $y' = ky$ is $y = Ce^{kt}$. Thus, $y_1 = C_1 e^{-t}$, $y_2 = C_2 e^{6t}$ and and $y_3 = C_3 e^{t}$.

15. This system has the matrix form

$$y' = \begin{bmatrix} y'_1 \\ y'_2 \end{bmatrix} = \begin{bmatrix} 1 & -4 \\ 0 & 2 \end{bmatrix} \begin{bmatrix} y_1 \\ y_2 \end{bmatrix} = A\mathbf{y}.$$

The eigenvalues of A are $\lambda_1 = 1$ and $\lambda_2 = 2$, with corresponding eigenvectors $(1, 0)$ and $(-4, 1)$, respectively. Thus, we may diagonalize A using a matrix P whose columns are the eigenvectors of A.

$$P = \begin{bmatrix} 1 & -4 \\ 0 & 1 \end{bmatrix} \quad \text{and} \quad P^{-1}AP = \begin{bmatrix} 1 & 0 \\ 0 & 2 \end{bmatrix}$$

The solution of the system $\mathbf{w}' = P^{-1}AP\mathbf{w}$ is $w_1 = C_1 e^{t}$ and $w_2 = C_2 e^{2t}$. We return to the original system by applying the substitution $\mathbf{y} = P\mathbf{w}$.

$$\mathbf{y} = \begin{bmatrix} y_1 \\ y_2 \end{bmatrix} = \begin{bmatrix} 1 & -4 \\ 0 & 1 \end{bmatrix} \begin{bmatrix} w_1 \\ w_2 \end{bmatrix} = \begin{bmatrix} w_1 - 4w_2 \\ w_2 \end{bmatrix}.$$

Thus, the solution is

$$y_1 = C_1 e^{t} - 4C_2 e^{2t}$$

$$y_2 = C_2 e^{2t}.$$

17. This system has the matrix form

$$y' = \begin{bmatrix} y_1' \\ y_2' \end{bmatrix} = \begin{bmatrix} 1 & 2 \\ 2 & 1 \end{bmatrix} \begin{bmatrix} y_1 \\ y_2 \end{bmatrix} = A\mathbf{y}.$$

The eigenvalues of A are $\lambda_1 = -1$ and $\lambda_2 = 3$ with corresponding eigenvectors $\mathbf{x}_1 = (1, -1)$ and $\mathbf{x}_2 = (1, 1)$, respectively. Thus, we may diagonalize A using a matrix P whose column vectors are the eigenvectors of A.

$$P = \begin{bmatrix} 1 & 1 \\ -1 & 1 \end{bmatrix} \quad \text{and} \quad P^{-1}AP = \begin{bmatrix} -1 & 0 \\ 0 & 3 \end{bmatrix}$$

The solution of the system $\mathbf{w}' = P^{-1}AP\mathbf{w}$ is $w_1 = C_1e^{-t}$ and $w_2 = C_2e^{3t}$. We return to the original system by applying the substitution $\mathbf{y} = P\mathbf{w}$.

$$\mathbf{y} = \begin{bmatrix} y_1 \\ y_2 \end{bmatrix} = \begin{bmatrix} 1 & 1 \\ -1 & 1 \end{bmatrix} \begin{bmatrix} w_1 \\ w_2 \end{bmatrix} = \begin{bmatrix} w_1 + w_2 \\ -w_1 + w_2 \end{bmatrix}$$

Thus, the solution is

$$y_1 = C_1e^{-t} + C_2e^{3t}$$

$$y_2 = -C_1e^{-t} + C_2e^{3t}.$$

19. This system has the matrix form

$$y' = \begin{bmatrix} y_1' \\ y_2' \\ y_3' \end{bmatrix} = \begin{bmatrix} 0 & -3 & 5 \\ -4 & 4 & -10 \\ 0 & 0 & 4 \end{bmatrix} \begin{bmatrix} y_1 \\ y_2 \\ y_3 \end{bmatrix} = A\mathbf{y}.$$

The eigenvalues of A are $\lambda_1 = -2$, $\lambda_2 = 6$ and $\lambda_3 = 4$, with corresponding eigenvectors $(3, 2, 0)$, $(-1, 2, 0)$ and $(-5, 10, 2)$, respectively. Thus, we may diagonalize A using a matrix P whose column vectors are the eigenvectors of A.

$$P = \begin{bmatrix} 3 & -1 & -5 \\ 2 & 2 & 10 \\ 0 & 0 & 2 \end{bmatrix} \quad \text{and} \quad P^{-1}AP = \begin{bmatrix} -2 & 0 & 0 \\ 0 & 6 & 0 \\ 0 & 0 & 4 \end{bmatrix}$$

The solution of the system $\mathbf{w}' = P^{-1}AP\mathbf{w}$ is $w_1 = C_1e^{-2t}$, $w_2 = C_2e^{6t}$ and $w_3 = C_3e^{4t}$. We return to the original system by applying the substitution $\mathbf{y} = P\mathbf{w}$.

$$\mathbf{y} = \begin{bmatrix} y_1 \\ y_2 \\ y_3 \end{bmatrix} = \begin{bmatrix} 3 & -1 & -5 \\ 2 & 2 & 10 \\ 0 & 0 & 2 \end{bmatrix} \begin{bmatrix} w_1 \\ w_2 \\ w_3 \end{bmatrix} = \begin{bmatrix} 3w_1 - w_2 - 5w_3 \\ 2w_1 + 2w_2 + 10w_3 \\ 2w_3 \end{bmatrix}$$

Thus, the solution is

$$y_1 = 3C_1e^{-2t} - C_2e^{6t} - 5C_3e^{4t}$$

$$y_2 = 2C_1e^{-2t} + 2C_2e^{6t} + 10C_3e^{4t}$$

$$y_3 = 2C_3e^{4t}.$$

21. This system has the matrix form

$$y' = \begin{bmatrix} y'_1 \\ y'_2 \\ y'_3 \end{bmatrix} = \begin{bmatrix} 1 & -2 & 1 \\ 0 & 2 & 4 \\ 0 & 0 & 3 \end{bmatrix} \begin{bmatrix} y_1 \\ y_2 \\ y_3 \end{bmatrix} = A\mathbf{y}.$$

The eigenvalues of A are $\lambda_1 = 1$, $\lambda_2 = 2$, and $\lambda_3 = 3$ with corresponding eigenvectors
$\mathbf{x}_1 = (1, 0, 0)$, $\mathbf{x}_2 = (-2, 1, 0)$, and $\mathbf{x}_3 = (-7, 8, 2)$. Thus, we may diagonalize A using
a matrix P whose column vectors are the eigenvectors of A.

$$P = \begin{bmatrix} 1 & -2 & -7 \\ 0 & 1 & 8 \\ 0 & 0 & 2 \end{bmatrix} \quad \text{and} \quad P^{-1}AP = \begin{bmatrix} 1 & 0 & 0 \\ 0 & 2 & 0 \\ 0 & 0 & 3 \end{bmatrix}$$

The solution of the system $\mathbf{w}' = P^{-1}AP\mathbf{w}$ is $w_1 = C_1 e^t$, $w_2 = C_2 e^{2t}$, and $w_3 = C_3 e^{3t}$.
We return to the original system by applying the substitution $\mathbf{y} = P\mathbf{w}$.

$$\mathbf{y} = \begin{bmatrix} y_1 \\ y_2 \\ y_3 \end{bmatrix} = \begin{bmatrix} 1 & -2 & -7 \\ 0 & 1 & 8 \\ 0 & 0 & 2 \end{bmatrix} \begin{bmatrix} w_1 \\ w_2 \\ w_3 \end{bmatrix} = \begin{bmatrix} w_1 - 2w_2 - 7w_3 \\ w_2 + 8w_3 \\ 2w_3 \end{bmatrix}$$

Thus, the solution is

$$y_1 = C_1 e^t - 2C_2 e^{2t} - 7C_3 e^{3t}$$

$$y_2 = \qquad\qquad C_2 e^{2t} + 8C_3 e^{3t}$$

$$y_3 = \qquad\qquad\qquad\qquad 2C_3 e^{3t}.$$

23. Since

$$y' = \begin{bmatrix} y'_1 \\ y'_2 \end{bmatrix} = \begin{bmatrix} 1 & 1 \\ 0 & 1 \end{bmatrix} \begin{bmatrix} y_1 \\ y_2 \end{bmatrix} = A\mathbf{y}$$

the system represented by $y' = A\mathbf{y}$ is

$$y'_1 = y_1 + y_2$$

$$y'_2 = \qquad y_2.$$

Note that

$$y'_1 = C_1 e^t + C_2 t e^t + C_2 e^t = y_1 + y_2$$

and

$$y'_2 = C_2 e^t = y_2.$$

25. Since

$$y' = \begin{bmatrix} y'_1 \\ y'_2 \\ y'_3 \end{bmatrix} = \begin{bmatrix} 0 & 1 & 0 \\ 0 & 0 & 1 \\ 0 & -4 & 0 \end{bmatrix} \begin{bmatrix} y_1 \\ y_2 \\ y_3 \end{bmatrix} = A\mathbf{y}$$

the system represented by $y' = A\mathbf{y}$ is

$$y'_1 = \quad y_2$$
$$y'_2 = \qquad y_3$$
$$y'_3 = -4y_2$$

Note that

$$y'_1 = -2C_2 \sin 2t + 2C_3 \cos 2t = y_2$$
$$y'_2 = -4C_3 \sin 2t - 4C_2 \cos 2t = y_3$$
$$y'_3 = \quad 8C_2 \sin 2t - 8C_3 \cos 2t = -4y_2.$$

27. The matrix of the quadratic form is

$$A = \begin{bmatrix} a & b/2 \\ b/2 & c \end{bmatrix} = \begin{bmatrix} 1 & 0 \\ 0 & 1 \end{bmatrix}.$$

29. The matrix of the quadratic form is

$$A = \begin{bmatrix} a & b/2 \\ b/2 & c \end{bmatrix} = \begin{bmatrix} 9 & 5 \\ 5 & -4 \end{bmatrix}.$$

31. The matrix of the quadratic form is

$$A = \begin{bmatrix} a & b/2 \\ b/2 & c \end{bmatrix} = \begin{bmatrix} 0 & 5 \\ 5 & -10 \end{bmatrix}.$$

33. The matrix of the quadratic form is

$$A = \begin{bmatrix} a & b/2 \\ b/2 & c \end{bmatrix} = \begin{bmatrix} 2 & -\frac{3}{2} \\ -\frac{3}{2} & -2 \end{bmatrix}.$$

The eigenvalues of A are $\lambda_1 = -\frac{5}{2}$ and $\lambda_2 = \frac{5}{2}$ with corresponding eigenvectors $\mathbf{x}_1 = (1, 3)$ and $\mathbf{x}_2 = (-3, 1)$ respectively. Using unit vectors in the direction of $\mathbf{x}_1$ and $\mathbf{x}_2$ to form the columns of P yields

$$P = \begin{bmatrix} \frac{1}{\sqrt{10}} & -\frac{3}{\sqrt{10}} \\ \frac{3}{\sqrt{10}} & \frac{1}{\sqrt{10}} \end{bmatrix}.$$

Note that

$$P^T A P = \begin{bmatrix} \frac{1}{\sqrt{10}} & \frac{3}{\sqrt{10}} \\ -\frac{3}{\sqrt{10}} & \frac{1}{\sqrt{10}} \end{bmatrix} \begin{bmatrix} 2 & -\frac{3}{2} \\ -\frac{3}{2} & -2 \end{bmatrix} \begin{bmatrix} \frac{1}{\sqrt{10}} & -\frac{3}{\sqrt{10}} \\ \frac{3}{\sqrt{10}} & \frac{1}{\sqrt{10}} \end{bmatrix} = \begin{bmatrix} -\frac{5}{2} & 0 \\ 0 & \frac{5}{2} \end{bmatrix}.$$

35. The matrix of the quadratic form is

$$A = \begin{bmatrix} a & b/2 \\ b/2 & c \end{bmatrix} = \begin{bmatrix} 13 & 3\sqrt{3} \\ 3\sqrt{3} & 7 \end{bmatrix}.$$

The eigenvalues of A are $\lambda_1 = 4$ and $\lambda_2 = 16$, with corresponding eigenvectors $\mathbf{x}_1 = (1, -\sqrt{3})$ and $\mathbf{x}_2 = (\sqrt{3}, 1)$, respectively. Using unit vectors in the direction of $\mathbf{x}_1$ and $\mathbf{x}_2$ to form the columns of P, we have

$$P = \begin{bmatrix} \frac{1}{2} & \frac{\sqrt{3}}{2} \\ -\frac{\sqrt{3}}{2} & \frac{1}{2} \end{bmatrix} \quad \text{and} \quad P^T A P = \begin{bmatrix} 4 & 0 \\ 0 & 16 \end{bmatrix}.$$

37. The matrix of the quadratic form is

$$A = \begin{bmatrix} a & b/2 \\ b/2 & c \end{bmatrix} = \begin{bmatrix} 16 & -12 \\ -12 & 9 \end{bmatrix}.$$

The eigenvalues of A are $\lambda_1 = 0$ and $\lambda_2 = 25$, with corresponding eigenvectors $\mathbf{x}_1 = (3, 4)$ and $\mathbf{x}_2 = (-4, 3)$, respectively. Using unit vectors in the direction of $\mathbf{x}_1$ and $\mathbf{x}_2$ to form the columns of P, we have

$$P = \begin{bmatrix} \frac{3}{5} & -\frac{4}{5} \\ \frac{4}{5} & \frac{3}{5} \end{bmatrix} \quad \text{and} \quad P^T A P = \begin{bmatrix} 0 & 0 \\ 0 & 25 \end{bmatrix}.$$

39. The matrix of the quadratic form is

$$A = \begin{bmatrix} a & b/2 \\ b/2 & c \end{bmatrix} = \begin{bmatrix} 13 & -4 \\ -4 & 7 \end{bmatrix}.$$

This matrix has eigenvalues of 5 and 15 with corresponding unit eigenvectors $\left(\frac{1}{\sqrt{5}}, \frac{2}{\sqrt{5}}\right)$ and $\left(-\frac{2}{\sqrt{5}}, \frac{1}{\sqrt{5}}\right)$, respectively. Thus, we let

$$P = \begin{bmatrix} \frac{1}{\sqrt{5}} & -\frac{2}{\sqrt{5}} \\ \frac{2}{\sqrt{5}} & \frac{1}{\sqrt{5}} \end{bmatrix} \quad \text{and} \quad P^T A P = \begin{bmatrix} 5 & 0 \\ 0 & 15 \end{bmatrix}.$$

This implies that the rotated conic is an ellipse with equation

$$5(x')^2 + 15(y')^2 = 45.$$

41. The matrix of the quadratic form is

$$A = \begin{bmatrix} a & b/2 \\ b/2 & c \end{bmatrix} = \begin{bmatrix} 7 & 16 \\ 16 & -17 \end{bmatrix}.$$

This matrix has eigenvalues of -25 and 15, with corresponding unit eigenvectors $\left(1/\sqrt{5}, -2/\sqrt{5}\right)$ and $\left(2/\sqrt{5}, 1/\sqrt{5}\right)$ respectively. Thus, we let

$$P = \begin{bmatrix} \frac{1}{\sqrt{5}} & \frac{2}{\sqrt{5}} \\ -\frac{2}{\sqrt{5}} & \frac{1}{\sqrt{5}} \end{bmatrix} \quad \text{and} \quad P^T A P = \begin{bmatrix} -25 & 0 \\ 0 & 15 \end{bmatrix}.$$

This implies that the rotated conic is a hyperbola with equation

$$-25(x')^2 + 15(y')^2 - 50 = 0.$$

43. The matrix of the quadratic form is

$$A = \begin{bmatrix} a & b/2 \\ b/2 & c \end{bmatrix} = \begin{bmatrix} 2 & 2 \\ 2 & 2 \end{bmatrix}.$$

The matrix has eigenvalues 0 and 4, with corresponding unit eigenvectors $(1/\sqrt{2}, -1/\sqrt{2})$ and $(1/\sqrt{2}, 1/\sqrt{2})$ respectively. Thus, we let

$$P = \begin{bmatrix} \frac{1}{\sqrt{2}} & \frac{1}{\sqrt{2}} \\ -\frac{1}{\sqrt{2}} & \frac{1}{\sqrt{2}} \end{bmatrix} \quad \text{and} \quad P^T A P = \begin{bmatrix} 0 & 0 \\ 0 & 4 \end{bmatrix}.$$

This implies that the rotated conic is a parabola. Furthermore,

$$[\, d \quad e \,] P = [\, 6\sqrt{2} \quad 2\sqrt{2} \,] \begin{bmatrix} \frac{1}{\sqrt{2}} & \frac{1}{\sqrt{2}} \\ -\frac{1}{\sqrt{2}} & \frac{1}{\sqrt{2}} \end{bmatrix} = [\, 4 \quad 8 \,] = [\, d' \quad e' \,].$$

So, the equation in the $x'y'$-coordinate system is

$$4(y')^2 + 4x' + 8y' + 4 = 0.$$

45. The matrix of the quadratic form is

$$A = \begin{bmatrix} 0 & \frac{1}{2} \\ \frac{1}{2} & 0 \end{bmatrix}.$$

This matrix has eigenvalues of $-\frac{1}{2}$ and $\frac{1}{2}$ with corresponding unit eigenvectors $\left(-\frac{1}{\sqrt{2}}, \frac{1}{\sqrt{2}}\right)$ and $\left(\frac{1}{\sqrt{2}}, \frac{1}{\sqrt{2}}\right)$ respectively. Thus, we let

$$P = \begin{bmatrix} -\frac{1}{\sqrt{2}} & \frac{1}{\sqrt{2}} \\ \frac{1}{\sqrt{2}} & \frac{1}{\sqrt{2}} \end{bmatrix} \quad \text{and} \quad P^T A P = \begin{bmatrix} -\frac{1}{2} & 0 \\ 0 & \frac{1}{2} \end{bmatrix}.$$

This implies that the rotated conic is a hyperbola. Furthermore,

$$[\, d \quad e \,] P = [\, 1 \quad -2 \,] \begin{bmatrix} -\frac{1}{\sqrt{2}} & \frac{1}{\sqrt{2}} \\ \frac{1}{\sqrt{2}} & \frac{1}{\sqrt{2}} \end{bmatrix} = [\, -\frac{3}{\sqrt{2}} \quad -\frac{1}{\sqrt{2}} \,] = [\, d' \quad e' \,],$$

so the equation in the $x'y'$-coordinate system is

$$-\tfrac{1}{2}(x')^2 + \tfrac{1}{2}(y')^2 - \tfrac{3}{\sqrt{2}}x' - \tfrac{1}{\sqrt{2}}y' + 3 = 0.$$

47. The matrix of the quadratic form is

$$A = \begin{bmatrix} 3 & -1 & 0 \\ -1 & 3 & 0 \\ 0 & 0 & 8 \end{bmatrix}.$$

The eigenvalues of A are 2, 4, and 8 with corresponding unit eigenvectors
$\left(\frac{1}{\sqrt{2}}, \frac{1}{\sqrt{2}}, 0\right)$, $\left(-\frac{1}{\sqrt{2}}, \frac{1}{\sqrt{2}}, 0\right)$, and $(0, 0, 1)$ respectively.

Then we let

$$P = \begin{bmatrix} \frac{1}{\sqrt{2}} & -\frac{1}{\sqrt{2}} & 0 \\ \frac{1}{\sqrt{2}} & \frac{1}{\sqrt{2}} & 0 \\ 0 & 0 & 1 \end{bmatrix} \quad \text{and} \quad P^T A P = \begin{bmatrix} 2 & 0 & 0 \\ 0 & 4 & 0 \\ 0 & 0 & 8 \end{bmatrix}.$$

Furthermore,

$$[g \ h \ i] P = [0 \ 0 \ 0] \begin{bmatrix} \frac{1}{\sqrt{2}} & -\frac{1}{\sqrt{2}} & 0 \\ \frac{1}{\sqrt{2}} & \frac{1}{\sqrt{2}} & 0 \\ 0 & 0 & 1 \end{bmatrix} = [0 \ 0 \ 0] = [g' \ h' \ i'].$$

Thus, the equation of the rotated quadratic surface is

$$2(x')^2 + 4(y')^2 + 8(z')^2 - 16 = 0.$$

49. Let $P = \begin{bmatrix} a & b \\ c & d \end{bmatrix}$ be a 2×2 orthogonal matrix such that $|P| = 1$. We define $\theta \in (0, 2\pi)$
as follows.

(i)   If $a = 1$, then $c = 0$, $b = 0$ and $d = 1$, so let $\theta = 0$.

(ii) If $a = -1$, then $c = 0$, $b = 0$ and $d = -1$, so let $\theta = \pi$.

(iii) If $a \geq 0$ *and* $c > 0$, let $\theta = \arccos(a)$, $0 < \theta \leq \pi/2$.

(iv) If $a \geq 0$ *and* $c < 0$, let $\theta = 2\pi - \arccos(a)$, $3\pi/2 \leq \theta < 2\pi$.

(v)   If $a \leq 0$ *and* $c > 0$, let $\theta = \arccos(a)$, $\pi/2 \leq \theta < \pi$.

(vi) If $a \leq 0$ *and* $c < 0$, let $\theta = 2\pi - \arccos(a)$, $\pi < \theta \leq 3\pi/2$.

In each of these cases, we can check that

$$P = \begin{bmatrix} a & b \\ c & d \end{bmatrix} = \begin{bmatrix} \cos \theta & -\sin \theta \\ \sin \theta & \cos \theta \end{bmatrix}.$$

Chapter 7   Review Exercises

1. (a) The characteristic equation of A is given by

$$|\lambda I - A| = \begin{vmatrix} \lambda - 2 & -1 \\ -5 & \lambda + 2 \end{vmatrix} = \lambda^2 - 9 = 0.$$

   (b) The eigenvalues of A are $\lambda_1 = -3$ and $\lambda_2 = 3$.

   (c) To find the eigenvectors corresponding to $\lambda_1 = -3$, we solve the matrix equation $(\lambda_1 I - A)\mathbf{x} = \mathbf{0}$. We row-reduce the augmented matrix to yield

$$\begin{bmatrix} -5 & -1 & \vdots & 0 \\ -5 & -1 & \vdots & 0 \end{bmatrix} \Rightarrow \begin{bmatrix} 1 & \frac{1}{5} & \vdots & 0 \\ 0 & 0 & \vdots & 0 \end{bmatrix}.$$

   Thus, $\mathbf{x}_1 = (1, -5)$ is an eigenvector and $\{(1, -5)\}$ is a basis for the eigenspace corresponding to $\lambda_1 = -3$. Similarly, we solve $(\lambda_2 I - A)\mathbf{x} = \mathbf{0}$ for $\lambda_2 = 3$. Thus, $\mathbf{x}_2 = (1, 1)$ is an eigenvector and $\{(1, 1)\}$ is a basis for the eigenspace corresponding to $\lambda_2 = 3$.

3. (a) The characteristic equation of A is given by

$$|\lambda I - A| = \begin{vmatrix} \lambda - 9 & -4 & 3 \\ 2 & \lambda & -6 \\ 1 & 4 & \lambda - 11 \end{vmatrix} = \lambda^3 - 20\lambda^2 + 128\lambda - 256 = (\lambda - 4)(\lambda - 8)^2.$$

   (b) The eigenvalues of A are $\lambda_1 = 4$ and $\lambda_2 = 8$ (repeated).

   (c) To find the eigenvector corresponding to $\lambda_1 = 4$, we solve the matrix equation $(\lambda_1 I - A)\mathbf{x} = \mathbf{0}$. Row-reducing the augmented matrix,

$$\begin{bmatrix} -5 & -4 & 3 & \vdots & 0 \\ 2 & 4 & -6 & \vdots & 0 \\ 1 & 4 & -7 & \vdots & 0 \end{bmatrix} \Rightarrow \begin{bmatrix} 1 & 0 & 1 & \vdots & 0 \\ 0 & 1 & -2 & \vdots & 0 \\ 0 & 0 & 0 & \vdots & 0 \end{bmatrix}$$

   we see that a basis for the eigenspace of $\lambda_1 = 4$ is $\{(-1, 2, 1)\}$.
   Similarly, we solve $(\lambda_2 I - A)\mathbf{x} = \mathbf{0}$ for $\lambda_2 = 8$. Thus, a basis for the eigenspace of $\lambda_2 = 8$ is $\{(3, 0, 1), (-4, 1, 0)\}$.

5. (a) The characteristic equation of A is given by

$$|\lambda I - A| = \begin{vmatrix} \lambda - 2 & 0 & -1 \\ 0 & \lambda - 3 & -4 \\ 0 & 0 & \lambda - 1 \end{vmatrix} = (\lambda - 2)(\lambda - 3)(\lambda - 1) = 0.$$

(b) The eigenvalues of A are $\lambda_1 = 1$, $\lambda_2 = 2$ and $\lambda_3 = 3$.

(c) To find the eigenvector corresponding to $\lambda_1 = 1$, we solve the matrix equation $(\lambda_1 I - A)\mathbf{x} = \mathbf{0}$. Row-reducing the augmented matrix,

$$\begin{bmatrix} -1 & 0 & -1 & \vdots & 0 \\ 0 & -2 & -4 & \vdots & 0 \\ 0 & 0 & 0 & \vdots & 0 \end{bmatrix} \Rightarrow \begin{bmatrix} 1 & 0 & 1 & \vdots & 0 \\ 0 & 1 & 2 & \vdots & 0 \\ 0 & 0 & 0 & \vdots & 0 \end{bmatrix}$$

we see that a basis for the eigenspace of $\lambda_1 = 1$ is $\{(-1, -2, 1)\}$.

Similarly, we solve $(\lambda_2 I - A)\mathbf{x} = \mathbf{0}$ for $\lambda_2 = 2$, and see that $\{(1, 0, 0)\}$ is a basis for the eigenspace of $\lambda_2 = 2$. Finally, we solve $(\lambda_3 I - A)\mathbf{x} = \mathbf{0}$ for $\lambda_3 = 3$, and discover that $\{(0, 1, 0)\}$ is a basis for its eigenspace.

7. The eigenvalues of A are the solutions of

$$|\lambda I - A| = \begin{vmatrix} \lambda + 2 & 1 & -3 \\ 0 & \lambda - 1 & -2 \\ 0 & 0 & \lambda - 1 \end{vmatrix} = (\lambda + 2)(\lambda - 1)^2 = 0.$$

The eigenspace corresponding to the repeated eigenvalue $\lambda = 1$ has dimension 1, and hence, A is *not* diagonalizable.

9. The eigenvalues of A are the solutions to

$$|\lambda I - A| = \begin{vmatrix} \lambda - 1 & 0 & -2 \\ 0 & \lambda - 1 & 0 \\ -2 & 0 & \lambda - 1 \end{vmatrix} = (\lambda - 3)(\lambda - 1)(\lambda + 1) = 0.$$

Therefore, the eigenvalues are 3, 1, and -1. The corresponding eigenvectors are the solutions of $(\lambda I - A)\mathbf{x} = \mathbf{0}$. Thus, an eigenvector corresponding to 3 is $(1, 0, 1)$, an eigenvector corresponding to 1 is $(0, 1, 0)$, and eigenvector corresponding to -1 is $(1, 0, -1)$. We now form P using the eigenvectors of A as column vectors.

$$P = \begin{bmatrix} 1 & 0 & 1 \\ 0 & 1 & 0 \\ 1 & 0 & -1 \end{bmatrix}$$

Note that

$$P^{-1}AP = \begin{bmatrix} \frac{1}{2} & 0 & \frac{1}{2} \\ 0 & 1 & 0 \\ \frac{1}{2} & 0 & -\frac{1}{2} \end{bmatrix} \begin{bmatrix} 1 & 0 & 2 \\ 0 & 1 & 0 \\ 2 & 0 & 1 \end{bmatrix} \begin{bmatrix} 1 & 0 & 1 \\ 0 & 1 & 0 \\ 1 & 0 & -1 \end{bmatrix} = \begin{bmatrix} 3 & 0 & 0 \\ 0 & 1 & 0 \\ 0 & 0 & -1 \end{bmatrix}.$$

11. Consider the characteristic equation

$$|\lambda I - A| = \begin{vmatrix} \lambda - \cos\theta & \sin\theta \\ -\sin\theta & \lambda - \cos\theta \end{vmatrix} = \lambda^2 - 2\cos\theta \cdot \lambda + 1 = 0.$$

The discriminant of this quadratic equation in λ is

$$b^2 - 4ac = 4\cos^2\theta - 4 = -4\sin^2\theta.$$

Since $0 < \theta < \pi$, this discriminant is always negative, and the characteristic equation has no real roots.

13. The eigenvalue is $\lambda = 3$ (repeated). To find its corresponding eigenspace, we solve $(\lambda I - A)\mathbf{x} = \mathbf{0}$ with $\lambda = 3$.

$$\begin{bmatrix} \lambda - 3 & 0 & 0 & \vdots & 0 \\ -1 & \lambda - 3 & 0 & \vdots & 0 \\ 0 & 0 & \lambda - 3 & \vdots & 0 \end{bmatrix} = \begin{bmatrix} 0 & 0 & 0 & \vdots & 0 \\ -1 & 0 & 0 & \vdots & 0 \\ 0 & 0 & 0 & \vdots & 0 \end{bmatrix} \Rightarrow \begin{bmatrix} 1 & 0 & 0 & \vdots & 0 \\ 0 & 0 & 0 & \vdots & 0 \\ 0 & 0 & 0 & \vdots & 0 \end{bmatrix}$$

Since the eigenspace is only two-dimensional, the matrix A is not diagonalizable.

15. The eigenvalues of B are 1 and 2 with corresponding eigenvectors $(0, 1)$ and $(1, 0)$, respectively. We form the columns of P from the eigenvectors of B. Thus,

$$P = \begin{bmatrix} 0 & 1 \\ 1 & 0 \end{bmatrix}$$

$$P^{-1}BP = \begin{bmatrix} 0 & 1 \\ 1 & 0 \end{bmatrix} \begin{bmatrix} 2 & 0 \\ 0 & 1 \end{bmatrix} \begin{bmatrix} 0 & 1 \\ 1 & 0 \end{bmatrix} = \begin{bmatrix} 1 & 0 \\ 0 & 2 \end{bmatrix} = A.$$

Therefore, A and B are similar.

17. Since

$$A^T = \begin{bmatrix} -\frac{\sqrt{2}}{2} & \frac{\sqrt{2}}{2} \\ \frac{\sqrt{2}}{2} & \frac{\sqrt{2}}{2} \end{bmatrix} = A,$$

A is symmetric. Furthermore, the column vectors of A form an orthonormal set. Thus, A is both symmetric and orthogonal.

19. Since

$$A^T = \begin{bmatrix} 0 & 0 & 1 \\ 0 & 1 & 0 \\ 1 & 0 & 1 \end{bmatrix} = A,$$

A is symmetric. However, column 3 is not a unit vector, so A is *not* orthogonal.

21. The eigenvalues of A are 5 and -5 with corresponding unit eigenvectors $\left(\frac{2}{\sqrt{5}}, \frac{1}{\sqrt{5}}\right)$ and $\left(-\frac{1}{\sqrt{5}}, \frac{2}{\sqrt{5}}\right)$, respectively. We form the columns of P with the eigenvectors of A. Thus,

$$P = \begin{bmatrix} \frac{2}{\sqrt{5}} & -\frac{1}{\sqrt{5}} \\ \frac{1}{\sqrt{5}} & \frac{2}{\sqrt{5}} \end{bmatrix}.$$

23. The eigenvalues of A are 3 and 1 (repeated), with corresponding unit eigenvectors $\left(\frac{1}{\sqrt{2}}, 0, -\frac{1}{\sqrt{2}}\right)$, $\left(\frac{1}{\sqrt{2}}, 0, \frac{1}{\sqrt{2}}\right)$ and $(0, 1, 0)$. We form the columns of P from the eigenvectors of A_i

$$P = \begin{bmatrix} \frac{1}{\sqrt{2}} & \frac{1}{\sqrt{2}} & 0 \\ 0 & 0 & 1 \\ -\frac{1}{\sqrt{2}} & \frac{1}{\sqrt{2}} & 0 \end{bmatrix}.$$

25. The eigenvalues of A are $\frac{1}{6}$ and 1. The eigenvectors corresponding to $\lambda = 1$ are $\mathbf{x} = t(3, 2)$.

By choosing $t = \frac{1}{5}$, we find the steady state probability vector for A to be $\mathbf{v} = \frac{1}{5}(3, 2) = \left(\frac{3}{5}, \frac{2}{5}\right)$.
Note that

$$A\mathbf{v} = \begin{bmatrix} \frac{2}{3} & \frac{1}{2} \\ \frac{1}{3} & \frac{1}{2} \end{bmatrix} \begin{bmatrix} \frac{3}{5} \\ \frac{2}{5} \end{bmatrix} = \begin{bmatrix} \frac{3}{5} \\ \frac{2}{5} \end{bmatrix} = \mathbf{v}.$$

27. The eigenvalues of A are $0, \frac{1}{2}$ and 1. The eigenvectors corresponding to $\lambda = 1$ are $\mathbf{x} = t(1, 2, 1)$.

By choosing $t = \frac{1}{4}$, we find the steady state probability vector for A to be $\mathbf{v} = \left(\frac{1}{4}, \frac{1}{2}, \frac{1}{4}\right)$.
Note that

$$A\mathbf{v} = \begin{bmatrix} \frac{1}{2} & \frac{1}{4} & 0 \\ \frac{1}{2} & \frac{1}{2} & \frac{1}{2} \\ 0 & \frac{1}{4} & \frac{1}{2} \end{bmatrix} \begin{bmatrix} \frac{1}{4} \\ \frac{1}{2} \\ \frac{1}{4} \end{bmatrix} = \begin{bmatrix} \frac{1}{4} \\ \frac{1}{2} \\ \frac{1}{4} \end{bmatrix} = \mathbf{v}.$$

29. The eigenvalues of A are 0.6 and 1. The eigenvectors corresponding to $\lambda = 1$ are $\mathbf{x} = t(4, 5, 7)$. By choosing $t = \frac{1}{16}$, we find the steady state probability vector for A to be

$$\mathbf{v} = \tfrac{1}{16}(4, 5, 7) = \left(\tfrac{1}{4}, \tfrac{5}{16}, \tfrac{7}{16}\right).$$

Note that

$$A\mathbf{v} = \begin{bmatrix} 0.7 & 0.1 & 0.1 \\ 0.2 & 0.7 & 0.1 \\ 0.1 & 0.2 & 0.8 \end{bmatrix} \begin{bmatrix} 0.25 \\ 0.3125 \\ 0.4375 \end{bmatrix} = \begin{bmatrix} 0.25 \\ 0.3125 \\ 0.4375 \end{bmatrix} = \mathbf{v}.$$

31. $(P^T A P)^T = P^T A^T (P^T)^T = P^T A P$ (since A is symmetric), which shows that $P^T A P$ is symmetric.

33. From the form $p(\lambda) = a_0 + a_1\lambda + a_2\lambda^2$, we have $a_0 = 0$, $a_1 = -9$, and $a_2 = 4$. This implies that the companion matrix of p is

$$A = \begin{bmatrix} 0 & 1 \\ -a_0/a_2 & -a_1/a_2 \end{bmatrix} = \begin{bmatrix} 0 & 1 \\ 0 & 9/4 \end{bmatrix}.$$

The eigenvalues of A are 0 and $9/4$, the zeros of p.

35. $A^2 = 10A - 24I_2 = \begin{bmatrix} 80 & -40 \\ 20 & 20 \end{bmatrix} - \begin{bmatrix} 24 & 0 \\ 0 & 24 \end{bmatrix} = \begin{bmatrix} 56 & -40 \\ 20 & -4 \end{bmatrix}$

$A^3 = 10A^2 - 24A = \begin{bmatrix} 560 & -400 \\ 200 & -40 \end{bmatrix} - \begin{bmatrix} 192 & -96 \\ 48 & 48 \end{bmatrix} = \begin{bmatrix} 368 & -304 \\ 152 & -88 \end{bmatrix}$

37. (a) True. If $A\mathbf{x} = \lambda\mathbf{x}$, then

$$A^2\mathbf{x} = A(A\mathbf{x}) = A(\lambda\mathbf{x}) = \lambda(A\mathbf{x}) = \lambda^2\mathbf{x}$$

showing that $\mathbf{x}$ is an eigenvector of A^2.

(b) False. For example, $(1, 0)$ is an eigenvector of $A^2 = \begin{bmatrix} 1 & 0 \\ 0 & 1 \end{bmatrix}$, but not of

$$A = \begin{bmatrix} 0 & 1 \\ 1 & 0 \end{bmatrix}.$$

39. Since $A^{-1}(AB)A = BA$, we see that AB and BA are similar.

41. The eigenvalues of A are $a - b$ and $a + b$, with corresponding unit eigenvectors $\left(\frac{1}{\sqrt{2}}, \frac{1}{\sqrt{2}}\right)$ and $\left(-\frac{1}{\sqrt{2}}, \frac{1}{\sqrt{2}}\right)$, respectively. Thus,

$$P = \begin{bmatrix} \frac{1}{\sqrt{2}} & -\frac{1}{\sqrt{2}} \\ \frac{1}{\sqrt{2}} & \frac{1}{\sqrt{2}} \end{bmatrix}.$$

Note that

$$P^{-1}AP = \begin{bmatrix} \frac{1}{\sqrt{2}} & \frac{1}{\sqrt{2}} \\ -\frac{1}{\sqrt{2}} & \frac{1}{\sqrt{2}} \end{bmatrix} \begin{bmatrix} a & b \\ b & a \end{bmatrix} \begin{bmatrix} \frac{1}{\sqrt{2}} & -\frac{1}{\sqrt{2}} \\ \frac{1}{\sqrt{2}} & \frac{1}{\sqrt{2}} \end{bmatrix} = \begin{bmatrix} a - b & 0 \\ 0 & a + b \end{bmatrix}.$$

43. (a) *A* is diagonalizable if and only if $a = b = c = 0$.

(b) If exactly two of a, b, and c are zero, then the eigenspace of 2 has dimension 3. If exactly one of a, b, c is zero, then the dimension of the eigenspace is 2. If none of a, b, c is zero, the eigenspace is dimension 1.

45. The population after one transition is

$$\mathbf{x}_2 = A\mathbf{x}_1 = \begin{bmatrix} 0 & 1 \\ \frac{1}{4} & 0 \end{bmatrix} \begin{bmatrix} 100 \\ 100 \end{bmatrix} = \begin{bmatrix} 100 \\ 25 \end{bmatrix}$$

and after two transitions is

$$\mathbf{x}_3 = A\mathbf{x}_2 = \begin{bmatrix} 0 & 1 \\ \frac{1}{4} & 0 \end{bmatrix} \begin{bmatrix} 100 \\ 25 \end{bmatrix} = \begin{bmatrix} 25 \\ 25 \end{bmatrix}.$$

The eigenvalues of *A* are $-\frac{1}{2}$ and $\frac{1}{2}$. We choose the positive eigenvalue and find the corresponding eigenvectors to be multiples of $(2, 1)$.

47. The population after one transition is

$$\mathbf{x}_2 = \begin{bmatrix} 0 & 3 & 12 \\ 1 & 0 & 0 \\ 0 & \frac{1}{6} & 0 \end{bmatrix} \begin{bmatrix} 300 \\ 300 \\ 300 \end{bmatrix} = \begin{bmatrix} 4500 \\ 300 \\ 50 \end{bmatrix}$$

and after two transitions is

$$\mathbf{x}_3 = \begin{bmatrix} 0 & 3 & 12 \\ 1 & 0 & 0 \\ 0 & \frac{1}{6} & 0 \end{bmatrix} \begin{bmatrix} 4500 \\ 300 \\ 50 \end{bmatrix} = \begin{bmatrix} 1500 \\ 4500 \\ 50 \end{bmatrix}.$$

The positive eigenvalue 2 has corresponding eigenvector $(24, 12, 1)$, which is a stable distribution.

49. The matrix corresponding to the system $\mathbf{y}' = A\mathbf{y}$ is

$$A = \begin{bmatrix} 1 & 2 \\ 0 & 0 \end{bmatrix}.$$

This matrix has eigenvalues of 0 and 1, with corresponding eigenvectors $(-2, 1)$ and $(1, 0)$, respectively. Thus, a matrix P that diagonalizes A is

$$P = \begin{bmatrix} -2 & 1 \\ 1 & 0 \end{bmatrix} \quad \text{and} \quad P^{-1}AP = \begin{bmatrix} 0 & 0 \\ 0 & 1 \end{bmatrix}.$$

The system represented by $\mathbf{w}' = P^{-1}AP\mathbf{w}$ yields the solution $w'_1 = 0$ and $w'_2 = w_2$. Thus $w_1 = C_1$ and $w_2 = C_2 e^t$. We substitute $\mathbf{y} = P\mathbf{w}$ and write

$$\begin{bmatrix} y_1 \\ y_2 \end{bmatrix} = \begin{bmatrix} -2 & 1 \\ 1 & 0 \end{bmatrix} \begin{bmatrix} w_1 \\ w_2 \end{bmatrix} = \begin{bmatrix} -2w_1 + w_2 \\ w_1 \end{bmatrix}.$$

This implies that the solution is

$$y_1 = -2C_1 + C_2 e^t$$

$$y_2 = \quad C_1 \ .$$

51. The matrix corresponding to the system $\mathbf{y}' = A\mathbf{y}$ is $A = \begin{bmatrix} 0 & 1 \\ 1 & 0 \end{bmatrix}$.

This matrix has eigenvalues 1 and -1, with corresponding eigenvectors $(1, 1)$ and $(1, -1)$. Thus, a matrix P that diagonalizes A is

$$P = \begin{bmatrix} 1 & 1 \\ 1 & -1 \end{bmatrix} \quad \text{and} \quad P^{-1}AP = \begin{bmatrix} 1 & 0 \\ 0 & -1 \end{bmatrix}.$$

The system represented by $\mathbf{w}' = P^{-1}AP\mathbf{w}$ has solutions $w_1 = C_1 e^t$ and $w_2 = C_2 e^{-t}$. We substitute $\mathbf{y} = P\mathbf{w}$ and obtain

$$\begin{bmatrix} y_1 \\ y_2 \end{bmatrix} = \begin{bmatrix} 1 & 1 \\ 1 & -1 \end{bmatrix} \begin{bmatrix} w_1 \\ w_2 \end{bmatrix} = \begin{bmatrix} w_1 + w_2 \\ w_1 - w_2 \end{bmatrix}$$

which yields the solution

$$y_1 = C_1 e^t + C_2 e^{-t}$$

$$y_2 = C_1 e^t - C_2 e^{-t}.$$

53. The matrix of the quadratic form is

$$A = \begin{bmatrix} a & \frac{b}{2} \\ \frac{b}{2} & c \end{bmatrix} = \begin{bmatrix} 1 & \frac{3}{2} \\ \frac{3}{2} & 1 \end{bmatrix}.$$

The eigenvalues are $\frac{5}{2}$ and $-\frac{1}{2}$ with corresponding unit eigenvectors $\left(\frac{1}{\sqrt{2}}, \frac{1}{\sqrt{2}}\right)$ and $\left(-\frac{1}{\sqrt{2}}, \frac{1}{\sqrt{2}}\right)$, respectively. Then we form the columns of P from the eigenvectors of A.

$$P = \begin{bmatrix} \frac{1}{\sqrt{2}} & -\frac{1}{\sqrt{2}} \\ \frac{1}{\sqrt{2}} & \frac{1}{\sqrt{2}} \end{bmatrix} \quad \text{and} \quad P^T A P = \begin{bmatrix} \frac{5}{2} & 0 \\ 0 & -\frac{1}{2} \end{bmatrix}$$

This implies that the equation of the rotated conic is $\frac{5}{2}(x')^2 - \frac{1}{2}(y')^2 - 3 = 0$.

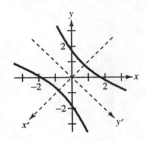

55. The matrix of the quadratic form is

$$A = \begin{bmatrix} a & \frac{b}{2} \\ \frac{b}{2} & c \end{bmatrix} = \begin{bmatrix} 0 & \frac{1}{2} \\ \frac{1}{2} & 0 \end{bmatrix}.$$

The eigenvalues are $\frac{1}{2}$ and $-\frac{1}{2}$, with corresponding unit eigenvectors $\left(\frac{1}{\sqrt{2}}, \frac{1}{\sqrt{2}}\right)$ and $\left(-\frac{1}{\sqrt{2}}, \frac{1}{\sqrt{2}}\right)$. We use these eigenvectors to form the columns of P.

$$P = \begin{bmatrix} \frac{1}{\sqrt{2}} & -\frac{1}{\sqrt{2}} \\ \frac{1}{\sqrt{2}} & \frac{1}{\sqrt{2}} \end{bmatrix} \quad \text{and} \quad P^T A P = \begin{bmatrix} \frac{1}{2} & 0 \\ 0 & -\frac{1}{2} \end{bmatrix}$$

This implies that the equation of the rotated conic is $\frac{1}{2}(x')^2 - \frac{1}{2}(y')^2 - 2 = 0$, a hyperbola.

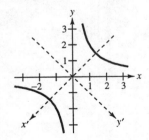

Chapters 6-7   Solutions — Cumulative Test

1. Yes, T is a linear transformation.

2. No, T is not a linear transformation. For example,

$$T\left(2\begin{pmatrix}1 & 0\\ 0 & 1\end{pmatrix}\right) = T\begin{pmatrix}2 & 0\\ 0 & 2\end{pmatrix} = \left|\begin{pmatrix}2 & 0\\ 0 & 2\end{pmatrix} + \begin{pmatrix}2 & 0\\ 0 & 2\end{pmatrix}\right| = \begin{vmatrix}4 & 0\\ 0 & 4\end{vmatrix} = 16$$

$$2T\begin{pmatrix}1 & 0\\ 0 & 1\end{pmatrix} = 2\left|\begin{pmatrix}1 & 0\\ 0 & 1\end{pmatrix} + \begin{pmatrix}1 & 0\\ 0 & 1\end{pmatrix}\right| = 2\begin{vmatrix}2 & 0\\ 0 & 2\end{vmatrix} = 2 \cdot 4 = 8$$

3. (a) $T(1, -2) = \begin{bmatrix}1 & 0\\ -1 & 0\\ 0 & 0\end{bmatrix}\begin{bmatrix}1\\ -2\end{bmatrix} = \begin{bmatrix}1\\ -1\\ 0\end{bmatrix}$

   (b) $\begin{bmatrix}1 & 0\\ -1 & 0\\ 0 & 0\end{bmatrix}\begin{bmatrix}x\\ y\end{bmatrix} = \begin{bmatrix}x\\ -y\\ 0\end{bmatrix} = \begin{bmatrix}1\\ 3\\ 0\end{bmatrix} \Rightarrow x = 1 \text{ and } y = -3$

   The preimage of $(1, 3, 0)$ is $(1, -3)$.

4. The kernel is the solution space of the homogenous system

$$\begin{aligned}x_1 - x_2 & = 0\\ -x_1 + x_2 & = 0\\ x_3 + x_4 & = 0\end{aligned}$$

$$\begin{bmatrix}1 & -1 & 0 & 0\\ -1 & 1 & 0 & 0\\ 0 & 0 & 1 & 1\end{bmatrix} \Rightarrow \begin{bmatrix}1 & -1 & 0 & 0\\ 0 & 0 & 0 & 0\\ 0 & 0 & 1 & 1\end{bmatrix}$$

$$\left.\begin{aligned}x_1 & = s\\ x_2 & = s\\ x_3 & = -t\\ x_4 & = t\end{aligned}\right\} \text{span of } \begin{pmatrix}1\\ 1\\ 0\\ 0\end{pmatrix} \text{ and } \begin{pmatrix}0\\ 0\\ -1\\ 1\end{pmatrix}$$

5. $A = \begin{bmatrix}1 & 0 & 1 & 0\\ 0 & -1 & 0 & -1\end{bmatrix} \Rightarrow \begin{bmatrix}1 & 0 & 1 & 0\\ 0 & 1 & 0 & 1\end{bmatrix}.$

   (a) basis for kernel: $\left\{\begin{bmatrix}0\\ -1\\ 0\\ 1\end{bmatrix}, \begin{bmatrix}1\\ 0\\ -1\\ 0\end{bmatrix}\right\}$

   (b) basis for range (column space of A): $\left\{\begin{pmatrix}1\\ 0\end{pmatrix}, \begin{pmatrix}0\\ 1\end{pmatrix}\right\}$

   (c) rank = 2, nullity = 2

6. $\begin{bmatrix} -1 & 1 & 0 \\ 0 & -1 & 1 \\ 1 & 0 & -1 \end{bmatrix}$

7. $T\begin{pmatrix} 1 \\ 0 \end{pmatrix} = \begin{bmatrix} \frac{1}{2} \\ -\frac{1}{2} \end{bmatrix}$, $T\begin{pmatrix} 0 \\ 1 \end{pmatrix} = \begin{bmatrix} -\frac{1}{2} \\ \frac{1}{2} \end{bmatrix}$, $A = \begin{bmatrix} \frac{1}{2} & -\frac{1}{2} \\ -\frac{1}{2} & \frac{1}{2} \end{bmatrix}$

$T\begin{pmatrix} 1 \\ 1 \end{pmatrix} = \begin{bmatrix} \frac{1}{2} & -\frac{1}{2} \\ -\frac{1}{2} & \frac{1}{2} \end{bmatrix} \begin{bmatrix} 1 \\ 1 \end{bmatrix} = \begin{bmatrix} 0 \\ 0 \end{bmatrix}$

$T\begin{pmatrix} -2 \\ 2 \end{pmatrix} = \begin{bmatrix} \frac{1}{2} & -\frac{1}{2} \\ -\frac{1}{2} & \frac{1}{2} \end{bmatrix} \begin{bmatrix} -2 \\ 2 \end{bmatrix} = \begin{bmatrix} -2 \\ 2 \end{bmatrix}$

8. Matrix of T is $A = \begin{bmatrix} 1 & -1 \\ 2 & 1 \end{bmatrix}$

$A^{-1} = \frac{1}{3} \begin{bmatrix} 1 & 1 \\ -2 & 1 \end{bmatrix} \cdot T^{-1}(x, y) = \left(\frac{1}{3}x + \frac{1}{3}y, -\frac{2}{3}x + \frac{1}{3}y \right)$

$T^{-1} \circ T (3, -2) = T^{-1} (5, 4) = (3, -2).$

9. $T(1, 1) = (1, 2, 2) = -1 (1, 0, 0) + 0 (1, 1, 0) + 2 (1, 1, 1)$

$T(1, 0) = (0, 2, 1) = -2 (1, 0, 0) + 1 (1, 1, 0) + 1 (1, 1, 1)$

$A = \begin{bmatrix} -1 & -2 \\ 0 & 1 \\ 2 & 1 \end{bmatrix}$

$T(0, 1) = A[\mathbf{v}]_B = \begin{bmatrix} -1 & -2 \\ 0 & 1 \\ 2 & 1 \end{bmatrix} \begin{bmatrix} 1 \\ -1 \end{bmatrix} = \begin{bmatrix} 1 \\ -1 \\ 1 \end{bmatrix} = (1, 0, 0) - (1, 1, 0) + (1, 1, 1)$

$= (1, 0, 1)$

10. (a) $A = \begin{bmatrix} 1 & -2 \\ 1 & 4 \end{bmatrix}$

(b) $[B : B'] \Rightarrow [I : P] \Rightarrow P = \begin{bmatrix} 1 & 1 \\ 1 & 2 \end{bmatrix}$

(c) $P^{-1} = \begin{bmatrix} 2 & -1 \\ -1 & 1 \end{bmatrix} \cdot A' = P^{-1}AP = \begin{bmatrix} -7 & -15 \\ 6 & 12 \end{bmatrix}$

(d) $\begin{bmatrix} -7 & -15 \\ 6 & 12 \end{bmatrix} \begin{bmatrix} 3 \\ -2 \end{bmatrix} = \begin{bmatrix} 9 \\ -6 \end{bmatrix} = [T(\mathbf{v})]_{B'}$

(e) $[\mathbf{v}]_{B'} = \begin{bmatrix} 3 \\ -2 \end{bmatrix} \Rightarrow \mathbf{v} = 3 \begin{pmatrix} 1 \\ 1 \end{pmatrix} - 2 \begin{pmatrix} 1 \\ 2 \end{pmatrix} = \begin{pmatrix} 1 \\ -1 \end{pmatrix} \Rightarrow [\mathbf{v}]_B = \begin{bmatrix} 1 \\ -1 \end{bmatrix}$

$T(\mathbf{v}) = 9 \begin{pmatrix} 1 \\ 1 \end{pmatrix} - 6 \begin{pmatrix} 1 \\ 2 \end{pmatrix} = \begin{pmatrix} 3 \\ -3 \end{pmatrix}$

$[T(\mathbf{v})]_B = \begin{bmatrix} 1 & -2 \\ 1 & 4 \end{bmatrix} \begin{bmatrix} 1 \\ -1 \end{bmatrix} = \begin{bmatrix} 3 \\ -3 \end{bmatrix}$

11. $|\lambda I - A| = \begin{vmatrix} \lambda - 3 & 0 & 0 \\ 0 & \lambda - 2 & -1 \\ 0 & 0 & \lambda - 2 \end{vmatrix} = (\lambda - 3)(\lambda - 2)^2 \cdot \lambda = 2, 2, 3$

12. $|\lambda I - A| = \begin{vmatrix} \lambda - 1 & -2 & -1 \\ 0 & \lambda - 3 & -1 \\ 0 & 3 & \lambda + 1 \end{vmatrix} = (\lambda - 1)[\lambda^2 - 2\lambda] = (\lambda - 1)\lambda(\lambda - 2)$

$$\lambda = 1: \begin{pmatrix} 0 & -2 & -1 \\ 0 & -2 & -1 \\ 0 & 3 & 2 \end{pmatrix} \Rightarrow \begin{pmatrix} 0 & 2 & 1 \\ 0 & 0 & 1 \\ 0 & 0 & 0 \end{pmatrix} \Rightarrow \begin{pmatrix} 1 \\ 0 \\ 0 \end{pmatrix}$$

$$\lambda = 0: \begin{pmatrix} -1 & -2 & -1 \\ 0 & -3 & -1 \\ 0 & 3 & 1 \end{pmatrix} \Rightarrow \begin{pmatrix} 1 & 2 & 1 \\ 0 & 3 & 1 \\ 0 & 0 & 0 \end{pmatrix} \Rightarrow \begin{pmatrix} -1 \\ -1 \\ 3 \end{pmatrix}$$

$$\lambda = 2: \begin{pmatrix} 1 & -2 & -1 \\ 0 & -1 & -1 \\ 0 & 3 & 3 \end{pmatrix} \Rightarrow \begin{pmatrix} 1 & -2 & -1 \\ 0 & 1 & 1 \\ 0 & 0 & 0 \end{pmatrix} \Rightarrow \begin{pmatrix} 1 \\ 1 \\ -1 \end{pmatrix}$$

13. $\lambda = 1, 1, 1$ (upper triangular)

$$\begin{pmatrix} 0 & 1 & -1 \\ 0 & 0 & -2 \\ 0 & 0 & 0 \end{pmatrix} \Rightarrow \begin{pmatrix} 0 & 1 & 0 \\ 0 & 0 & 1 \\ 0 & 0 & 0 \end{pmatrix} \Rightarrow \begin{pmatrix} 1 \\ 0 \\ 0 \end{pmatrix}$$

14. Eigenvalues and eigenvectors of A: $\lambda = 2, \begin{pmatrix} 3 \\ 1 \end{pmatrix}$; $\lambda = 4, \begin{pmatrix} 1 \\ 1 \end{pmatrix}$

$$P = \begin{pmatrix} 3 & 1 \\ 1 & 1 \end{pmatrix} \cdot P^{-1}AP = \begin{pmatrix} 2 & 0 \\ 0 & 4 \end{pmatrix}$$

15. Matrix of T relative to standard basis: $A = \begin{pmatrix} 2 & 0 & -2 \\ 0 & 2 & -2 \\ 3 & 0 & -3 \end{pmatrix}$
Eigenvalues and eigenvectors of A are

$$\lambda = 2, \begin{pmatrix} 0 \\ 1 \\ 0 \end{pmatrix}; \quad \lambda = 0, \begin{pmatrix} 1 \\ 1 \\ 1 \end{pmatrix}, \quad \lambda = -1, \begin{pmatrix} 2 \\ 2 \\ 3 \end{pmatrix}$$

Basis $B = \left\{ \begin{pmatrix} 0 \\ 1 \\ 0 \end{pmatrix}, \begin{pmatrix} 1 \\ 1 \\ 1 \end{pmatrix}, \begin{pmatrix} 2 \\ 2 \\ 3 \end{pmatrix} \right\}$.

16. Eigenvalues and eigenvectors of $A = \begin{bmatrix} 1 & 3 \\ 3 & 1 \end{bmatrix}$ are

$$\lambda = -2, \begin{pmatrix} 1 \\ -1 \end{pmatrix}, \quad \lambda = 4, \begin{pmatrix} 1 \\ 1 \end{pmatrix}. \quad P = \begin{pmatrix} \frac{1}{\sqrt{2}} & \frac{1}{\sqrt{2}} \\ -\frac{1}{\sqrt{2}} & \frac{1}{\sqrt{2}} \end{pmatrix}$$

17. Eigenvalues and eigenvectors of A are

$$\lambda = 2, \begin{pmatrix} 1 \\ 1 \\ 1 \end{pmatrix}; \quad \lambda = -1, \begin{pmatrix} 1 \\ 0 \\ -1 \end{pmatrix}, \begin{pmatrix} 1 \\ -1 \\ 0 \end{pmatrix}.$$

Using the Gram-Schmidt orthonormalization process, we obtain

$$P = \begin{pmatrix} \frac{1}{\sqrt{3}} & \frac{1}{\sqrt{2}} & \frac{1}{\sqrt{6}} \\ \frac{1}{\sqrt{3}} & 0 & -\frac{2}{\sqrt{6}} \\ \frac{1}{\sqrt{3}} & -\frac{1}{\sqrt{2}} & \frac{1}{\sqrt{6}} \end{pmatrix}$$

18. λ is an <u>eigenvalue</u> of A if there exists a nonzero vector $\mathbf{x}$ such that $A\mathbf{x} = \lambda\mathbf{x}$.
$\mathbf{x}$ is called an <u>eigenvector</u> of A. If A is $n \times n$, A can have n eigenvalues,
possibly complex and possibly repeated.

19. P is <u>orthogonal</u> if $P^{-1} = P^T$.
$1 = \det\left(P \cdot P^{-1}\right) = \det\left(P\, P^T\right) = (\det P)^2 \implies \det P = \pm 1$.

20. There exists P such that $P^{-1}AP = D$. A and B are similar implies that there exists Q such that
$A = Q^{-1}BQ$. Then $D = P^{-1}AP = P^{-1}\left(Q^{-1}BQ\right)P = (QP)^{-1}\, B(QP)$.

21. If 0 is an eigenvalue of A, then $|A - \lambda I| = |A| = 0$, and A is singular.

22. See proof of Theorem 7.9.

23. The range of T is nonempty because it contains $\mathbf{0}$. Let $T(\mathbf{u})$ and $T(\mathbf{v})$ be two vectors in the range
of T. Then $T(\mathbf{u}) + T(\mathbf{v}) = T(\mathbf{u} + \mathbf{v})$. But since $\mathbf{u}$ and $\mathbf{v}$ are in V, it follows that $\mathbf{u} + \mathbf{v}$ is also in
V, which in turn implies that $T(\mathbf{u} + \mathbf{v})$ is in the range.

Similarly, let $T(\mathbf{u})$ be in the range of T, and let c be a scalar. Then $cT(\mathbf{u}) = T(c\mathbf{u})$. But since $c\mathbf{u}$ is
in V, this implies that $T(c\mathbf{u})$ is in the range.

24. If T is one-to-one and $\mathbf{v} \in$ kernel, then $T(\mathbf{v}) = T(\mathbf{0}) = \mathbf{0} \implies \mathbf{v} = \mathbf{0}$.
If kernel $= \{\mathbf{0}\}$ and $T(\mathbf{v}_1) = T(\mathbf{v}_2)$,
then $T(\mathbf{v}_1 - \mathbf{v}_2) = \mathbf{0} \implies \mathbf{v}_1 - \mathbf{v}_2 \in$ kernel $\implies \mathbf{v}_1 = \mathbf{v}_2$.

25. If λ is an eigenvalue of A and $A^2 = 0$, then

$$A\mathbf{x} = \lambda\mathbf{x}, \mathbf{x} \neq \mathbf{0}$$

$$A^2\mathbf{x} = A(\lambda\mathbf{x}) = \lambda^2\mathbf{x}$$

$$\mathbf{0} = \lambda^2\mathbf{x} \implies \lambda^2 = 0 \implies \lambda = 0$$

CHAPTER 8
Complex Vector Spaces

Section 8.1   Complex Numbers

1. $\sqrt{-2}\,\sqrt{-3} = (\sqrt{2}i)(\sqrt{3}i) = (\sqrt{2})(\sqrt{3})i^2 = \sqrt{6}(-1) = -\sqrt{6}$

3. $\sqrt{-4}\,\sqrt{-4} = (\sqrt{4}i)(\sqrt{4}i) = (\sqrt{4})(\sqrt{4})i^2 = \sqrt{16}(-1) = -4$

5. $i^4 = i^2 i^2 = (-1)(-1) = 1$

7. We plot the complex numbers on a set of Cartesian axes. The real part is the horizontal distance from the vertical axis and the imaginary part is the vertical distance from the horizontal axis. The number $6 - 2i$ is plotted below.

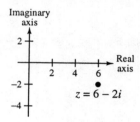

9. $z = -5 + 5i$.

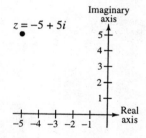

11. $z = 1 + 5i$.

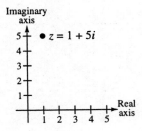

13. We have $-u = -(3 - i) = -3 + i$, and $2u = 2(3 - i) = 6 - 2i$. These two complex numbers are plotted below.

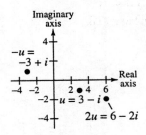

15. $x + 3i = 6 + 3i$

$x = 6$

17. The corresponding real and imaginary parts on each side must be equal. Equating the imaginary parts, we have

$2x = 6$

$x = 3.$

This satisfies the equality of the real parts also, since $x^2 + 6 = 3^2 + 6 = 15$.

19. Sum: $(2 + 6i) + (3 - 3i) = (2 + 3) + (6 - 3)i = 5 + 3i$

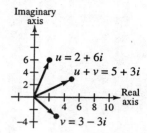

Difference: $(2 + 6i) - (3 - 3i) = (2 - 3) + (6 + 3)i = -1 + 9i$

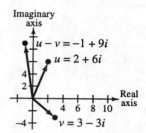

21. To find the sum, we add the corresponding real and imaginary parts.

$$(5 + i) + (5 - i) = (5 + 5) + (i - i) = 10$$

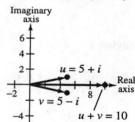

To find the difference, we find the difference of the corresponding real and imaginary parts.

$$(5 + i) - (5 - i) = (5 - 5) + (i + i) = 2i$$

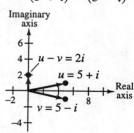

23. Sum: $6 + (-2i) = 6 - 2i$

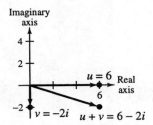

Difference: $6 - (-2i) = 6 + 2i$

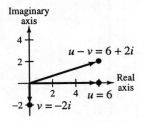

25. Sum: $(2 + i) + (2 + i) = (2 + 2) + (1 + 1)i = 4 + 2i$

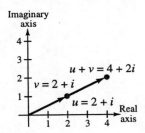

Difference: $(2 + i) - (2 + i) = (2 - 2) + (1 - 1)i = 0$

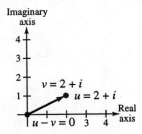

27. $(5 - 5i)(1 + 3i) = [(5)(1) - (-5)(3)] + [(5)(3) + (-5)(1)]i$

$$= (5 + 15) + (15 - 5)i$$

$$= 20 + 10i$$

29. To find the product of two complex numbers, use the distributive property as follows.

$$(\sqrt{7} - i)(\sqrt{7} + i) = \left[(\sqrt{7})(\sqrt{7}) - (-1)(1)\right] + \left[(\sqrt{7})(1) + (-1)(\sqrt{7})\right]i$$

$$= (7 + 1) + (\sqrt{7} - \sqrt{7})i$$

$$= 8$$

31. $(a + bi)^2 = (a + bi)(a + bi)$

$$= [a^2 - b^2] + [ab + ab]i$$

$$= (a^2 - b^2) + 2abi$$

33. To raise a complex number to a positive integer power, you can use repeated multiplication.

$$(1 + i)^3 = (1 + i)(1 + i)(1 + i)$$

$$= [(1 + i) + i(1 + i)](1 + i)$$

$$= 2i(1 + i) = 2i + 2i^2 = -2 + 2i$$

(Note that for higher powers, we will introduce an easier method in Section 8.3.)

35. $(a + bi)^3 = (a + bi)(a + bi)(a + bi)$

$$= \left[(a^2 - b^2) + (ab + ab)i\right](a + bi)$$

$$= \left[(a^2 - b^2) + (2ab)i\right](a + bi)$$

$$= \left[(a^2 - b^2)(a) - (2ab)(b)\right] + \left[(a^2 - b^2)(b) + (2ab)(a)\right]i$$

$$= (a^3 - ab^2 - 2ab^2) + (a^2b - b^3 + 2a^2b)i$$

$$= (a^3 - 3ab^2) + (3a^2b - b^3)i$$

37. The zeros of the polynomial are the solutions to

$$2x^2 + 2x + 5 = 0,$$

which we can solve using the Quadratic Formula.

$$x = \frac{-2 \pm \sqrt{2^2 - 4(2)(5)}}{2(2)}$$

$$= \frac{-2 \pm \sqrt{-36}}{4} = \frac{-2 \pm 6i}{4}$$

$$= -\frac{1}{2} \pm \frac{3}{2}i$$

39. $x^2 - 5x + 6 = 0$

$(x - 2)(x - 3) = 0$

$x - 2 = 0 \quad \text{or} \quad x - 3 = 0$

$\quad x = 2 \qquad\qquad x = 3$

41. $x^3 - 3x^2 + 4x - 2 = 0$

$(x - 1)(x^2 - 2x + 2) = 0$

$x - 1 = 0 \quad \text{or} \quad x^2 - 2x + 2 = 0$

$x = 1$

Completing the square we get

$$x^2 - 2x + 1 = -2 + 1$$

$$(x - 1)^2 = -1$$

$$x - 1 = \pm\sqrt{-1}$$

$$x - 1 = \pm i$$

$$x = 1 \pm i.$$

43. $x^4 - 16 = (x^2 - 4)(x^2 + 4) = 0.$

$x^2 - 4 = 0 \quad \text{or} \quad x^2 + 4 = 0$

$\quad x^2 = 4 \qquad\qquad x^2 = -4$

$\quad x = \pm 2 \qquad\qquad x = \pm\sqrt{-4}$

$\qquad\qquad\qquad\qquad\quad x = \pm 2i$

45. $A + B = \begin{bmatrix} 1 + i & 1 \\ 2 - 2i & -3i \end{bmatrix} + \begin{bmatrix} 1 - i & 3i \\ -3 & -i \end{bmatrix}$

$$= \begin{bmatrix} (1 + i) + (1 - i) & (1) + (3i) \\ (2 - 2i) + (-3) & (-3i) + (-i) \end{bmatrix}$$

$$= \begin{bmatrix} 2 & 1 + 3i \\ -1 - 2i & -4i \end{bmatrix}$$

47. $2A = 2\begin{bmatrix} 1 + i & 1 \\ 2 - 2i & -3i \end{bmatrix} = \begin{bmatrix} 2 + 2i & 2 \\ 4 - 4i & -6i \end{bmatrix}$

49. $2iA = 2i\begin{bmatrix} 1 + i & 1 \\ 2 - 2i & -3i \end{bmatrix} = \begin{bmatrix} 2i + 2i^2 & 2i \\ 4i - 4i^2 & -6i^2 \end{bmatrix}$

$$= \begin{bmatrix} -2 + 2i & 2i \\ 4 + 4i & 6 \end{bmatrix}$$

51. Using the matrix $A + B$ found in Exercise 45, we have

$$\det(A + B) = \begin{vmatrix} 2 & 1 + 3i \\ -1 - 2i & -4i \end{vmatrix}$$

$$= 2(-4i) - (1 + 3i)(-1 - 2i)$$

$$= -8i - [(-1 - 2i) + 3i(-1 - 2i)]$$

$$= -8i - (5 - 5i)$$

$$= -5 - 3i.$$

53. $5AB = 5 \begin{bmatrix} 1 + i & 1 \\ 2 - 2i & -3i \end{bmatrix} \begin{bmatrix} 1 - i & 3i \\ -3 & -i \end{bmatrix}$

$$= 5 \begin{bmatrix} (1 + i)(1 - i) - 3 & 3i(1 + i) - i \\ (2 - 2i)(1 - i) + 9i & 3i(2 - 2i) - 3 \end{bmatrix}$$

$$= 5 \begin{bmatrix} -1 & -3 + 2i \\ 5i & 3 + 6i \end{bmatrix} = \begin{bmatrix} -5 & -15 + 10i \\ 25i & 15 + 30i \end{bmatrix}$$

55. We verify that the set of complex numbers C is a vector space by verifying the definition from Section 4.2.

1. If $(a + bi)$ and $(c + di)$ are complex numbers, then so is their sum, $(a + c) + (b + d)i$.

2. $(a + bi) + (c + di) = (c + di) + (a + bi)$.

3. $(a + bi) + [(c + di) + (e + fi)] = [(a + bi) + (c + di)] + (e + fi)$.

4. The zero vector is $0 + 0i$.

5. For any complex number $a + bi, (a + bi) + (-a - bi) = 0$.

6. If r is a real number, then $r(a + bi) = ra + rbi \in C$.

7. $r\left[(a + bi) + (c + di)\right] = r(a + bi) + r(c + di)$.

8. $(r + s)(a + bi) = r(a + bi) + s(a + bi)$.

9. $r\left(s(a + bi)\right) = (rs)(a + bi)$.

10. $1(a + bi) = a + bi$.

The dimension of C as a vector space over the real numbers is two, since a basis is $\{1, i\}$.

57. (a) $A^1 = A = \begin{bmatrix} 0 & i \\ i & 0 \end{bmatrix}$

$A^2 = \begin{bmatrix} -1 & 0 \\ 0 & -1 \end{bmatrix}$

$A^3 = \begin{bmatrix} 0 & -i \\ -i & 0 \end{bmatrix}$

$A^4 = \begin{bmatrix} 1 & 0 \\ 0 & 1 \end{bmatrix}$

$A^5 = A = \begin{bmatrix} 0 & i \\ i & 0 \end{bmatrix}$

(b) $A^{57} = (A^4)^{14}A = A = \begin{bmatrix} 0 & i \\ i & 0 \end{bmatrix}$

$A^{1995} = A^3 = \begin{bmatrix} 0 & -i \\ -i & 0 \end{bmatrix}$

(c) $A^n = \begin{cases} \begin{bmatrix} 0 & i \\ i & 0 \end{bmatrix}, & n = 1, 5, 9, \ldots \\[2em] \begin{bmatrix} -1 & 0 \\ 0 & -1 \end{bmatrix}, & n = 2, 6, 10, \ldots \\[2em] \begin{bmatrix} 0 & -i \\ -i & 0 \end{bmatrix}, & n = 3, 7, 11, \ldots \\[2em] \begin{bmatrix} 1 & 0 \\ 0 & 1 \end{bmatrix}, & n = 4, 8, 12, \ldots \end{cases}$

Section 8.2   Conjugates and Division of Complex Numbers

1. To find the complex conjugate, we negate the imaginary part of *z*.

$$z = 6 - 3i$$

$$\bar{z} = 6 + 3i$$

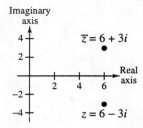

3. $z = -8i$
   $\bar{z} = 8i$

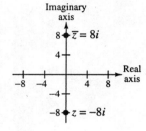

5. Applying the definition of the modulus of a complex number, we have

$$|z| = |(2 + i)| = \sqrt{2^2 + 1^2} = \sqrt{5}.$$

7. $|zw| = |(2 + i)(-3 + 2i)| = |(-6 - 2) + (4 - 3)i|$
$$= |-8 + i|$$
$$= \sqrt{(8)^2 + (1)^2} = \sqrt{65}$$

9. $|v| = |(-5i)| = \sqrt{(-5)^2} = \sqrt{25} = 5$

11. $|wz| = |(-1 + 2i)(1 + i)| = |(-1 - 2) + (-1 + 2)i|$
$$= |-3 + i| = \sqrt{(-3)^2 + (1)^2} = \sqrt{10}$$
$|w||z| = |(-1 + 2i)||1 + i| = \sqrt{(-1)^2 + (2)^2}\sqrt{(1)^2 + (1)^2}$
$$= \sqrt{5}\sqrt{2} = \sqrt{10}$$
$|zw| = |(1 + i)(-1 + 2i)| = |-3 + i|$
$$= \sqrt{(-3^2) + (1)^2} = \sqrt{10}$$

13. $\dfrac{2+i}{i} = \dfrac{2+i}{i} \cdot \dfrac{-i}{i}$

$\quad\quad = 1 - 2i$

15. Using the complex conjugate of the denominator,

$$\dfrac{3 - \sqrt{2}i}{3 + \sqrt{2}i} = \dfrac{3 - \sqrt{2}i}{3 + \sqrt{2}i} \cdot \dfrac{3 - \sqrt{2}i}{3 - \sqrt{2}i} = \dfrac{(9 - 2) + (-3\sqrt{2}i - 3\sqrt{2}i)}{9 + 2} = \dfrac{7 - 6\sqrt{2}i}{11}.$$

17. $\dfrac{(2 + i)(3 - i)}{4 - 2i} = \dfrac{(6 + 1) + (-2 + 3)i}{4 - 2i} = \dfrac{7 + i}{4 - 2i}$

$$\quad\quad = \dfrac{(7)(4) + (1)(-2)}{(4)^2 + (-2)^2} + \dfrac{(1)(4) - (7)(-2)}{(4)^2 + (-2)^2}i$$

$$\quad\quad = \dfrac{28 - 2}{20} + \dfrac{4 + 14}{20i} = \dfrac{26}{20} + \dfrac{18}{20}i$$

$$\quad\quad = \dfrac{13}{10} + \dfrac{9}{10}i$$

19. (a) $z^2 = (2 - i)^2 = (4 - 1) + 2(2)(-i) = 3 - 4i$

(b) $z^3 = z^2 \cdot z = (3 - 4i)(2 - i) = (6 - 4) + (-8i - 3i) = 2 - 11i$

(c) $z^{-1} = \dfrac{1}{2 - i} = \dfrac{1}{2 - i} \cdot \dfrac{2 + i}{2 + i} = \dfrac{2 + i}{4 + 1} = \dfrac{2}{5} + \dfrac{1}{5}i$

(d) $z^{-2} = \dfrac{1}{z^2} = \dfrac{1}{3 - 4i} = \dfrac{1}{3 - 4i} \cdot \dfrac{3 + 4i}{3 + 4i} = \dfrac{3 + 4i}{9 + 16} = \dfrac{3}{25} + \dfrac{4}{25}i$

21. A has an inverse since $|A| = 6i - 3i(2 - i) = 6i - 6i + 3i^2 = -3 \neq 0$. We find the inverse by using the rule for 2×2 matrices,

$$A^{-1} = \dfrac{1}{|A|} \begin{bmatrix} i & -3i \\ -2 + i & 6 \end{bmatrix} = \begin{bmatrix} -\frac{i}{3} & i \\ \frac{2}{3} - \frac{i}{3} & -2 \end{bmatrix}.$$

To verify our work, we find AA^{-1}.

$$AA^{-1} = \begin{bmatrix} 6 & 3i \\ 2 - i & i \end{bmatrix} \begin{bmatrix} -\frac{i}{3} & i \\ \frac{2}{3} - \frac{i}{3} & -2 \end{bmatrix}$$

$$= \begin{bmatrix} 6\left(-\frac{i}{3}\right) + 3i\left(\frac{2 - i}{3}\right) & 6(i) + 3i(-2) \\ (2 - i)\left(-\frac{i}{3}\right) + i\left(\frac{2 - i}{3}\right) & (2 - i)i + i(-2) \end{bmatrix}$$

$$= \begin{bmatrix} 1 & 0 \\ 0 & 1 \end{bmatrix} = I$$

23. *A* does not have an inverse since

$$|A| = (1 - i)(1 + i) - 2 = 1 + 1 - 2 = 0.$$

25.
$$A = \begin{bmatrix} 1 & 0 & 0 \\ 0 & 1 - i & 0 \\ 0 & 0 & 1 + i \end{bmatrix}. \quad A^{-1} = \begin{bmatrix} 1 & 0 & 0 \\ 0 & a & 0 \\ 0 & 0 & b \end{bmatrix}.$$

$$(1 - i)(a) = 1$$

$$a = \frac{1}{1 - i} \cdot \frac{1 + i}{1 + i} = \frac{1 + i}{1 + i} = \frac{1}{2}(1 + i)$$

$$(1 + i)(b) = 1$$

$$b = \frac{1}{1 + i} \cdot \frac{1 - i}{1 - i} = \frac{1 - i}{1 + i} = \frac{1}{2}(1 - i)$$

Thus,

$$A^{-1} = \begin{bmatrix} 1 & 0 & 0 \\ 0 & \frac{1}{2}(1 + i) & 0 \\ 0 & 0 & \frac{1}{2}(1 - i) \end{bmatrix}$$

Verification

$$AA^{-1} = \begin{bmatrix} 1 & 0 & 0 \\ 0 & 1 - i & 0 \\ 0 & 0 & 1 + i \end{bmatrix} \begin{bmatrix} 1 & 0 & 0 \\ 0 & \frac{1}{2}(1 + i) & 0 \\ 0 & 0 & \frac{1}{2}(1 - i) \end{bmatrix}$$

$$= \begin{bmatrix} 1 & 0 & 0 \\ 0 & 1 & 0 \\ 0 & 0 & 1 \end{bmatrix}$$

27. Letting $z = a + bi$, where a and b are real numbers, we have

$$\det(A) = 5(2 - i) - z(3i) = (10 + 3b) + (-5i - 3ai).$$

Setting $\det(A) = 0$,

$$10 + 3b = 0 \qquad \text{and} \qquad -5i - 3ai = 0$$

$$b = -\frac{10}{3} \qquad\qquad a = -\frac{5}{3}$$

Thus,

$$z = -\frac{5}{3} - \frac{10}{3}i.$$

29. Let $z = a + bi$. Then the following are equivalent.

$$z = \bar{z} \Longleftrightarrow a + bi = \overline{a + bi}$$

$$\Longleftrightarrow a + bi = a - bi$$

$$\Longleftrightarrow b = 0$$

$$\Longleftrightarrow z \text{ is real.}$$

31. (a) $|z| = 3$

Circle of radius 3 with center at origin.

(b) Circle of radius 5 with center at $(1, -i)$.

(c) Interior and borders of circle of radius 2 and center $(0, i)$.

(d) Closed region between concentric circles centered at origin, and radii 2 and 5.

33. (a) $\left(\frac{1}{i}\right)^1 = \left(\frac{1}{i}\right) = -i$

$\left(\frac{1}{i}\right)^2 = (-i)^2 = -1$

$\left(\frac{1}{i}\right)^3 = (-1)(-i) = i$

$\left(\frac{1}{i}\right)^4 = 1$

$\left(\frac{1}{i}\right)^5 = -i$

(b) $\left(\frac{1}{i}\right)^{57} = \left(\frac{1}{i}\right)^{56}\left(\frac{1}{i}\right) = -i$

$\left(\frac{1}{i}\right)^{1995} = \left(\frac{1}{i}\right)^3 = i$

(c)
$$\left(\frac{1}{i}\right)^n = \begin{cases} -i & \text{for} \quad n = 1, 5, 9, \ldots \\ -1 & \text{for} \quad n = 2, 6, 10, \ldots \\ i & \text{for} \quad n = 3, 7, 11, \ldots \\ 1 & \text{for} \quad n = 4, 8, 12, \ldots \end{cases}$$

Section 8.3   Polar Form and DeMoivre's Theorem

1. Using the definition of the modulus of a complex number,

   $$r = \sqrt{2^2 + (-2)^2} = \sqrt{4 + 4} = 2\sqrt{2}.$$

   The argument is found by solving $\tan \theta = b/a$ for θ as follows.

   $$\tan \theta = \frac{-2}{2} = -1$$

   $$\theta = -\frac{\pi}{4} \quad \text{(Quadrant IV)}$$

   Thus, the polar form of $2 - 2i$ is $z = 2\sqrt{2}\left[\cos\left(-\frac{\pi}{4}\right) + i \sin\left(-\frac{\pi}{4}\right)\right]$.

3. -6 in polar form.

   $a = -6, b = 0$. Therefore, $r = \sqrt{(-6)^2} = 6$.

   $\tan \theta = 0 \Rightarrow \theta = \pi$.

   Thus, polar form is $z = 6(\cos \pi + i \sin \pi)$.

5. The graph of $-2 - 2i$ is sketched below.

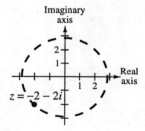

   We find the modulus and argument as follows.

   $$r = \sqrt{(-2)^2 + (-2)^2} = 2\sqrt{2}$$

   $$\tan \theta = \frac{-2}{-2} = 1$$

   $$\theta = \frac{-3\pi}{4} \quad \text{(Quadrant III)}$$

   Thus, the polar form of $-2 - 2i$ is $z = 2\sqrt{2}\left(\cos\frac{-3\pi}{4} + i \sin\frac{-3\pi}{4}\right)$.

7. $-2\left(1 + \sqrt{3}i\right)$ (Quadrant III)

$a = -2, b = -2\sqrt{3}, r = \sqrt{(-2)^2 + \left(-2\sqrt{3}\right)^2} = \sqrt{4 + 12} = 4$

$\tan \theta = \dfrac{2\sqrt{3}}{2} = \sqrt{3} \Rightarrow \theta = \dfrac{-2\pi}{3}$

Polar form: $z = 4\left(\cos \dfrac{-2\pi}{3} + i \sin \dfrac{-2\pi}{3}\right)$

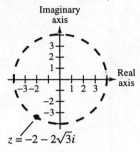

$z = -2 - 2\sqrt{3}i$

9. $6i$ along positive imaginary axis.

$a = 0, b = 6 \Rightarrow r = \sqrt{(0)^2 + (6)^2} = 6.$

$\tan \theta = \text{undefined} \Rightarrow \theta = \dfrac{\pi}{2}.$

Polar form: $z = 6\left(\cos \dfrac{\pi}{2} + i \sin \dfrac{\pi}{2}\right)$

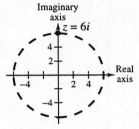

11. 7 along positive real axis.

$a = 7, b = 0 \Rightarrow r = \sqrt{(7)^2 + (0)^2} = 7$

$\tan \theta = 0 \Rightarrow \theta = 0$

$z = 7(\cos 0 + i \sin 0)$

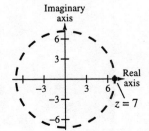

13. The graph of $1 + 6i$ is sketched below.

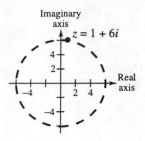

We find the modulus and argument as follows.

$$r = \sqrt{1^2 + 6^2} = \sqrt{37}$$

$$\tan \theta = \frac{6}{1} = 6$$

$$\theta \approx 80.5° \quad \text{(Quadrant I)}$$

Thus, the polar form of $1 + 6i$ is $z = \sqrt{37} (\cos 80.5° + i \sin 80.5°)$.

15. $-3 - i$ (Quadrant III)

$$a = -3, b = -1 \Rightarrow r = \sqrt{(-3)^2 + (-1)^2} = \sqrt{10}$$

$$\tan \theta = \frac{1}{3} \Rightarrow \theta \approx -161.6°$$

Polar form: $z = \sqrt{10} [\cos(-161.6°) + i \sin(-161.6°)]$

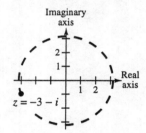

17. To plot a complex number in polar form, we draw a circle with radius equal to the modulus of the complex number. We then find the intersection of the terminal side of the argument with the circle. The graph of the given complex number is sketched below. $z = 2i$

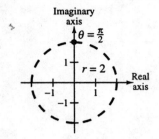

19. $z = \dfrac{3}{2}\left(\cos\dfrac{5\pi}{3} + i\sin\dfrac{5\pi}{3}\right)$

$$= \dfrac{3}{2}\left(\dfrac{1}{2} - i\left(\dfrac{\sqrt{3}}{2}\right)\right)$$

$$= \dfrac{3}{2}\left(\dfrac{1}{2} - \dfrac{\sqrt{3}}{2}i\right)$$

$$= \dfrac{3}{4} - \dfrac{3\sqrt{3}}{4}i$$

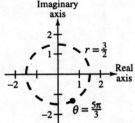

21. To plot a complex number in polar form, we draw a circle with radius equal to the modulus of the complex number. We then find the intersection of the terminal side of the argument with the circle. The graph of the given complex number is sketched below.

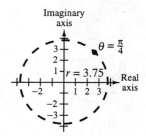

We find the standard form by evaluating the polar form.

$$3.75\left(\cos\frac{\pi}{4} + i\sin\frac{\pi}{4}\right) = 3.75\left(\frac{\sqrt{2}}{2} + \frac{\sqrt{2}}{2}i\right) \approx 2.65 + 2.65i$$

23. $4\left(\cos\frac{3\pi}{2} + i\sin\frac{3\pi}{2}\right) = 4(0 - i) = -4i$

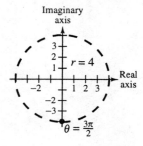

25. $7(\cos 0 + i\sin 0) = 7\left(1 + i(0)\right) = 7$

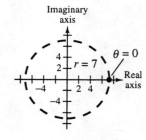

27. $\left[3\left(\cos\frac{\pi}{3} + i\sin\frac{\pi}{3}\right)\right]\left[4\left(\cos\frac{\pi}{6} + i\sin\frac{\pi}{6}\right)\right] = (3)(4)\left[\cos\left(\frac{\pi}{3} + \frac{\pi}{6}\right) + i\sin\left(\frac{\pi}{3} + \frac{\pi}{6}\right)\right]$

$$= 12\left(\cos\frac{\pi}{2} + i\sin\frac{\pi}{2}\right)$$

29. To multiply two complex numbers in polar form, we multiply moduli and add arguments.

$$[0.5(\cos \pi + i \sin \pi)][0.5(\cos[-\pi] + i \sin[-\pi])] = (0.5)(0.5)[\cos(\pi + [-\pi]) + i \sin(\pi + [-\pi])]$$

$$= 0.25(\cos 0 + i \sin 0)$$

31. $\dfrac{2[\cos(2\pi/3) + i \sin(2\pi/3)]}{4[\cos(2\pi/9) + i \sin(2\pi/9)]} = \dfrac{2}{4}\left[\cos\left(\dfrac{2\pi}{3} - \dfrac{2\pi}{9}\right) + i \sin\left(\dfrac{2\pi}{3} - \dfrac{2\pi}{9}\right)\right]$

$$= \dfrac{1}{2}\left(\cos\dfrac{4\pi}{9} + i \sin\dfrac{4\pi}{9}\right)$$

33. To divide two complex numbers in polar form, we divide moduli and subtract arguments.

$$\dfrac{12[\cos(\pi/3) + i \sin(\pi/3)]}{3[\cos(\pi/6) + i \sin(\pi/6)]} = \dfrac{12}{3}\left[\cos\left(\dfrac{\pi}{3} - \dfrac{\pi}{6}\right) + i \sin\left(\dfrac{\pi}{3} - \dfrac{\pi}{6}\right)\right]$$

$$= 4\left(\cos\dfrac{\pi}{6} + i \sin\dfrac{\pi}{6}\right)$$

35. $(1 + i)^4 \Rightarrow r = \sqrt{1^2 + 1^2} = \sqrt{2}$. Furthermore, $\theta = \dfrac{\pi}{4}$.

Thus,

$$(1 + i)^4 = (\sqrt{2})^4\left(\cos\left[(4)\left(\dfrac{\pi}{4}\right)\right] + i \sin\left[(4)\left(\dfrac{\pi}{4}\right)\right]\right)$$

$$= 4(\cos \pi + i \sin \pi)$$

$$= 4(-1 + i(0)) = -4.$$

37. We begin by finding the modulus and argument of $-1 + i$ as follows.

$$r = \sqrt{(-1)^2 + 1^2} = \sqrt{2}$$
$$\tan \theta = \dfrac{1}{-1} = -1$$

$$\theta = \dfrac{3\pi}{4} \quad \text{(Quadrant II)}$$

Then, we raise the modulus to the indicated power, and multiply the argument by that power.

$$(-1 + i)^{10} = (\sqrt{2})^{10}\left[\cos\dfrac{15\pi}{2} + i \sin\dfrac{15\pi}{2}\right]$$

$$= 32\left(\cos\dfrac{3\pi}{2} + i \sin\dfrac{3\pi}{2}\right) = 32(0 - i) = -32i$$

39. $(1 - \sqrt{3}i)^3 \Rightarrow r = \sqrt{(1)^2 + (-\sqrt{3})^2} = \sqrt{4} = 2$ and $\theta = \dfrac{5\pi}{3}$

Thus,

$$(1 - \sqrt{3}i)^3 = (2)^3 (\cos 5\pi + i \sin 5\pi)$$

$$= 8(-1 + 0) = -8.$$

41. We raise the modulus to the indicated power, and multiply the argument by that power.

$$\left[3\left(\cos\frac{5\pi}{6} + i\sin\frac{5\pi}{6}\right)\right]^4 = 3^4\left(\cos\frac{20\pi}{6} + i\sin\frac{20\pi}{6}\right)$$

$$= 81\left(\cos\frac{4\pi}{3} + i\sin\frac{4\pi}{3}\right)$$

$$= 81\left(-\frac{1}{2} - \frac{\sqrt{3}}{2}i\right) = -\frac{81}{2} - \frac{81\sqrt{3}}{2}i$$

43. $\left[2\left(\cos\frac{\pi}{2} + i\sin\frac{\pi}{2}\right)\right]^8 \Rightarrow r = 2, \theta = \frac{\pi}{2}$

$$\left[2\left(\cos\frac{\pi}{2} + i\sin\frac{\pi}{2}\right)\right]^8 = (2)^8[\cos(4\pi) + i\sin(4\pi)]$$

$$= 256\big(1 + i(0)\big)$$

$$= 256$$

45. $z^2 = 16\left(\cos\frac{\pi}{3} + i\sin\frac{\pi}{3}\right)$

$$z = \sqrt{16}\left[\cos\frac{\pi/3 + 2\pi k}{2} + i\sin\frac{\pi/3 + 2\pi k}{2}\right]$$

for $k = 0$,

$$z = 4\left(\cos\frac{\pi}{6} + i\sin\frac{\pi}{6}\right) = 2\sqrt{3} + 2i$$

for $k = 1$,

$$= 4\left(\cos\frac{7\pi}{6} + i\sin\frac{7\pi}{6}\right) = -2\sqrt{3} - 2i$$

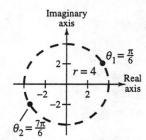

47. $z^4 = 16\left(\cos\dfrac{4\pi}{3} + i\sin\dfrac{4\pi}{3}\right)$

$$z = \sqrt[4]{16}\left(\cos\frac{4\pi/3 + 2\pi k}{4} + i\sin\frac{4\pi/3 + 2\pi k}{4}\right)$$

for $k = 0$,

$$z = 2\left(\cos\frac{\pi}{3} + i\sin\frac{\pi}{3}\right) = 1 + \sqrt{3}i$$

for $k = 1$,

$$z = 2\left(\cos\frac{5\pi}{6} + i\sin\frac{5\pi}{6}\right) = -\sqrt{3} + i$$

for $k = 2$,

$$z = 2\left(\cos\frac{4\pi}{3} + i\sin\frac{4\pi}{3}\right) = -1 - \sqrt{3}i$$

for $k = 3$,

$$z = 2\left(\cos\frac{11\pi}{6} + i\sin\frac{11\pi}{6}\right) = \sqrt{3} - i$$

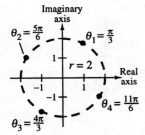

49. (a) First, we find the polar form of $-25i$.

$$-25i = 25\left(\cos\frac{3\pi}{2} + i\sin\frac{3\pi}{2}\right) = z^2$$

Then we apply Theorem 9.6 to find the general form of the roots.

$$z_k = \sqrt{25}\left(\cos\frac{(3\pi/2) + 2\pi k}{2} + i\sin\frac{(3\pi/2) + 2\pi k}{2}\right)$$

Finally, we can plug in $k = 0$ and $k = 1$ to obtain the two roots

$$z_0 = 5\left(\cos\frac{3\pi}{4} + i\sin\frac{3\pi}{4}\right)$$

$$z_1 = 5\left(\cos\frac{7\pi}{4} + i\sin\frac{7\pi}{4}\right).$$

(b) Drawing a circle of radius 5, we find the intersection with the terminal rays of the angles $3\pi/4$ and $7\pi/4$. We plot the intersection points as shown below.

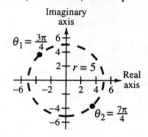

(c) To express the roots in standard form, we evaluate the polar forms as follows.

$$z_0 = 5\left(\cos\frac{3\pi}{4} + i\sin\frac{3\pi}{4}\right) = -\frac{5\sqrt{2}}{2} + \frac{5\sqrt{2}}{2}i$$

$$z_1 = 5\left(\cos\frac{7\pi}{4} + i\sin\frac{7\pi}{4}\right) = \frac{5\sqrt{2}}{2} - \frac{5\sqrt{2}}{2}i$$

51. $z^3 = -\dfrac{125}{2}\left(1 + \sqrt{3}i\right) = 125\left(-\dfrac{1}{2} - \dfrac{\sqrt{3}}{2}i\right)$

$r = 125, \tan\theta = \dfrac{\sqrt{3}}{2}\cdot 2 = \sqrt{3} \Rightarrow \theta = \dfrac{4\pi}{3}$

$z^3 = 125\left(\cos\dfrac{4\pi}{3} + i\sin\dfrac{4\pi}{3}\right)$

$z = \sqrt[3]{125}\left(\cos\dfrac{4\pi/3 + 2\pi k}{3} + i\sin\dfrac{4\pi/3 + 2\pi k}{3}\right)$

for $k = 0$,

$z = 5\left(\cos\dfrac{4\pi}{9} + i\sin\dfrac{4\pi}{9}\right) \approx 0.87 + 4.92i.$

for $k = 1$,

$z = 5\left(\cos\dfrac{10\pi}{9} + i\sin\dfrac{10\pi}{9}\right) \approx -4.7 - 1.71i.$

for $k = 2$,

$z = 5\left(\cos\dfrac{16\pi}{9} + i\sin\dfrac{16\pi}{9}\right) \approx 3.83 - 3.21i.$

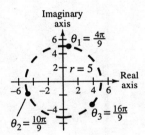

53. (a) First, we find the polar form of 8.

$$8 = 8(\cos 0 + i \sin 0) = z^3$$

Then we apply Theorem 9.6 to find the general form of the roots.

$$z = \sqrt[3]{8}\left(\cos\frac{2\pi k}{3} + i\sin\frac{2\pi k}{3}\right)$$

Finally, we can plug in $k = 0, 1$ and 2 to obtain the three roots

$$z_0 = 2(\cos 0 + i \sin 0)$$

$$z_1 = 2\left(\cos\frac{2\pi}{3} + i\sin\frac{2\pi}{3}\right)$$

$$z_2 = 2\left(\cos\frac{4\pi}{3} + i\sin\frac{4\pi}{3}\right).$$

(b) Drawing a circle of radius 2, we find the intersection with the terminal rays of the angles $0, 2\pi/3$ and $4\pi/3$. We plot the intersection points as shown below.

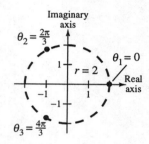

(c) To express the roots in standard form, we evaluate the polar forms as follows.

$$z_0 = 2(\cos 0 + i \sin 0) = 2$$

$$z_1 = 2\left(\cos\frac{2\pi}{3} + i\sin\frac{2\pi}{3}\right) = -1 + \sqrt{3}i$$

$$z_2 = 2\left(\cos\frac{4\pi}{3} + i\sin\frac{4\pi}{3}\right) = -1 - \sqrt{3}i$$

55. $1 = \cos 0 + i \sin 0 = z^4$

$$z = \cos\left(\frac{0 + 2\pi k}{4}\right) + i \sin\left(\frac{0 + 2\pi k}{4}\right)$$

for $k = 0$,

$\cos 0 + i \sin 0 = 1$

for $k = 1$,

$\cos\dfrac{\pi}{2} + i \sin\dfrac{\pi}{2} = i$

for $k = 2$,

$\cos \pi + i \sin \pi = -1$

for $k = 3$,

$\cos\dfrac{3\pi}{2} + i \sin\dfrac{3\pi}{2} = -i$

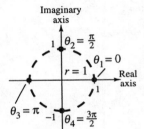

57. We can rewirte $x^4 - i = 0$ as $x^4 = i$ and apply Theorem 9.6 to find the fourth roots of i as follows.

$$x^4 = i = 1\left(\cos\frac{\pi}{2} + i\sin\frac{\pi}{2}\right)$$

$$x_k = 1\left(\cos\frac{(\pi/2) + 2\pi k}{4} + i\sin\frac{(\pi/2) + 2\pi k}{4}\right)$$

$$x_0 = \cos\frac{\pi}{8} + i\sin\frac{\pi}{8}$$

$$x_1 = \cos\frac{5\pi}{8} + i\sin\frac{5\pi}{8}$$

$$x_2 = \cos\frac{9\pi}{8} + i\sin\frac{9\pi}{8}$$

$$x_3 = \cos\frac{13\pi}{8} + i\sin\frac{13\pi}{8}$$

Drawing a circle of radius 1, we find the intersection with the terminal rays of the angles $\pi/8, 5\pi/8, 9\pi/8,$ and $13\pi/8$. We plot the intersection points as shown below.

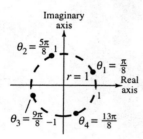

59. $x^5 + 243 = 0 \Rightarrow x^5 = -243 = 243(\cos \pi + i \sin \pi)$

$$x = \sqrt[5]{243}\left(\cos \frac{\pi + 2\pi k}{5} + i \sin \frac{\pi + 2\pi k}{5}\right), k = 0, 1, 2, 3, 4.$$

for $k = 0$,

$$3\left(\cos \frac{\pi}{5} + i \sin \frac{\pi}{5}\right) \approx 2.4 + 1.8i$$

for $k = 1$,

$$3\left(\cos \frac{3\pi}{5} + i \sin \frac{3\pi}{5}\right) \approx -0.9 + 2.9i$$

for $k = 2$,

$$3(\cos \pi + i \sin \pi) = -3$$

for $k = 3$,

$$3\left(\cos \frac{7\pi}{5} + i \sin \frac{7\pi}{5}\right) \approx -0.9 - 2.9i$$

for $k = 4$,

$$3\left(\cos \frac{9\pi}{5} + i \sin \frac{9\pi}{5}\right) \approx 2.4 - 1.8i$$

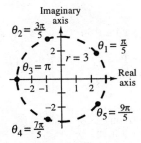

Solutions: $2.4 + 1.8i, -0.9 + 2.9i, -3, -0.9 - 2.9i, 2.4 - 1.8i$.

61. $x^3 + 64i = 0 \Rightarrow x^3 = -64i = 64\left(\cos \frac{3\pi}{2} + i \sin \frac{3\pi}{2}\right)$

$$x = \sqrt[3]{64}\left(\cos \frac{3\pi/2 + 2\pi k}{3} + i \sin \frac{3\pi/2 + 2\pi k}{3}\right)$$

$k = 0, 1, 2$

for $k = 0$,

$$4\left(\cos \frac{\pi}{2} + i \sin \frac{\pi}{2}\right) = 4i$$

for $k = 1$,

$$4\left(\cos \frac{7\pi}{6} + i \sin \frac{7\pi}{6}\right) = -2\sqrt{3} - 2i$$

for $k = 2$,

$$4\left(\cos \frac{11\pi}{6} + i \sin \frac{11\pi}{6}\right) = 2\sqrt{3} - 2i$$

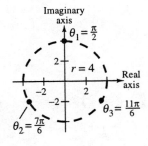

Solutions: $4i, -2\sqrt{3} - 2i, 2\sqrt{3} - 2i$

63. $\dfrac{z_1}{z_2} = \dfrac{r_1(\cos\theta_1 + i\sin\theta_1)}{r_2(\cos\theta_2 + i\sin\theta_2)} \cdot \dfrac{\cos\theta_2 - i\sin\theta_2}{\cos\theta_2 - i\sin\theta_2}$

$\qquad = \dfrac{r_1}{r_2}\Big[\cos\theta_1\cos\theta_2 + \sin\theta_1\sin\theta_2 + i(\cos\theta_2\sin\theta_1 - \cos\theta_1\sin\theta_2)\Big]$

$\qquad = \dfrac{r_1}{r_2}\Big[\cos(\theta_1 - \theta_2) + i\sin(\theta_1 - \theta_2)\Big]$

65. (a) $z\bar{z} = [r(\cos\theta + i\sin\theta)]\,[r(\cos(-\theta) + \sin(-\theta))]$

$\qquad = (r)\,(r)\,[\cos(\theta - \theta) + i\sin(\theta - \theta)]$

$\qquad = r^2\,(\cos 0 + i\sin 0)$

$\qquad = r^2$

$\quad$ **(b)** $z/\bar{z} = \dfrac{r(\cos\theta + \sin\theta)}{r(\cos(-\theta) + i\sin(-\theta))}$

$\qquad = \dfrac{r}{r}[\cos(\theta + \theta) + i\sin(\theta + \theta)]$

$\qquad = (\cos(2\theta) + i\sin(2\theta)$

67. (a) $z = 2\left(\cos\frac{\pi}{6} + i\sin\frac{\pi}{6}\right)$

$\qquad = \sqrt{3} + i$

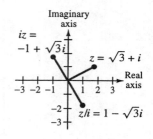

$\quad iz = 2\left(\cos\frac{\pi}{6} + i\sin\frac{\pi}{6}\right)\left(\cos\frac{\pi}{2} + i\sin\frac{\pi}{2}\right)$

$\qquad = 2\left(\cos\frac{2\pi}{3} + i\sin\frac{2\pi}{3}\right)$

$\qquad = -1 + \sqrt{3}i$ $\qquad\qquad\qquad$ (90° rotation counterclockwise)

$\quad z/i = [2\left(\cos\frac{\pi}{6} + i\sin\frac{\pi}{6}\right) / \left(\cos\frac{\pi}{2} + i\sin\frac{\pi}{2}\right)$

$\qquad = 2\left(\cos\left(-\frac{\pi}{3}\right) + i\sin\left(-\frac{\pi}{3}\right)\right)$

$\qquad = 1 - \sqrt{3}i$ $\qquad\qquad\qquad$ (90° rotation clockwise)

$\quad$ **(b)** The geometric effect of multiplication by i is to rotate z by 90° in the counterclockwise direction. The geometric effect of division by i is to rotate z by 90° in the clockwise direction.

Section 8.4   Complex Vector Spaces and Inner Products

1. $3\mathbf{u} = 3(i, 3 - i) = (3i, 9 - 3i)$

3. $(1 + 2i)\mathbf{w} = (1 + 2i)(4i, 6)$
$$= (4i + 8i^2, 6 + 12i)$$
$$= (-8 + 4i, 6 + 12i)$$

5. $\mathbf{u} - (2 - i)\mathbf{v} = (i, 3 - i) - (2 - i)(2 + i, 3 + i)$
$$= (i, 3 - i) - \left(4 - i^2, 6 - i - i^2\right)$$
$$= (i, 3 - i) - (5, 7 - i)$$
$$= (i - 5, 3 - i - 7 + i)$$
$$= (-5 + i, -4)$$

7. $\mathbf{u} + i\mathbf{v} + 2i\mathbf{w} = (i, 3 - i) + i(2 + i, 3 + i) + 2i(4i, 6)$
$$= (i, 3 - i) + (-1 + 2i, -1 + 3i) + (-8, 12i)$$
$$= (i - 1 + 2i - 8, 3 - i - 1 + 3i + 12i)$$
$$= (-9 + 3i, 2 + 14i)$$

9. We can show that S is not a basis for C^2 showing that the vectors in S are multiples of each other.

$$c_1\mathbf{v}_1 = \mathbf{v}_2$$
$$i(1, i) = (i, -1)$$

11. $S = \{(i, 0, 0), (0, i, i), (0, 0, 1)\}$
$$c_1\mathbf{v}_1 + c_2\mathbf{v}_2 + c_3\mathbf{v}_3 = \mathbf{0}$$
$$(c_1 i, 0, 0) + (0, c_2 i, c_2 i) + (0, 0, c_3) = (0, 0, 0)$$
$$(c_1 i, c_2 i, c_2 i + c_3) = \mathbf{0}$$
$$c_1 i = 0 \Rightarrow c_1 = 0$$
$$c_2 i = 0 \Rightarrow c_2 = 0$$
$$c_2 i + c_3 = 0 \Rightarrow 0 + c_3 = 0 \Rightarrow c_3 = 0$$

S is a basis in C^3.

13. (a) We begin by expressing **v** as a linear combination of the basis vectors.

$$\mathbf{v} = c_1\mathbf{v}_1 + c_2\mathbf{v}_2 + c_3\mathbf{v}_3$$

$$= c_1(i, 0, 0) + c_2(i, i, 0) + c_3(i, i, i)$$

$$= \left(c_1 i, 0, 0\right) + \left(c_2 i, c_2 i, 0\right) + \left(c_3 i, c_3 i, c_3 i\right)$$

$$= \left(c_1 i + c_2 i + c_3 i, c_2 i + c_3 i, c_3 i\right)$$

$$= (1, 2, 0)$$

This gives us the following system.

$$c_1 i + c_2 i + c_3 i = 1$$

$$c_2 i + c_3 i = 2$$

$$c_3 i = 0$$

Solving this system yields $c_1 = i$, $c_2 = -2i$, and $c_3 = 0$.
Therefore, $\mathbf{v} = i(i, 0, 0) - 2i(i, i, 0) + 0(i, i, i)$.

(b) We begin by expressing **v** as a linear combination of the basis vectors.

$$\mathbf{v} = c_1\mathbf{v}_1 + c_2\mathbf{v}_2 + c_3\mathbf{v}_3$$

$$= c_1(1, 0, 0) + c_2(1, 1, 0) + c_3(0, 0, 1 + i)$$

$$= \left(c_1, 0, 0\right) + \left(c_2, c_2, 0\right) + \left(0, 0, c_3 + c_3 i\right)$$

$$= \left(c_1 + c_2, c_2, c_3[1 + i]\right)$$

$$= (1, 2, 0)$$

This gives us the following system.

$$c_1 + c_2 = 1$$

$$c_2 = 2$$

$$c_3(1 + i) = 0$$

Solving this system yields $c_1 = -1$, $c_2 = 2$, and $c_3 = 0$.
Therefore, $\mathbf{v} = -(1, 0, 0) + 2(1, 1, 0) + 0(0, 0, 1 + i)$.

15. (a) $\mathbf{v} = c_1\mathbf{v}_1 + c_2\mathbf{v}_2 + c_3\mathbf{v}_3$

$\quad = i(c_1 + c_2 + c_3), i(c_2 + c_3), c_3 i)$

$\quad = (-i, 2 + i, -1)$

$\qquad i(c_1 + c_2 + c_3) = -i$

$\qquad\qquad i(c_2 + c_3) = 2 + i$

$\qquad\qquad c_3 i = -1 \Longrightarrow c_3 = -\dfrac{1}{i} = i$

$\qquad\qquad i(c_2 + i) = 2 + i$

$\qquad\qquad c_2 i = 2 + i + 1 = 3 + i$

$\qquad\qquad c_2 = \dfrac{3 + i}{i} = 1 - 3i$

$\qquad c_1 + 1 - 3i + i = -1$

$c_1 = -1 - 1 + 3i - 1 = -2 + 2i$

Therefore, $\mathbf{v} = (-2 + 2i)\mathbf{v}_1 + (1 - 3i)\mathbf{v}_2 + i\mathbf{v}_3$.

(b) $\mathbf{v} = c_1\mathbf{v}_1 + c_2\mathbf{v}_2 + c_3\mathbf{v}_3$

$\quad = (c_1 + c_2, c_2, c_3 + c_3 i)$

$\quad = (-i, 2 + i, -1)$

$c_1 + c_2 = -i \Longrightarrow c_1 = -i - 2 - i = -2 - 2i$

$\qquad\qquad c_2 = 2 + i$

$\qquad\qquad c_3 + c_3 i = -1$

$\qquad\qquad c_3(1 + i) = -1 \Longrightarrow c_3 = -\dfrac{1}{1 + i} = \dfrac{1}{2}(-1 + i)$

Therefore, $\mathbf{v} = (-2 - 2i)\mathbf{v}_1 + (2 + i)\mathbf{v}_2 + \dfrac{1}{2}(-1 + i)\mathbf{v}_3$.

17. $\|\mathbf{v}\| = (\mathbf{v} \cdot \mathbf{v})^{\frac{1}{2}} = (|v_1|^2 + |v_2|^2)^{\frac{1}{2}}$

$\quad = \sqrt{(1)^2 + (1)^2} = \sqrt{1 + 1} = \sqrt{2}$

19. $\|\mathbf{v}\| = \sqrt{\mathbf{v} \cdot \mathbf{v}} = \sqrt{3^2[(6 + i)(6 - i) + (2 - i)(2 + i)]}$

$\quad = 3\sqrt{(36 + 1) + (4 + 1)} = 3\sqrt{42}$.

21. $\|\mathbf{v}\| = \sqrt{1^2 + (2^2 + 1^2) + 1^2} = \sqrt{1 + 5 + 1} = \sqrt{7}$

23. $\|\mathbf{v}\| = \sqrt{(1^2 + 2^2) + 1^2 + 3^2 + (1^2 + 1^2)} = \sqrt{5 + 1 + 9 + 2} = \sqrt{17}$

25. $d(\mathbf{u}, \mathbf{v}) = \|\mathbf{u} - \mathbf{v}\| = \|(1 - i, -i)\|$

$\quad = \sqrt{(1^2 + 1^2) + (1)^2} = \sqrt{1 + 1 + 1} = \sqrt{3}$

27. $d(\mathbf{u}, \mathbf{v}) = \|\mathbf{u} - \mathbf{v}\| = \|(i, 2i - 1, 3i)\|$

$$= \sqrt{1^2 + (2^2 + 1^2) + 3^2} = \sqrt{1 + 4 + 1 + 9}$$

$$= \sqrt{15}.$$

29. $d(\mathbf{u}, \mathbf{v}) = \|\mathbf{u} - \mathbf{v}\| = \|(1, -1)\|$

$$= \sqrt{1^2 + 1^2} = \sqrt{2}$$

31. Since $i(1, i) = (i, -1)$, the vectors are linearly dependent.

33. Consider

$$c_1\mathbf{v}_1 + c_2\mathbf{v}_2 + c_3\mathbf{v}_3 = \mathbf{0}$$

$$c_1(1, i, 1 + i) + c_2(0, i, -i) + c_3(0, 0, 1) = (0, 0, 0)$$

$$(c_1, c_1 i, c_1[1 + i]) + (0, c_2 i, -c_2 i) + (0, 0, c_3) = (0, 0, 0)$$

$$(c_1, c_1 i + c_2 i, c_1[1 + i] - c_2 i + c_3) = (0, 0, 0)$$

This gives us the following system.

$$c_1 \qquad\qquad\qquad = 0$$

$$c_1 i \quad + c_2 i \qquad\quad = 0$$

$$c_1(1 + i) - c_2 i + c_3 = 0$$

Since this system has only the trivial solution $c_1 = c_2 = c_3 = 0$, the given set of vectors is linearly independent.

35. $\langle \mathbf{u}, \mathbf{v} \rangle = u_1 + u_2 u_2$ is *not* an inner product. For instance, if $\mathbf{u} = (1, 3)$ and $\mathbf{v} = (2, 5)$, then

$$\langle \mathbf{u}, \mathbf{v} \rangle = \langle (1, 3), (2, 5) \rangle = 1 + 3 \cdot 5 = 16, \quad \text{whereas}$$

$$\overline{\langle \mathbf{v}, \mathbf{u} \rangle} = \overline{\langle (2, 5), (1, 3) \rangle} = 2 + 5 \cdot 3 = 17.$$

37. To show that the given function is a complex inner product, we verify the definition of complex inner products.

(1) $\overline{\langle \mathbf{v}, \mathbf{u} \rangle} = \overline{4v_1\overline{u_1} + 6v_2\overline{u_2}}$

$\qquad = 4u_1\overline{v_1} + 6u_2\overline{v_2} = \langle \mathbf{u}, \mathbf{v} \rangle$

(2) $\langle \mathbf{u} + \mathbf{v}, \mathbf{w} \rangle = (4u_1 + v_1)\overline{w_1} + 6(u_2 + v_2)\overline{w_2}$

$\qquad = 4u_1\overline{w_1} + 4v_1\overline{w_1} + 6u_2\overline{w_2} + 6v_2\overline{w_2}$

$\qquad = (4u_1\overline{w_1} + 6u_2\overline{w_2}) + (4u_1\overline{w_1} + 6v_2\overline{w_2})$

$\qquad = \langle \mathbf{u}, \mathbf{w} \rangle + \langle \mathbf{v}, \mathbf{w} \rangle$

(3) $\langle k\mathbf{u}, \mathbf{v} \rangle = 4ku_1\overline{v_1} + 6ku_2\overline{v_2}$

$\qquad = k(4u_1\overline{v_1} + 6u_2\overline{v_2})$

$\qquad = k\langle \mathbf{u}, \mathbf{v} \rangle$

(4) $\langle \mathbf{u}, \mathbf{u} \rangle = 4u_1\overline{u_1} + 6u_2\overline{u_2}$

$\qquad = 4|u_1|^2 + 6|u_2|^2 \geq 0$

$\langle \mathbf{u}, \mathbf{u} \rangle = 0$ if and only if $u_1 = u_2 = 0$

Since all four properties hold, the given function is a complex inner product.

39. $v_1 = (i, 0, 0)$, $v_2 = (i, i, 0)$, $v_3 = (z_1, z_2, z_3)$ and $\{v_1, v_2, v_3\}$ is not a basis for C^3. Then,

$$\begin{vmatrix} i & 0 & 0 \\ i & i & 0 \\ z_1 & z_2 & z_3 \end{vmatrix} = 0$$

which implies that $z_3 = 0$.

41. $(\mathbf{u} + \mathbf{v}) \cdot \mathbf{w} = \left[(u_1, \ldots, u_n) + (v_1, \ldots, u_n) \right] \cdot (w_1, \ldots, w_n)$

$\qquad = (u_1 + v_1, \ldots, u_n + v_n) \cdot (w_1, \ldots, w_n)$

$\qquad = ((u_1 + v_1)\overline{w_1}, \ldots, (u_n + v_n)\overline{w_n})$

$\qquad = (u_1\overline{w_1} + v_1\overline{w_1}, \ldots, u_n\overline{w_n} + v_n\overline{w_n})$

$\qquad = (u_1\overline{w_1}, \ldots, u_n\overline{w_n}) + (v_1\overline{w_1}, \ldots, u_n\overline{w_n})$

$\qquad = \mathbf{u} \cdot \mathbf{w} + \mathbf{v} \cdot \mathbf{w}$

43. $\mathbf{u} \cdot k\mathbf{v} = \overline{k\mathbf{v} \cdot \mathbf{u}} = \overline{k}\,\overline{\mathbf{v} \cdot \mathbf{u}} = \overline{k}(\mathbf{u} \cdot \mathbf{v})$

45. From Exercise 44, we see that $\mathbf{u} \cdot \mathbf{u} = 0$ if and only if $u_1 = u_2 = \cdots = u_n = 0$; that is, if $\mathbf{u} = \mathbf{0}$.

47. We use the properties of linear transformations to find T.

$$
\begin{aligned}
T(x, y) &= T(x, 0) + T(0, y) \\
&= xT(1, 0) + yT(0, 1) \\
&= x(2 + i, 1) + y(0, -i) \\
&= (2x + xi, x) + (0, -yi) \\
&= (2x + xi, x - yi)
\end{aligned}
$$

49. $A = \begin{bmatrix} 1 & 0 \\ i & i \end{bmatrix}$, $\mathbf{v} = \begin{bmatrix} 1 + i \\ 1 - i \end{bmatrix}$, $\mathbf{w} = \begin{bmatrix} 0 \\ 0 \end{bmatrix}$

Image:

$$
A\mathbf{v} = \begin{bmatrix} 1 & 0 \\ i & i \end{bmatrix} \begin{bmatrix} 1 + i \\ 1 - i \end{bmatrix} = \begin{bmatrix} 1 + i \\ i - 1 + i + 1 \end{bmatrix} = \begin{bmatrix} 1 + i \\ 2i \end{bmatrix}
$$

Preimage:

$$
\begin{bmatrix} 1 & 0 \\ i & i \end{bmatrix} \begin{bmatrix} w_1 \\ w_2 \end{bmatrix} = \begin{bmatrix} 0 \\ 0 \end{bmatrix}
$$

$$
\begin{bmatrix} w_1 \\ w_1 i + w_2 i \end{bmatrix} = \begin{bmatrix} 0 \\ 0 \end{bmatrix} \Rightarrow w_1 = w_2 = 0
$$

Thus, the preimage is $\begin{bmatrix} 0 \\ 0 \end{bmatrix}$.

51. The image of $\mathbf{v}$ is given by

$$
A\mathbf{v} = \begin{bmatrix} 1 & 0 \\ i & 0 \\ i & i \end{bmatrix} \begin{bmatrix} 2 - i \\ 3 + 2i \end{bmatrix} = \begin{bmatrix} 2 - i \\ 1 + 2i \\ -1 + 5i \end{bmatrix}.
$$

The preimage of $\mathbf{w}$ is given by solving $A\mathbf{u} = \mathbf{w}$,

$$
\begin{bmatrix} 1 & 0 \\ i & 0 \\ i & i \end{bmatrix} \begin{bmatrix} u_1 \\ u_2 \end{bmatrix} = \begin{bmatrix} 2 \\ 2i \\ 3i \end{bmatrix},
$$

which yields

$$
u_1 = 2
$$

$$
u_1 i + u_2 i = 3i \Rightarrow 2i + u_2 i = 3i \Rightarrow u_2 = 1.
$$

Thus, the preimage of $\mathbf{w}$ is $\begin{bmatrix} 2 \\ 1 \end{bmatrix}$.

53. $T(\mathbf{v}) = A\mathbf{v}$

$$T(v_1, v_2) = \begin{bmatrix} 1 & 0 \\ i & i \end{bmatrix} \begin{bmatrix} v_1 \\ v_2 \end{bmatrix} = \begin{bmatrix} v_1 \\ v_1 i + v_2 i \end{bmatrix} = \begin{bmatrix} 0 \\ 0 \end{bmatrix} \Rightarrow v_1 = 0 \Rightarrow v_2 = 0.$$

Thus, the kernel of T is $\mathbf{v} = \begin{bmatrix} 0 \\ 0 \end{bmatrix}$.

55. $\quad T_2 \circ T_1 = \begin{bmatrix} -i & i \\ i & -i \end{bmatrix} \begin{bmatrix} 0 & i \\ i & 0 \end{bmatrix} = \begin{bmatrix} -1 & 1 \\ 1 & -1 \end{bmatrix}$

$$(T_2 \circ T_1)\mathbf{v} = \begin{bmatrix} -1 & 1 \\ 1 & -1 \end{bmatrix} \begin{bmatrix} i \\ i \end{bmatrix} = \begin{bmatrix} 0 \\ 0 \end{bmatrix}$$

57. (a) Yes, this set is a subspace. It is nonempty because it contains the zero matrix. The sum of two symmetric matrices is again symmetric, and a scalar multiple of a symmetric matrix is again symmetric, which implies that the set is closed under both addition and scalar multiplication.

(b) No. This is not a subspace. For example, let $A = \begin{bmatrix} 1 & 0 \\ 0 & 1 \end{bmatrix}$ be in the set and i a scalar. Then,

$$(\overline{iA})^T = \left(\overline{i \begin{bmatrix} 1 & 0 \\ 0 & 1 \end{bmatrix}} \right)^T = \left(\overline{\begin{bmatrix} i & 0 \\ 0 & i \end{bmatrix}} \right)^T = \begin{bmatrix} -i & 0 \\ 0 & -i \end{bmatrix}^T$$

$$= \begin{bmatrix} -i & 0 \\ 0 & -i \end{bmatrix} \neq i \begin{bmatrix} 1 & 0 \\ 0 & 1 \end{bmatrix} = iA$$

(c) This is not a subspace. For example, $A = \begin{bmatrix} 1 & 0 \\ 0 & 1 \end{bmatrix}$ is in the set, but iA is not.

(d) Yes, this set is a subspace. It is nonempty because the zero matrix is diagonal. The sum of 2 diagonal matrices is diagonal, and the scalar multiples of diagonal matrices are diagonal, which shows that the set is closed under both addition and scalar multiplication.

Section 8.5 Unitary and Hermitian Matrices

1. $A^* = \overline{A}^T = \begin{bmatrix} -i & i \\ 2 & -3i \end{bmatrix}^T = \begin{bmatrix} -i & 2 \\ i & -3i \end{bmatrix}$

3. $A = \begin{bmatrix} 0 & 1 \\ 2 & 0 \end{bmatrix} \Rightarrow \overline{A} = \begin{bmatrix} 0 & 1 \\ 2 & 0 \end{bmatrix}$

$\overline{A}^T = \begin{bmatrix} 0 & 2 \\ 1 & 0 \end{bmatrix} = A^*$

5. $A^* = \overline{A}^T = \begin{bmatrix} 0 & 5-i & -\sqrt{2}i \\ 5+i & 6 & 4 \\ \sqrt{2}i & 4 & 3 \end{bmatrix}^T = \begin{bmatrix} 0 & 5+i & \sqrt{2}i \\ 5-i & 6 & 4 \\ -\sqrt{2}i & 4 & 3 \end{bmatrix}$

7. $A = \begin{bmatrix} 7+5i \\ 2i \\ 4 \end{bmatrix} \Rightarrow \overline{A} = \begin{bmatrix} 7-5i \\ -2i \\ 4 \end{bmatrix}$

$\overline{A}^T = [\, 7-5i \quad -2i \quad 4 \,] = A^*$

9. Since $\det(A) = 0$, does not have an inverse, and thus cannot be unitary.

11. $A = \begin{bmatrix} \frac{1+i}{\sqrt{2}} & 0 & -\frac{i}{\sqrt{2}} \\ 0 & 1 & 0 \end{bmatrix}$ which is not square. Therefore, it is not a unitary matrix.

13. $A = \begin{bmatrix} 1+i & 1+i \\ 1-i & 1-i \end{bmatrix} \Rightarrow \overline{A} = \begin{bmatrix} 1-i & 1-i \\ 1+i & 1+i \end{bmatrix}$

$\overline{A}^T = \begin{bmatrix} 1-i & 1+i \\ 1-i & 1+i \end{bmatrix} = A^*$

$AA^* = \begin{bmatrix} 1+i & 1+i \\ 1-i & 1-i \end{bmatrix} \begin{bmatrix} 1-i & 1+i \\ 1-i & 1+i \end{bmatrix} = \begin{bmatrix} 4 & 4i \\ -4i & 4 \end{bmatrix} \neq I_2$

Therefore, A is not unitary.

15. $I_n^* = \overline{I_n}^T = I_n^T = I_n \Rightarrow I_n I_n^* = I_n I_n = I_n.$

Therefore, I_n is unitary, since $I_n^{-1} = I_n^*$.

17. $A = \begin{bmatrix} -\frac{i}{\sqrt{2}} & \frac{i}{\sqrt{3}} & \frac{i}{\sqrt{6}} \\ \frac{i}{\sqrt{2}} & \frac{i}{\sqrt{3}} & \frac{i}{\sqrt{6}} \\ 0 & \frac{i}{\sqrt{3}} & -\frac{i}{\sqrt{6}} \end{bmatrix} \Rightarrow \overline{A} = \begin{bmatrix} \frac{i}{\sqrt{2}} & -\frac{i}{\sqrt{3}} & -\frac{i}{\sqrt{6}} \\ -\frac{i}{\sqrt{2}} & -\frac{i}{\sqrt{3}} & -\frac{i}{\sqrt{6}} \\ 0 & -\frac{i}{\sqrt{3}} & \frac{i}{\sqrt{6}} \end{bmatrix}$

$\overline{A}^T = A^* = \begin{bmatrix} \frac{i}{\sqrt{2}} & -\frac{i}{\sqrt{2}} & 0 \\ -\frac{i}{\sqrt{3}} & -\frac{i}{\sqrt{3}} & -\frac{i}{\sqrt{3}} \\ -\frac{i}{\sqrt{6}} & -\frac{i}{\sqrt{6}} & \frac{i}{\sqrt{6}} \end{bmatrix}$

$AA^* = \begin{bmatrix} -\frac{i}{\sqrt{2}} & \frac{i}{\sqrt{3}} & \frac{i}{\sqrt{6}} \\ \frac{i}{\sqrt{2}} & \frac{i}{\sqrt{2}} & \frac{i}{\sqrt{6}} \\ 0 & \frac{i}{\sqrt{3}} & -\frac{i}{\sqrt{6}} \end{bmatrix} \begin{bmatrix} \frac{i}{\sqrt{2}} & -\frac{i}{\sqrt{2}} & 0 \\ -\frac{i}{\sqrt{3}} & -\frac{i}{\sqrt{3}} & -\frac{i}{\sqrt{3}} \\ -\frac{i}{\sqrt{6}} & -\frac{i}{\sqrt{6}} & \frac{i}{\sqrt{6}} \end{bmatrix}$

$= \begin{bmatrix} 1 & 0 & \frac{1}{6} \\ 0 & 1 & \frac{1}{6} \\ \frac{1}{6} & \frac{1}{6} & \frac{1}{2} \end{bmatrix} \neq I_3$

Therefore, A is not a unitary matrix.

19. (a) $r_1 = \left(-\frac{4}{5}, \frac{3}{5}i \right) \quad \Rightarrow \quad \|r_1\| = \sqrt{\frac{16}{25} + \frac{9}{25}} = 1$

$r_2 = \left(\frac{3}{5}, \frac{4}{5}i \right) \quad \Rightarrow \quad \|r_2\| = \sqrt{\frac{9}{25} + \frac{16}{25}} = 1$

$r_1 \cdot r_2 = \left(-\frac{4}{5} \right)\left(\frac{3}{5} \right) + \left(\frac{3}{5}i \right)\left(-\frac{4}{5}i \right) = -\frac{12}{25} + \frac{12}{25} = 0$

Therefore, row vectors of A form an orthonormal set in C^2.

(b) Since A is unitary, $A^{-1} = A^*$.

$\overline{A} = \begin{bmatrix} -\frac{4}{5} & -\frac{3}{5}i \\ \frac{3}{5} & -\frac{4}{5}i \end{bmatrix} \quad \Rightarrow \quad \overline{A}^T = A^* = A^{-1} = \begin{bmatrix} -\frac{4}{5} & \frac{3}{5} \\ -\frac{3}{5}i & -\frac{4}{5}i \end{bmatrix}$

21. (a) Let $\mathbf{r}_1 = \dfrac{1}{2\sqrt{2}}(\sqrt{3} - i, 1 + \sqrt{3}i)$ and $\mathbf{r}_2 = \dfrac{1}{2\sqrt{2}}(\sqrt{3} + i, 1 - \sqrt{3}i)$ be the row vectors of A. Since

$$\|\mathbf{r}_1\| = \sqrt{\mathbf{r}_1 \cdot \mathbf{r}_1} = \sqrt{\frac{1}{8}[(3 + 1) + (1 + 3)]} = 1$$

$$\|\mathbf{r}_2\| = \sqrt{\mathbf{r}_2 \cdot \mathbf{r}_2} = \sqrt{\frac{1}{8}[(3 + 1) + (1 + 3)]} = 1$$

$$\mathbf{r}_1 \cdot \mathbf{r}_2 = \frac{1}{8}\left[(3 - 2\sqrt{3}i - 1) + (1 + 2\sqrt{3}i - 3)\right] = 0$$

$\mathbf{r}_1$ and $\mathbf{r}_2$ form an orthonormal set of vectors, so (by Theorem 9.9) A is unitary.

(b) Since A is unitary,

$$A^{-1} = A^* = \overline{A}^T = \frac{1}{2\sqrt{2}}\begin{bmatrix} \sqrt{3} + i & 1 - \sqrt{3}i \\ \sqrt{3} - i & 1 + \sqrt{3}i \end{bmatrix}^T = \frac{1}{2\sqrt{2}}\begin{bmatrix} \sqrt{3} + i & \sqrt{3} - i \\ 1 - \sqrt{3}i & 1 + \sqrt{3}i \end{bmatrix}.$$

23. $A = \begin{bmatrix} 0 & 2 + i & 1 \\ 2 - i & i & 0 \\ 1 & 0 & 1 \end{bmatrix}$

Not Hermitian since not all the entries on the main diagonal, namely a_{22}, are real.

25. Since

$$A^* = \overline{A}^T = \begin{bmatrix} 0 & -i \\ i & 0 \end{bmatrix}^T = \begin{bmatrix} 0 & i \\ -i & 0 \end{bmatrix} = A,$$

A is Hermitian.

27. $A = \begin{bmatrix} 0 & 0 \\ 0 & 0 \end{bmatrix}.$

Hermitian since both properties hold.

29. We solve the equation $|\lambda I - A| = 0$ as follows.

$$|\lambda I - A| = \begin{vmatrix} \lambda & -i \\ i & \lambda \end{vmatrix} = \lambda^2 + i^2 = \lambda^2 - 1 = 0 \Rightarrow \lambda = \pm 1$$

Therefore, the eigenvalues are $\lambda = \pm 1$.

31. $A = \begin{bmatrix} 3 & 1 - i \\ 1 + i & 2 \end{bmatrix}$

$|\lambda I - A| = \begin{vmatrix} \lambda - 3 & -1 + i \\ -1 - i & \lambda - 2 \end{vmatrix} = (\lambda - 3)(\lambda - 2) - (-1 + i)(-1 - i)$

$$= \lambda^2 - 5\lambda + 6 - 1 - 1$$

$$= \lambda^2 - 5\lambda + 4 = (\lambda - 4)(\lambda - 1).$$

Eigenvalues: $\lambda = 4$, $\lambda = 1$.

33. $A = \begin{bmatrix} 2 & -\frac{i}{\sqrt{2}} & \frac{i}{\sqrt{2}} \\ \frac{i}{\sqrt{2}} & 2 & 0 \\ -\frac{i}{\sqrt{2}} & 0 & 2 \end{bmatrix}$

$|\lambda I - A| = \begin{vmatrix} \lambda - 2 & \frac{i}{\sqrt{2}} & -\frac{i}{\sqrt{2}} \\ -\frac{i}{\sqrt{2}} & \lambda - 2 & 0 \\ \frac{i}{\sqrt{2}} & 0 & \lambda - 2 \end{vmatrix}$

$(\lambda - 2)(\lambda - 2)(\lambda - 2) - \left[\left(\frac{i}{\sqrt{2}} \right)(\lambda - 2)\left(-\frac{i}{\sqrt{2}} \right) \right] + \left[(\lambda - 2)\left(-\frac{i}{\sqrt{2}} \right)\left(\frac{-i}{\sqrt{2}} \right) \right]$

$(\lambda - 2)(\lambda^2 - 4\lambda + 4) - \left(-\frac{i^2(\lambda - 2)}{2} + \frac{-i^2(\lambda - 2)}{2} \right)$

$= (\lambda - 2)(\lambda^2 - 4\lambda + 4) - (\lambda - 2)$

$= (\lambda - 2)[\lambda^2 - 4\lambda + 4 - 1]$

$= (\lambda - 2)(\lambda - 3)(\lambda - 1)$

Eigenvalues: $\lambda = 1, 2, 3$.

35. For each eigenvalue, we solve the equation

$$(\lambda I - A)\mathbf{v} = \begin{bmatrix} \lambda & -i \\ i & \lambda \end{bmatrix} \begin{bmatrix} v_1 \\ v_2 \end{bmatrix} = \begin{bmatrix} 0 \\ 0 \end{bmatrix} = \mathbf{0}.$$

For $\lambda = -1$, we have

$$\begin{bmatrix} -1 & -i \\ i & -1 \end{bmatrix} \begin{bmatrix} v_1 \\ v_2 \end{bmatrix} = \begin{bmatrix} 0 \\ 0 \end{bmatrix} \Rightarrow -v_1 - v_2 i = 0$$

$$v_1 i - v_2 = 0$$

$$\Rightarrow \mathbf{v} = t \begin{bmatrix} 1 \\ i \end{bmatrix}.$$

For $\lambda = 1$, we have

$$\begin{bmatrix} 1 & -i \\ i & 1 \end{bmatrix} \begin{bmatrix} v_1 \\ v_2 \end{bmatrix} = \begin{bmatrix} 0 \\ 0 \end{bmatrix} \Rightarrow v_1 - v_2 i = 0$$

$$v_1 i + v_2 = 0$$

$$\Rightarrow \mathbf{v} = t \begin{bmatrix} 1 \\ -i \end{bmatrix}.$$

37. Eigenvector for $\lambda = 1$.

$$\begin{bmatrix} -1 & \frac{i}{\sqrt{2}} & -\frac{i}{\sqrt{2}} \\ -\frac{i}{\sqrt{2}} & -1 & 0 \\ \frac{i}{\sqrt{2}} & 0 & -1 \end{bmatrix} \begin{bmatrix} v_1 \\ v_2 \\ v_3 \end{bmatrix} = \begin{bmatrix} 0 \\ 0 \\ 0 \end{bmatrix} \Rightarrow \qquad -v_1 + \frac{i}{\sqrt{2}} v_2 - \frac{i}{\sqrt{2}} v_3 = 0$$

$$-\frac{i}{\sqrt{2}} v_1 - \quad v_2 \qquad = 0$$

$$\frac{i}{\sqrt{2}} v_1 \qquad - \quad v_3 = 0$$

$$\mathbf{v} = t \begin{bmatrix} \sqrt{2} \\ -i \\ i \end{bmatrix}$$

Eigenvector for $\lambda = 2$.

$$\begin{bmatrix} 0 & \frac{i}{\sqrt{2}} & -\frac{i}{\sqrt{2}} \\ -\frac{i}{\sqrt{2}} & 0 & 0 \\ \frac{i}{\sqrt{2}} & 0 & 0 \end{bmatrix} \begin{bmatrix} v_1 \\ v_2 \\ v_3 \end{bmatrix} = \begin{bmatrix} 0 \\ 0 \\ 0 \end{bmatrix} \Rightarrow \qquad \frac{i}{\sqrt{2}} v_2 - \frac{i}{\sqrt{2}} v_3 = 0$$

$$-\frac{i}{\sqrt{2}} v_1 \qquad = 0$$

$$\frac{i}{\sqrt{2}} v_1 \qquad = 0$$

$$\mathbf{v} = t \begin{bmatrix} 0 \\ 1 \\ 1 \end{bmatrix}$$

Eigenvector for $\lambda = 3$.

$$\begin{bmatrix} 1 & \frac{i}{\sqrt{2}} & -\frac{i}{\sqrt{2}} \\ -\frac{i}{\sqrt{2}} & 1 & 0 \\ \frac{i}{\sqrt{2}} & 0 & 1 \end{bmatrix} \begin{bmatrix} v_1 \\ v_2 \\ v_3 \end{bmatrix} = \begin{bmatrix} 0 \\ 0 \\ 0 \end{bmatrix} \Rightarrow \qquad v_1 + \frac{i}{\sqrt{2}} v_2 - \frac{i}{\sqrt{2}} v_3 = 0$$

$$-\frac{i}{\sqrt{2}} v_1 + \quad v_2 \qquad = 0$$

$$\frac{i}{\sqrt{2}} v_1 \qquad + \quad v_3 = 0$$

$$\mathbf{v} = t \begin{bmatrix} \sqrt{2} \\ i \\ -i \end{bmatrix}$$

39. The eigenvectors of A are given in Exercise 35. We form the matrix P by normalizing these two eigenvectors and using the resulting unit vectors to create the columns of P.

$$\|\mathbf{v}_1\| = \|(1, i)\| = \sqrt{1 + 1} = \sqrt{2}$$

$$\|\mathbf{v}_2\| = \|(1, -i)\| = \sqrt{1 + 1} = \sqrt{2}$$

Thus,

$$P = \begin{bmatrix} \frac{1}{\sqrt{2}} & \frac{1}{\sqrt{2}} \\ \frac{i}{\sqrt{2}} & -\frac{i}{\sqrt{2}} \end{bmatrix}.$$

41. From Exercise 37, we have

$$\|\mathbf{v}_1\| = \|(\sqrt{2}, -i, i)\| = \sqrt{2 + 1 + 1} = 2$$

$$\|\mathbf{v}_2\| = \|(0, 1, 1)\| = \sqrt{0 + 1 + 1} = \sqrt{2}$$

$$\|\mathbf{v}_3\| = \|(\sqrt{2}, i, -i)\| = \sqrt{2 + 1 + 1} = 2$$

$$P = \begin{bmatrix} \frac{\sqrt{2}}{2} & 0 & \frac{\sqrt{2}}{2} \\ -\frac{i}{2} & \frac{\sqrt{2}}{2} & \frac{i}{2} \\ \frac{i}{2} & \frac{\sqrt{2}}{2} & -\frac{i}{2} \end{bmatrix} = \frac{1}{2}\begin{bmatrix} \sqrt{2} & 0 & \sqrt{2} \\ -i & \sqrt{2} & i \\ i & \sqrt{2} & -i \end{bmatrix}$$

43.

$$A = \begin{bmatrix} -1 & 0 & 0 \\ 0 & -1 & -1+i \\ 0 & -1-i & 0 \end{bmatrix}$$

$$|\lambda I - A| = \begin{bmatrix} \lambda+1 & 0 & 0 \\ 0 & \lambda+1 & 1-i \\ 0 & 1+i & \lambda \end{bmatrix}$$

$$= (\lambda+1)\left[(\lambda+1)\lambda - (1-i)(1+i)\right]$$

$$= (\lambda+1)\left[(\lambda^2 + \lambda - 2)\right]$$

$$= (\lambda+1)(\lambda+2)(\lambda-1)$$

Eigenvalues: $\lambda = -1, -2, 1$.

Eigenvector for $\lambda = -1$.

$$\begin{bmatrix} 0 & 0 & 0 \\ 0 & 0 & 1-i \\ 0 & 1+i & -1 \end{bmatrix} \Rightarrow \mathbf{v} = t \begin{bmatrix} 1 \\ 0 \\ 0 \end{bmatrix}$$

Eigenvector for $\lambda = 1$.

$$\begin{bmatrix} 2 & 0 & 0 \\ 0 & 2 & 1-i \\ 0 & 1+i & 1 \end{bmatrix} \begin{bmatrix} v_1 \\ v_2 \\ v_2 \end{bmatrix} = \begin{bmatrix} 0 \\ 0 \\ 0 \end{bmatrix} \Rightarrow \begin{aligned} 2v_1 &= 0 \\ 2v_2 + (1-i)v_3 &= 0 \\ (1+i)v_2 + v_3 &= 0 \end{aligned}$$

$$\mathbf{v} = t \begin{bmatrix} 0 \\ -1+i \\ 2 \end{bmatrix}$$

Eigenvector for $\lambda = -2$.

$$\begin{bmatrix} -1 & 0 & 0 \\ 0 & -1 & 1-i \\ 0 & 1+i & -2 \end{bmatrix} \begin{bmatrix} v_1 \\ v_2 \\ v_3 \end{bmatrix} = \begin{bmatrix} 0 \\ 0 \\ 0 \end{bmatrix} \Rightarrow \begin{aligned} -v_1 &= 0 \\ -v_2 + (1-i)v_3 &= 0 \\ (1+i)v_2 - 2v_3 &= 0 \end{aligned}$$

$$\mathbf{v} = t \begin{bmatrix} 0 \\ 2 \\ 1+i \end{bmatrix}$$

$$\|\mathbf{v}_1\| = \|(1, 0, 0)\| = 1$$

$$\|\mathbf{v}_2\| = \|(0, -1+i, 2)\| = \sqrt{1+1+4} = \sqrt{6}$$

$$\|\mathbf{v}_3\| = \|(0, 2, 1+i)\| = \sqrt{4+1+1} = \sqrt{6}$$

$$P = \frac{1}{\sqrt{6}} \begin{bmatrix} \sqrt{6} & 0 & 0 \\ 0 & -1+i & 2 \\ 0 & 2 & 1+i \end{bmatrix}$$

45. $z = -1 \Rightarrow \bar{z} = -1, iz = -i$, and $-i\bar{z} = i$. Therefore $a = \bar{z} = -1, b = iz = -i$, and $c = -i\bar{z} = i$. Using the results of Exercise 44, A is unitary if

$$A = \frac{1}{\sqrt{2}} \begin{bmatrix} -1 & -1 \\ -i & i \end{bmatrix}.$$

47. $A = \dfrac{1}{\sqrt{2}} \begin{bmatrix} i & a \\ b & c \end{bmatrix}$

$z = i, \bar{z} = -i, iz = -1, -i\bar{z} = -1$

Therefore, $a = -i, b = -1, c = -1$ and

$$A = \frac{1}{\sqrt{2}} \begin{bmatrix} i & -i \\ -1 & -1 \end{bmatrix}.$$

49. $(A*)* = \left(\overline{A^T}\right)^T = \overline{\overline{A}} = A.$

51. $(kA)* = \overline{kA^T} = \bar{k}\,\overline{A^T} = \bar{k}\,A*.$

53. $(iA)* = \bar{i}\,A* = -iA* = -i(-A) = iA,$
which shows that (iA) is Hermitian.

55. $\det(A*) = \det\left(\overline{A^T}\right) = \det\overline{A} = \overline{\det A}.$

57. (a) $A = \overline{A^T} = \left(\dfrac{A + \overline{A}}{2}\right) + i\left(\dfrac{A - \overline{A}}{2i}\right) = B + iC.$

B is real and symmetric, since

$$B^T = \left(\dfrac{A + \overline{A}}{2}\right)^T = \dfrac{A^T + \overline{A}^T}{2} = \dfrac{A + A^T}{2} = \dfrac{A + \overline{A}}{2} = B.$$

C is real and skew-symmetric, since

$$C^T = \left(\dfrac{A - \overline{A}}{2i}\right)^T = \dfrac{A^T - \overline{A}^T}{2i} = \dfrac{A^T - A}{2i} = \dfrac{\overline{A} - A}{2i} = -C.$$

(b) $A = \begin{bmatrix} 2 & 1 + i \\ 1 - i & 3 \end{bmatrix}, \quad A^T = \begin{bmatrix} 2 & 1 - i \\ 1 + i & 3 \end{bmatrix}$

$$\dfrac{A + A^T}{2} = \begin{bmatrix} 2 & 1 \\ 1 & 3 \end{bmatrix}; \quad \dfrac{A - \overline{A}}{2i} = \dfrac{\begin{bmatrix} 0 & 2i \\ -2i & 0 \end{bmatrix}}{2i} = \begin{bmatrix} 0 & 1 \\ -1 & 0 \end{bmatrix}$$

Thus, $A = \begin{bmatrix} 2 & 1 \\ 1 & 3 \end{bmatrix} + i\begin{bmatrix} 0 & 1 \\ -1 & 0 \end{bmatrix} = B + iC.$

(c) $A = \left(\dfrac{A + \overline{A^T}}{2}\right) + i\left(\dfrac{A - \overline{A^T}}{2i}\right) = B + iC.$

$$\overline{B}^T = \overline{\left(\dfrac{A + \overline{A^T}}{2}\right)}^T = \left(\dfrac{\overline{A} + A^T}{2}\right)^T = \dfrac{A + \overline{A}^T}{2} = B$$

$$\overline{C}^T = \overline{\left(\dfrac{A - \overline{A^T}}{2i}\right)}^T = \left(\dfrac{\overline{A} - A^T}{-2i}\right)^T = \dfrac{\overline{A}^T - A}{-2i} = \dfrac{A - \overline{A}^T}{2i} = C.$$

(d) $A = \begin{bmatrix} i & 2 \\ i + 2 & 1 - 2i \end{bmatrix}, \quad \overline{A}^T = \begin{bmatrix} -i & 2 - i \\ 2 & 1 + 2i \end{bmatrix}$

$$A = \begin{bmatrix} 0 & 2 - \frac{i}{2} \\ 2 + \frac{i}{2} & 1 \end{bmatrix} + i\begin{bmatrix} 1 & \frac{1}{2} \\ \frac{1}{2} & -2 \end{bmatrix}$$

59. (a) Let $A = A^*$ be Hermitian. Then $AA^* = AA = A^*A$ which shows that A is normal.

(b) Let A be unitary, $A^{-1} = A^*$. Then $AA^* = AA^{-1} = A^{-1}A = A^*A$, which shows that A is normal.

(c) $A = \begin{bmatrix} 1 & 2 \\ 2 & 1 \end{bmatrix}$ is Hermitian, but not unitary.

(d) $A = \dfrac{1}{2}\begin{bmatrix} 1 + i & 1 - i \\ 1 - i & 1 + i \end{bmatrix}$ is unitary, but not Hermitian.

(e) $A = \begin{bmatrix} 1 & i \\ i & 1 \end{bmatrix}$ is normal, but neither Hermitian nor unitary.

(f) $\lambda_1 = 1 - i, \begin{bmatrix} 1 \\ -1 \end{bmatrix}, \quad \lambda_2 = 1 + i, \begin{bmatrix} 1 \\ 1 \end{bmatrix}.$

(g) Eigenvalue of $\begin{bmatrix} i & 1 \\ 0 & i \end{bmatrix}$ is $\lambda = i$ (repeated). There is no basis of eigenvectors. The matrix is not normal.

Chapter 8   Review Exercises

1. $u = 2 - 4i,$

$z = 4i$

$u + z = (2 - 4i) + (4i)$

$= 2$

3. $u = 4 - 2i,$

$z = 4 + 2i$

$uz = (4 - 2i)(4 + 2i)$

$= 16 - 4i^2$

$= 16 + 4$

$= 20$

5. $\dfrac{u}{z} = \dfrac{6 - 2i}{3 - 3i}$

$= \dfrac{6 - 2i}{3 - 3i} \cdot \dfrac{3 + 3i}{3 + 3i}$

$= \dfrac{(6 - 2i)(3 + 3i)}{9 - 9i^2}$

$= \dfrac{1}{18}\left(18 + 18i - 6i - 6i^2\right)$

$= \dfrac{1}{18}(24 + 12i)$

$= \dfrac{4}{3} + \dfrac{2}{3}i$

7. $x^2 - 4x + 8 = 0.$

Completing the square we get

$x^2 - 4x + 4 = -8 + 4$

$(x - 2)^2 = -4$

$x - 2 = \pm 2i$

$x = 2 \pm 2i.$

9. We use the Quadratic Formula to solve $3x^2 + 3x + 3 = 0.$

$$x = \frac{-3 \pm \sqrt{3^2 - 4(3)(3)}}{2(3)} = \frac{-3 \pm 3\sqrt{-3}}{6} = -\frac{1}{2} \pm \frac{\sqrt{3}}{2}i$$

11. $A + B = \begin{bmatrix} 4 - i & 2 \\ 3 & 3 + i \end{bmatrix} + \begin{bmatrix} 1 + i & i \\ 2i & 2 + i \end{bmatrix}$

$\qquad = \begin{bmatrix} 5 & 2 + i \\ 3 + 2i & 5 + 2i \end{bmatrix}$

13. $\det(A - B) = \det \left(\begin{bmatrix} 4 - i & 2 \\ 3 & 3 + i \end{bmatrix} - \begin{bmatrix} 1 + i & i \\ 2i & 2 + i \end{bmatrix} \right)$

$\qquad = \det \begin{bmatrix} 3 - 2i & 2 - i \\ 3 - 2i & 1 \end{bmatrix}$

$\qquad = 3 - 2i - (2 - i)(3 - 2i) = 3 - 2i - (4 - 7i) = -1 + 5i$

15. $z = \overline{(-1 + 2i)} = -1 - 2i.$

17. $|w| = |2 - 2i| = \sqrt{2^2 + (-2)^2} = \sqrt{4 + 4} = 2\sqrt{2}$

19. $\overline{wv} = \overline{(2 - 2i)(3 + 1)} = \overline{6 - 4i + 2}$

$\qquad = \overline{8 - 4i}$

$\qquad = 8 + 4i$

21. $\dfrac{2 + i}{2 - i} = \dfrac{2 + i}{2 - i} \cdot \dfrac{2 + i}{2 + i} = \dfrac{3 + 4i}{4 + 1} = \dfrac{3}{5} + \dfrac{4}{5}i$

23. $\dfrac{(1 - 2i)(1 + 2i)}{3 - 3i} = \dfrac{1 + 4}{3 - 3i} = \dfrac{5}{3 - 3i} \cdot \dfrac{3 + 3i}{3 + 3i}$

$\qquad\qquad = \dfrac{5(3 + 3i)}{9 + 9}$

$\qquad\qquad = \dfrac{5}{18}(3 + 3i) = \dfrac{5}{6}(1 + i)$

25. $A = \begin{bmatrix} 3 - i & -1 - 2i \\ -\frac{23}{5} + \frac{11}{5}i & 2 + 3i \end{bmatrix}$

$\qquad |A| = (3 - i)(2 + 3i) - (-1 - 2i)\left(-\dfrac{23}{5} + \dfrac{11}{5}i \right)$

$\qquad = (6 + 7i + 3) - \left(\dfrac{23}{5} + \dfrac{46}{5}i - \dfrac{11}{5}i + \dfrac{22}{5} \right)$

$\qquad = 9 + 7i - (9 + 7i) = 0$

Therefore, A^{-1} does not exist (A is singular.)

27. $4 + 4i, a = 4, b = 4, \Longrightarrow$

$\qquad r = \sqrt{16 + 16} = \sqrt{32} = 4\sqrt{2}$

$\qquad \tan \theta = 1 \Longrightarrow \theta = \dfrac{\pi}{4}$

$\qquad z = 4\sqrt{2} \left(\cos \dfrac{\pi}{4} + i \sin \dfrac{\pi}{4} \right)$

29. The modulus is given by

$$r = \sqrt{7^2 + (-4)^2} = \sqrt{49 + 16} = \sqrt{65}, \text{ and the argument is the solution of}$$

$$\tan \theta = -\frac{4}{7} \Longrightarrow \theta \approx -0.519 \quad \text{(Quadrant IV)}.$$

Therefore,

$$z = \sqrt{65}(\cos[-0.519] + i \sin[-0.519]).$$

31. $5\left[\cos\left(-\frac{\pi}{6}\right) + i \sin\left(-\frac{\pi}{6}\right)\right] = 5\left(\frac{\sqrt{3}}{2} + i\left[-\frac{1}{2}\right]\right) = \frac{5\sqrt{3}}{2} - \frac{5}{2}i$

33. To find the standard form, we simply evaluate the polar form of the complex number.

$$6\left(\cos\frac{2\pi}{3} + i \sin\frac{2\pi}{3}\right) = 6\left(-\frac{1}{2} + i\frac{\sqrt{3}}{2}\right) = -3 + 3\sqrt{3}i$$

35. $\left[4\left(\cos\frac{\pi}{2} + i \sin\frac{\pi}{2}\right)\right]\left[3\left(\cos\frac{\pi}{6} + i \sin\frac{\pi}{6}\right)\right] =$

$$(4)(3)\left[\cos\left(\frac{\pi}{2} + \frac{\pi}{6}\right) + i \sin\left(\frac{\pi}{2} + \frac{\pi}{6}\right)\right] = 12\left(\cos\frac{2\pi}{3} + i \sin\frac{2\pi}{3}\right)$$

37. We divide complex numbers in polar form by dividing moduli and subtracting arguments.

$$\frac{9[\cos(\pi/2) + i \sin(\pi/2)]}{6[\cos(2\pi/3) + i \sin(2\pi/3)]} = \frac{9}{6}\left[\cos\left(\frac{\pi}{2} - \frac{2\pi}{3}\right) + i \sin\left(\frac{\pi}{2} - \frac{2\pi}{3}\right)\right]$$

$$= \frac{3}{2}\left[\cos\left(-\frac{\pi}{6}\right) + i \sin\left(-\frac{\pi}{6}\right)\right]$$

39. $(-1 - i)^4; a = -1, b = -1$

$$r = \sqrt{1 + 1} = \sqrt{2}$$

$$\tan \theta = 1 \Longrightarrow \theta = \frac{\pi}{4}; \left[\sqrt{2}\left(\cos\frac{\pi}{4} + i \sin\frac{\pi}{4}\right)\right]^4$$

$$= (\sqrt{2})^4\left[\cos\left(4 \cdot \frac{\pi}{4}\right) + i \sin\left(4 \cdot \frac{\pi}{4}\right)\right]$$

$$= 4(\cos \pi + i \sin \pi)$$

41. By Demoivre's Theorem, we raise the modulus to the indicated power and multiply the argument by that power.

$$\left[\sqrt{2}\left(\cos\frac{\pi}{6} + i \sin\frac{\pi}{6}\right)\right]^7 = (\sqrt{2})^7\left(\cos\frac{7\pi}{6} + i \sin\frac{7\pi}{6}\right)$$

$$= 8\sqrt{2}\left(\cos\frac{7\pi}{6} + i \sin\frac{7\pi}{6}\right)$$

43. $\left[25 \left(\cos \dfrac{2\pi}{3} + i \sin \dfrac{2\pi}{3} \right) \right]$ (square roots)

$$\sqrt{25} \left[\cos \left(\dfrac{\dfrac{2\pi}{3} + 2\pi k}{2} \right) + i \sin \left(\dfrac{\dfrac{2\pi}{3} + 2\pi k}{2} \right) \right]$$

$$k = 0 : 5 \left(\cos \dfrac{\pi}{3} + i \sin \dfrac{\pi}{3} \right) = 5 \left(\dfrac{1}{2} + \dfrac{\sqrt{3}}{2} i \right) = \dfrac{5}{2} + \dfrac{5\sqrt{3}}{2} i$$

$$k = 1 : 5 \left(\cos \dfrac{4\pi}{3} + i \sin \dfrac{4\pi}{3} \right) = 5 \left(-\dfrac{1}{2} - \dfrac{\sqrt{3}}{2} i \right) = -\dfrac{5}{2} - \dfrac{5\sqrt{3}}{2} i$$

45. Note that

$$i = 1 \left(\cos \dfrac{\pi}{2} + i \sin \dfrac{\pi}{2} \right),$$

so the cube roots of i are given by

$$\sqrt[3]{i} = \sqrt[3]{1} \left(\cos \dfrac{(\pi/2) + 2\pi k}{3} + i \sin \dfrac{(\pi/2) + 2\pi k}{3} \right)$$

Substituting in the values $k = 0$, 1, and 2, we get the following roots.

$$z_0 = \cos \dfrac{\pi}{6} + i \sin \dfrac{\pi}{6} = \dfrac{\sqrt{3}}{2} + \dfrac{1}{2} i$$

$$z_1 = \cos \dfrac{5\pi}{6} + i \sin \dfrac{5\pi}{6} = -\dfrac{\sqrt{3}}{2} + \dfrac{1}{2} i$$

$$z_2 = \cos \dfrac{3\pi}{2} + i \sin \dfrac{3\pi}{2} = -i$$

47. $A^* = \overline{A^T} = \begin{bmatrix} -1 - 4i & 3 - i \\ 3 + i & 2 - i \end{bmatrix}^T = \begin{bmatrix} -1 - 4i & 3 + i \\ 3 - i & 2 - i \end{bmatrix}.$

49. $7\mathbf{u} - \mathbf{v} = 7(4i, 2 + i) - (3, -i)$

$\qquad = (28i, 14 + 7i) - (3, -i)$

$\qquad = (-3 + 28i, 14 + 8i)$

51. $i\mathbf{u} + i\mathbf{v} - i\mathbf{w} = i(4i, 2 + i) + i(3, -i) - i(3 - i, 4 + i)$

$\qquad\qquad = (-4, -1 + 2i) + (3i, 1) + (-1 - 3i, 1 - 4i)$

$\qquad\qquad = (-5, 1 - 2i)$

53. $\|\mathbf{v}\| = \sqrt{\mathbf{v} \cdot \mathbf{v}}$

$\qquad = \sqrt{(3 - 5i)(3 + 5i) + (2i)(-2i)}$

$\qquad = \sqrt{3^2 + 5^2 + 2^2} = \sqrt{38}.$

55.
$$\mathbf{v} = (2 - i, i), \mathbf{u} = (i, 2 - i)$$

$$d(\mathbf{v}, \mathbf{u}) = \|\mathbf{v} - \mathbf{u}\| = \|(2 - 2i, -2 + 2i)\|$$

$$= \sqrt{(2)^2 + (2)^2 + (2)^2 + (2)^2}$$

$$= \sqrt{4 + 4 + 4 + 4} = \sqrt{16} = 4$$

57. The conjugate transpose of A is

$$A^* = \overline{A}^T = \frac{1}{\sqrt{2}}\begin{bmatrix} -i & -1 \\ -i & 1 \end{bmatrix}^T = \frac{1}{\sqrt{2}}\begin{bmatrix} -i & -i \\ -1 & 1 \end{bmatrix}.$$

Then, since

$$AA^* = \left(\frac{1}{\sqrt{2}}\right)^2 \begin{bmatrix} i & -1 \\ i & 1 \end{bmatrix}\begin{bmatrix} -i & -i \\ -1 & 1 \end{bmatrix} = \frac{1}{2}\begin{bmatrix} 2 & 0 \\ 0 & 2 \end{bmatrix} = \begin{bmatrix} 1 & 0 \\ 0 & 1 \end{bmatrix} = I_2,$$

A is unitary.

59. $\begin{bmatrix} 1 & 0 \\ i & -i \end{bmatrix} = A \Rightarrow \overline{A} = \begin{bmatrix} 1 & 0 \\ -i & i \end{bmatrix}$

$$\overline{A}^T = A^* = \begin{bmatrix} 1 & -i \\ 0 & i \end{bmatrix}$$

$$AA^* = \begin{bmatrix} 1 & 0 \\ i & -i \end{bmatrix}\begin{bmatrix} 1 & -i \\ 0 & i \end{bmatrix}$$

$$= \begin{bmatrix} 1 & -i \\ i & 2 \end{bmatrix} \neq I_2$$

Therefore, A is not unitary.

61. Since

$$A^* = \overline{A}^T = \begin{bmatrix} 1 & -1 - i & 2 + i \\ 1 + i & 3 & -i \\ 2 - i & i & 4 \end{bmatrix}^T = \begin{bmatrix} 1 & 1 + i & 2 - i \\ -1 - i & 3 & i \\ 2 + i & -i & 4 \end{bmatrix} \neq A,$$

A is not Hermitian.

63. The eigenvalues are given by the solutions of $|\lambda I - A| = 0$.

$$|\lambda I - A| = \begin{vmatrix} \lambda - 4 & -2 + i \\ -2 - i & \lambda \end{vmatrix}$$

$$= \lambda^2 - 4\lambda - 5 = 0 \Longrightarrow \lambda = -1, 5$$

The eigenvalues are given by the solutions to the equation $|\lambda I - A|\mathbf{x} = \mathbf{0}$.

$$\lambda = -1: \quad \begin{bmatrix} -5 & -2 + i \\ -2 - i & -1 \end{bmatrix} \begin{bmatrix} x_1 \\ x_2 \end{bmatrix} = \begin{bmatrix} 0 \\ 0 \end{bmatrix} \Longrightarrow -5x_1 + (-2 + i)x_2 = 0$$

$$-5t + (-2 + i)x_2 = 0$$

$$\Longrightarrow \mathbf{x} = t \begin{bmatrix} 1 \\ -2 - i \end{bmatrix}$$

$$\lambda = 5: \quad \begin{bmatrix} 1 & -2 + i \\ -2 - i & 5 \end{bmatrix} \begin{bmatrix} x_1 \\ x_2 \end{bmatrix} = \begin{bmatrix} 0 \\ 0 \end{bmatrix} \Longrightarrow x_1 + (-2 + i)x_2 = 0$$

$$t + (-2 + i)x_2 = 0$$

$$\Longrightarrow \mathbf{x} = t \begin{bmatrix} 1 \\ \frac{2 + i}{5} \end{bmatrix}.$$

65. The inverse of A^* is $(A^{-1})^*$, since

$$(A^{-1})^*A^* = [A(A^{-1})]^* = I^* = I.$$

67. Let $z_1 z_2 = 0$, and suppose $z_1 \neq 0$. then z_1^{-1} exists, and

$$\frac{1}{z}(z_1 z_2) = \left(\frac{1}{z_1} z_1\right) z_2 = z_2 = 0.$$

69. AB is Hermitian $\Longleftrightarrow (AB)^* = AB$

$$\Longleftrightarrow B^*A^* = AB$$

$$\Longleftrightarrow BA = AB.$$

71. The Theorem is trivial for $n = 1$. So assume DeMoivre's Theorem holds for n. Consider z^{n+1}

$$z^{n+1} = zz^n = r(\cos\theta + i\sin\theta)\left(r^n(\cos(n\theta) + i\sin(n\theta))\right)$$

$$= r^{n+1}\left[\cos\theta\cos(n\theta) - \sin\theta\sin(n\theta)\right]$$

$$+ \left[(\sin\theta\cos(n\theta) + \cos\theta\sin(n\theta))i\right]$$

$$= r^{n+1}\left[\cos(n + 1)\theta + i\sin(n + 1)\theta\right].$$

73. Clearly, z_1 and z_2 cannot be zero. Consider $z_1 + z_2 = x \in R$ and $z_1 \bar{z}_2 = y \in R$. Then,

$$\bar{z}_1 = x - \bar{z}_2 = x - y/z_1 \Longrightarrow$$

$$z_1 \bar{z}_1 = z_1(x - y/z_1) = xz_1 - y \Longrightarrow$$

$$|z_1|^2 = xz_{1-y} \Longrightarrow$$

$$z_1 = \left(|z_1|^2 + y\right) / x \in R.$$

Finally, $z_2 = x - z_1 \in R$ as well.

75. Expanding the right-hand side, we obtain

$$\frac{1}{4}\left[\|\mathbf{u} + \mathbf{v}\|^2 - \|\mathbf{u} - \mathbf{v}\|^2 + i\|\mathbf{u} + i\mathbf{v}\|^2 - i\|\mathbf{u} - i\mathbf{v}\|^2\right]$$

$$= \frac{1}{4}\left[\langle\mathbf{u} + \mathbf{v}, \mathbf{u} + \mathbf{v}\rangle - \langle\mathbf{u} - \mathbf{v}, \mathbf{u} - \mathbf{v}\rangle + i\langle\mathbf{u} + i\mathbf{v}, \mathbf{u} + i\mathbf{v}\rangle - i\langle\mathbf{u} - i\mathbf{v}, \mathbf{u} - i\mathbf{v}\rangle\right]$$

$$= \frac{1}{4}\left[\langle\mathbf{u}, \mathbf{u}\rangle + \langle\mathbf{v}, \mathbf{v}\rangle + \langle\mathbf{u}, \mathbf{v}\rangle + \langle\mathbf{v}, \mathbf{u}\rangle - \langle\mathbf{u}, \mathbf{u}\rangle - \langle\mathbf{v}, \mathbf{v}\rangle + \langle\mathbf{u}, \mathbf{v}\rangle + \langle\mathbf{v}, \mathbf{u}\rangle\right]$$

$$+ \left[i\langle\mathbf{u}, \mathbf{u}\rangle + i\langle i\mathbf{v}, i\mathbf{v}\rangle + i\langle\mathbf{u}, i\mathbf{v}\rangle + i\langle i\mathbf{v}, \mathbf{u}\rangle\right]$$

$$\left[- i\langle\mathbf{u}, \mathbf{u}\rangle - i\langle i\mathbf{v}, i\mathbf{v}\rangle + i\langle\mathbf{u}, i\mathbf{v}\rangle + i\langle i\mathbf{v}, \mathbf{u}\rangle\right]$$

$$= \frac{1}{4}\left[2\langle\mathbf{u}, \mathbf{v}\rangle + 2\langle\mathbf{v}, \mathbf{u}\rangle + 2i\langle\mathbf{u}, i\mathbf{v}\rangle + 2i\langle i\mathbf{v}, \mathbf{u}\rangle\right]$$

$$= \frac{1}{4}\left[2\langle\mathbf{u}, \mathbf{v}\rangle + 2\langle\mathbf{v}, \mathbf{u}\rangle + 2\langle\mathbf{u}, \mathbf{v}\rangle - 2\langle\mathbf{v}, \mathbf{u}\rangle\right]$$

$$= \langle\mathbf{u}, \mathbf{v}\rangle.$$

CHAPTER 9
Linear Programming

Section 9.1 Systems of Linear Inequalities

1. f

3. a

5. b

7. $x \geq 2$

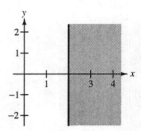

9. $y \geq -1$

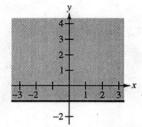

11. $y < 2 - x$

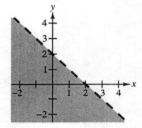

13. $2y - x \geq 4$

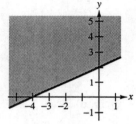

15. $y \leq x$

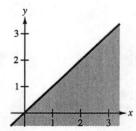

17. $y \geq 4 - 2x$

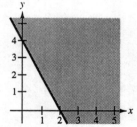

19. $3y + 4 \geq x$

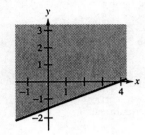

21. $4x - 2y \leq 12$

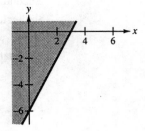

23. $x \geq 0$
   $y \geq 0$
   $x \leq 2$
   $y \leq 4$

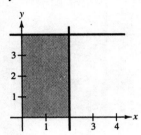

25. $x + y \leq 1$
   $-x + y \leq 1$
   $y \geq 0$

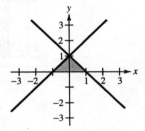

27. $x + y \leq 5$
   $x \geq 2$
   $y \geq 0$

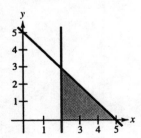

29. $-3x + 2y < 6$
   $x + 4y > -2$
   $2x + y < 3$

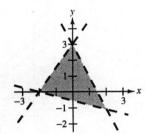

31.
$$x \geq 1$$
$$x - 2y \leq 3$$
$$3x + 2y \geq 9$$
$$x + y \leq 6$$

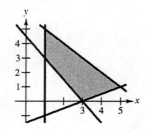

33. First, plot the vertices.

Second, sketch the lines that bound the rectangle.

Third, write equations of the boundary lines:

$$x = 2, x = 5, y = 1, \text{ and } y = 7.$$

Fourth, write appropriate inequalities.

$$x \geq 2$$
$$x \leq 5$$
$$y \geq 1$$
$$y \leq 7$$

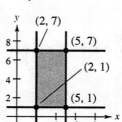

35. The line through $(0, 0)$ and $(2, 3)$
has equation $y = \frac{3}{2}x$.
The line through $(2, 3)$ and $(5, 0)$
has equation $y = -x + 5$.
The appropriate inequalities are:

$$y \geq 0$$
$$y \leq \frac{3}{2}x$$
$$y \leq -x + 5.$$

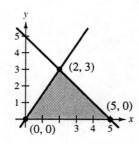

37.
$$1 \cdot x + \frac{3}{2}y \leq 12$$
$$\frac{4}{3} \cdot x + \frac{3}{2}y \leq 15$$
$$x \qquad \geq 0$$
$$\qquad y \geq 0$$

39. Let $x be invested in the smaller account and let $y be invested in the other account.

$$y \geq 2x$$
$$x + y \leq 20,000$$
$$x \geq 5,000$$

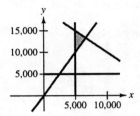

41. Let x ounces of food X and y ounces of food Y be in the diet.

$$2x + y \geq 30$$
$$3x + 2y \geq 30$$
$$x + 2y \geq 20$$
$$x \geq 0$$
$$y \geq 0$$

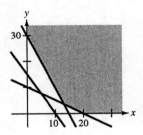

Section 9.2   Linear Programming Involving Two Variables

1.

Vertex: (x, y)	$(0, 0)$	$(4, 0)$	$(3, 4)$	$(0, 5)$
$z = 3x + 2y$	0	12	17	10

The maximum value of z is 17; the minimum is 0.

3.

Vertex: (x, y)	$(0, 0)$	$(4, 0)$	$(3, 4)$	$(0, 5)$
$z = 5x + 0.5y$	0	20	17	2.5

The maximum value of z is 20; the minimum is 0.

5.

Vertex: (x, y)	$(0, 0)$	$(60, 0)$	$(60, 20)$	$(30, 45)$	$(0, 45)$
$z = 10x + 7y$	0	600	740	615	315

The maximum value of z is 740; the minimum is 0.

7.

Vertex: (x, y)	$(0, 0)$	$(60, 0)$	$(60, 20)$	$(30, 45)$	$(0, 45)$
$z = 25x + 30y$	0	1500	2100	2100	1350

The maximum value of z is 2100; the minimum is 0.

9.

Vertex: (x, y)	$(0, 9)$	$(3, 5)$	$(5, 3)$	$(10, 0)$
$z = 4x + 5y$	45	37	35	40

The minimum value of z is 35; there is no maximum value.

11.

Vertex: (x, y)	$(0, 9)$	$(3, 5)$	$(5, 3)$	$(10, 0)$
$z = 2x + 7y$	63	41	31	20

The minimum value of z is 20; there is no maximum value.

13.

Vertex: (x, y)	$(36, 0)$	$(40, 0)$	$(24, 8)$
$z = 4x + y$	144	160	104

The maximum value of z is 160; the minimum is 104.

15.

Vertex: (x, y)	$(36, 0)$	$(40, 0)$	$(24, 8)$
$z = x + 4y$	36	40	56

The maximum value of z is 56; the minimum is 36.

17.

Vertex: (x_1, x_2)	(0, 0)	(5, 0)	(3, 6)	(0, 10)
$z = 2x_1 + x_2$	0	10	12	10

The maximum value of z is 12.

19.

Vertex: (x_1, x_2)	(0, 0)	(5, 0)	(3, 6)	(0, 10)
$z = x_1 + x_2$	0	5	9	10

The maximum value of z is 10.

21. Let x units of the $250 computer and y units of the $400 model be sold.
The profit is $P = 45x + 50y$ dollars.

$$x + y \leq 250$$
$$250x + 400y \leq 70{,}000$$
$$x, y \geq 0$$

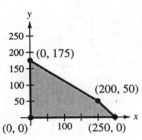

Vertex: (x, y)	(0, 0)	(250, 0)	(200,50)	(0, 175)
$P = 45x + 50y$	0	11,250	11,500	8,750

Stock 200 of the $250 model and 50 of the $400 model.

23. Let the mixture contain x bags of Brand X and y bags of Brand Y.
The cost of the mixture is $C = 25x + 20y$ dollars.

$$2x + y \geq 12$$
$$2x + 9y \geq 36$$
$$2x + 3y \geq 24$$
$$x, y \geq 0$$

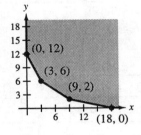

Vertex: (x, y)	(0, 12)	(3, 6)	(9, 2)	(18, 0)
$C = 25x + 20y$	240	195	265	450

Mix 3 bags of Brand X with 6 bags of Brand Y.

25.
$$x \geq 0$$
$$y \geq 0$$
$$3x + 5y \leq 15$$
$$5x + 2y \leq 10$$

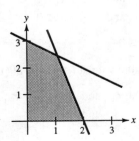

Vertex: (x, y)	(0, 0)	(2, 0)	$\left(\frac{20}{19}, \frac{45}{19}\right)$	(0, 3)
$z = 2.5x + y$	0	5	5	3

Unusual characteristic: The maximum value of z occurs at every
point on the line segment connecting the vertices (2, 0) and $\left(\frac{20}{19}, \frac{45}{19}\right)$.

27. $x \geq 0$
$y \geq 0$
$x \leq 10$
$x + y \leq 7$

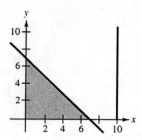

Unusual characteristic: One of the constraints, $x \leq 10$, is irrelevant.

29. $x \geq 0$
$y \geq 0$
$x + y \leq 1$
$2x + y \geq 4$

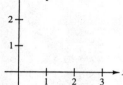

No solution points

Unusual characteristic: The solution region is empty.

31. $x \geq 0$
$y \geq 0$
$x \leq 1$
$y \leq 1$

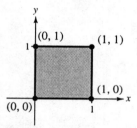

Vertex: (x, y)	$(0, 0)$	$(1, 0)$	$(1, 1)$	$(0, 1)$
$z = x + ty$	0	1	$1 + t$	t

(a) The maximum value of z cannot occur at $(0, 0)$ since z has a larger value at $(1, 0)$.

(b) The maximum value of z occurs at $(1, 0)$ if two conditions hold:

$t \leq 1$ and $1 + t \leq 1$
$t \leq 1$ and $t \leq 0$

Answer: $t \leq 0$

(c) The maximum value of z occurs at $(1, 1)$ if two conditions hold:

$1 \leq 1 + t$ and $t \leq 1 + t$
$0 \leq t$ and $0 \leq 1$

Answer: $0 \leq t$

(d) The maximum value of z cannot occur at $(0, 1)$ since it would follow that
$1 + t \leq t$; that is, $1 \leq 0$.

Section 9.3   The Simplex Method: Maximization

1.

x_1	x_2	s_1	s_2	b	Basic Variables
2	1	1	0	8	s_1
1	1	0	1	5	s_2
−1	−2	0	0	0	

3.

x_1	x_2	x_3	s_1	s_2	b	Basic Variables
1	2	0	1	0	12	s_1
1	0	1	0	1	8	s_2
−2	−3	−4	0	0	0	

5. The given problem does not seek to maximize the objective function.

7. The sense (direction) of the inequality in the constraint $2x_1 - 2x_3 \geq 1$ is reversed.

9.

x_1	x_2	s_1	s_2	b	Basic Variables
1	4	1	0	8	s_1 ← Departing
1	1	0	1	12	s_2
−1	−2	0	0	0	

↑
Entering

x_1	x_2	s_1	s_2	b	Basic Variables
0.25	1	0.25	0	2	x_2 ← Departing
0.75	0	−0.25	1	10	s_2
−0.5	0	0.5	0	4	

↑
Entering

x_1	x_2	s_1	s_2	b	Basic Variables
1	4	1	0	8	x_1
0	−3	−1	1	4	s_2
1	2	1	0	8	

$(x_1, x_2, s_1, s_2) = (8, 0, 0, 4)$ gives a maximum value of $z = 8$.

11.

x_1	x_2	x_3	s_1	s_2	s_3	b	Basic Variables	
2	-4	1	1	0	0	42	s_1	
2	3	-1	0	1	0	42	s_2	
6	-1	3	0	0	1	42	s_3	$\leftarrow$ Departing
-5	-2	-8	0	0	0	0		

$$\underset{\text{Entering}}{\uparrow}$$

(under x_3 column)

x_1	x_2	x_3	s_1	s_2	s_3	b	Basic Variables	
0	$-\frac{11}{3}$	0	1	0	$-\frac{1}{3}$	28	s_1	
4	$\frac{8}{3}$	0	0	1	$\frac{1}{3}$	56	s_2	$\leftarrow$ Departing
2	$-\frac{1}{3}$	1	0	0	$\frac{1}{3}$	14	x_3	
11	$-\frac{14}{3}$	0	0	0	$\frac{8}{3}$	112		

$$\underset{\text{Entering}}{\uparrow}$$

(under x_2 column)

x_1	x_2	x_3	s_1	s_2	s_3	b	Basic Variables
$\frac{11}{2}$	0	0	1	$\frac{11}{8}$	$\frac{1}{8}$	105	s_1
$\frac{3}{2}$	1	0	0	$\frac{3}{8}$	$\frac{1}{8}$	21	x_2
$\frac{5}{2}$	0	1	0	$\frac{1}{8}$	$\frac{3}{8}$	21	x_3
18	0	0	0	$\frac{7}{4}$	$\frac{13}{4}$	210	

$(x_1, x_2, x_3, s_1, s_2, s_3) = (0, 21, 21, 105, 0, 0)$ gives a maximum value of $z = 210$.

13.

x_1	x_2	s_1	s_2	b	Basic Variables	
1	1	1	0	10	s_1	← Departing
3	7	0	1	42	s_2	
−4	−5	0	0	0		
	↑					
	Entering					

x_1	x_2	s_1	s_2	b	Basic Variables	
$\frac{4}{7}$	0	1	$-\frac{1}{7}$	4	s_1	← Departing
$\frac{3}{7}$	1	0	$\frac{1}{7}$	6	x_2	
$-\frac{13}{7}$	0	0	$\frac{5}{7}$	30		
↑						
Entering						

x_1	x_2	s_1	s_2	b	Basic Variables
1	0	$\frac{7}{4}$	$-\frac{1}{4}$	7	x_1
0	1	$-\frac{3}{4}$	$\frac{1}{4}$	3	x_2
0	0	$\frac{13}{4}$	$\frac{1}{4}$	43	

$(x_1, x_2, s_1, s_2) = (7, 3, 0, 0)$ gives a maximum value of $z = 43$.

15.

x_1	x_2	x_3	x_4	s_1	s_2	s_3	b	Basic Variables
8	3	4	1	1	0	0	7	s_1
2	6	1	5	0	1	0	3	s_2 ← Departing
1	4	5	2	0	0	1	8	s_3
-3	-4	-1	-7	0	0	0	0	

$$\uparrow$$
Entering

x_1	x_2	x_3	x_4	s_1	s_2	s_3	b	Basic Variables
7.6	1.8	3.8	0	1	-0.2	0	6.4	s_1 ← Departing
0.4	1.2	0.2	1	0	0.2	0	0.6	x_4
0.2	1.6	4.6	0	0	-0.4	1	6.8	s_3
-0.2	4.4	0.4	0	0	1.4	0	4.2	

$$\uparrow$$
Entering

x_1	x_2	x_3	x_4	s_1	s_2	s_3	b	Basic Variables
1	$\frac{9}{38}$	$\frac{1}{2}$	0	$\frac{5}{38}$	$-\frac{1}{38}$	0	$\frac{16}{19}$	x_1
0	$\frac{21}{19}$	0	1	$-\frac{1}{19}$	$\frac{4}{19}$	0	$\frac{5}{19}$	x_4
0	$\frac{59}{38}$	$\frac{9}{2}$	0	$-\frac{1}{38}$	$-\frac{15}{38}$	1	$\frac{126}{19}$	s_3
0	$\frac{169}{38}$	$\frac{1}{2}$	0	$\frac{1}{38}$	$\frac{53}{38}$	0	$\frac{83}{19}$	

$(x_1, x_2, x_3, x_4, s_1, s_2, s_3) = \left(\frac{16}{19}, 0, 0, \frac{5}{19}, 0, 0, \frac{126}{19}\right)$ gives a maximum value of $z = \frac{83}{19}$.

17.

x_1	x_2	x_3	s_1	s_2	s_3	b	Basic Variables
2	1	−3	1	0	0	40	s_1 ← Departing
1	0	1	0	1	0	25	s_2
0	2	3	0	0	1	32	s_3
−1	1	−1	0	0	0	0	

↑
Entering

x_1	x_2	x_3	s_1	s_2	s_3	b	Basic Variables
1	0.5	−1.5	0.5	0	0	20	x_1
0	−0.5	2.5	−0.5	1	0	5	s_2 ← Departing
0	2	3	0	0	1	32	s_3
0	1.5	−2.5	0.5	0	0	20	

↑
Entering

x_1	x_2	x_3	s_1	s_2	s_3	b	Basic Variables
1	0.2	0	0.2	0.6	0	23	x_1
0	−0.2	1	−0.2	0.4	0	2	x_3
0	2.6	0	0.6	−1.2	1	26	s_3
0	1	0	0	1	0	25	

$\left(x_1, x_2, x_3, s_1, s_2, s_3\right) = (23, 0, 2, 0, 0, 26)$ gives a maximum value of $z = 25$.

19.

x_1	x_2	x_3	x_4	s_1	s_2	b	Basic Variables
1	2	3	0	1	0	24	s_1 ← Departing
0	3	7	1	0	1	42	s_2
−1	−2	0	1	0	0	0	

↑
Entering

x_1	x_2	x_3	x_4	s_1	s_2	b	Basic Variables
0.5	1	1.5	0	0.5	0	12	x_2
−1.5	0	2.5	1	−1.5	1	6	s_2
0	0	3	1	1	0	24	

$\left(x_1, x_2, x_3, x_4, s_1, s_2\right) = (0, 12, 0, 0, 0, 6)$ gives a maximum value of $z = 24$.

21. Let x units of the $250 computer and y units of the $400 model be sold.

The profit is $P = 45x + 50y$ dollars.

$$x + y \le 250$$

$$250x + 400y \le 70{,}000$$

$$x, y \ge 0$$

x	y	s_1	s_2	b	Basic Variables	
1	1	1	0	250	s_1	
250	400	0	1	70,000	s_2	← Departing
-45	-50	0	0	0		

↑
Entering

x	y	s_1	s_2	b	Basic Variables	
$\frac{3}{8}$	0	1	$-\frac{1}{400}$	75	s_1	← Departing
$\frac{5}{8}$	1	0	$\frac{1}{400}$	175	y	
$-\frac{55}{4}$	0	0	$\frac{1}{8}$	8,750		

↑
Entering

x	y	s_1	s_2	b	Basic Variables
1	0	$\frac{8}{3}$	$-\frac{1}{150}$	200	x
0	1	$-\frac{5}{3}$	$\frac{1}{150}$	50	y
0	0	$\frac{110}{3}$	$\frac{1}{30}$	11,500	

Stock 200 of the $250 model and 50 of the $400 model.

23. Let x_1, x_2, and x_3 acres be planted in carrots, celery, and lettuce, respectively.

The profit is $P = 60x_1 + 20x_2 + 30x_3$ dollars.

$$x_1 + x_2 + x_3 \leq 50$$

$$200x_1 + 80x_2 + 140x_3 \leq 10,000$$

$$x_1, x_2, x_3 \geq 0$$

x_1	x_2	x_3	s_1	s_2	b	Basic Variables	
1	1	1	1	0	50	s_1	← Departing
200	80	140	0	1	10,000	s_2	
−60	−20	−30	0	0	0		

↑
Entering

x_1	x_2	x_3	s_1	s_2	b	Basic Variables
1	1	1	1	0	50	x_1
0	−120	−60	−200	1	0	s_2
0	40	30	60	0	3,000	

Plant all 50 acres in carrots.

25. Let bicycles of types A, B, and C be produced in quantities x_1, x_2, and x_3, respectively. The profit is $P = 45x_1 + 50x_2 + 55x_3$ dollars.

$$2x_1 + 2.5x_2 + 3x_3 \leq 4{,}006$$
$$1.5x_1 + 2x_2 + x_3 \leq 2{,}495$$
$$x_1 + 0.75x_2 + 1.25x_3 \leq 1{,}500$$
$$x_1, x_2, x_3 \geq 0$$

x_1	x_2	x_3	s_1	s_2	s_3	b	Basic Variables	
2	2.5	3	1	0	0	4006	s_1	
1.5	2	1	0	1	0	2495	s_2	
1	0.75	1.25	0	0	1	1500	s_3	← Departing
−45	−50	−55	0	0	0	0		

              ↑
         Entering

x_1	x_2	x_3	s_1	s_2	s_3	b	Basic Variables	
−0.4	0.7	0	1	0	−2.4	406	s_1	← Departing
0.7	1.4	0	0	1	−0.8	1,295	s_2	
0.8	0.6	1	0	0	0.8	1,200	x_3	
−1	−17	0	0	0	44	66,000		

       ↑
    Entering

x_1	x_2	x_3	s_1	s_2	s_3	b	Basic Variables	
$-\frac{4}{7}$	1	0	$\frac{10}{7}$	0	$-\frac{24}{7}$	580	x_2	
$\frac{3}{2}$	0	0	−2	1	4	483	s_2	← Departing
$\frac{8}{7}$	0	1	$-\frac{6}{7}$	0	$\frac{20}{7}$	852	x_3	
$-\frac{75}{7}$	0	0	$\frac{170}{7}$	0	$-\frac{100}{7}$	75,860		

                         ↑
                     Entering

x_1	x_2	x_3	s_1	s_2	s_3	b	Basic Variables	
$\frac{5}{7}$	1	0	$-\frac{2}{7}$	$\frac{6}{7}$	0	994	x_2	
$\frac{3}{8}$	0	0	$-\frac{1}{2}$	$\frac{1}{4}$	1	$\frac{483}{4}$	s_3	← Departing
$\frac{1}{14}$	0	1	$\frac{4}{7}$	$-\frac{5}{7}$	0	507	x_3	
$-\frac{75}{14}$	0	0	$\frac{120}{7}$	$\frac{25}{7}$	0	77,585		

↑
Entering

x_1	x_2	x_3	s_1	s_2	s_3	b	Basic Variables
0	1	0	$\frac{2}{3}$	$\frac{8}{21}$	$-\frac{40}{21}$	764	x_2
1	0	0	$-\frac{4}{3}$	$\frac{2}{3}$	$\frac{8}{3}$	322	x_1
0	0	1	$\frac{2}{3}$	$-\frac{16}{21}$	$-\frac{4}{21}$	484	x_3
0	0	0	10	$\frac{50}{7}$	$\frac{100}{7}$	79,310	

Produce 322 bicycles of type A, 764 of type B, and 484 of type C.

27. Let x_1 television minutes and x_2 newspaper pages be purchased. Assuming that each television ad is one minute long, the total expected audience is $15x_1 + 3x_2$ million people.

$$60{,}000x_1 + 15{,}000x_2 \leq 600{,}000$$

$$60{,}000x_1 \qquad\qquad \leq (0.9)\,(600{,}000)$$

$$x_1, x_2 \geq 0$$

$$4x_1 + \qquad x_2 \leq 40$$

$$x_1 + \qquad\quad\; \leq 9$$

$$x_1, x_2 \geq 0$$

x_1	x_2	s_1	s_2	b	Basic Variables	
4	1	1	0	40	s_1	
1	0	0	1	9	s_2	← Departing
−15	−3	0	0	0		

Entering (↑ under x_1)

x_1	x_2	s_1	s_2	b	Basic Variables	
0	1	1	−4	4	s_1	← Departing
1	0	0	1	9	x_1	
0	−3	0	15	135		

Entering (↑ under x_2)

x_1	x_2	s_1	s_2	b	Basic Variables
0	1	1	−4	4	x_2
1	0	0	1	9	x_1
0	0	3	3	147	

Spend \$540,000 on television and \$60,000 on newspapers.

29. Let x_1, x_2 and x_3 dollars be allocated to type A, B, and C investments, repsectively.
The return is $P = 0.08x_1 + 0.1x_2 + 0.14x_3$ dollars.

$$x_1 + x_2 + x_3 \leq 250{,}000$$
$$0.06x_2 + 0.1x_3 \leq 0.05 \left(x_1 + x_2 + x_3\right)$$
$$x_1 \geq 0.25 \left(x_1 + x_2 + x_3\right)$$
$$x_2 \geq 0.25 \left(x_1 + x_2 + x_3\right)$$
$$x_1, x_2, x_3 \geq 0$$

$$x_1 + x_2 + x_3 \leq 250{,}000$$
$$-5x_1 + x_2 + 5x_3 \leq 0$$
$$-3x_1 + x_2 + x_3 \leq 0$$
$$x_1 - 3x_2 + x_3 \leq 0$$
$$x_1, x_2, x_3 \geq 0$$

x_1	x_2	x_3	s_1	s_2	s_3	s_4	b	Basic Variables	
1	1	1	1	0	0	0	250,000	s_1	
−5	1	5	0	1	0	0	0	s_2	← Departing
−3	1	1	0	0	1	0	0	s_3	
1	−3	1	0	0	0	1	0	s_4	
−0.08	−0.1	−0.14	0	0	0	0	0		

$\uparrow$
Entering

x_1	x_2	x_3	s_1	s_2	s_3	s_4	b	Basic Variables	
2	0.8	0	1	−0.2	0	0	250,000	s_1	
−1	0.2	1	0	0.2	0	0	0	x_3	
−2	0.8	0	0	−0.2	1	0	0	s_3	
2	−3.2	0	0	−0.2	0	1	0	s_4	← Departing
−0.22	−0.072	0	0	0.028	0	0	0		

↑
Entering

x_1	x_2	x_3	s_1	s_2	s_3	s_4	b	Basic Variables	
0	4	0	1	0	0	−1	250,000	s_1	← Departing
0	−1.4	1	0	0.1	0	0.5	0	x_3	
0	−2.4	0	0	−0.4	1	1	0	s_3	
1	−1.6	0	0	−0.1	0	0.5	0	x_1	
0	−0.424	0	0	0.006	0	0.11	0		

↑
Entering

x_1	x_2	x_3	s_1	s_2	s_3	s_4	b	Basic Variables
0	1	0	0.25	0	0	−0.25	62,500	x_2
0	0	1	0.35	0.1	0	0.15	87,500	x_3
0	0	0	0.6	−0.4	1	0.4	150,000	s_3
1	0	0	0.4	−0.1	0	0.1	100,000	x_1
0	0	0	0.106	0.006	0	0.004	26,500	

Allocate $100,000 to type A investments, $62,500 to type B investments, and $87,500 to type C investments.

31. Let x_1 be the number of audits and let x_2 be the number of tax returns.

The revenue produced is $R = 2000x_1 + 300x_2$ dollars.

$$100x_1 + 12.5x_2 \le 900$$

$$10x_1 + 2.5x_2 \le 100$$

$$x_1, x_2 \ge 0$$

x_1	x_2	s_1	s_2	b	Basic Variables	
100	12.5	1	0	900	s_1	← Departing
10	2.5	0	1	100	s_2	
−2000	−300	0	0	0		

↑
Entering

x_1	x_2	s_1	s_2	b	Basic Variables	
1	0.125	0.01	0	9	x_1	
0	1.25	−0.1	1	10	s_2	← Departing
0	−50	20	0	18,000		

↑
Entering

x_1	x_2	s_1	s_2	b	Basic Variables
1	0	0.02	−0.1	8	x_1
0	1	−0.08	0.8	8	x_2
0	0	16	40	18,400	

Do 8 audits and 8 tax returns to maximize revenue.

33.

x_1	x_2	s_1	s_2	b	Basic Variables
1	−3	1	0	1	s_1
−1	2	0	1	4	s_2 ← Departing
−1	−2	0	0	0	

$$\underset{\text{Entering}}{\uparrow}$$

x_1	x_2	s_1	s_2	b	Basic Variables
$-\frac{1}{2}$	0	1	$\frac{3}{2}$	7	s_1
$-\frac{1}{2}$	1	0	$\frac{1}{2}$	2	x_2
−2	0	0	1	4	

$$\underset{\text{Entering}}{\uparrow}$$

$$x_1 - 3x_2 \leq 1$$

$$-x_1 + 2x_2 \leq 4$$

$$x_1, x_2 \geq 0$$

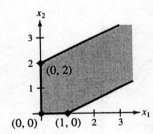

The negative entries in column one of the second tableau prevent selection of a departing variable. The region determined by the constraints is illustrated and the objective function $z = x_1 + 2x_2$ has no maximum value there.

35.

x_1	x_2	s_1	s_2	b	Basic Variables
3	5	1	0	15	s_1
5	2	0	1	10	s_2 ← Departing
−2.5	−1	0	0	0	

↑
Entering

x_1	x_2	s_1	s_2	b	Basic Variables
0	3.8	1	−0.6	9	s_1
1	0.4	0	0.2	2	x_1
0	0	0	0.5	5	

The simplex method has terminated with the basic solution $(x_1, x_2, s_1, s_2) = (2, 0, 9, 0)$; so x_1 and s_1 are in the final basis. Let x_2, which has a bottom-row entry of zero, be brought into the basis and let s_1 depart.

x_1	x_2	s_1	s_2	b	Basic Variables
0	1	$\frac{5}{19}$	$-\frac{3}{19}$	$\frac{45}{19}$	x_2
1	0	$-\frac{2}{19}$	$\frac{6}{95}$	$\frac{20}{19}$	x_1
0	0	0	$\frac{1}{2}$	5	

The new optimal solution is $(x_1, x_2, s_1, s_2) = \left(\frac{20}{19}, \frac{45}{19}, 0, 0\right)$.

Section 9.4   The Simplex Method: Minimization

1. The augmented matrix for the given minimization problem:

$$\begin{bmatrix} 2 & 1 & \vdots & 4 \\ 1 & 2 & \vdots & 4 \\ \hdotsfor{4} \\ 3 & 3 & \vdots & 0 \end{bmatrix}$$

Its transpose:

$$\begin{bmatrix} 2 & 1 & \vdots & 3 \\ 1 & 2 & \vdots & 3 \\ \hdotsfor{4} \\ 4 & 4 & \vdots & 0 \end{bmatrix}$$

The dual maximization problem:

Objective function:

$$z = 4y_1 + 4y_2$$

Constraints:

$$2y_1 + y_2 \le 3$$
$$y_1 + 2y_2 \le 3$$
$$y_1, y_2 \ge 0$$

3. The augmented matrix for the given minimization problem:

$$\begin{bmatrix} 3 & 2 & 1 & \vdots & 23 \\ 1 & 0 & 1 & \vdots & 10 \\ 8 & 1 & 2 & \vdots & 40 \\ \cdots & \cdots & \cdots & \vdots & \cdots \\ 4 & 1 & 1 & \vdots & 0 \end{bmatrix}$$

Its transpose:

$$\begin{bmatrix} 3 & 1 & 8 & \vdots & 4 \\ 2 & 0 & 1 & \vdots & 1 \\ 1 & 1 & 2 & \vdots & 1 \\ \cdots & \cdots & \cdots & \vdots & \cdots \\ 23 & 10 & 40 & \vdots & 0 \end{bmatrix}$$

The dual maximization problem:

Objective function:

$$z = 23y_1 + 10y_2 + 40y_3$$

Constraints:

$$3y_1 + y_2 + 8y_3 \leq 4$$
$$2y_1 \quad + y_3 \leq 1$$
$$y_1 + y_2 + 2y_3 \leq 1$$
$$y_1, y_2, y_3 \geq 0$$

5. The augmented matrix for the given minimization problem:

$$\begin{bmatrix} 1 & 1 & 2 & \vdots & 7 \\ 1 & 2 & 1 & \vdots & 4 \\ \cdots & \cdots & \cdots & \vdots & \cdots \\ 14 & 20 & 24 & \vdots & 0 \end{bmatrix}$$

Its transpose:

$$\begin{bmatrix} 1 & 1 & \vdots & 14 \\ 1 & 2 & \vdots & 20 \\ 2 & 1 & \vdots & 24 \\ \cdots & \cdots & \vdots & \cdots \\ 7 & 4 & \vdots & 0 \end{bmatrix}$$

The dual maximization problem:

Objective function:

$$z = 7y_1 + 4y_2$$

Constraints:

$$y_1 + y_2 \leq 14$$
$$y_1 + 2y_2 \leq 20$$
$$2y_1 + y_2 \leq 24$$
$$y_1, y_2 \geq 0$$

7. (a)

Vertex: (x_1, x_2)	$(0, \frac{5}{2})$	$(1, 1)$	$(3, 0)$
$w = 2x_1 + 2x_2$	5	4	6

Answer:

$(x_1, x_2) = (1, 1)$ gives a minimum value of $w = 4$.

(b) The dual maximization problem:

Objective function:

$$z = 3y_1 + 5y_2$$

Constraints:

$$y_1 + 3y_2 \leq 2$$

$$2y_1 + 2y_2 \leq 2$$

$$y_1, y_2 \geq 0$$

Augmented matrices:

Given:

$$\begin{bmatrix} 1 & 2 & \vdots & 3 \\ 3 & 2 & \vdots & 5 \\ \cdots & \cdots & \cdots & \cdots \\ 2 & 2 & \vdots & 0 \end{bmatrix}$$

Dual:

$$\begin{bmatrix} 1 & 3 & \vdots & 2 \\ 2 & 2 & \vdots & 2 \\ \cdots & \cdots & \cdots & \cdots \\ 3 & 5 & \vdots & 0 \end{bmatrix}$$

(c)

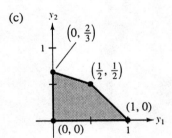

Vertex: (y_1, y_2)	$(0, 0)$	$(1, 0)$	$(\frac{1}{2}, \frac{1}{2})$	$(0, \frac{2}{3})$
$z = 3y_1 + 5y_2$	0	3	4	$\frac{10}{3}$

Answer:

$(y_1, y_2) = (\frac{1}{2}, \frac{1}{2})$ gives a maximum value of $z = 4$.

9.   (a)

Vertex: (x_1, x_2)	$(0, 3)$	$\left(\frac{4}{3}, \frac{5}{3}\right)$
$w = x_1 + 4x_2$	12	8

Answer:
$(x_1, x_2) = \left(\frac{4}{3}, \frac{5}{3}\right)$ gives a minimum value of $w = 8$.

(b)   The dual maximization problem:

Objective function:
$$z = 3y_1 + 2y_2$$

Constraints:
$$y_1 - y_2 \le 1$$
$$y_1 + 2y_2 \le 4$$
$$y_1, y_2 \ge 0$$

Augmented matrices:

Given:
$$\begin{bmatrix} 1 & 1 & \vdots & 3 \\ -1 & 2 & \vdots & 2 \\ \cdots & \cdots & \vdots & \cdots \\ 1 & 4 & \vdots & 0 \end{bmatrix}$$

Dual:
$$\begin{bmatrix} 1 & -1 & \vdots & 1 \\ 1 & 2 & \vdots & 4 \\ \cdots & \cdots & \vdots & \cdots \\ 3 & 2 & \vdots & 0 \end{bmatrix}$$

(c)

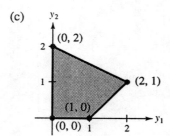

Vertex: (y_1, y_2)	$(0, 0)$	$(1, 0)$	$(2, 1)$	$(0, 2)$
$z = 3y_1 + 2y_2$	0	3	8	4

Answer:
$(y_1, y_2) = (2, 1)$ gives a maximum value of $z = 8$.

11. (a)

Vertex: (x_1, x_2)	$(0, 4)$	$\left(\frac{1}{2}, 2\right)$
$w = 6x_1 + 3x_2$	12	9

Answer:

$(x_1, x_2) = \left(\frac{1}{2}, 2\right)$ gives a minimum value of $w = 9$.

(b) The dual maximization problem:

Objective function:

$$z = 4y_1 + 2y_2$$

Constraints:

$$4y_1 \qquad \leq 6$$

$$y_1 + y_2 \leq 3$$

$$y_1, y_2 \geq 0$$

Augmented matrices:

Given:
$$\begin{bmatrix} 4 & 1 & \vdots & 4 \\ 0 & 1 & \vdots & 2 \\ \cdots & \cdots & \cdots & \cdots \\ 6 & 3 & \vdots & 0 \end{bmatrix}$$

Dual:
$$\begin{bmatrix} 4 & 0 & \vdots & 6 \\ 1 & 1 & \vdots & 3 \\ \cdots & \cdots & \cdots & \cdots \\ 4 & 2 & \vdots & 0 \end{bmatrix}$$

(c)

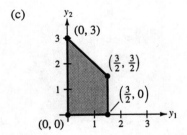

Vertex: (y_1, y_2)	$(0, 0)$	$\left(\frac{3}{2}, 0\right)$	$\left(\frac{3}{2}, \frac{3}{2}\right)$	$(0, 3)$
$z = 4y_1 + 2y_2$	0	6	9	6

Answer:

$(y_1, y_2) = \left(\frac{3}{2}, \frac{3}{2}\right)$ gives a maximum value of $z = 9$.

13. Augmented matrices:

$$
\text{Given:} \quad
\begin{bmatrix}
1 & 5 & : & 10 \\
-6 & 5 & : & 3 \\
\cdots & \cdots & \cdots & \cdots \\
0 & 1 & : & 0
\end{bmatrix}
$$

$$
\text{Dual:} \quad
\begin{bmatrix}
1 & -6 & : & 0 \\
5 & 5 & : & 1 \\
\cdots & \cdots & \cdots & \cdots \\
10 & 3 & : & 0
\end{bmatrix}
$$

The dual maximization problem:

Objective function:

$$z = 10y_1 + 3y_2$$

Constraints:

$$y_1 - 6y_2 \leq 0$$

$$5y_1 + 5y_2 \leq 1$$

$$y_1, y_2 \geq 0$$

y_1	y_2	s_1	s_2	b	Basic Variables	
1	−6	1	0	0	s_1	← Departing
5	5	0	1	1	s_2	
−10	−3	0	0	0		

↑
Entering

y_1	y_2	s_1	s_2	b	Basic Variables	
1	−6	1	0	0	y_1	
0	35	−5	1	1	s_2	← Departing
0	−63	10	0	0		

↑
Entering

y_1	y_2	s_1	s_2	b	Basic Variables
1	0	$\frac{1}{7}$	$\frac{6}{35}$	$\frac{6}{35}$	y_1
0	1	$-\frac{1}{7}$	$\frac{1}{35}$	$\frac{1}{35}$	y_2
0	0	1	$\frac{9}{5}$	$\frac{9}{5}$	

Answer:

$(x_1, x_2) = \left(1, \frac{9}{5}\right)$ gives a minimum value of $w = \frac{9}{5}$.

15. Augmented matrices:

Given: $\begin{bmatrix} 5 & 1 & : & 9 \\ 2 & 2 & : & 10 \\ \cdots & \cdots & : & \cdots \\ 2 & 1 & : & 0 \end{bmatrix}$

Dual: $\begin{bmatrix} 5 & 2 & : & 2 \\ 1 & 2 & : & 1 \\ \cdots & \cdots & : & \cdots \\ 9 & 10 & : & 0 \end{bmatrix}$

The dual maximization problem:

Objective function:

$$z = 9y_1 + 10y_2$$

Constraints:

$$5y_1 + 2y_2 \le 2$$
$$y_1 + 2y_2 \le 1$$
$$y_1, y_2 \ge 0$$

y_1	y_2	s_1	s_2	b	Basic Variables	
5	2	1	0	2	s_1	
1	2	0	1	1	s_2	← Departing
−9	−10	0	0	0		
	↑					
	Entering					

y_1	y_2	s_1	s_2	b	Basic Variables	
4	0	1	−1	1	s_1	← Departing
$\frac{1}{2}$	1	0	$\frac{1}{2}$	$\frac{1}{2}$	y_2	
−4	0	0	5	5		
↑						
Entering						

y_1	y_2	s_1	s_2	b	Basic Variables
1	0	$\frac{1}{4}$	$-\frac{1}{4}$	$\frac{1}{4}$	y_1
See the NOTE below.					y_2
0	0	1	4	6	

Answer:

$(x_1, x_2) = (1, 4)$ gives a minimum value of $w = 6$.

NOTE: In dual problems, it is convenient to calculate the pivot row and then the bottom row of each tableau. If there are no negative entries in the bottom row (except for the last column), then the answer has been found and further computation is unnecessary.

17. Augmented matrices:

Given:
$$\begin{bmatrix} 3 & 2 & 1 & \vdots & 6 \\ 4 & 1 & 3 & \vdots & 7 \\ 2 & 1 & 4 & \vdots & 8 \\ \cdots & \cdots & \cdots & \vdots & \cdots \\ 8 & 4 & 6 & \vdots & 0 \end{bmatrix}$$

Dual:
$$\begin{bmatrix} 3 & 4 & 2 & \vdots & 8 \\ 2 & 1 & 1 & \vdots & 4 \\ 1 & 3 & 4 & \vdots & 6 \\ \cdots & \cdots & \cdots & \vdots & \cdots \\ 6 & 7 & 8 & \vdots & 0 \end{bmatrix}$$

The dual maximization problem:

Objective function:

$$z = 6y_1 + 7y_2 + 8y_3$$

Constraints:

$$3y_1 + 4y_2 + 2y_3 \le 8$$
$$2y_1 + y_2 + y_3 \le 4$$
$$y_1 + 3y_2 + 4y_3 \le 6$$
$$y_1, y_2, y_3 \ge 0$$

y_1	y_2	y_3	s_1	s_2	s_3	b	Basic Variables
3	4	2	1	0	0	8	s_1
2	1	1	0	1	0	4	s_2
1	3	4	0	0	1	6	s_3 ← Departing
−6	−7	−8	0	0	0	0	

Entering (↑ under y_3)

y_1	y_2	y_3	s_1	s_2	s_3	b	Basic Variables
2.5	2.5	0	1	0	−0.5	5	s_1
1.75	0.25	0	0	1	−0.25	2.5	s_2 ← Departing
0.25	0.75	1	0	0	0.25	1.5	y_3
−4	−1	0	0	0	2	12	

Entering (↑ under y_1)

y_1	y_2	y_3	s_1	s_2	s_3	b	Basic Variables
0	$\frac{15}{7}$	0	1	$-\frac{10}{7}$	$-\frac{1}{7}$	$\frac{10}{7}$	s_1 ← Departing
1	$\frac{1}{7}$	0	0	$\frac{4}{7}$	$-\frac{1}{7}$	$\frac{10}{7}$	y_1
1	$\frac{5}{7}$	1	0	$-\frac{1}{7}$	$\frac{2}{7}$	$\frac{8}{7}$	y_3
0	$-\frac{3}{7}$	0	0	$\frac{16}{7}$	$\frac{10}{7}$	$\frac{124}{7}$	

Entering (↑ under y_2)

y_1	y_2	y_3	s_1	s_2	s_3	b	Basic Variables
0	1	0	$\frac{7}{15}$	$-\frac{2}{3}$	$-\frac{1}{15}$	$\frac{2}{3}$	y_2
		See NOTE in Exercise 15.			·		y_1
							y_3
0	0	0	$\frac{1}{5}$	2	$\frac{7}{5}$	18	

Answer:

$(x_1, x_2, x_3) = \left(\frac{1}{5}, 2, \frac{7}{5}\right)$ gives a minimum value of $w = 18$.

19. Augmented matrices:

$$\text{Given:} \begin{bmatrix} 3 & 2 & 1 & \vdots & 28 \\ 6 & 0 & 1 & \vdots & 24 \\ 3 & 1 & 2 & \vdots & 40 \\ \hdotsfor{5} \\ 6 & 2 & 3 & \vdots & 0 \end{bmatrix}$$

$$\text{Dual:} \begin{bmatrix} 3 & 6 & 3 & \vdots & 6 \\ 2 & 0 & 1 & \vdots & 2 \\ 1 & 1 & 2 & \vdots & 3 \\ \hdotsfor{5} \\ 28 & 24 & 40 & \vdots & 0 \end{bmatrix}$$

The dual maximization problem:

Objective function:

$$z = 28y_1 + 24y_2 + 40y_3$$

Constraints:

$$3y_1 + 6y_2 + 3y_3 \le 6$$
$$2y_1 \qquad + y_3 \le 2$$
$$y_1 + y_2 + 2y_3 \le 3$$
$$y_1, y_2, y_3 \ge 0$$

y_1	y_2	y_3	s_1	s_2	s_3	b	Basic Variables
3	6	3	1	0	0	6	s_1
2	0	1	0	1	0	2	s_2
1	1	2	0	0	1	3	s_3 ← Departing
−28	−24	−40	0	0	0	0	

↑ Entering (under y_3)

y_1	y_2	y_3	s_1	s_2	s_3	b	Basic Variables
1.5	4.5	0	1	0	−1.5	1.5	s_1
1.5	−0.5	0	0	1	−0.5	0.5	s_2 ← Departing
0.5	0.5	1	0	0	0.5	1.5	y_3
−8	−4	0	0	0	20	60	

↑ Entering (under y_1)

y_1	y_2	y_3	s_1	s_2	s_3	b	Basic Variables
0	5	0	1	−1	−1	1	s_1 ← Departing
1	$-\frac{1}{3}$	0	0	$\frac{2}{3}$	$-\frac{1}{3}$	$\frac{1}{3}$	y_1
0	$\frac{2}{3}$	1	0	$-\frac{1}{3}$	$\frac{2}{3}$	$\frac{4}{3}$	y_3
0	$-\frac{20}{3}$	0	0	$\frac{16}{3}$	$\frac{52}{3}$	$\frac{188}{3}$	

↑ Entering (under y_2)

y_1	y_2	y_3	s_1	s_2	s_3	b	Basic Variables
0	1	0	$\frac{1}{5}$	$-\frac{1}{5}$	$-\frac{1}{5}$	$\frac{1}{5}$	y_2
			See NOTE in Exercise 15.				y_1
							y_3
0	0	0	$\frac{4}{3}$	4	16	64	

Answer:

$(x_1, x_2, x_3) = \left(\frac{4}{3}, 4, 16\right)$ gives a minimum value of $w = 64$.

21. Let x_1 liters of the first drink and x_2 liters of the second drink be consumed.

$$x_1 + 2x_2 \geq 3$$

$$3x_1 + 2x_2 \geq 5$$

$$x_1, x_2 \geq 0$$

The cost to be minimized is $C = 2x_1 + 3x_2$ dollars.

Augmented matrices:

Given: $\begin{bmatrix} 1 & 2 & : & 3 \\ 3 & 2 & : & 5 \\ \cdots & \cdots & \cdots & \cdots \\ 2 & 3 & : & 0 \end{bmatrix}$

Dual: $\begin{bmatrix} 1 & 3 & : & 2 \\ 2 & 2 & : & 3 \\ \cdots & \cdots & \cdots & \cdots \\ 3 & 5 & : & 0 \end{bmatrix}$

The dual maximization problem:

Objective function:

$$z = 3y_1 + 5y_2$$

Constraints:

$$y_1 + 3y_2 \leq 2$$

$$2y_1 + 2y_2 \leq 3$$

$$y_1, y_2 \geq 0$$

y_1	y_2	s_1	s_2	b	Basic Variables	
1	3	1	0	2	s_1	← Departing
2	2	0	1	3	s_2	
−3	−5	0	0	0		
	↑ Entering					

y_1	y_2	s_1	s_2	b	Basic Variables	
$\frac{1}{3}$	1	$\frac{1}{3}$	0	$\frac{2}{3}$	y_2	
$\frac{4}{3}$	0	$-\frac{2}{3}$	1	$\frac{5}{3}$	s_2	← Departing
$-\frac{4}{3}$	0	$\frac{5}{3}$	0	$\frac{10}{3}$		
↑ Entering						

y_1	y_2	s_1	s_2	b	Basic Variables
See NOTE in Exercise 15.					y_2
1	0	−0.5	0.75	1.25	y_1
0	0	1	1	5	

Answer: Consume a liter of each drink for a minimum cost of $5.00.

23. This setup is just like the one for solving Exercise 21 except that the cost is $C = x_1 + 3x_2$. Consequently, the dual problem for this exercise has the same initial tableau as in Exercise 21 except for column b.

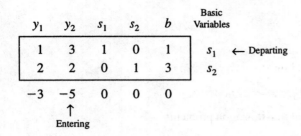

y_1	y_2	s_1	s_2	b	Basic Variables	
1	3	1	0	1	s_1	← Departing
2	2	0	1	3	s_2	
−3	−5	0	0	0		
	↑					
	Entering					

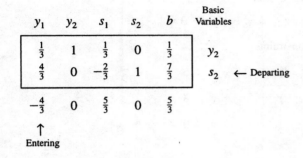

y_1	y_2	s_1	s_2	b	Basic Variables	
$\frac{1}{3}$	1	$\frac{1}{3}$	0	$\frac{1}{3}$	y_2	
$\frac{4}{3}$	0	$-\frac{2}{3}$	1	$\frac{7}{3}$	s_2	← Departing
$-\frac{4}{3}$	0	$\frac{5}{3}$	0	$\frac{5}{3}$		
↑						
Entering						

y_1	y_2	s_1	s_2	b	Basic Variables
1	3	1	0	1	y_1
See NOTE in Exercise 15.					s_2
0	4	3	0	3	

Answer: Consume 3 liters of the first drink only for a minimum cost of $3.00.

25. Let x_1 liters of Drink I and x_2 liters of Drink II be combined. Assume that the given table lists units of nutrients per liter.

$$4x_1 + x_2 \geq 4$$

$$2x_1 + 5x_2 \geq 10$$

$$x_1 + x_2 \geq 3$$

$$x_1, x_2 \geq 0$$

The cost to be minimized is $C = 5x_1 + 8x_2$ dollars.

Augmented matrices:

Given:
$$\begin{bmatrix} 4 & 1 & \vdots & 4 \\ 2 & 5 & \vdots & 10 \\ 1 & 1 & \vdots & 3 \\ \cdots & \cdots & \vdots & \\ 5 & 8 & \vdots & 0 \end{bmatrix}$$

Dual:
$$\begin{bmatrix} 4 & 2 & 1 & \vdots & 5 \\ 1 & 5 & 1 & \vdots & 8 \\ \cdots & \cdots & \cdots & \vdots & \\ 4 & 10 & 3 & \vdots & 0 \end{bmatrix}$$

The dual maximization problem:

Objective function:

$$z = 4y_1 + 10y_2 + 3y_3$$

Constraints:

$$4y_1 + 2y_2 + y_3 \leq 5$$

$$y_1 + 5y_2 + y_3 \leq 8$$

$$y_1, y_2, y_3 \geq 0$$

y_1	y_2	y_3	s_1	s_2	b	Basic Variables
4	2	1	1	0	5	s_1
1	5	1	0	1	8	s_2 ← Departing
−4	−10	−3	0	0	0	

Entering (y_2)

y_1	y_2	y_3	s_1	s_2	b	Basic Variables
3.6	0	0.6	1	−0.4	1.8	s_1 ← Departing
0.2	1	0.2	0	0.2	1.6	y_2
−2	0	−1	0	2	16	

Entering (y_1)

y_1	y_2	y_3	s_1	s_2	b	Basic Variables
1	0	$\frac{1}{6}$	$\frac{5}{18}$	$-\frac{1}{9}$	$\frac{1}{2}$	y_1 ← Departing
0	1	$\frac{1}{6}$	$-\frac{1}{18}$	$\frac{2}{9}$	$\frac{3}{2}$	y_2
0	0	$-\frac{2}{3}$	$\frac{5}{9}$	$\frac{16}{9}$	17	

Entering (y_3)

y_1	y_2	y_3	s_1	s_2	b	Basic Variables
6	0	1	$\frac{5}{3}$	$-\frac{2}{3}$	3	y_3
See NOTE in Exercise 15.						y_2
4	0	0	$\frac{5}{3}$	$\frac{4}{3}$	19	

Answer: Consume $\frac{5}{3}$ liters of Drink I and $\frac{4}{3}$ liters of Drink II for a minimum cost of $19.00.

27. This setup is just like the one for solving Exercise 25 except that the cost is $C = x_1 + 5x_2$. Consequently, the dual problem for this exercise has the same initial tableau as in Exercise 25 except for column b.

y_1	y_2	y_3	s_1	s_2	b	Basic Variables
4	2	1	1	0	1	s_1 ← Departing
1	5	1	0	1	5	s_2
−4	−10	−3	0	0	0	

$\uparrow$
Entering

y_1	y_2	y_3	s_1	s_2	b	Basic Variables
2	1	0.5	0.5	0	0.5	y_2
		See NOTE in Exercise 15.				s_2
16	0	2	5	0	5	

Answer: Use 5 liters of Drink I only for a minimum cost of $5.00.

29. Let plants 1, 2, and 3 operate for $x_1, x_2,$ and x_3 days, respectively. The operating cost is $C = 55x_1 + 60x_2 + 60x_3$ thousand dollars.

$$8x_1 + 6x_2 + 12x_3 \geq 300$$

$$4x_1 + 6x_2 + 4x_3 \geq 172$$

$$8x_1 + 3x_2 + 8x_3 \geq 249.5$$

$$x_1, x_2, x_3 \geq 0$$

Augmented matrices:

Given:
$$\begin{bmatrix} 8 & 6 & 12 & : & 300 \\ 4 & 6 & 4 & : & 172 \\ 8 & 3 & 8 & : & 249.5 \\ \cdots & \cdots & \cdots & : & \cdots \\ 55 & 60 & 60 & : & 0 \end{bmatrix}$$

Dual:
$$\begin{bmatrix} 8 & 4 & 8 & : & 55 \\ 6 & 6 & 3 & : & 60 \\ 12 & 4 & 8 & : & 60 \\ \cdots & \cdots & \cdots & : & \cdots \\ 300 & 172 & 249.5 & : & 0 \end{bmatrix}$$

The dual maximization problem:

Objective function:

$$z = 300y_1 + 172y_2 + 249.5y_3$$

Constraints:

$$8y_1 + 4y_2 + 8y_3 \leq 55$$

$$6y_1 + 6y_2 + 3y_3 \leq 60$$

$$12y_1 + 4y_2 + 8y_3 \leq 60$$

$$y_1, y_2, y_3 \geq 0$$

y_1	y_2	y_3	s_1	s_2	s_3	b	Basic Variables	
8	4	8	1	0	0	55	s_1	
6	6	3	0	1	0	60	s_2	
12	4	8	0	0	1	60	s_3	← Departing

$$-300 \quad -172 \quad -249.5 \quad 0 \quad 0 \quad 0 \quad 0$$
$$\uparrow$$
$$\text{Entering}$$

y_1	y_2	y_3	s_1	s_2	s_3	b	Basic Variables	
0	$\frac{4}{3}$	$\frac{8}{3}$	1	0	$-\frac{2}{3}$	15	s_1	
0	4	-1	0	1	$-\frac{1}{2}$	30	s_2	← Departing
1	$\frac{1}{3}$	$\frac{2}{3}$	0	0	$\frac{1}{12}$	5	y_1	

$$0 \quad -72 \quad -49.5 \quad 0 \quad 0 \quad 25 \quad 1{,}500$$
$$\uparrow$$
$$\text{Entering}$$

y_1	y_2	y_3	s_1	s_2	s_3	b	Basic Variables	
0	0	3	1	$-\frac{1}{3}$	$-\frac{1}{2}$	5	s_1	← Departing
0	1	$-\frac{1}{4}$	0	$\frac{1}{4}$	$-\frac{1}{8}$	$\frac{15}{2}$	y_2	
1	0	$\frac{3}{4}$	0	$-\frac{1}{12}$	$\frac{1}{8}$	$\frac{5}{2}$	y_1	

$$0 \quad 0 \quad -67.5 \quad 0 \quad 18 \quad 16 \quad 2{,}040$$
$$\uparrow$$
$$\text{Entering}$$

y_1	y_2	y_3	s_1	s_2	s_3	b	Basic Variables
0	0	1	$\frac{1}{3}$	$-\frac{1}{9}$	$-\frac{1}{6}$	$\frac{5}{3}$	y_3
		See NOTE in Exercise 15.					y_2
							y_1

$$0 \quad 0 \quad 0 \quad 22.5 \quad 10.5 \quad 4.75 \quad 2{,}152.5$$

Answer: The minimum cost of $2,152,500 occurs when Plants 1, 2, and 3 operate for 22.5 days, 10.5 days, and 4.75 days, respectively.

31. Let Refinery 1 operate for x_1 days and let Refinery 2 operate for x_2 days. The cost to minimize is
$C = 25x_1 + 30x_2$ thousand dollars.

$$300x_1 + 300x_2 \geq 35,000$$

$$200x_2 + 250x_2 \geq 30,000$$

$$150x_1 + 400x_2 \geq 40,000$$

$$x_1, x_2 \geq 0$$

Augmented matrices:

Given:
$$\begin{bmatrix} 300 & 300 & \vdots & 35,000 \\ 200 & 250 & \vdots & 30,000 \\ 150 & 400 & \vdots & 40,000 \\ \cdots & \cdots & \vdots & \cdots \\ 25 & 30 & \vdots & 0 \end{bmatrix}$$

Dual:
$$\begin{bmatrix} 300 & 200 & 150 & \vdots & 25 \\ 300 & 250 & 400 & \vdots & 30 \\ \cdots & \cdots & \cdots & \vdots & \cdots \\ 35,000 & 30,000 & 40,000 & \vdots & 0 \end{bmatrix}$$

The dual maximization problem:

Objective function:

$$z = 35,000y_1 + 30,000y_2 + 40,000y_3$$

Constraints:

$$300y_1 + 200y_2 + 150y_3 \leq 25$$

$$300y_1 + 250y_2 + 400y_3 \leq 30$$

$$y_1, y_2, y_3 \geq 0$$

y_1	y_2	y_3	s_1	s_2	b	Basic Variables
300	200	150	1	0	25	s_1
300	250	400	0	1	30	s_2 ← Departing
−35,000	−30,000	−40,000	0	0	0	

↑ Entering (under y_3)

y_1	y_2	y_3	s_1	s_2	b	Basic Variables
187.5	106.25	0	1	0.375	13.75	s_1
0.75	0.625	1	0	0.0025	0.075	y_3 ← Departing
−5,000	−5,000	0	0	100	3,000	

↑ Entering (under y_1)

y_1	y_2	y_3	s_1	s_2	b	Basic Variables
		See NOTE in Exercise 15.				s_1
1.2	1	1.6	0	0.004	0.12	y_2
1,000	0	8,000	0	120	3,600	

Answer: The minimum cost of $3,600,000 occurs when Refinery 1 is idle and Refinery 2 operates for 120 days.

33. The dual maximization problem:

Objective function:

$$z = 35y_1 + 120y_2 + 50y_3 + 75y_4$$

Constraints:

$$1.5y_1 \qquad + y_3 + 0.5y_4 \le 1$$
$$y_1 + 2y_2 + y_3 \qquad \le 0.5$$
$$6y_2 + y_3 + 2.5y_4 \le 2.5$$
$$2y_1 + 4y_2 + y_3 + 1.5y_4 \le 2.5$$
$$y_1, \qquad y_2, \qquad y_3, \qquad y_4 \le 0$$

y_1	y_2	y_3	y_4	s_1	s_2	s_3	s_4	b	Basic Variables	
1.5	0	1	0.5	1	0	0	0	1	s_1	
1	2	1	0	0	1	0	0	0.5	s_2	
0	6	1	2.5	0	0	1	0	2.5	s_3	
2	4	1	1.5	0	0	0	1	3	s_4	← Departing
−35	−120	−50	−75	0	0	0	0	0		

$\uparrow$
Entering

The minimum is 87.14 at (21.43, 2.86, 25.71, 0).

Section 9.5   The Simplex Method: Mixed Constraints

1. Introduce a surplus variable in the first inequality and a slack variable in the second inequality.

x_1	x_2	s_1	s_2	b	Basic Variables
2	1	−1	0	4	s_1
1	1	0	1	8	s_2
−10	−4	0	0	0	

3. Introduce a slack variable in the first inequality and a surplus variable in the second inequality.

x_1	x_2	s_1	s_2	b	Basic Variables
2	1	1	0	4	s_1
1	3	0	−1	2	s_2
1	1	0	0	0	

5. Introduce surplus variables in the first and third inequalities and introduce a slack variable in the second inequality.

x_1	x_2	x_3	s_1	s_2	s_3	b	Basic Variables
4	1	0	−1	0	0	10	s_1
1	1	3	0	1	0	30	s_2
2	1	4	0	0	−1	16	s_3
−1	0	−1	0	0	0	0	

7.

x_1	x_2	s_1	s_2	b	Basic Variables	
1	1	−1	0	3	s_1	← Departing
1	1	0	1	6	s_2	
1	−2	0	0	0		

       ↑
    Entering

x_1	x_2	s_1	s_2	b	Basic Variables	
1	1	−1	0	3	x_2	
0	0	1	1	3	s_2	← Departing
3	0	−2	0	6		

       ↑
    Entering

x_1	x_2	s_1	s_2	b	Basic Variables
1	1	0	1	6	x_2
0	0	1	1	3	s_1
3	0	0	2	12	

The maximum value of w is 12 and it occurs when $x_1 = 0$ and $x_2 = 6$.

9.

x_1	x_2	s_1	s_2	b	Basic Variables
2	3	1	0	25	s_1
1	2	0	−1	16	s_2 ← Departing
1	2	0	0	0	

↑
Entering

x_1	x_2	s_1	s_2	b	Basic Variables
0.5	0	1	1.5	1	s_1
0.5	1	0	−0.5	8	x_2
0	0	0	1	−16	

The minimum value of w is 16 and it occurs when $x_1 = 0$ and $x_2 = 8$, for example.

11.

x_1	x_2	x_3	s_1	s_2	s_3	b	Basic Variables
−4	3	1	1	0	0	40	s_1
−2	1	1	0	−1	0	10	s_2 ← Departing
0	1	1	0	0	1	20	s_3
−1	−1	0	0	0	0	0	

↑
Entering

x_1	x_2	x_3	s_1	s_2	s_3	b	Basic Variables
2	0	−2	1	3	0	10	s_1 ← Departing
−2	1	1	0	−1	0	10	x_2
2	0	0	0	1	1	10	s_3
−3	0	1	0	−1	0	10	

↑
Entering

x_1	x_2	x_3	s_1	s_2	s_3	b	Basic Variables
1	0	−1	0.5	1.5	0	5	x_1
0	1	−1	1	2	0	20	x_2
0	0	2	−1	−2	1	0	s_3 ← Departing
0	0	−2	1.5	3.5	0	25	

↑
Entering

x_1	x_2	x_3	s_1	s_2	s_3	b	Basic Variables
1	0	0	0	0.5	0.5	5	x_1
0	1	0	0.5	1	0.5	20	x_2
0	0	1	−0.5	−1	0.5	0	x_3
0	0	0	0.5	1.5	1	25	

The maximum value of w is 25 and it occurs when $x_1 = 5$, $x_2 = 20$, and $x_3 = 0$, for example.

13.

x_1	x_2	s_1	s_2	b	Basic Variables	
1	2	-1	0	4	s_1	$\leftarrow$ Departing
1	1	0	1	8	s_2	
-2	-5	0	0	0		

$\uparrow$
Entering

x_1	x_2	s_1	s_2	b	Basic Variables	
0.5	1	-0.5	0	2	x_2	
0.5	0	-0.5	1	6	s_2	$\leftarrow$ Departing
0.5	0	-2.5	0	10		

$\uparrow$
Entering

x_1	x_2	s_1	s_2	b	Basic Variables
1	1	0	1	8	x_2
1	0	1	2	12	s_1
3	0	0	5	40	

The maximum value of w is 40 and it occurs when $x_1 = 0$ and $x_2 = 8$.

15.

x_1	x_2	x_3	s_1	s_2	s_3	b	Basic Variables	
1	4	2	1	0	0	85	s_1	
0	1	-5	0	-1	0	20	s_2	$\leftarrow$ Departing
3	2	11	0	0	-1	49	s_3	
-2	-1	-3	0	0	0	0		

$\uparrow$
Entering

x_1	x_2	x_3	s_1	s_2	s_3	b	Basic Variables	
1	0	22	1	4	0	5	s_1	$\leftarrow$ Departing
0	1	-5	0	-1	0	20	x_2	
3	0	21	0	2	-1	9	s_3	
-2	0	-8	0	-1	0	20		

$\uparrow$
Entering

x_1	x_2	x_3	s_1	s_2	s_3	b	Basic Variables
1	0	22	1	4	0	5	x_1
0	1	-5	0	-1	0	20	x_2
0	0	-45	-3	-10	-1	-6	s_3
0	0	36	2	7	0	30	

$(x_1, x_2, x_3, s_1, s_2, s_3) = (5, 20, 0, 0, 0, 6)$ gives a maximum value of $w = 30$.

17.

x_1	x_2	s_1	s_2	b	Basic Variables
1	2	−1	0	25	s_1 ← Departing
2	5	0	1	60	s_2
1	1	0	0	0	

↑
Entering

x_1	x_2	s_1	s_2	b	Basic Variables
1	2	−1	0	25	x_1
0	1	2	1	10	s_2 ← Departing
0	−1	1	0	−25	

↑
Entering

x_1	x_2	s_1	s_2	b	Basic Variables
1	0	−5	−2	5	x_1
0	1	2	1	10	s_2
0	0	3	1	−15	

The minimum value of w is 15 and it occurs when $x_1 = 5$ and $x_2 = 10$.

19.

x_1	x_2	x_3	s_1	s_2	b	Basic Variables
3	−6	4	1	0	30	s_1
2	−8	10	0	−1	18	s_2 ← Departing
−2	4	−1	0	0	0	

↑
Entering

x_1	x_2	x_3	s_1	s_2	b	Basic Variables
0	6	−11	1	1.5	3	s_1 ← Departing
1	−4	5	0	−0.5	9	x_1
0	−4	9	0	−1	18	

↑
Entering

x_1	x_2	x_3	s_1	s_2	b	Basic Variables
0	1	$-\frac{11}{6}$	$\frac{1}{6}$	$\frac{1}{4}$	$\frac{1}{2}$	x_2
1	0	$-\frac{7}{3}$	$\frac{2}{3}$	$\frac{1}{2}$	11	x_1
0	0	$\frac{5}{3}$	$\frac{2}{3}$	0	20	

The minimum value of w is −20 and it occurs when $x_1 = 11$, $x_2 = 0.5$, and $x_3 = 0$, for example.

21.

x_1	x_2	s_1	s_2	s_3	b	Basic Variables
1	1	1	0	0	5	s_1
−1	1	0	1	0	3	s_2
0	1	0	0	−1	1	s_3 ← Departing
−2	−1	0	0	0	0	

       ↑
    Entering

x_1	x_2	s_1	s_2	s_3	b	Basic Variables
1	0	1	0	1	4	s_1 ← Departing
−1	0	0	1	1	2	s_2
0	1	0	0	−1	1	x_2
−2	0	0	0	−1	1	

↑
Entering

x_1	x_2	s_1	s_2	s_3	b	Basic Variables
1	0	1	0	1	4	x_1
0	0	1	1	2	6	s_2
0	1	0	0	−1	1	x_2
0	0	2	0	1	9	

The maximum value of w is 9 and it occurs when $x_1 = 4$ and $x_2 = 1$.

23.

x_1	x_2	s_1	s_2	s_3	b	Basic Variables
1	1	1	0	0	5	s_1
−1	1	0	1	0	3	s_2
0	1	0	0	−1	1	s_3 ← Departing
0	−1	0	0	0	0	

    ↑
   Entering

x_1	x_2	s_1	s_2	s_3	b	Basic Variables
1	0	1	0	1	4	s_1
−1	0	0	1	1	2	s_2 ← Departing
0	1	0	0	−1	1	x_2
0	0	0	0	−1	1	

    ↑
   Entering

x_1	x_2	s_1	s_2	s_3	b	Basic Variables
2	0	1	−1	0	2	s_1 ← Departing
−1	0	0	1	1	2	s_3
−1	1	0	1	0	3	x_2
−1	0	0	1	0	3	

↑
Entering

x_1	x_2	s_1	s_2	s_3	b	Basic Variables
1	0	0.5	−0.5	0	1	x_1
0	0	0.5	0.5	1	3	s_3
0	1	0.5	0.5	0	4	x_2
0	0	0.5	0.5	0	4	

The maximum value of w is 4 and it occurs when $x_1 = 1$ and $x_2 = 4$.

25.

x_1	x_2	s_1	s_2	s_3	s_4	b	Basic Variables	
3	2	−1	0	0	0	6	s_1	
1	−1	0	1	0	0	2	s_2	
−1	2	0	0	1	0	6	s_3	← Departing
1	0	0	0	0	1	4	s_4	
−1	−1	0	0	0	0	0		

$\uparrow$
Entering

x_1	x_2	s_1	s_2	s_3	s_4	b	Basic Variables	
4	0	−1	0	−1	0	0	s_1	← Departing
0.5	0	0	1	0.5	0	5	s_2	
−0.5	1	0	0	0.5	0	3	x_2	
1	0	0	0	0	1	4	s_4	
−1.5	0	0	0	0.5	1	3		

$\uparrow$
Entering

x_1	x_2	s_1	s_2	s_3	s_4	b	Basic Variables	
1	0	−0.25	0	−0.25	0	0	x_1	
0	0	0.125	1	0.625	0	5	s_2	
0	1	−0.125	0	0.375	0	3	x_2	
0	0	0.25	0	0.25	1	4	s_4	← Departing
0	0	−0.375	0	0.125	0	3		

$\uparrow$
Entering

x_1	x_2	s_1	s_2	s_3	s_4	b	Basic Variables
1	0	0	0	0	1	4	x_1
0	0	0	1	0.5	−0.5	3	s_2
0	1	0	0	0.5	0.5	5	x_2
0	0	1	0	1	4	16	s_1
0	0	0	0	0.5	1.5	9	

The maximum value of w is 9 and it occurs when $x_1 = 4$ and $x_2 = 5$.

27.

x_1	x_2	s_1	s_2	s_3	s_4	b	Basic Variables
3	2	-1	0	0	0	6	s_1
1	-1	0	1	0	0	2	s_2
-1	2	0	0	1	0	6	s_3 ← Departing
1	0	0	0	0	1	4	s_4
4	-1	0	0	0	0	0	

Entering (under x_2)

x_1	x_2	s_1	s_2	s_3	s_4	b	Basic Variables
4	0	-1	0	-1	0	0	s_1 ← Departing
0.5	0	0	1	0.5	0	5	s_2
-0.5	1	0	0	0.5	0	3	x_2
1	0	0	0	0	1	4	s_4
3.5	0	0	0	0.5	0	3	

Entering (under x_1)

x_1	x_2	s_1	s_2	s_3	s_4	b	Basic Variables
1	0	-0.25	0	-0.25	0	0	x_1
0	0	0.125	1	0.625	0	5	s_2
0	1	-0.125	0	0.375	0	3	x_2
0	0	0.25	0	0.25	1	4	s_4
0	0	0.875	0	1.375	0	3	

The maximum value of w is 3 and it occurs when $x_1 = 0$ and $x_2 = 3$.

29. Let x_1 tires be shipped from supplier S_1 to customer C_1, and let x_2 tires be shipped from S_1 to C_2.

$$0 \le x_1 \le 500$$

$$0 \le x_2 \le 600$$

$$x_1 + x_2 \le 900$$

$$(500 - x_1) + (600 - x_2) \le 800$$

The last inequality is equivalent to $x_1 + x_2 \ge 300$. The cost to minimize is

$$C = 0.6x_1 + 1.2x_2 + (500 - x_1) + 1.8(600 - x_2) = 1580 - 0.4x_1 - 0.6x_2.$$

A convenient objective function to maximize is $z = 0.4x_1 + 0.6x_2$ since $C = 1580 - z$.

x_1	x_2	s_1	s_2	s_3	s_4	b	Basic Variables	
1	0	1	0	0	0	500	s_1	
0	1	0	1	0	0	600	s_2	
1	1	0	0	1	0	900	s_3	
1	1	0	0	0	−1	300	s_4	← Departing
−0.4	−0.6	0	0	0	0	0		

↑
Entering

x_1	x_2	s_1	s_2	s_3	s_4	b	Basic Variables	
1	0	1	0	0	0	500	s_1	
−1	0	0	1	0	1	300	s_2	← Departing
0	0	0	0	1	0	600	s_3	
1	1	0	0	0	−1	300	x_2	
0.2	0	0	0	0	−0.6	180		

↑
Entering

x_1	x_2	s_1	s_2	s_3	s_4	b	Basic Variables	
1	0	1	0	0	0	500	s_1	
−1	0	0	1	0	1	300	s_4	
1	0	0	−1	1	0	300	s_3	← Departing
0	1	0	1	0	0	600	x_2	
−0.4	0	0	0.6	0	0	360		

↑
Entering

x_1	x_2	s_1	s_2	s_3	s_4	b	Basic Variables
0	0	1	1	−1	0	200	s_1
0	0	0	0	1	1	600	s_4
1	0	0	−1	1	0	300	x_1
0	1	0	1	0	0	600	x_2
0	0	0	0.2	0.4	0	480	

The value $C = 1580 - 480 = 1100$ is minimal and it occurs when the following shipping schedule for tires is implemented.

	C_1	C_2
S_1	300	600
S_2	200	0

31. This setup is just like the one for solving Exercise 29 except that the cost is

$$C = 1.2x_1 + x_2 + (500 - x_1) + 1.2(600 - x_2) = 1220 + 0.2x_1 - 0.2x_2.$$

A convenient objective function to maximize is $z = -0.2x_1 + 0.2x_2$ since $C = 1220 - z$.

x_1	x_2	s_1	s_2	s_3	s_4	b	Basic Variables	
1	0	1	0	0	0	500	s_1	
0	1	0	1	0	0	600	s_2	← Departing
1	1	0	0	1	0	900	s_3	
1	1	0	0	0	−1	300	s_4	
0.2	−0.2	0	0	0	0	0		

↑
Entering

x_1	x_2	s_1	s_2	s_3	s_4	b	Basic Variables
1	0	1	0	0	0	500	s_1
0	1	0	1	0	0	600	x_2
1	0	0	−1	1	0	300	s_3
1	0	0	−1	0	−1	−300	s_4
0.2	0	0	0.2	0	0	120	

The solution represented by this tableau is $(x_1, x_2, s_1, s_2, s_3, s_4) = (0, 600, 500, 0, 300, 300)$.

Answer:

The value $C = 1220 - 120 = 1100$ is minimal and is realized when the following schedule for shipping tires is used.

	C_1	C_2
S_1	0	600
S_2	500	0

33. Let x_1 cars and x_2 cars be shipped from Factory 1 to Customers 1 and 2, respectively.

$$0 \leq x_2 \leq 200$$

$$0 \leq x_2 \leq 300$$

$$x_1 + x_2 \leq 400$$

$$(200 - x_1) + (300 - x_2) \leq 300$$

The last inequality is equivalent to $x_1 + x_2 \geq 200$. The cost in dollars to minimize is

$$C = 36x_1 + 30x_2 + 30(200 - x_1) + 25(300 - x_2) = 13,500 + 6x_1 + 5x_2.$$

A convenient objective function to maximize is $z = -6x_1 - 5x_2$ since $C = 13,500 - z$.

x_1	x_2	s_1	s_2	s_3	s_4	b	Basic Variables
1	0	1	0	0	0	200	s_1
0	1	0	1	0	0	300	s_2
1	1	0	0	1	0	400	s_3
1	1	0	0	0	-1	200	s_4 ← Departing
6	5	0	0	0	0	0	

↑ Entering

x_1	x_2	s_1	s_2	s_3	s_4	b	Basic Variables
1	0	1	0	0	0	200	s_1
-1	0	0	1	0	1	100	s_2
0	0	0	0	1	1	200	s_3
1	1	0	0	0	-1	200	x_2
1	0	0	0	0	5	-1000	

The minimum value of C is $13,500 - (-1000) = 14,500$. To achieve it, use the following schedule of cars to be shipped.

	Customer 1	Customer 2
Factory 1	0	200
Factory 2	200	100

35. Let x_1 television minutes and x_2 newspaper pages be purchased. Assuming that each television ad lasts one minute, the size of the audience to be maximized is expected to be $15x_1 + 3x_2$ million people.

$$60x_1 + 15x_2 \leq 600$$
$$x_1 \geq 6$$
$$x_2 \geq 4$$

x_1	x_2	s_1	s_2	s_3	b	Basic Variables
60	15	1	0	0	600	s_1
1	0	0	−1	0	6	s_2
0	1	0	0	−1	4	s_3 ← Departing
−15	−3	0	0	0	0	

↑
Entering

x_1	x_2	s_1	s_2	s_3	b	Basic Variables
60	0	1	0	15	540	s_1 ← Departing
1	0	0	−1	0	6	s_2
0	1	0	0	−1	4	x_2
−15	0	0	0	−3	12	

↑
Entering

x_1	x_2	s_1	s_2	s_3	b	Basic Variables
1	0	$\frac{1}{60}$	0	$\frac{1}{4}$	9	x_1
1	0	$-\frac{1}{60}$	−1	$-\frac{1}{4}$	−3	s_2
0	1	0	0	−1	4	x_2
0	0	$\frac{1}{4}$	0	$\frac{3}{4}$	147	

This tableau represents the solution $(x_1, x_2, s_1, s_2, s_3) = (9, 4, 0, 3, 0)$.
Purchase 9 television ads for \$540,000 and 4 newspaper ads for \$60,000
to realize the maximum audience of 147 million people.

37. Let x_1 computers be shipped from Plant A to Outlet I and let x_2 computers be shipped from Plant A to Outlet II.

$$0 \leq x_1 \leq 3000$$
$$0 \leq x_2 \leq 5000$$
$$x_1 + x_2 \leq 5000$$
$$(3000 - x_1) + (5000 - x_2) \leq 4000$$

The last inequality is equivalent to $x_1 + x_2 \geq 4000$. The cost in dollars to be minimized is

$$C = 4x_1 + 5x_2 + 5(3000 - x_1) + 6(5000 - x_2) = 45{,}000 - x_1 - x_2.$$

A convenient function to maximize is $z = x_1 + x_2$ since $C = 45{,}000 - z$.

x_1	x_2	s_1	s_2	s_3	s_4	b	Basic Variables	
1	0	1	0	0	0	3000	s_1	← Departing
0	1	0	1	0	0	5000	s_2	
1	1	0	0	1	0	5000	s_3	
1	1	0	0	0	−1	4000	s_4	
−1	−1	0	0	0	0	0		

↑
Entering

x_1	x_2	s_1	s_2	s_3	s_4	b	Basic Variables	
1	0	1	0	0	0	3000	x_1	
0	1	0	1	0	0	5000	s_2	
0	1	−1	0	1	0	2000	s_3	← Departing
0	1	−1	0	0	−1	1000	s_4	
0	−1	1	0	0	0	3000		

↑
Entering

x_1	x_2	s_1	s_2	s_3	s_4	b	Basic Variables
1	0	1	0	0	0	3000	x_1
0	0	1	1	−1	0	3000	s_2
0	1	−1	0	1	0	2000	x_2
0	0	0	0	−1	−1	−1000	s_4
0	0	0	0	1	0	5000	

This tableau represents the solution $(x_1, x_2, s_1, s_2, s_3, s_4) = (3000, 2000, 0, 3000, 0, 1000)$. The minimum cost is $C = 45{,}000 - 5{,}000 = 40{,}000$ dollars; it is obtained by using the following shipping schedule, for example.

	Outlet I	Outlet II
Plant A	3000	2000
Plant B	0	3000

Chapter 9   Review Exercises

1. $x + 2y \leq 160$

$3x + y \leq 180$

$x, y \geq 0$

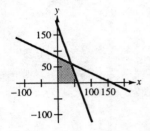

3. $3x + 2y \geq 24$

$x + 2y \geq 12$

$2 \leq x \leq 15$

$y \leq 15$

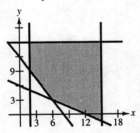

5. $2x - 3y \geq 0$

$2x - y \leq 8$

$y \geq 0$

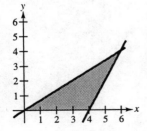

7.   Let $x_1 = \#$ apples for Harrisburg

$x_2 = \#$ apples for Philadelphia

$x_1 \geq 400$

$x_2 \geq 600$

$x_1 + x_2 \leq 1500$

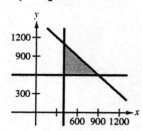

9. Maximize $z = 3x + 4y$

at $(0,0)$ $z = \ \ 0$

at $(0, 10)$ $z = 40$

at $(5, 8)$ $z = 47$

at $(7, 0)$ $z = 21$

Maximize is 47 at $(5, 8)$.

11. $x \geq 0$

$y \geq 0$

$x \leq 5$

$x + y \geq 3$

$x - y \leq 3$

$-x + y \leq 3$

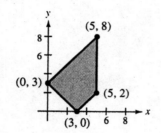

Vertex: (x, y)	$(3, 0)$	$(5, 2)$	$(5, 8)$	$(0, 3)$
$z = x + 3y$	3	11	29	9

$(x, y) = (3, 0)$ gives a minimum value of $z = 3$. $(x, y) = (5, 8)$
gives a maximum value of $z = 29$.

13.

$$x \geq 0$$

$$y \geq 0$$

$$x \leq 3y$$

$$-x + 2y \leq 12$$

$$4x + 3y \leq 40$$

$$x + 2y \leq 15$$

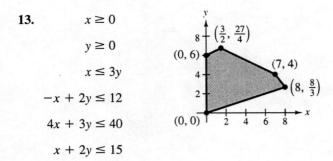

Vertex: (x, y)	$(0, 0)$	$\left(8, \frac{8}{3}\right)$	$(7, 4)$	$\left(\frac{3}{2}, \frac{27}{4}\right)$	$(0, 6)$
$z = 3x - y$	0	$\frac{64}{3}$	17	$-\frac{21}{4}$	-6

$(x, y) = (0, 6)$ gives a minimum value of $z = -6$. $(x, y) = \left(8, \frac{8}{3}\right)$ gives a maximum value of $z = \frac{64}{3}$.

15.

	x_1	x_2	s_1	s_2	b	Basic Variables
	2	1	1	0	31	s_1
	1	4	0	1	40	s_2 ← Departing
	-1	-2	0	0	0	

↑
Entering

	x_1	x_2	s_1	s_2	b	Basic Variables
	1.75	0	1	-0.25	21	s_1 ← Departing
	0.25	1	0	0.25	10	x_2
	-0.5	0	0	0.5	20	

↑
Entering

	x_1	x_2	s_1	s_2	b	Basic Variables
	1	0	$\frac{4}{7}$	$-\frac{1}{7}$	12	x_1
	0	1	$-\frac{1}{7}$	$\frac{2}{7}$	7	x_2
	0	0	$\frac{2}{7}$	$\frac{3}{7}$	26	

$\left(x_1, x_2\right) = (12, 7)$ gives a maximum value of $z = 26$.

17.

x_1	x_2	x_3	s_1	s_2	s_3	b	Basic Variables
2	2	1	1	0	0	20	s_1
1	1	−2	0	1	0	23	s_2
−2	1	−2	0	0	1	8	s_3 ← Departing
−1	−2	−1	0	0	0	0	

Entering (x_2)

x_1	x_2	x_3	s_1	s_2	s_3	b	Basic Variables
6	0	5	1	0	−2	4	s_1 ← Departing
3	0	0	0	1	−1	15	s_2
−2	1	−2	0	0	1	8	x_2
−5	0	−5	0	0	2	16	

Entering (x_3)

x_1	x_2	x_3	s_1	s_2	s_3	b	Basic Variables
1.2	0	1	0.2	0	−0.4	0.8	x_3
3	0	0	0	1	−1	15	s_2
0.4	1	0	0.4	0	0.2	9.6	x_2
1	0	0	1	0	0	20	

The maximum value of z is 20 and it occurs when $(x_1, x_2, x_3, s_1, s_2, s_3) = (0, 9.6, 0.8, 0, 15, 0)$, for example.

19.

x_1	x_2	s_1	s_2	b	Basic Variables
3	1	1	0	432	s_1 ← Departing
1	4	0	1	628	s_2
−1	−1	0	0	0	

Entering (x_1)

x_1	x_2	s_1	s_2	b	Basic Variables
1	$\frac{1}{3}$	$\frac{1}{3}$	0	144	x_1
0	$\frac{11}{3}$	$-\frac{1}{3}$	1	484	s_2 ← Departing
0	$-\frac{2}{3}$	$\frac{1}{3}$	0	144	

Entering (x_2)

x_1	x_2	s_1	s_2	b	Basic Variables
1	0	$\frac{4}{11}$	$-\frac{1}{11}$	100	x_1
0	1	$-\frac{1}{11}$	$\frac{3}{11}$	132	x_2
0	0	$\frac{3}{11}$	$\frac{2}{11}$	232	

$(x_1, x_2, s_1, s_2) = (100, 132, 0, 0)$ gives a maximum value of $z = 232$.

21.

x_1	x_2	x_3	s_1	s_2	s_3	b	Basic Variables
6	−2	3	1	0	0	24	s_1
3	−3	9	0	1	0	33	s_2
−2	1	−2	0	0	1	25	s_3 ← Departing
−3	−5	−4	0	0	0	0	

    ↑
  Entering

x_1	x_2	x_3	s_1	s_2	s_3	b	Basic Variables
2	0	−1	1	0	2	74	s_1
−3	0	3	0	1	3	108	s_2 ← Departing
−2	1	−2	0	0	1	25	x_2
−13	0	−14	0	0	5	125	

    ↑
  Entering

x_1	x_2	x_3	s_1	s_2	s_3	b	Basic Variables
1	0	0	1	$\frac{1}{3}$	3	110	s_1 ← Departing
−1	0	1	0	$\frac{1}{3}$	1	36	x_3
−4	1	0	0	$\frac{2}{3}$	3	97	x_2
−27	0	0	0	$\frac{14}{3}$	19	629	

↑
Entering

x_1	x_2	x_3	s_1	s_2	s_3	b	Basic Variables
1	0	0	1	$\frac{1}{3}$	3	110	s_1
0	0	1	1	$\frac{2}{3}$	4	146	x_3
0	1	0	4	2	15	537	x_2
0	0	0	27	$\frac{41}{3}$	100	3599	

$(x_1, x_2, x_3, s_1, s_2, s_3) = (110, 537, 146, 0, 0, 0)$ gives a maximum value of $z = 3599$.

23. Augmented matrices:

Given:
$$\begin{bmatrix} 1 & 1 & 2 & : & 30 \\ 3 & 6 & 4 & : & 75 \\ \cdots & \cdots & \cdots & \cdots & \cdots \\ 7 & 3 & 1 & : & 0 \end{bmatrix}$$

Dual:
$$\begin{bmatrix} 1 & 3 & : & 7 \\ 1 & 6 & : & 3 \\ 2 & 4 & : & 1 \\ \cdots & \cdots & \cdots & \cdots \\ 30 & 75 & : & 0 \end{bmatrix}$$

The dual maximization problem:

Objective function:

$$z = 30y_1 + 75y_2$$

Constraints:

$$y_1 - 3y_2 \leq 7$$
$$y_1 + 6y_2 \leq 3$$
$$2y_1 + 4y_2 \leq 1$$
$$y_1, y_2 \geq 0$$

25. Augmented matrices:

$$\text{Given: } \begin{bmatrix} 1 & 5 & : & 15 \\ 4 & -10 & : & 0 \\ \cdots & \cdots & : & \cdots \\ 9 & 15 & : & 0 \end{bmatrix}$$

$$\text{Dual: } \begin{bmatrix} 1 & 4 & : & 9 \\ 5 & -10 & : & 15 \\ \cdots & \cdots & : & \cdots \\ 15 & 0 & : & 0 \end{bmatrix}$$

The dual maximization problem:

Objective function:

$$z = 15y_1$$

Constraints:

$$y_1 + 4y_2 \le 9$$
$$5y_1 - 10y_2 \le 15$$
$$y_1, y_2 \ge 0$$

y_1	y_2	s_1	s_2	b	Basic Variables	
1	4	1	0	9	s_1	
5	-10	0	1	15	s_2	← Departing
-15	0	0	0	0		

↑
Entering

y_1	y_2	s_1	s_2	b	Basic Variables	
0	6	1	-0.2	6	s_1	← Departing
1	-2	0	0.2	3	y_1	
0	-30	0	3	45		

↑
Entering

y_1	y_2	s_1	s_2	b	Basic Variables
0	1	$\frac{1}{6}$	$-\frac{1}{30}$	1	y_2
See the NOTE below.					y_1

0	0	5	2	75

$(x_1, x_2) = (5, 2)$ gives a minimum value of $w = 75$.

NOTE: In dual problems, it is convenient to calculate the pivot row and then the bottom row of each tableau. If there are no negative entries in the bottom row (except for the last column), then the answer has been found and further computation is unnecessary.

27. Augmented matrices:

Given:
$$\begin{bmatrix} 2 & 2 & -3 & : & 24 \\ 6 & 0 & -2 & : & 21 \\ -8 & -4 & 8 & : & 12 \\ \cdots & \cdots & \cdots & : & \cdots \\ 24 & 22 & 18 & : & 0 \end{bmatrix}$$

Dual:
$$\begin{bmatrix} 2 & 6 & -8 & : & 24 \\ 2 & 0 & -4 & : & 22 \\ -3 & -2 & 8 & : & 18 \\ \cdots & \cdots & \cdots & : & \cdots \\ 24 & 21 & 12 & : & 0 \end{bmatrix}$$

The dual maximization problem:

Objective function:

$$z = 24y_1 + 21y_2 + 12y_3$$

Constraints:

$$2y_1 + 6y_2 - 8y_3 \le 24$$
$$2y_1 \quad\quad - 4y_3 \le 22$$
$$-3y_1 - 2y_2 + 8y_3 \le 18$$
$$y_1, y_2, y_3 \ge 0$$

y_1	y_2	y_3	s_1	s_2	s_3	b	Basic Variables	
2	6	−8	1	0	0	24	s_1	
2	0	−4	0	1	0	22	s_2	← Departing
−3	−2	8	0	0	1	18	s_3	
−24	−21	−12	0	0	0	0		

↑
Entering

y_1	y_2	y_3	s_1	s_2	s_3	b	Basic Variables	
0	6	−4	1	−1	0	2	s_1	
1	0	−2	0	−0.5	0	11	y_1	
0	−2	2	0	1.5	1	51	s_3	← Departing
0	−21	−60	0	12	0	264		

↑
Entering

y_1	y_2	y_3	s_1	s_2	s_3	b	Basic Variables	
0	2	0	1	2	2	104	s_1	← Departing
1	−2	0	0	2	1	62	y_1	
0	−1	1	0	0.75	0.5	25.5	y_3	
0	−81	0	0	57	30	1794		

↑
Entering

y_1	y_2	y_3	s_1	s_2	s_3	b	Basic Variables
0	1	0	0.5	1	1	52	y_2
			See NOTE in Exercise 25.				y_1
							y_3
0	0	0	40.5	138	111	6006	

$(x_1, x_2, x_3) = (40.5, 138, 111)$ gives a minimum value of $w = 6006$.

29. Augmented matrices:

$$
\text{Given:} \quad
\begin{bmatrix}
1 & 2 & 3 & \vdots & 2 \\
2 & 7 & 4 & \vdots & 5 \\
1 & 3 & 4 & \vdots & 1 \\
\hdotsfor{5} \\
16 & 54 & 48 & \vdots & 0
\end{bmatrix}
$$

$$
\text{Dual:} \quad
\begin{bmatrix}
1 & 2 & 1 & \vdots & 16 \\
2 & 7 & 3 & \vdots & 54 \\
3 & 4 & 4 & \vdots & 48 \\
\hdotsfor{5} \\
2 & 5 & 1 & \vdots & 0
\end{bmatrix}
$$

The dual maximization problem:

Objective function:

$$z = 2y_1 + 5y_2 + y_3$$

Constraints:

$$
\begin{aligned}
y_1 + 2y_2 + y_3 &\le 16 \\
2y_1 + 7y_2 + 3y_3 &\le 54 \\
3y_1 + 4y_2 + 4y_3 &\le 48 \\
y_1, y_2, y_3 &\ge 0
\end{aligned}
$$

y_1	y_2	y_3	s_1	s_2	s_3	b	Basic Variables
1	2	1	1	0	0	16	s_1
2	7	3	0	1	0	54	s_2 ← Departing
3	4	4	0	0	1	48	s_3
-2	-5	-1	0	0	0	0	

Entering (y_2)

y_1	y_2	y_3	s_1	s_2	s_3	b	Basic Variables
$\frac{3}{7}$	0	$\frac{1}{7}$	1	$-\frac{2}{7}$	0	$\frac{4}{7}$	s_1 ← Departing
$\frac{2}{7}$	1	$\frac{3}{7}$	0	$\frac{1}{7}$	0	$\frac{54}{7}$	y_2
$\frac{13}{7}$	0	$\frac{16}{7}$	0	$-\frac{4}{7}$	1	$\frac{120}{7}$	s_3
$-\frac{4}{7}$	0	$\frac{8}{7}$	0	$\frac{5}{7}$	0	$\frac{270}{7}$	

Entering (y_1)

y_1	y_2	y_3	s_1	s_2	s_3	b	Basic Variables
0	1	$\frac{1}{3}$	$\frac{7}{3}$	$-\frac{2}{3}$	0	$\frac{4}{3}$	y_1
		See NOTE in Exercise 25.					y_2
							s_3
0	0	$\frac{4}{3}$	$\frac{4}{3}$	$\frac{1}{3}$	0	$\frac{118}{3}$	

$(x_1, x_2, x_3) = \left(\frac{4}{3}, \frac{1}{3}, 0\right)$ gives a minimum value of $w = \frac{118}{3}$.

31.

x_1	x_2	s_1	s_2	b	Basic Variables
-4	2	1	0	26	s_1
-3	1	0	-1	12	s_2 ← Departing
-1	-2	0	0	0	

Entering (x_2)

x_1	x_2	s_1	s_2	b	Basic Variables
2	0	1	2	2	s_1 ← Departing
-3	1	0	-1	12	x_2
-7	0	0	-2	24	

Entering (x_1)

x_1	x_2	s_1	s_2	b	Basic Variables
1	0	0.5	1	1	x_1
0	1	1.5	2	15	x_2
0	0	3.5	5	31	

$(x_1, x_2) = (1, 15)$ gives the maximum value of $z = 31$.

33.

x_1	x_2	x_3	s_1	s_2	s_3	b	Basic Variables
1	1	1	1	0	0	60	s_1
−4	2	1	0	−1	0	52	s_2
2	0	1	0	0	−1	40	s_3 ← Departing
−2	−1	−1	0	0	0	0	

↑ Entering (under x_3)

x_1	x_2	x_3	s_1	s_2	s_3	b	Basic Variables
−1	1	0	1	0	1	20	s_1
−6	2	0	0	−1	1	12	s_2 ← Departing
2	0	1	0	0	−1	40	x_3
0	−1	0	0	0	−1	40	

↑ Entering (under x_2)

x_1	x_2	x_3	s_1	s_2	s_3	b	Basic Variables
2	0	0	1	0.5	0.5	14	s_1 ← Departing
−3	1	0	0	−0.5	0.5	6	x_2
2	0	1	0	0	−1	40	x_3
−3	0	0	0	−0.5	−0.5	46	

↑ Entering (under x_1)

x_1	x_2	x_3	s_1	s_2	s_3	b	Basic Variables
1	0	0	0.5	0.25	0.25	7	x_1
0	1	0	1.5	0.25	1.25	27	x_2
0	0	1	−1	−0.5	−1.5	26	x_3
0	0	0	1.5	0.25	0.25	67	

$(x_1, x_2, x_3) = (7, 27, 26)$ gives a maximum value of $z = 67$.

35.

x_1	x_2	x_3	s_1	s_2	s_3	b	Basic Variables
32	16	8	1	0	0	344	s_1
20	−40	20	0	−1	0	200	s_2 ← Departing
−45	15	30	0	0	1	525	s_3
9	4	10	0	0	0	0	

↑ Entering (under x_1)

x_1	x_2	x_3	s_1	s_2	s_3	b	Basic Variables
0	80	−24	1	1.6	0	24	s_1
1	−2	1	0	−0.05	0	10	x_1
0	−75	75	0	−2.25	1	975	s_3
0	22	1	0	0.45	0	−90	

$(x_1, x_2, x_3) = (10, 0, 0)$ gives a minimum value of $z = 90$.

37. Suppose x_1 purses and x_2 vests are made. The profit to be maximized is $P = 80x_1 + 50x_2$ dollars.

$$2x_1 + x_2 \le 12$$

$$x_1 + 2x_2 \le 21$$

$$x_1 + 3x_2 \le 11$$

$$x_1, x_2 \ge 0$$

x_1	x_2	s_1	s_2	s_3	b	Basic Variables	
2	1	1	0	0	12	s_1	← Departing
1	2	0	1	0	21	s_2	
1	3	0	0	1	11	s_3	
−80	−50	0	0	0	0		

↑
Entering

x_1	x_2	s_1	s_2	s_3	b	Basic Variables	
1	0.5	0.5	0	0	6	x_1	
0	1.5	−0.5	1	0	15	s_2	
0	2.5	−0.5	0	1	5	s_3	← Departing
0	−10	40	0	0	480		

↑
Entering

x_1	x_2	s_1	s_2	s_3	b	Basic Variables
1	0	0.6	0	−0.2	5	x_1
0	0	−0.2	1	−0.6	12	s_2
0	1	−0.2	0	0.4	2	x_2
0	0	38	0	4	500	

To attain the maximum profit of $500, the tailor should make 5 purses and 2 vests.

39. Suppose Mines A, B, and C operate for x_1, x_2, and x_3 days respectively. The cost to be minimized is $C = 200x_1 + 200x_2 + 100x_3$ dollars.

$$x_1 + x_2 + 2x_3 \geq 60$$

$$2x_1 + 2x_2 + x_3 \geq 48$$

$$3x_1 + 2x_2 + x_3 \geq 55$$

$$x_1, x_2, x_3 \geq 0$$

This is a standard minimization problem and it can be solved by treating the dual maximization problem. For the sake of variety, however, the solution method for mixed constraint problems is used.

x_1	x_2	x_3	s_1	s_2	s_3	b	Basic Variables	
1	1	2	−1	0	0	60	s_1	← Departing
2	2	1	0	−1	0	48	s_2	
3	2	1	0	0	−1	55	s_3	
200	200	100	0	0	0	0		

Entering (↑ under x_3)

x_1	x_2	x_3	s_1	s_2	s_3	b	Basic Variables	
0.5	0.5	1	−0.5	0	0	30	x_3	
1.5	1.5	0	0.5	−1	0	18	s_2	← Departing
2.5	1.5	0	0.5	0	−1	25	s_3	
150	150	0	50	0	0	−3000		

Entering (↑ under s_1)

x_1	x_2	x_3	s_1	s_2	s_3	b	Basic Variables	
2	2	1	0	−1	0	48	x_3	
3	3	0	1	−2	0	36	s_1	
1	0	0	0	1	−1	7	s_3	← Departing
0	0	0	0	100	0	−4800		

Entering (↑ under s_2)

x_1	x_2	x_3	s_1	s_2	s_3	b	Basic Variables
0	2	1	0	−3	2	34	x_3
0	3	0	1	−5	3	15	s_1
1	0	0	0	1	−1	7	x_1
0	0	0	0	100	0	−4800	

Operate Mine A for 7 days and Mine C for 34 days to attain the minimum cost of $4800. Mine B remains idle. There are other solutions.

CHAPTER 10
Numerical Methods

Section 10.1   Gaussian Elimination with Partial Pivoting

1. We express the number as a sign and a mantissa M where $0.1 \leq M < 1$ multiplied by 10^k where k is an integer. Thus, $4281 = 0.4281 \times 10^4$ in floating point form.

3. We express the number as a sign and a mantissa M where $0.1 \leq M < 1$ multiplied by 10^k where k is an integer. Thus, $-2.62 = -0.262 \times 10^1$.

5. We express the number as a sign and a mantissa M where $0.1 \leq M < 1$ multiplied by 10^k where k is an integer. Thus, $-0.00121 = -0.121 \times 10^{-2}$ in floating point form.

7. We express the number as a sign and a mantissa M where $0.1 \leq M < 1$ multiplied by 10^k where k is an integer. Thus, $\frac{1}{8} = 0.125 \times 10^0$.

9. (a) The floating point form is 0.331×10^3. To three significant digits this rounds to 0.331×10^3.

    (b) The floating point form is 0.331×10^3. To four significant digits this rounds to 0.3310×10^3.

11. (a) The floating point form is -0.92646×10^2. To three significant digits this rounds to -0.926×10^2.

    (b) The floating point form is -0.92646×10^2. To four significant digits this rounds to -0.9265×10^2.

13. (a) The floating point form is 0.4375×10^0. To three significant digits this rounds to 0.438×10^0.

    (b) The floating point form is 0.4375×10^0. This representation is already correct to four significant digits.

15. (a) The floating point form is $0.\overline{142857} \times 10^0$. To three significant digits this rounds to 0.143×10^0.

    (b) To four significant digits this rounds to 0.1429×10^0.

17. The exact value of the determinant is

$$\begin{vmatrix} 1.24 & 56.00 \\ 66.00 & 1.02 \end{vmatrix} = 1.24(1.02) - 56.00(66.00)$$

$$= 1.2648 - 3696.00$$

$$= -3694.7352.$$

Rounding each intermediate calculation to three significant digits yields

$$\begin{vmatrix} 1.24 & 56.00 \\ 66.00 & 1.02 \end{vmatrix} = 1.24(1.02) - 56.00(66.0)$$

$$= 1.26 - 3700$$

$$= -3700.$$

The percentage of accumulated error is

$$100 \left| \frac{-3694.7352 + 3700}{-3694.7352} \right| \approx 0.142\%.$$

19. We row-reduce the augmented matrix of the system, rounding to three significant digits after each intermediate calculation.

$$\begin{bmatrix} 1.21 & 16.7 & 28.8 \\ 4.66 & 64.4 & 111.0 \end{bmatrix} \Rightarrow \begin{bmatrix} 1 & 13.8 & 23.8 \\ 4.66 & 64.4 & 111.0 \end{bmatrix}$$

$$\Rightarrow \begin{bmatrix} 1 & 13.8 & 23.8 \\ 0 & 0.1 & 0 \end{bmatrix}$$

We then use back-substitution to obtain $y = 0$ and $x = 23.8$. The exact answer is $z = 10$ and $y = 1$, which is quite different!

21. The augmented matrix for this system is

$$\begin{bmatrix} 1.00 & 1.04 & 2.04 \\ 6.00 & 6.20 & 12.2 \end{bmatrix}.$$

Adding -6.00 times row one to row two yields

$$\begin{bmatrix} 1 & 1.04 & 2.04 \\ 0 & -0.0400 & 0.000 \end{bmatrix}.$$

Dividing row two by -0.0400 yields

$$\begin{bmatrix} 1 & 1.04 & 2.04 \\ 0 & 1 & 0.000 \end{bmatrix}.$$

We then use back-substitution to obtain $y = 0.000$ and $x = 2.04 - 1.04(0.000) = 2.04$.
If we reduce the same augmented matrix with partial pivoting we must begin by interchanging rows one and two.

$$\begin{bmatrix} 6.00 & 6.20 & 12.2 \\ 1.00 & 1.04 & 2.04 \end{bmatrix}$$

Then we divide row one by 6.00 to obtain

$$\begin{bmatrix} 1 & 1.03 & 2.03 \\ 1.00 & 1.04 & 2.04 \end{bmatrix}.$$

Adding -1.00 times row one to row two yields

$$\begin{bmatrix} 1 & 1.03 & 2.03 \\ 0 & 0.0100 & 0.0100 \end{bmatrix}.$$

Dividing row two by 0.0100 yields

$$\begin{bmatrix} 1 & 1.03 & 2.03 \\ 0 & 1 & 1.00 \end{bmatrix}.$$

Using back-substitution produces $y = 1.00$ and $x = 2.03 - 1.03(1.00) = 2.03 - 1.03 = 1.00$.
Thus, Gaussian elimination without partial pivoting yields a grossly incorrect solution, while partial pivoting (in this case) eliminated the error.

23. We row-reduce the augmented matrix of the system, rounding to three digits after each intermediate calculation.

$$\begin{bmatrix} 1 & 4.01 & 0.00445 & 0.00 \\ -1 & -4.00 & 0.00600 & 0.21 \\ 2 & -4.05 & 0.0500 & -0.385 \end{bmatrix} \Rightarrow \begin{bmatrix} 1 & 4.01 & 0.00445 & 0.0 \\ 0 & 0.01 & 0.0104 & 0.21 \\ 0 & -12.1 & 0.0411 & -0.385 \end{bmatrix}$$

$$\Rightarrow \begin{bmatrix} 1 & 4.01 & 0.00445 & 0.0 \\ 0 & 1 & 1.04 & 21.0 \\ 0 & 0 & 12.6 & 254.0 \end{bmatrix}$$

We then use back-substitution to obtain $z = 20.2$, $y = 21 - 1.04(20.2) = 0$, and $x = -0.00445(20.2) - 4.01(0) = -0.0899$. If we use partial pivoting, we first exchange the first and third rows.

$$\begin{bmatrix} 2 & 4.05 & 0.0500 & -0.385 \\ -1 & -4.00 & 0.00600 & 0.21 \\ 1 & 4.01 & 0.00445 & 0.0 \end{bmatrix} \Rightarrow \begin{bmatrix} 1 & -2.02 & 0.025 & -0.192 \\ 0 & -6.02 & 0.031 & 0.018 \\ 0 & 6.03 & -0.0206 & 0.192 \end{bmatrix}$$

$$\Rightarrow \begin{bmatrix} 1 & -2.02 & 0.025 & -0.192 \\ 0 & 6.03 & -0.0206 & 0.192 \\ 0 & -6.02 & 0.031 & 0.018 \end{bmatrix}$$

$$\Rightarrow \begin{bmatrix} 1 & -2.02 & 0.025 & -0.192 \\ 0 & 1 & -0.00342 & 0.0318 \\ 0 & 0 & 0.0104 & 0.209 \end{bmatrix}$$

Back-substitution now yields

$z = 20.1$,

$y = 0.0318 + (0.00342)(20.1)$

$\quad = 0.0318 + 0.0687 = 0.100$, and

$x = -0.192 - 0.025(20.1) + (2.02)(0.100)$

$\quad = -0.192 - 0.502 + 0.202 = -0.492$.

Thus, Gaussian elimination with partial pivoting yields a grossly incorrect solution, while partial pivoting (in this case) produces a much more accurate solution.

25. We row-reduce the augmented matrix, rounding each intermediate calculation to three significant digits

$$\begin{bmatrix} 1 & 1 & 2 \\ 1 & \frac{600}{601} & 20 \end{bmatrix} \Rightarrow \begin{bmatrix} 1 & 1 & 2 \\ 0 & -0.002 & 18 \end{bmatrix}.$$

Hence, $y = 18/(-0.002) = -9000$ and $x = 2 + 9000 = 9000$. Note that the exact solution is quite different: $x = 10,820$ and $y = -10,818$.

27. We solve the two systems by row-reduction.

$$\begin{bmatrix} 1 & 1 & 2 \\ 1 & 1.0001 & 2 \end{bmatrix} \Rightarrow \begin{bmatrix} 1 & 1 & 2 \\ 0 & 0.001 & 0 \end{bmatrix} \Rightarrow x = 2 \text{ and } y = 0$$

$$\begin{bmatrix} 1 & 1 & 2 \\ 1 & 1.0001 & 2.0001 \end{bmatrix} \Rightarrow \begin{bmatrix} 1 & 1 & 2 \\ 0 & 0.001 & 0.001 \end{bmatrix} \Rightarrow x = 1 \text{ and } y = 1$$

29. The augmented matrix for this system is

$$\begin{bmatrix} 1.0 & 0.50 & 0.33 & 1.0 \\ 0.50 & 0.33 & 0.25 & 1.0 \\ 0.33 & 0.25 & 0.20 & 1.0 \end{bmatrix}.$$

Adding -0.50 times row one to row two and -0.33 times row one to row three yields

$$\begin{bmatrix} 1 & 0.50 & 0.33 & 1.0 \\ 0 & 0.080 & 0.090 & 0.50 \\ 0 & 0.090 & 0.090 & 0.67 \end{bmatrix}.$$

Dividing row two by 0.080 yields

$$\begin{bmatrix} 1 & 0.50 & 0.33 & 1.0 \\ 0 & 1 & 1.1 & 6.2 \\ 0 & 0.090 & 0.090 & 0.67 \end{bmatrix}.$$

Adding -0.090 times row two to row three yields

$$\begin{bmatrix} 1 & 0.50 & 0.33 & 1.0 \\ 0 & 1 & 1.1 & 6.2 \\ 0 & 0 & -0.0090 & 0.11 \end{bmatrix}.$$

Dividing row three by -0.0090 yields

$$\begin{bmatrix} 1 & 0.50 & 0.33 & 1.0 \\ 0 & 1 & 1.1 & 6.2 \\ 0 & 0 & 1 & -12 \end{bmatrix}.$$

Using back-substitution we obtain

$$x_3 = -12$$

$$x_2 = 6.2 - 1.1(-12) = 6.2 + 13 = 19$$

$$x_1 = 1.0 - 0.50(19) - 0.33(-12) = 1.0 - 9.5 + 4.0 = -8.5 + 4.0 = -4.5.$$

Note that these values for x_1, x_2 and x_3 are grossly incorrect as compared with the exact solution.

31. Matlab gives the following inverses for the Hilbert matrices of order 4, 5, 6 and 7.

>> inv(hilb(4))

ans =

1.0e+03 *

0.0160	−0.1200	0.2400	−0.1400
−0.1200	1.2000	−2.7000	1.6800
0.2400	−2.7000	6.4800	−4.2000
−0.1400	1.6800	−4.2000	2.8000

>> inv(hilb(5))

ans =

1.0e+05 *

0.0002	−0.0030	0.0105	−0.0140	0.0063
−0.0030	0.0480	−0.1890	0.2688	−0.1260
0.0105	−0.1890	0.7938	−1.1760	0.5670
−0.0140	0.2688	−1.1760	1.7920	−0.8820
0.0063	−0.1260	0.5670	−0.8820	0.4410

>> inv(hilb(6))

ans =

1.0e+06 *

0.0000	−0.0006	0.0034	−0.0076	0.0076	−0.0028
−0.0006	0.0147	−0.0882	0.2117	−0.2205	0.0832
0.0034	−0.0882	0.5645	−1.4112	1.5120	−0.5821
−0.0076	0.2117	−1.4112	3.6288	−3.9690	1.5523
0.0076	−0.2205	1.5120	−3.9690	4.4100	−1.7464
−0.0028	0.0832	−0.5821	1.5523	−1.7464	0.6985

>> inv(hilb(7))

ans =

1.0e+08 *

0.0000	−0.0000	0.0001	−0.0003	0.0005	−0.0004	0.0001
−0.0000	0.0004	−0.0032	0.0113	−0.0194	0.0160	−0.0050
0.0001	−0.0032	0.0286	−0.1058	0.1871	−0.1572	0.0505
−0.0003	0.0113	−0.1058	0.4032	−0.7277	0.6209	−0.2018
0.0005	−0.0194	0.1871	−0.7277	1.3340	−1.1526	0.3784
0.0004	0.0160	−0.1572	0.6209	−1.1526	1.0059	−0.3330
0.0001	−0.0050	0.0505	−0.2018	0.3784	−0.3330	0.1110

Your answers will depend on the software used.

Section 10.2 Iterative Methods for Solving Linear Systems

1. First, we write the system in the form

$$x_1 = \tfrac{2}{3} + \tfrac{1}{3}x_2$$

$$x_2 = \tfrac{5}{4} - \tfrac{1}{4}x_1.$$

The first approximation is

$$x_1 = \tfrac{2}{3} + \tfrac{1}{3}(0) = \tfrac{2}{3} \approx 0.667$$

$$x_2 = \tfrac{5}{4} - \tfrac{1}{4}(0) = \tfrac{5}{4} = 1.25 \ .$$

We continue this procedure, with the results summarized below.

n	0	1	2	3	4	5	6	7
x_1	0.000	0.667	1.08	1.03	0.993	0.998	1.00	1.00
x_2	0.000	1.25	1.08	0.979	0.993	1.00	1.00	1.00

3. First, we write the system in the form

$$x_1 = 1 + \tfrac{1}{2}x_2$$

$$x_2 = \tfrac{2}{3} + \tfrac{1}{3}x_1 + \tfrac{1}{3}x_3$$

$$x_3 = 2 - \tfrac{1}{3}x_1 + \tfrac{1}{3}x_2.$$

The first approximation is

$$x_1 = 1 + \tfrac{1}{2}(0) = 1$$

$$x_2 = \tfrac{2}{3} + \tfrac{1}{3}(0) + \tfrac{1}{3}(0) = \tfrac{2}{3} \approx 0.667$$

$$x_3 = 2 - \tfrac{1}{3}(0) + \tfrac{1}{3}(0) = 2.$$

We continue this procedure, with the results summarized below.

n	0	1	2	3	4	. . .	
x_1	0	1.0	1.333	1.83	1.87	. . .	2.0
x_2	0	0.667	1.667	1.74	1.98	. . .	2.0
x_3	0	2.0	1.8$\overline{8}$	2.11	1.97	. . .	2.0

5. We use the same form of the original system.

$$x_1 = \tfrac{2}{3} + \tfrac{1}{3}x_2$$
$$x_2 = \tfrac{5}{4} - \tfrac{1}{4}x_1$$

This method, however, requires us to use the most recently calculated value of x_1 and x_2 in each iteration. Thus, we begin with

$$x_1 = \tfrac{2}{3} + \tfrac{1}{3}(0) = \tfrac{2}{3} \approx 0.667$$
$$x_2 = \tfrac{5}{4} - \tfrac{1}{4}\left(\tfrac{2}{3}\right) = \tfrac{13}{12} \approx 1.08 \ .$$

We continue this procedure, with the results summarized below.

n	0	1	2	3	4	5
x_1	0.000	0.667	1.03	0.998	1.00	1.00
x_2	0.000	1.08	0.993	1.00	1.00	1.00

7. We use the same form of the original system

$$x_1 = 1 + \tfrac{1}{2}x_2$$
$$x_2 = \tfrac{2}{3} + \tfrac{1}{3}x_1 + \tfrac{1}{3}x_3$$
$$x_3 = 2 - \tfrac{1}{3}x_1 + \tfrac{1}{3}x_2.$$

This method, however, requires us to use the most recently calculated value of x_1, x_2 and x_3 in each iteration. Thus, we begin with

$$x_1 = 1 + \tfrac{1}{2}(0) = 1$$
$$x_2 = \tfrac{2}{3} + \tfrac{1}{3}(1) + \tfrac{1}{3}(0) = 1$$
$$x_3 = 2 - \tfrac{1}{3}(1) + \tfrac{1}{3}(1) = 2.$$

We continue this procedure, with the results summarized below.

n	0	1	2	3	4	5	6
x_1	0	1	1.5	1.92	2.01	2.0	2.0
x_2	0	1	1.83	2.01	2.01	2.0	2.0
x_3	0	2	2.11	2.03	2.0	2.0	2.0

9. We write the system in the form

$$x_1 = -1 + 2x_2$$
$$x_2 = 3 - 2x_1.$$

Then we find the first approximation.

$$x_1 = -1 + 2(0) = -1$$
$$x_2 = 3 - 2(-1) = 5$$

A second iteration yields

$$x_1 = -1 + 2(5) = 9$$
$$x_2 = 3 - 2(9) = -15,$$

and a third yields

$$x_1 = -1 + 2(-15) = -31$$
$$x_2 = 3 - 2(-31) = 65.$$

Since the actual solution is $x_1 = 1$ and $x_2 = 1$ and since the approximations are getting continually worse, we conclude that the method diverges for this system.

11. We write the system in the form

$$x_1 = -\tfrac{7}{2} + \tfrac{3}{2}x_2$$
$$x_2 = 3 - \tfrac{1}{3}x_1 + \tfrac{10}{3}x_3$$
$$x_3 = 13 - 3x_1.$$

Then we find the first approximation

$$x_1 = -\tfrac{7}{2} + \tfrac{3}{2}(0) = -3.5$$
$$x_2 = 3 - \tfrac{1}{3}(-3.5) + \tfrac{10}{8}(0) = 4.167$$
$$x_3 = 13 - 3(-3.5) = 23.5$$

Continuing this procedure, we obtain the following.

n	0	1	2	3	4
x_1	0	-3.5	2.75	117.0	-33.8
x_2	0	4.167	80.40	-20.2	-1114.0
x_3	0	23.5	4.75	-338.0	114.0

We see that the approximations are getting continually further from the exact solution $\left(x_1 = 4, x_2 = 5, x_3 = 1\right)$. We conclude that the method diverges for this case.

13. Since

$$|a_{11}| = 2 > 1 = |a_{12}|$$
$$|a_{22}| = 5 > 3 = |a_{21}|$$

the matrix *is* strictly diagonally dominant.

15. Since

$$|a_{22}| = 3 < 2 + 2 = |a_{21}| + |a_{23}|$$

the matrix is *not* strictly diagonally dominant.

17. The system with rows interchanged is

$$2x_1 + x_2 = 3$$
$$x_1 - 2x_2 = -1.$$

We write this system in the form

$$x_1 = \tfrac{3}{2} - \tfrac{1}{2}x_2$$
$$x_2 = \tfrac{1}{2} + \tfrac{1}{2}x_1.$$

Then the first approximation is

$$x_1 = \tfrac{3}{2} - \tfrac{1}{2}(0) = \tfrac{3}{2} = 1.5$$
$$x_2 = \tfrac{1}{2} + \tfrac{1}{2}\left(\tfrac{3}{2}\right) = \tfrac{5}{4} = 1.25.$$

We continue this procedure, with the results summarized below.

n	0	1	2	3	4	5	6
x_1	0.00	1.5	0.88	1.0	0.99	1.0	1.0
x_2	0.00	1.3	0.94	1.0	1.0	1.0	1.0

19. The system with rows interchanged is

$$3x_1 \qquad + \quad x_3 = 13$$
$$2x_1 - 3x_2 \qquad = -7$$
$$x_1 + 3x_2 - 10x_3 = 9.$$

We write this system in the form

$$x_1 = \tfrac{13}{3} - \tfrac{1}{3}x_3$$
$$x_2 = \tfrac{7}{3} + \tfrac{2}{3}x_1$$
$$x_3 = -\tfrac{9}{10} + \tfrac{1}{10}x_1 + \tfrac{3}{10}x_2.$$

The the first approximation is

$$x_1 = \tfrac{13}{3} - \tfrac{1}{3}(0) = 4.33$$
$$x_2 = \tfrac{7}{3} + \tfrac{2}{3}(4.33) = 5.22$$
$$x_3 = -\tfrac{9}{10} + \tfrac{1}{10}(4.33) + \tfrac{3}{10}(5.22) = 1.1.$$

We continue this procedure with the results summarized below.

n	0	1	2	3	4
x_1	0	4.33	3.967	4.003	4.0
x_2	0	5.22	4.978	5.002	5.0
x_3	0	1.1	0.99	1.001	1.0

21. We write the system in the form

$$x_1 = -\tfrac{1}{4} + \tfrac{5}{4}x_2$$
$$x_2 = \tfrac{3}{2} - \tfrac{1}{2}x_1.$$

Then using the Jacobi Method, the first iteration yields

$$x_1 = -\tfrac{1}{4} + \tfrac{5}{4}(0) = -\tfrac{1}{4}$$
$$x_2 = \tfrac{3}{2} - \tfrac{1}{2}(0) = \tfrac{3}{2}.$$

After 31 iterations, the Jacobi Method has converged to three significant digits.

$$x_1 = 1.00$$

$$x_2 = 1.00$$

Similarly, using the Gauss-Seidel Method, the first iteration yields

$$x_1 = -\tfrac{1}{4} + \tfrac{5}{4}(0) = -\tfrac{1}{4}$$
$$x_2 = \tfrac{3}{2} - \tfrac{1}{2}(-\tfrac{1}{4}) = \tfrac{13}{8}.$$

After 19 iterations, the Gauss-Seidel Method has converged to three significant digits.

$$x_1 = 1.00$$

$$x_2 = 1.00$$

23. Refer to the computer program on in the Answers to Odd-Numbered Exercises that applies the Gauss-Seidel Method to solve the given system of linear equations

$$
\begin{aligned}
4x_1 + x_2 - x_3 &= 3 \\
x_1 + 6x_2 - 2x_3 + x_4 - x_5 &= -6 \\
x_2 + 5x_3 - x_5 + x_6 &= -5 \\
2x_2 + 5x_4 - x_5 - x_7 - x_8 &= 0 \\
-x_3 - x_4 + 6x_5 - x_6 - x_8 &= 12 \\
-x_3 - x_5 + 5x_6 &= -12 \\
-x_4 + 4x_7 - x_8 &= -2 \\
-x_4 - x_5 - x_7 + 5x_8 &= 2.
\end{aligned}
$$

The final solution is

$$X1 = 1.000$$

$$X2 = -1.000$$

$$X3 = 0.000$$

$$X4 = 1.000$$

$$X5 = 2.000$$

$$X6 = -2.000$$

$$X7 = 0.000$$

$$X8 = 1.000.$$

Section 10.3   Power Method for Approximating Eigenvalues

1. The eigenvalues of A are given by solving the characteristic equation

$$|\lambda I - A| = \begin{vmatrix} \lambda - 2 & -1 \\ 0 & \lambda + 4 \end{vmatrix} = (\lambda + 4)(\lambda - 2) = 0.$$

The solutions of this equation are $\lambda_1 = -4$ and $\lambda_2 = 2$. Thus, -4 is a dominant eigenvalue with dominant eigenvector $\left(-\frac{1}{6}, 1\right)$.

3. The eigenvalues of A are given by solving

$$|\lambda I - A| = \begin{vmatrix} \lambda - 1 & 5 \\ 3 & \lambda + 1 \end{vmatrix} = (\lambda^2 - 16) = 0.$$

The solutions of this equation are $\lambda_1 = -4$ and $\lambda_2 = 4$. Thus, A has no dominant eigenvalue.

5. The eigenvalues of A are the entries along the main diagonal $\lambda_1 = 2$, $\lambda_2 = -1$ and $\lambda_3 = 3$. Thus, 3 is a dominant eigenvalue, with corresponding eigenvector $(5, 1, 2)$.

7. $$A\mathbf{x} = \begin{bmatrix} 4 & -5 \\ 2 & -3 \end{bmatrix} \begin{bmatrix} 5 \\ 2 \end{bmatrix} = \begin{bmatrix} 10 \\ 4 \end{bmatrix}$$

$$A\mathbf{x} \cdot \mathbf{x} = \begin{bmatrix} 10 \\ 4 \end{bmatrix} \cdot \begin{bmatrix} 5 \\ 2 \end{bmatrix} = 58$$

$$\mathbf{x} \cdot \mathbf{x} = \begin{bmatrix} 5 \\ 2 \end{bmatrix} \cdot \begin{bmatrix} 5 \\ 2 \end{bmatrix} = 29$$

Therefore, the Rayleigh quotient is

$$\lambda = \frac{A\mathbf{x} \cdot \mathbf{x}}{\mathbf{x} \cdot \mathbf{x}} = \frac{58}{29} = 2.$$

9. $$A\mathbf{x} = \begin{bmatrix} 1 & 2 & -2 \\ -2 & 5 & -2 \\ -6 & 6 & -3 \end{bmatrix} \begin{bmatrix} 1 \\ 1 \\ 3 \end{bmatrix} = \begin{bmatrix} -3 \\ -3 \\ -9 \end{bmatrix}$$

$$A\mathbf{x} \cdot \mathbf{x} = \begin{bmatrix} -3 \\ -3 \\ -9 \end{bmatrix} \cdot \begin{bmatrix} 1 \\ 1 \\ 3 \end{bmatrix} = -33$$

$$\mathbf{x} \cdot \mathbf{x} = \begin{bmatrix} 1 \\ 1 \\ 3 \end{bmatrix} \cdot \begin{bmatrix} 1 \\ 1 \\ 3 \end{bmatrix} = 11$$

Therefore, the Rayleigh quotient is

$$\lambda = \frac{A\mathbf{x} \cdot \mathbf{x}}{\mathbf{x} \cdot \mathbf{x}} = \frac{-33}{11} = -3.$$

11. We begin to form the sequence of approximations as follows.

$$\mathbf{x}_1 = A\mathbf{x}_0 = \begin{bmatrix} 2 & 1 \\ 0 & -7 \end{bmatrix} \begin{bmatrix} 1 \\ 1 \end{bmatrix} = \begin{bmatrix} 3 \\ -7 \end{bmatrix} \Rightarrow \mathbf{x}_1' = \begin{bmatrix} -3/7 \\ 1 \end{bmatrix}$$

$$\mathbf{x}_2 = A\mathbf{x}_1' = \begin{bmatrix} 2 & 1 \\ 0 & -7 \end{bmatrix} \begin{bmatrix} -3/7 \\ 1 \end{bmatrix} = \begin{bmatrix} 1/7 \\ -7 \end{bmatrix} \Rightarrow \mathbf{x}_2' = \begin{bmatrix} -1/49 \\ 1 \end{bmatrix}.$$

Continuing in this fashion, we find

$$\mathbf{x}_3' = \begin{bmatrix} -0.137 \\ 1 \end{bmatrix}, \quad \mathbf{x}_4' = \begin{bmatrix} -0.1037 \\ 1 \end{bmatrix}, \quad \mathbf{x}_5' = \begin{bmatrix} -0.1132 \\ 1.0 \end{bmatrix}.$$

Finally, using the Rayleigh quotient, we approximate the dominant eigenvalue

$$\lambda = \frac{A\mathbf{x}_5' \cdot \mathbf{x}_5'}{\mathbf{x}_5' \cdot \mathbf{x}_5'} = -6.9979 \, (-7).$$

13. We begin to form the sequence of approximations as follows.

$$\mathbf{x}_1 = A\mathbf{x}_0 = \begin{bmatrix} 1 & -4 \\ -2 & 8 \end{bmatrix} \begin{bmatrix} 1 \\ 1 \end{bmatrix} = \begin{bmatrix} -3 \\ 6 \end{bmatrix} \qquad \Rightarrow \quad \mathbf{x}_1' = \begin{bmatrix} -1/2 \\ 1 \end{bmatrix}$$

$$\mathbf{x}_2 = A\mathbf{x}_1' = \begin{bmatrix} 1 & -4 \\ -2 & 8 \end{bmatrix} \begin{bmatrix} -1/2 \\ 1 \end{bmatrix} = \begin{bmatrix} -1/2 \\ 1 \end{bmatrix} = \begin{bmatrix} -9/2 \\ 9 \end{bmatrix} \qquad \Rightarrow \quad \mathbf{x}_2' = \begin{bmatrix} -1/2 \\ 1 \end{bmatrix}$$

Thus, all subsequent approximations will be the same, so $\mathbf{x}_5 = \left(-\frac{1}{2}, 1 \right)$. (Note that in this case, the approximation is exact.) Using the known dominant eigenvector we obtain the following.

$$A\mathbf{x}_5 = \begin{bmatrix} 1 & -4 \\ -2 & 8 \end{bmatrix} \begin{bmatrix} -1/2 \\ 1 \end{bmatrix} = \begin{bmatrix} -9/2 \\ 9 \end{bmatrix}$$

$$A\mathbf{x}_5 \cdot \mathbf{x}_5 = \begin{bmatrix} -9/2 \\ 9 \end{bmatrix} \cdot \begin{bmatrix} -1/2 \\ 1 \end{bmatrix} = \frac{45}{4}$$

$$\mathbf{x}_5 \cdot \mathbf{x}_5 = \begin{bmatrix} -1/2 \\ 1 \end{bmatrix} \cdot \begin{bmatrix} -1/2 \\ 1 \end{bmatrix} = \frac{5}{4}$$

Finally, using the Rayleigh quotient we find the dominant eigenvalue to be

$$\lambda = \frac{A\mathbf{x}_5 \cdot \mathbf{x}_5}{\mathbf{x}_5 \cdot \mathbf{x}_5} = \frac{45/4}{5/4} = 9.$$

15. We form the sequence of approximations as follows.

$$\mathbf{x}_1 = A\mathbf{x}_0 = \begin{bmatrix} 3 & 0 & 0 \\ 1 & -1 & 0 \\ 0 & 2 & 8 \end{bmatrix} \begin{bmatrix} 1 \\ 1 \\ 1 \end{bmatrix} = \begin{bmatrix} 3 \\ 0 \\ 10 \end{bmatrix} \qquad \Rightarrow \quad \mathbf{x}_1' = \begin{bmatrix} 0.3 \\ 0 \\ 1 \end{bmatrix}$$

$$\mathbf{x}_2 = A\mathbf{x}_1' = \begin{bmatrix} 3 & 0 & 0 \\ 1 & -1 & 0 \\ 0 & 2 & 8 \end{bmatrix} \begin{bmatrix} 0.3 \\ 0 \\ 1 \end{bmatrix} = \begin{bmatrix} 0.9 \\ 0.3 \\ 8 \end{bmatrix} \qquad \Rightarrow \quad \mathbf{x}_2' = \begin{bmatrix} 0.1125 \\ 0.0375 \\ 1 \end{bmatrix}$$

$$\mathbf{x}_3 = A\mathbf{x}_2' = \begin{bmatrix} 3 & 0 & 0 \\ 1 & -1 & 0 \\ 0 & 2 & 8 \end{bmatrix} \begin{bmatrix} 0.1125 \\ 0 \\ 1 \end{bmatrix} = \begin{bmatrix} 0.3375 \\ 0.075 \\ 8.075 \end{bmatrix} \qquad \Rightarrow \quad \mathbf{x}_3' = \begin{bmatrix} 0.0418 \\ 0.0093 \\ 1 \end{bmatrix}$$

$$\mathbf{x}_4 = A\mathbf{x}_3' = \begin{bmatrix} 3 & 0 & 0 \\ 1 & -1 & 0 \\ 0 & 2 & 8 \end{bmatrix} \begin{bmatrix} 0.0418 \\ 0.0093 \\ 1 \end{bmatrix} = \begin{bmatrix} 0.1254 \\ 0.03251 \\ 8.019 \end{bmatrix} \qquad \Rightarrow \quad \mathbf{x}_4' = \begin{bmatrix} 0.01564 \\ 0.004054 \\ 1 \end{bmatrix}$$

Therefore, we approximate a dominant eigenvector of A to be $\mathbf{x} = \mathbf{x}_4'$.

$$A\mathbf{x} = \begin{bmatrix} 3 & 0 & 0 \\ 1 & -1 & 0 \\ 0 & 2 & 8 \end{bmatrix} \begin{bmatrix} 0.01564 \\ 0.004054 \\ 0 \end{bmatrix} = \begin{bmatrix} 0.04691 \\ 0.01158 \\ 8.008 \end{bmatrix}$$

$$A\mathbf{x} \cdot \mathbf{x} = \begin{bmatrix} 0.04691 \\ 0.01158 \\ 8.008 \end{bmatrix} \cdot \begin{bmatrix} 0.01564 \\ 0.004054 \\ 1 \end{bmatrix} = 8.009$$

$$\mathbf{x} \cdot \mathbf{x} = \begin{bmatrix} 0.01564 \\ 0.004054 \\ 1 \end{bmatrix} \cdot \begin{bmatrix} 0.01564 \\ 0.004054 \\ 1 \end{bmatrix} = 1.000$$

Finally, using the Rayleigh quotient, we approximate the dominant eigenvalue to be

$$\lambda = \frac{A\mathbf{x} \cdot \mathbf{x}}{\mathbf{x} \cdot \mathbf{x}} = \frac{8.009}{1.000} \approx 8.007.$$

Note that all calculated digits were retained on a calculator, while only four significant digits are displayed in the final answers here.

17. We form the sequence of approximations as follows.

$$\mathbf{x}_1 = \begin{bmatrix} -1 & -6 & 0 \\ 2 & 7 & 0 \\ 1 & 2 & -1 \end{bmatrix} \begin{bmatrix} 1 \\ 1 \\ 1 \end{bmatrix} = \begin{bmatrix} -7 \\ 9 \\ 2 \end{bmatrix} \implies \mathbf{x}_1' = \begin{bmatrix} -7/9 \\ 1 \\ 2/9 \end{bmatrix}$$

$$\mathbf{x}_2 = \begin{bmatrix} -1 & -6 & 0 \\ 2 & 7 & 0 \\ 1 & 2 & -1 \end{bmatrix} \begin{bmatrix} -7/9 \\ 1 \\ 2/9 \end{bmatrix} = \begin{bmatrix} 47/9 \\ 49/9 \\ 1 \end{bmatrix} \implies \mathbf{x}_2' = \begin{bmatrix} -47/49 \\ 15 \\ 9/49 \end{bmatrix}$$

Continuing in this fashion, we find

$$\mathbf{x}_3' = \begin{bmatrix} -0.9920 \\ 1 \\ 0.1687 \end{bmatrix} \quad \text{and} \quad \mathbf{x}_4' = \begin{bmatrix} -0.9984 \\ 1 \\ 0.1673 \end{bmatrix}.$$

Finally, using the Rayleigh quotient, we approximate the dominant eigenvalue

$$\lambda = \frac{A\mathbf{x}_4' \cdot \mathbf{x}_4'}{\mathbf{x}_4' \cdot \mathbf{x}_4'} = 5.0061.$$

19. $\mathbf{x}_1 = A\mathbf{x}_0 = \begin{bmatrix} 1 & 1 & 0 \\ 3 & -1 & 0 \\ 0 & 0 & -2 \end{bmatrix} \begin{bmatrix} 1 \\ 1 \\ 1 \end{bmatrix} = \begin{bmatrix} 2 \\ 2 \\ -2 \end{bmatrix} \implies \mathbf{x}_1' = \begin{bmatrix} 1 \\ 1 \\ -1 \end{bmatrix}$

$\mathbf{x}_2 = A\mathbf{x}_1' = \begin{bmatrix} 1 & 1 & 0 \\ 3 & -1 & 0 \\ 0 & 0 & -2 \end{bmatrix} \begin{bmatrix} 1 \\ 1 \\ -1 \end{bmatrix} = \begin{bmatrix} 2 \\ 2 \\ 2 \end{bmatrix} \implies \mathbf{x}_2' = \begin{bmatrix} 1 \\ 1 \\ 1 \end{bmatrix}$

$\mathbf{x}_3 = A\mathbf{x}_2' = A\mathbf{x}_0 = \begin{bmatrix} 2 \\ 2 \\ -2 \end{bmatrix} \implies \mathbf{x}_3' = \begin{bmatrix} 1 \\ 1 \\ -1 \end{bmatrix}$

$\mathbf{x}_4 = A\mathbf{x}_3' = A\mathbf{x}_1' = \begin{bmatrix} 2 \\ 2 \\ 2 \end{bmatrix} \implies \mathbf{x}_4' = \begin{bmatrix} 1 \\ 1 \\ 1 \end{bmatrix}$

Note that for any integer $n \geq 0$, $\mathbf{x}_{2n}' = (1, 1, 1)$ and $\mathbf{x}_{2n+1}' = (1, 1, -1)$, so the power method fails.

21. (a) The eigenvalues are the solutions to the characteristic equation

$$|\lambda I - A| = \begin{vmatrix} \lambda - 3 & 1 \\ 2 & \lambda - 4 \end{vmatrix} = \lambda^2 - 7\lambda + 10 = (\lambda - 5)(\lambda - 2) = 0.$$

Thus, the eigenvalues are $\lambda_1 = 5$ and $\lambda_2 = 2$, with corresponding eigenvectors $(-1/2, 1)$ and $(1, 1)$.

(b) $\mathbf{x}_1 = A\mathbf{x}_0 = \begin{bmatrix} 3 & -1 \\ -2 & 4 \end{bmatrix} \begin{bmatrix} 1 \\ 1 \end{bmatrix} = \begin{bmatrix} 2 \\ 2 \end{bmatrix} \Rightarrow \mathbf{x}_1' = \begin{bmatrix} 1 \\ 1 \end{bmatrix}$

$\mathbf{x}_2 = A\mathbf{x}_1' = \begin{bmatrix} 3 & -1 \\ -2 & 4 \end{bmatrix} \begin{bmatrix} 1 \\ 1 \end{bmatrix} = \begin{bmatrix} 2 \\ 2 \end{bmatrix} \Rightarrow \mathbf{x}_2' = \begin{bmatrix} 1 \\ 1 \end{bmatrix}$

The initial guess was precisely an eigenvector for $\lambda = 2$.

23. $\mathbf{x}_1 = A^{-1}\mathbf{x}_0 = \begin{bmatrix} -5/2 & 6 \\ -1/2 & 1 \end{bmatrix} \begin{bmatrix} 1 \\ 1 \end{bmatrix} = \begin{bmatrix} 7/2 \\ 1/2 \end{bmatrix} \qquad \Rightarrow \mathbf{x}_1' = \begin{bmatrix} 1 \\ 1/7 \end{bmatrix}$

$\mathbf{x}_2 = A^{-1}\mathbf{x}_1' = \begin{bmatrix} -5/2 & 6 \\ -1/2 & 1 \end{bmatrix} \begin{bmatrix} 1 \\ 1/7 \end{bmatrix} = \begin{bmatrix} -23/14 \\ -5/14 \end{bmatrix} \qquad \Rightarrow \mathbf{x}_2' = \begin{bmatrix} 1 \\ 5/23 \end{bmatrix}$

$\mathbf{x}_3 = A^{-1}\mathbf{x}_2' = \begin{bmatrix} -5/2 & 6 \\ -1/2 & 1 \end{bmatrix} \begin{bmatrix} 1 \\ 5/23 \end{bmatrix} = \begin{bmatrix} -55/46 \\ -13/46 \end{bmatrix} \qquad \Rightarrow \mathbf{x}_3' = \begin{bmatrix} 1 \\ 13/55 \end{bmatrix}$

$\mathbf{x}_4 = A^{-1}\mathbf{x}_3' = \begin{bmatrix} -5/2 & 6 \\ -1/2 & 1 \end{bmatrix} \begin{bmatrix} 1 \\ 13/55 \end{bmatrix} = \begin{bmatrix} -119/110 \\ -29/110 \end{bmatrix} \qquad \Rightarrow \mathbf{x}_4' = \begin{bmatrix} 1 \\ 29/119 \end{bmatrix}$

$\mathbf{x}_5 = A^{-1}\mathbf{x}_4' = \begin{bmatrix} -5/2 & 6 \\ -1/2 & 1 \end{bmatrix} \begin{bmatrix} 1 \\ 29/119 \end{bmatrix} = \begin{bmatrix} -247/238 \\ -61/238 \end{bmatrix} \qquad \Rightarrow \mathbf{x}_5' = \begin{bmatrix} 1 \\ 61/247 \end{bmatrix}$

The Rayleigh quotient produces

$$\frac{1}{\lambda} = \frac{A^{-1}\mathbf{x} \cdot \mathbf{x}}{\mathbf{x} \cdot \mathbf{x}} \approx -1.019$$

and we conclude that $\lambda \approx -0.9818$ (the actual value is $\lambda = -1$).

25. (a) $|\lambda I - A| = \begin{vmatrix} \lambda - 2 & -1 \\ -1 & \lambda - 2 \end{vmatrix} = \lambda^2 - 4\lambda + 3 = (\lambda - 3)(\lambda - 1) \Rightarrow \lambda = 1, 3$

$|\lambda I - B| = \begin{vmatrix} \lambda - 2 & -3 \\ -1 & \lambda - 4 \end{vmatrix} = \lambda^2 - 6\lambda + 5 = (\lambda - 5)(\lambda - 1) \Rightarrow \lambda = 1, 5$

(b) For the matrix A, we find

$$\mathbf{x}_1 = A\mathbf{x}_0 = \begin{bmatrix} 2 & 1 \\ 1 & 2 \end{bmatrix} \begin{bmatrix} -1 \\ 2 \end{bmatrix} = \begin{bmatrix} 0 \\ 3 \end{bmatrix} \Rightarrow \mathbf{x}_1' = \begin{bmatrix} 0 \\ 1 \end{bmatrix}$$

and $\mathbf{x}_2' = (1/2, 1)$, $\mathbf{x}_3' = (0.8, 1)$ and $\mathbf{x}_4' = (0.9286, 1)$.
For the matrix B, we have

$$\mathbf{x}_1 = A\mathbf{x}_0 = \begin{bmatrix} 2 & 3 \\ 1 & 4 \end{bmatrix} \begin{bmatrix} -1 \\ 2 \end{bmatrix} = \begin{bmatrix} 4 \\ 7 \end{bmatrix} \Rightarrow \mathbf{x}_1' = \begin{bmatrix} 4/7 \\ 1 \end{bmatrix}$$

and $\mathbf{x}_2' = (0.9063, 1)$, $\mathbf{x}_3' = (0.9809, 1)$ and $\mathbf{x}_4' = (0.9962, 1)$.

(c) For A, $\lambda_1/\lambda_2 = 1/3$, while for B, $\lambda_1/\lambda_2 = 1/5$. Hence, B should converge faster.

27. $\mathbf{x}_1 = A\mathbf{x}_0 = \begin{bmatrix} 5 & 6 \\ 4 & 3 \end{bmatrix} \begin{bmatrix} 1 \\ 1 \end{bmatrix} = \begin{bmatrix} 11 \\ 7 \end{bmatrix} \qquad \Rightarrow \quad \mathbf{x}_1' \approx \begin{bmatrix} 0.8437 \\ 0.5369 \end{bmatrix}$

$\mathbf{x}_2 = A\mathbf{x}_1' = \begin{bmatrix} 5 & 6 \\ 4 & 3 \end{bmatrix} \begin{bmatrix} 0.8437 \\ 0.5369 \end{bmatrix} = \begin{bmatrix} 7.440 \\ 4.985 \end{bmatrix} \quad \Rightarrow \quad \mathbf{x}_2' = \begin{bmatrix} 0.8307 \\ 0.5567 \end{bmatrix}$

$\mathbf{x}_3 = A\mathbf{x}_2' = \begin{bmatrix} 5 & 6 \\ 4 & 3 \end{bmatrix} \begin{bmatrix} 0.8307 \\ 0.5567 \end{bmatrix} = \begin{bmatrix} 7.494 \\ 4.992 \end{bmatrix} \quad \Rightarrow \quad \mathbf{x}_3' = \begin{bmatrix} 0.8322 \\ 0.5545 \end{bmatrix}$

$\mathbf{x}_4 = A\mathbf{x}_3' = \begin{bmatrix} 5 & 6 \\ 4 & 3 \end{bmatrix} \begin{bmatrix} 0.8322 \\ 0.5545 \end{bmatrix} = \begin{bmatrix} 7.488 \\ 4.992 \end{bmatrix} \quad \Rightarrow \quad \mathbf{x}_4' = \begin{bmatrix} 0.8320 \\ 0.5547 \end{bmatrix}$

Using the Rayleigh quotient, we have

$$\lambda = \frac{A\mathbf{x}_4' \cdot \mathbf{x}_4'}{\mathbf{x}_4' \cdot \mathbf{x}_4'} = A\mathbf{x}_4' \cdot \mathbf{x}_4' \approx 9.000.$$

Values are shown to four significant digits, but all calculated digits were retained in a calculator during intermediate steps.

Section 10.4   Applications of Numerical Methods

1. We display the summations in the following table.

i	x_i	x_i^2	x_i^3	x_i^4	y_i	$x_i y_i$	$x_i^2 y_i$
1	−2	4	−8	16	1	−2	4
2	−1	1	−1	1	0	0	0
3	0	0	0	0	0	0	0
4	1	1	1	1	1	1	1
5	3	9	27	81	2	6	18
$\sum$	1	15	19	99	4	5	23

The coefficients of the least squares regression quadratic are the solution to the system.

$$5a_0 + a_1 + 15a_2 = 4$$

$$a_0 + 15a_1 + 19a_2 = 5$$

$$5a_0 + 19a_1 + 99a_3 = 23.$$

Gaussian elimination with pivoting on the matrix

$$\begin{bmatrix} 5 & 1 & 15 & 4 \\ 1 & 15 & 19 & 5 \\ 15 & 19 & 99 & 23 \end{bmatrix}$$

produces

$$\begin{bmatrix} 1 & 1.2667 & 6.6000 & 1.5333 \\ 0 & 1 & 0.90291 & 0.25243 \\ 0 & 0 & 1 & 0.17599 \end{bmatrix}.$$

Thus, by back-substitution we find the solution to be $a_2 = 0.1760$, $a_1 = 0.09352$, and $a_0 = 0.2533$ and the regression quadratic is

$$y = 0.1760x^2 + 0.09352x + 0.2533.$$

(Final values are to four significant digits.)

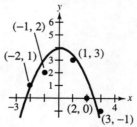

3. We display the summations in the following table.

i	x_i	x_i^2	x_i^3	x_i^4	y_i	$x_i y_i$	$x_i^2 y_i$
1	-2	4	-8	16	1	-2	4
2	-1	1	-1	1	2	-2	2
3	0	0	0	0	6	0	0
4	1	1	1	1	3	3	3
5	2	4	8	16	0	0	0
6	3	9	27	81	-1	-3	-9
$\sum$	3	19	27	115	11	-4	0

The coefficients of the least squares regression quadratic are the solutions to the system.

$$6a_0 + 3a_1 + 19a_2 = 11$$

$$3a_0 + 19a_1 + 27a_2 = -4$$

$$19a_0 + 27a_1 + 115a_2 = 0.$$

Using Gaussian elimination, we find that $a_0 = 3.9143$, $a_1 = 0.1357$, and $a_2 = -0.6786$. Thus, the least squares quadratic is

$$y = -0.6786x^2 + 0.1357x + 3.9143.$$

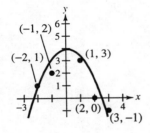

5.   We display the summations in the following table.

i	x_i	x_i^2	x_i^3	x_i^4	x_i^5	x_i^6	y_i	$x_i y_i$	$x_i^2 y_i$	$x_i^3 y_i$
1	0	0	0	0	0	0	0	0	0	0
2	1	1	1	1	1	1	2	2	2	2
3	2	4	8	16	32	64	4	8	16	32
4	3	9	27	81	243	729	1	3	9	27
5	4	16	64	256	1024	4096	0	0	0	0
6	5	25	125	625	3125	15625	1	5	25	125
$\sum$	15	55	225	979	4425	20515	8	18	52	186

The coefficients of the least squares regression cubic are the solution to the system.

$$6a_0 + 15a_1 + 55a_2 + 225a_3 = 8$$
$$15a_0 + 55a_1 + 225a_2 + 979a_3 = 18$$
$$55a_0 + 225a_1 + 979a_2 + 4425a_3 = 52$$
$$225a_0 + 979a_1 + 4425a_2 + 20515a_3 = 186$$

Gaussian elimination with pivoting on the matrix

$$\begin{bmatrix} 6 & 15 & 55 & 225 & 8 \\ 15 & 55 & 225 & 979 & 18 \\ 55 & 225 & 979 & 4425 & 52 \\ 225 & 979 & 4425 & 20515 & 186 \end{bmatrix}$$

produces

$$\begin{bmatrix} 1 & 4.3511 & 19.667 & 91.178 & 0.82667 \\ 0 & 1 & 7.1739 & 41.211 & -0.45652 \\ 0 & 0 & 1 & 8.1355 & -0.12174 \\ 0 & 0 & 0 & 1 & 0.28704 \end{bmatrix} .$$

Thus, by back-substitution we find the solution to be

$$a_3 = 0.2870, \ a_2 = -2.456, \ a_1 = 5.336 \text{ and } a_0 = -0.2540$$

and the regression cubic is

$$y = 0.2870x^3 - 2.456x^2 + 5.336x - 0.2540.$$

(Final values are to four significant digits.)

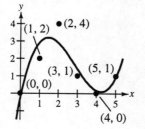

7. We display the summations in the following table.

i	x_i	x_i^2	x_i^3	x_i^4	x_i^5	x_i^6	y_i	$x_i y_i$	$x_i^2 y_i$	$x_i^3 y_i$
1	-3	9	-27	81	-243	729	4	-12	36	-108
2	-1	1	-1	1	-1	1	1	-1	1	-1
3	3	0	0	0	0	0	0	0	0	0
4	1	1	1	1	1	1	2	2	2	2
5	2	4	8	16	32	64	5	10	20	40
$\sum$	-1	15	-19	99	-211	795	12	-1	59	-67

The coefficients of the least squares regression cubic are the solution to the system.

$$5a_0 - a_1 + 15a_2 - 19a_3 = 12$$

$$-a_0 + 15a_1 - 19a_2 + 99a_3 = -1$$

$$15a_0 - 19a_1 + 99a_2 - 211a_3 = 59$$

$$-19a_0 + 99a_1 - 211a_2 + 795a_3 = -67$$

Using Gaussian elimination, we find that $a_0 = 0.4313$, $a_1 = 0.3518$, $a_2 = 0.7992$ and $a_3 = 0.09434$. Thus, the least squares cubic is

$$y = 0.09434x^3 + 0.7992x^2 + 0.3518x + 0.4313.$$

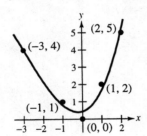

9. We display the summations in the following table.

i	x_i	x_i^2	x_i^3	x_i^4	y_i	$x_i y_i$	$x_i^2 y_i$
1	$-\pi/2$	$\pi^2/4$	$-\pi3/8$	$\pi^4/16$	0	0	0
2	$-\pi/3$	$\pi^2/9$	$-\pi^3/27$	$\pi^4/81$	1/2	$-\pi/6$	$\pi^2/18$
3	0	0	0	0	1	0	0
4	$\pi/3$	$\pi^2/9$	$\pi^3/27$	$\pi^4/81$	1/2	$\pi/6$	$\pi^2/18$
5	$\pi/2$	$\pi^2/4$	$\pi^3/8$	$\pi^4/16$	0	0	0
$\sum$	0	$\pi^2(13/18)$	0	$\pi^4(97/648)$	2	0	$\pi^2/9$
decimal	0.0	7.1280	0.0	14.5813	2.0	0.0	1.0966

The coefficients of the least squares regression quadratic are the solutions to the system.

$$5a_0 \qquad\qquad + 7.1280a_2 = \quad 2.0$$

$$7.1280a_1 \qquad\qquad = \quad 0.0$$

$$7.1280a_0 \qquad + 14.5813a_2 = 1.0966.$$

Using Gaussian elimination, we find $a_0 = 0.966$, $a_1 = 0$ and $a_2 = -0.397$.
Thus, the least squares polynomial of degree two is

$$y = 0.397x^2 + 0.966.$$

Evaluating $y(\pi/4) = 0.721$, we see that this is close to the exact value, $\cos(\pi/4) = 0.707$.

11. We display the summations in the following table, where $d = 0.01$ (depth) and $t = 0.01$ (time).

i	d_i	d_i^2	d_i^3	d_i^4	t_i	$d_i t_i$	$d_i^2 t_i$
1	0.35	0.1225	0.042875	0.01500625	3.10	1.085	0.37975
2	0.40	0.1600	0.064000	0.02560000	2.00	0.800	0.32000
3	0.50	0.2500	0.125000	0.06250000	1.00	0.500	0.25000
4	0.60	0.3600	0.216000	0.12960000	0.60	0.360	0.21600
5	0.70	0.4900	0.343000	0.24010000	0.50	0.350	0.24500
6	0.80	0.6400	0.512000	0.40960000	0.40	0.320	0.25600
7	0.90	0.8100	0.729000	0.65610000	0.30	0.270	0.24300
8	1.00	1.0000	1.000000	1.00000000	0.25	0.250	0.25000
9	1.10	1.2100	1.331000	1.46410000	0.20	0.220	0.24200
	6.35	5.0425	4.362875	4.00260625	8.35	4.155	2.40175

(a) The coefficients of the least squares regression line are the solution to the system.

$$9a_0 + 6.35a_1 = 8.35$$
$$6.35a_0 + 5.0425a_1 = 4.155$$

Using Gaussian elimination with partial pivoting and back-substitution yields $a_1 = -3.088$ and $a_0 = 3.107$. Thus, the regression line is $t = -3.088d + 3.107$.

(b) The coefficients of the least squares regression quadratic are the solution to the system.

$$9a_0 + 6.35a_1 + 5.0425a_2 = 8.35$$
$$6.35a_0 + 5.0425a_1 + 4.362875a_2 = 4.155$$
$$5.0425a_0 + 4.362875a_1 + 4.00260625a_2 = 2.40175$$

Using Gaussian elimination with partial pivoting and back-substitution yields $a_2 = 8.579$, $a_1 = -15.37$ and $a_0 = 6.968$. Thus, the regression quadratic is $t = 8.59d^2 - 15.37d + 6.968$.

(c) Note that by letting $d = 0.01x$ and $t = 0.01y$, where x is the unscaled depth and y is the unscaled time, we obtain the following equations.

$$y = -3.088x + 310.7 \qquad \text{(linear)}$$
$$y = 0.08579x^2 - 15.37x + 696.8 \qquad \text{(quadratic)}$$

The graph of each equation and data points follows.

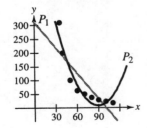

(d) When $x = 120$, the linear model yields

$$y = -3.088(120) + 310.7 \approx -59.9 \text{ minutes}$$

and the quadratic model yields

$$y = 0.08579(120)^2 - 15.37(120) + 696.8 \approx 87.8 \text{ minutes}.$$

Note that neither model is a good predictor for values outside the range of the sample data.

13. We first let 1977 correspond to $x = 0$, and display the summations.

i	x_i	x_i^2	x_i^3	x_i^4	y_i	$x_i y_i$	$x_i^2 y_i$
1	-7	49	-343	2401	7.5	-52.5	367.5
2	-5	25	-125	625	9.1	-45.5	227.5
3	-3	9	-27	81	13.1	-39.3	117.9
4	-1	1	-1	1	19.3	-19.3	19.3
5	1	1	1	1	25.9	25.9	25.9
6	3	9	27	81	36.8	110.4	993.6
7	5	25	125	625	52.4	262.0	1310.0
8	7	49	343	2401	64.8	453.6	3175.2
$\sum$	0	168	0	6216	228.9	695.3	6236.9

The coefficients of the least squares quadratic are the solutions to the system.

$$8a_0 \qquad\quad + \;\; 168a_2 = \;\; 228.9$$

$$168a_1 \qquad\qquad\quad = \;\; 695.3$$

$$168a_0 \qquad + \; 6216a_2 = 6236.9.$$

Using Gaussian elimination, we find $a_0 = 22.62$, $a_1 = 4.139$ and $a_2 = 0.2856$. Thus, the least squares quadratic is

$$y = 0.2856x^2 + 4.139x + 22.62 \; (x = 0 \text{ is } 1977).$$

For 1986 ($x = 9$), we have $y = 83.00$, and for 1988 ($x = 11$), we have $y = 102.7$.

15. From Example 1 we have the information

$$n = 8, \quad \sum_{i=1}^{8} x_i = -4, \quad \sum_{i=1}^{8} x_i^2 = 44, \quad \sum_{i=1}^{8} y_i = 28.87, \quad \sum_{i=1}^{8} x_i y_i = -0.24.$$

Thus, the coefficients of the least squares regression line are the solution to the system.

$$8a_0 - \; 4a_1 = 28.87$$

$$-4a_0 - 44a_1 = -0.24$$

We use Gaussian elimination and back-substitution to obtain $a_1 = 0.3380$ and $a_0 = 3.778$. The regression line is $y = 0.3380x + 3.778$. In 1990, $x = 4$ and $y = 0.3380(4) + 3.778 \approx 5.13$ billion

while in 1995, $x = 5$ and

$$y = 0.3380(5) + 3.778 \approx 5.47 \text{ billion.}$$

(Compare this to the predictions in Example 1 of 5.32 billion and 5.79 billion, respectively.)

17. We express the probability of winning (reaching the food) at each intersection with the following six equations.

$$p_1 = \tfrac{1}{4}(0) + \tfrac{1}{4}p_2 + \tfrac{1}{4}p_4 + \tfrac{1}{4}(0)$$

$$p_2 = \tfrac{1}{4}(0) + \tfrac{1}{4}p_3 + \tfrac{1}{4}p_5 + \tfrac{1}{4}p_1$$

$$p_3 = \tfrac{1}{4}(0) + \tfrac{1}{4}(0) + \tfrac{1}{4}p_6 + \tfrac{1}{4}p_2$$

$$p_4 = \tfrac{1}{4}p_1 + \tfrac{1}{4}p_5 + \tfrac{1}{4}(1) + \tfrac{1}{4}(0)$$

$$p_5 = \tfrac{1}{4}p_2 + \tfrac{1}{4}p_6 + \tfrac{1}{4}(1) + \tfrac{1}{4}p_4$$

$$p_6 = \tfrac{1}{4}p_3 + \tfrac{1}{4}(0) + \tfrac{1}{4}(1) + \tfrac{1}{4}p_5$$

In standard form these equations form the system of linear equations.

$$
\begin{aligned}
4p_1 - p_2 \quad\;\; - p_4 \qquad\qquad\qquad &= 0\\
-p_1 + 4p_2 - p_3 \qquad\;\; - p_5 \qquad\quad &= 0\\
-p_2 + 4p_3 \qquad\qquad - p_6 &= 0\\
-p_1 \qquad\qquad + 4p_4 - p_5 \qquad\quad &= 1\\
-p_2 \qquad\quad - p_4 + 4p_5 - p_6 &= 1\\
-p_3 \qquad\qquad - p_5 + 4p_6 &= 1
\end{aligned}
$$

Applying the Gauss-Seidel method with initial approximation $p_1 = p_2 = \cdots = p_6 = 0$ produces (after 8 iterations) an approximation of

$$p_1 = 0.155, \quad p_2 = 0.205, \quad p_3 = 0.155,$$

$$p_4 = 0.416, \quad p_5 = 0.509, \quad p_6 = 0.416.$$

19. At each point we assume that the temperature is the average of the temperatures at the four closest neighboring points. This produces the following nine equations.

$$T_1 = \tfrac{1}{4}\left(100 + 100 + T_2 + T_4\right)$$

$$T_2 = \tfrac{1}{4}\left(100 + T_1 + T_3 + T_5\right)$$

$$T_3 = \tfrac{1}{4}\left(0 + 100 + T_2 + T_6\right)$$

$$T_4 = \tfrac{1}{4}\left(100 + T_1 + T_5 + T_7\right)$$

$$T_5 = \tfrac{1}{4}\left(T_2 + T_4 + T_6 + T_8\right)$$

$$T_6 = \tfrac{1}{4}\left(0 + T_3 + T_5 + T_9\right)$$

$$T_7 = \tfrac{1}{4}\left(100 + T_4 + T_8 + 0\right)$$

$$T_8 = \tfrac{1}{4}\left(T_7 + T_5 + T_9 + 0\right)$$

$$T_9 = \tfrac{1}{4}\left(T_8 + T_6 + 0 + 0\right)$$

We express the equations as a 9×9 linear system and apply the Gauss-Seidel method with initial approximation $T_1 = T_2 = \cdots = T_9 = 0$. We obtain

$$T_1 = 85.7143, \quad T_2 = 71.4286, \quad T_3 = 50,$$

$$T_4 = 71.4286, \quad T_5 = 50, \quad\;\; T_6 = 28.5714,$$

$$T_7 = 50, \qquad\quad\; T_8 = 28.5714, \quad T_9 = 14.2857.$$

21. We choose $\mathbf{x}_0 = (1, 1)$ and begin the sequence of approximations to a dominant eigenvector by finding

$$\mathbf{x}_1 = A\mathbf{x}_0 = \begin{bmatrix} 1 & 4 \\ 1/2 & 0 \end{bmatrix} \begin{bmatrix} 1 \\ 1 \end{bmatrix} = \begin{bmatrix} 5 \\ 1/2 \end{bmatrix} \implies \mathbf{x}_1' = \begin{bmatrix} 1 \\ 0.1 \end{bmatrix}.$$

Continuing this process and letting $\mathbf{x}_{n+1} = A\mathbf{x}_n'$, we find that $\mathbf{x} = (4, 1)$ represents a stable age distribution for this population.

23. We choose $\mathbf{x}_0 = (1, 1, 1)$ and begin the sequence of approximations to a dominant eigenvector by finding

$$\mathbf{x}_1 = A\mathbf{x}_0 = \begin{bmatrix} 0 & 1 & 2 \\ 1/2 & 0 & 0 \\ 0 & 1/4 & 0 \end{bmatrix} \begin{bmatrix} 1 \\ 1 \\ 1 \end{bmatrix} = \begin{bmatrix} 3 \\ 1/2 \\ 1/4 \end{bmatrix} \implies \mathbf{x}_1' = \begin{bmatrix} 1 \\ 1/6 \\ 1/12 \end{bmatrix}.$$

Continuing this process and letting $\mathbf{x}_{n+1} = A\mathbf{x}_n'$, we find that $\mathbf{x} \approx (1, 0.565, 0.160)$.
This represents a stable age distribution for this population.

25. We choose $\mathbf{x}_0 = (1, 1, 1)$ and use the power method with scaling to find an approximation of the dominant eigenvector.

$$\mathbf{x}_1 = A\mathbf{x}_0 = \begin{bmatrix} 0 & 6 & 8 \\ 0.5 & 0 & 0 \\ 0 & 0.5 & 0 \end{bmatrix} \begin{bmatrix} 1 \\ 1 \\ 1 \end{bmatrix} = \begin{bmatrix} 14 \\ 0.5 \\ 0.5 \end{bmatrix} \implies \mathbf{x}_1' \approx \begin{bmatrix} 1 \\ 0.03571 \\ 0.03571 \end{bmatrix}.$$

Continuing this process and letting $\mathbf{x}_{n+1} = A\mathbf{x}_n'$, we find that $\mathbf{x} \approx (1.00, 0.250, 0.0625)$.
This represents a stable age distribution for this population.

27. We calculate $\mathbf{x}_{n+1} = A\mathbf{x}_n$ as follows.

$$\mathbf{x}_1 = A\mathbf{x}_0 = \begin{bmatrix} 1 & 1 \\ 1 & 0 \end{bmatrix} \begin{bmatrix} 1 \\ 1 \end{bmatrix} = \begin{bmatrix} 2 \\ 1 \end{bmatrix} \implies \mathbf{x}_1' = \begin{bmatrix} 1 \\ 1/2 \end{bmatrix}$$

$$\mathbf{x}_2 = A\mathbf{x}_1' = \begin{bmatrix} 1 & 1 \\ 1 & 0 \end{bmatrix} \begin{bmatrix} 1 \\ 1/2 \end{bmatrix} = \begin{bmatrix} 1.5 \\ 1 \end{bmatrix} \implies \mathbf{x}_2' = \begin{bmatrix} 1 \\ 2/3 \end{bmatrix}.$$

Continuing in this fashion, we find that the dominant eigenvector is approximately $\mathbf{x} = (1, 0.618)$.
Using the Rayleigh quotient, we see that the dominant eigenvalue is

$$\lambda = \frac{A\mathbf{x} \cdot \mathbf{x}}{\mathbf{x} \cdot \mathbf{x}} \approx 1.618.$$

29. The matrix found in Exercise 9 of Section 2.5 is

$$A = \begin{bmatrix} 0.93 & 0.10 & 0.05 \\ 0.05 & 0.80 & 0.10 \\ 0.02 & 0.10 & 0.85 \end{bmatrix}.$$

Using an initial approximation of $x_0 = (1, 1, 1)$, we use the power method to approximate a dominant eigenvector.

$$x_1 = Ax_0 = \begin{bmatrix} 0.93 & 0.10 & 0.05 \\ 0.05 & 0.80 & 0.10 \\ 0.02 & 0.10 & 0.85 \end{bmatrix} \begin{bmatrix} 1 \\ 1 \\ 1 \end{bmatrix} = \begin{bmatrix} 1.08 \\ 0.950 \\ 0.970 \end{bmatrix} \implies x_1' \approx \begin{bmatrix} 1 \\ 0.880 \\ 0.898 \end{bmatrix}$$

$$\vdots$$

$$x_{48} = Ax_{47}' = \begin{bmatrix} 0.93 & 0.10 & 0.05 \\ 0.05 & 0.80 & 0.10 \\ 0.02 & 0.10 & 0.85 \end{bmatrix} \begin{bmatrix} 1 \\ 0.475 \\ 0.450 \end{bmatrix} = \begin{bmatrix} 1.00 \\ 0.475 \\ 0.450 \end{bmatrix}$$

Thus, $x \approx (1.0, 0.49, 0.48)$ is an approximation of the dominant eigenvector of A.
This represents a stable population distribution of 51% nonsmokers, 25% moderate smokers, and 24% heavy smokers.